APPLIED
MATHEMATICS

12

SECOND EDITION

THE McGRAW-HILL RYERSON MATHEMATICS PROGRAM

MATH 1 SOURCE BOOK
MATH 2 SOURCE BOOK
MATH 3
MATH 4
MATH 5
MATH 6

TEACHER'S EDITION FOR:
MATH 3
MATH 4
MATH 5
MATH 6

BLACKLINE MASTERS FOR:
MATH 3
MATH 4
MATH 5
MATH 6

LIFE MATH 1
LIFE MATH 2
LIFE MATH 3

INTERMEDIATE MATHEMATICS 1
INTERMEDIATE MATHEMATICS 2
INTERMEDIATE MATHEMATICS 3

TEACHER'S EDITION FOR:
INTERMEDIATE MATHEMATICS 1
INTERMEDIATE MATHEMATICS 2
INTERMEDIATE MATHEMATICS 3

BLACKLINE MASTERS FOR:
INTERMEDIATE MATHEMATICS 1
INTERMEDIATE MATHEMATICS 2

APPLIED MATHEMATICS 9
APPLIED MATHEMATICS 10
APPLIED MATHEMATICS 11
APPLIED MATHEMATICS 12

TEACHER'S EDITION FOR:
APPLIED MATHEMATICS 9

TEACHER'S GUIDE FOR:
AM 10
AM 11
AM 12

FOUNDATIONS OF MATHEMATICS 9
FOUNDATIONS OF MATHEMATICS 10
FOUNDATIONS OF MATHEMATICS 11
FOUNDATIONS OF MATHEMATICS 12

TEACHER'S EDITION FOR:
FOUNDATIONS OF MATHEMATICS 9

TEACHER'S GUIDE FOR:
FM 10
FM 11
FM 12

APPLIED
MATHEMATICS

12

SECOND EDITION

Dino Dottori, B.Sc., M.S.Ed.
George Knill, B.Sc., M.S.Ed.
John Seymour, B.A., M.Ed.
Ann Jones, B.A., M.Ed.
Robert Alderson, B.A., M.Ed.
Darrell McPhail, B.Sc., M.Sc.

McGRAW-HILL RYERSON LIMITED

TORONTO MONTREAL NEW YORK AUCKLAND BOGOTÁ CAIRO CARACAS
HAMBURG LISBON LONDON MADRID MEXICO MILAN NEW DELHI PANAMA
PARIS SAN JUAN SÃO PAULO SINGAPORE SYDNEY TOKYO

APPLIED MATHEMATICS 12
SECOND EDITION

ISBN 0-07-548740-3

1234567890   JD   7654321098

Technical illustrations by Frank Zsigo

A complete list of notes and photograph credits appears on page 550.

Printed and bound in Canada

Canadian Cataloguing in Publication Data
Main entry under title:

Applied mathematics 12

2nd ed.
ISBN 0-07-548740-3

1. Mathematics — 1961–   . I. Dottori, Dino, date –   .

QA39.2.A69 1988   510   C88-093812-9

Communications Branch, Consumer and Corporate Affairs Canada, has granted permission for the use of the National Symbol for Metric Conversion.

RATIONAL NUMBERS
AND REAL NUMBERS

REVIEW **AND PREVIEW** TO CHAPTER

CALCULATING SKILLS

EXERCISE 1

1. Calculate mentally and record your answers.
(a) $12 - 7 + 8 - 5 + 4 - 6$
(b) $3 \times 2 + 4 + 7 - 1 - 2 - 3$
(c) $100 - 5 - 6 - 9 - 4 - 3 - 1$
(d) $1 + 2 + 3 + 4 + 5 + 6 + 7$
(e) $1 \times 2 \times 2 \times 2 \times 2 \times 2 \times 2$
(f) $200 \div 2 \div 2$
(g) $6 + 7 - 6 + 12 - 4 - 3 + 6$
(h) $(5 \times 2) + (12 \div 4) - (3 \times 6)$
(i) $9 + 8 - (5 \times 2) + 3 + (32 \div 4)$
(j) $14 + 12 + 5 - 30 + 5 - 15 - 9$
(k) $8\frac{1}{2} - 5\frac{1}{2} + 3\frac{1}{2} + 2\frac{1}{2} + 4 - 8$
(l) $5 - 3 + 15 + 2 - 9 - 2 + 11$
(m) $8 - (5 - 3) + (18 \div 6) + (7 \times 3)$

2. Calculate mentally and record your answers.
(a) $39 - (5 + 7 + 3) + (16 - 5)$
(b) $(8 \times 6 \div 12) + (18 \div 6 \times 2)$
(c) $42 \div 7 + 5 - 3 + 2(\frac{2}{3}$ of $24)$
(d) $1.5 + 1.5 + 2.5 + 3.5$
(e) $4.0 + 5.2 + 6.3 + 7.4$
(f) $100 \div 2 \div 2 \div 5 \div 5$
(g) $4 \times 6 - (16 - 11)$
(h) $15 - 7 - 2 + 8$
(i) $1.2 + 3.2 + 5.2 + 7.2 + 9.2$
(j) $200 - 20 - 10 - 15 - 30 - 10$
(k) $1 \times 2 \times 3 \times 4 \times 2 \times 1$
(l) $(20 - 5 - 10) \times 2 \times 3$
(m) $8 - 2 + 3 - 4 + 1 - 2$
(n) $11 - 2 \times 3 + 5$
(o) $20 - 30 \div 15 + 7$
(p) $8 \times 2 - 40 \div 5 + 1$
(q) $7 - 1 + 5 - 2 + 4 - 3 + 1$

3. Find the missing lengths mentally and record your results.

(a)

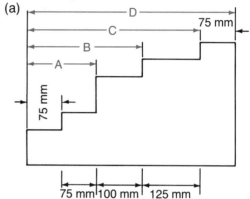

(b)

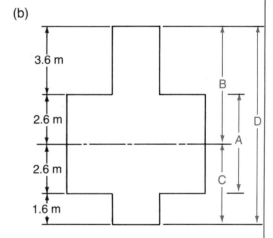

(c)

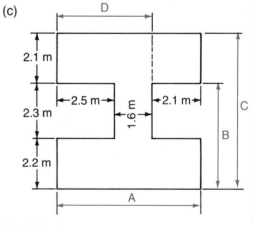

4. Multiply mentally and record your results.

(a) (2)(0.3)   (b) (12)(0.5)
(c) (0.03)(21)   (d) (41)(0.02)
(e) (2.4)(0.5)   (f) (32)(3)
(g) (0.4)(1.7)   (h) (23)(5)
(i) 25×0.8 (j) 15×0.3
(k) 20×0.6 (l) 7.5×6
(m) 3100×7 (n) 420×4
(o) 102×8 (p) 304×5
(q) 3100×4 (r) 1007×7

5. Divide mentally and total.

(a) $378 \div 9$ = ▓
    $20 \div 4$ = ▓
    $276 \div 4$ = ▓
    $888 \div 4$ = ▓
    $40 \div 5$ = ▓

    Total = ▓

(b) $63 \div 9$ = ▓
    $72 \div 6$ = ▓
    $154 \div 2$ = ▓
    $56 \div 8$ = ▓
    $972 \div 9$ = ▓

    Total = ▓

(c) $25 \div 5$ = ▓
    $84 \div 7$ = ▓
    $28 \div 4$ = ▓
    $536 \div 8$ = ▓
    $455 \div 7$ = ▓

    Total = ▓

(d) $912 \div 6$ = ▓
    $72 \div 9$ = ▓
    $64 \div 8$ = ▓
    $120 \div 5$ = ▓
    $160 \div 10$ = ▓

    Total = ▓

6. From the sum of 2.43 and 0.0176, subtract 1.271.

7. From the sum of 7.0234 and 1.0078, subtract 4.9328.

8. From the sum of 23.78 and 56.96, subtract the sum of 19.89 and 11.79.

9. From the product of 56 and 93, subtract 228.

10. From the product of 123 and 9, subtract the sum of 18 and 56.

11. From the product of 76 and 88, subtract the product of 18 and 21.

12. Simplify.

(a) $\frac{1}{3} + \frac{1}{4}$ (b) $\frac{5}{8} - \frac{1}{6}$

(c) $\frac{3}{4} \times \frac{5}{8}$ (d) $\frac{2}{3} \div \frac{1}{2}$

(e) $1\frac{3}{4} + 3\frac{4}{5}$ (f) $5 - 1\frac{5}{6}$

(g) $2\frac{2}{3} \times 3\frac{1}{4}$ (h) $1\frac{3}{4} \div 2\frac{2}{5}$

(i) $7 \div \frac{5}{8}$ (j) $\frac{5}{8} \div 7$

(k) $\frac{3}{5} \times 0.4$ (l) $\frac{3}{8} + 0.62$

(m) $1\frac{3}{5} - 0.74$ (n) $1.68 - \frac{4}{5}$

(o) $1\frac{3}{4} \div 0.5$ (p) $0.8 \div \frac{1}{2}$

MIND BENDER

There are four married women seated in fixed positions around a table.

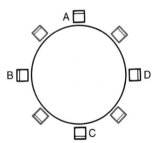

How many ways can the husbands be seated so that men and women alternate and no husband is seated next to his wife?

NUMBERS

We are familiar with the following sets of numbers.

Natural numbers   1, 2, 3, 4, ...
Whole numbers   0, 1, 2, 3, 4, 5, ...
Integers   ..., -2, -1, 0, 1, 2, ...

The following are examples of rational numbers.

$$\frac{7}{8}, \quad \frac{5}{3}, \quad \text{and} \quad -\frac{3}{7}$$

A rational number is a number that can be expressed in the form $\frac{a}{b}$, where a and b are integers, and $b \neq 0$.

Every rational number can be expressed as a decimal by dividing the numerator by the denominator. These decimals will be terminating decimals or non-terminating repeating decimals. For example,

$\frac{1}{8}$ becomes $8\overline{)1.000}$ 0.125

$\frac{2}{11}$ becomes $11\overline{)2.0000}$ 0.1818 ...   or $0.\overline{18}$

Thus $\frac{1}{8}$ becomes a terminating decimal.

Thus $\frac{2}{11}$ becomes a non-terminating repeating decimal.

Numbers that cannot be expressed in the form $\frac{a}{b}$ are called irrational numbers.

Examples of irrational numbers are

$$\sqrt{2}, \quad \sqrt{7}, \quad \text{and} \quad \sqrt{11}$$

Furthermore, these numbers cannot be represented as terminating decimals or non-terminating repeating decimals. They can be written as non-terminating non-repeating decimals.

We can get a decimal approximation of these numbers using a calculator.

$\sqrt{2}$ Press **2** √   The display is `1.414213562`

$\sqrt{7}$ Press **7** √   The display is `2.645751311`

$\sqrt{11}$ Press **1** **1** √   The display is `3.31662479`

The union of the rational numbers and the irrational numbers forms the set of real numbers.

EXERCISE 2

1. Identify each of the following numbers as rational or irrational.

(a) $\frac{22}{7}$ (b) $\sqrt{26}$ (c) $\sqrt{25}$

(d) $\frac{2}{3}$ (e) 1.62 (f) $0.\overline{72}$

(g) $1 + \sqrt{3}$ (h) $\frac{1}{7}$ (i) $\sqrt{3}$

2. Without using a calculator, express each as a decimal.

(a) $\frac{1}{2}$ (b) $\frac{1}{3}$ (c) $\frac{3}{4}$

(d) $\frac{3}{8}$ (e) $\frac{3}{5}$ (f) $\frac{1}{11}$

(g) $\frac{5}{6}$ (h) $2\frac{5}{8}$ (i) $3\frac{4}{5}$

3. Using a calculator, express each as a decimal.

(a) $\frac{1}{7}$ (b) $\frac{2}{7}$ (c) $\frac{3}{13}$

(d) $\frac{5}{9}$ (e) $\frac{5}{21}$ (f) $\frac{3}{11}$

(g) $\frac{7}{6}$ (h) $1\frac{3}{7}$ (i) $3\frac{6}{11}$

4. Using a calculator, express each irrational number as a decimal.

(a) $\sqrt{3}$ (b) $\sqrt{5}$
(c) $\sqrt{13}$ (d) $\sqrt{17}$
(e) $\sqrt{19}$ (f) $\sqrt{24}$

5. Simplify.
(a) $1.23 + 11.45 + 76.89$
(b) $234 + 56.8 + 2314$
(c) $0.345 + 11.78 + 18$
(d) $456.8 - 199.9$
(e) $26 - 0.543$
(f) $1.001 - 0.789$

6. Simplify.
(a) 7.8×56
(b) 234×0.9
(c) 0.23×1.1
(d) 0.82×0.67
(e) 4.9×9.5
(f) 1.44×0.22
(g) 7.89×0.3

7. Simplify.
(a) $1.61 \div 0.7$
(b) $22.4 \div 0.04$
(c) $20.7 \div 0.9$
(d) $0.342 \div 6$
(e) $6.24 \div 8$
(f) $0.255 \div 0.3$

POWERS OF TEN

EXERCISE 3

1. Calculate.
(a) 123×100 (b) 9.8×10
(c) 0.45×1000 (d) 1100×10
(e) 0.05×100 (f) 2.3×1000

2. Calculate.
(a) 300×0.1 (b) 5.4×0.1
(c) 125×0.01 (d) 0.6×0.01
(e) $12\,000 \times 0.1$ (f) 0.07×0.1

3. Calculate.
(a) $456 \div 10$ (b) $23 \div 1000$
(c) $7.6 \div 10$ (d) $0.67 \div 10$
(e) $0.09 \div 100$ (f) $8000 \div 1000$

4. Calculate.
(a) $670 \div 0.1$ (b) $99 \div 0.01$
(c) $6.9 \div 0.1$ (d) $0.5 \div 0.01$
(e) $0.07 \div 0.1$ (f) $6000 \div 0.01$

5. Calculate.
(a) 6700×0.1 (b) 8.45×1000
(c) 0.03×100 (d) $1.2 \div 0.01$
(e) 0.004×1000 (f) $55.5 \div 0.1$
(g) $19 \div 10$ (h) 0.6×100
(i) $1000 \div 0.01$ (j) 0.34×0.1
(k) 34.5×100 (l) $2.02 \div 0.01$

6. Calculate.
(a) $45 \div 100 \div 0.1$
(b) $62 \times 0.01 \times 0.01$
(c) $3.8 \times 100 \times 0.01$
(d) $0.4 \div 0.1 \div 100$
(e) $4.08 \times 100 \times 0.1$

PERCENT

Percent means "out of one hundred."
The percent symbol is made up of a 1
and two 0s.

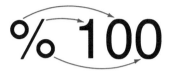

A percent can be written as a

decimal
$$15\% = \frac{15}{100}$$
$$= 0.15$$

fraction
$$15\% = \frac{15}{100}$$
$$= \frac{3}{20}$$

ratio
$$15\% = 15 : 100$$
$$= 3 : 20$$

EXERCISE 4

1. Write each of the following as
decimals.
(a) 23%   (b) 46%   (c) 87%
(d) 5%   (e) 99%   (f) 1%

2. Write each of the following as
fractions.
(a) 50%   (b) 25%   (c) 10%
(d) 1%   (e) 45%   (f) 150%
(g) 110%   (h) 7.5%   (i) 9.6%

3. Write each of the following as ratios.
(a) 50%   (b) 60%   (c) 15%
(d) 20%   (e) 30%   (f) 70%
(g) 10%   (h) 8%   (i) 5%

4. Write as percents.
(a) $\frac{1}{2}$ (b) $\frac{1}{4}$ (c) $\frac{7}{10}$

(d) $\frac{1}{5}$ (e) $\frac{3}{5}$ (f) $\frac{1}{8}$

5. Write as percents.
(a) 0.5   (b) 0.35   (c) 0.86
(d) 0.02   (e) 0.17   (f) 0.9

PERCENT OF A NUMBER

Example. At a school with 720
students, 65% of the
students had taken a course
in computers.
How many had taken a
computer course?

Solution: 65% of 720 = 0.65 × 720
= 468

A computer course had been
taken by 468 students.

EXERCISE 5

1. Calculate.
(a) 20% of 300   (b) 35% of 460
(c) 88% of 550   (d) 120% of 50
(e) 7% of 1250   (f) 24.5% of 900
(g) 9.1% of 7000   (h) 0.5% of 2000

2. In a poll 30% of the 800 people
surveyed preferred sports cars.
How many people preferred sports
cars?

3. A sweater was priced at $90.00.
During a sale the price of the sweater
was reduced by 25%.
What was the new price of the
sweater?

4. A painting that sold for $20 000.00
increased in value by 10% after one
year.
What was the increase in value?

5. Sandra sold a house for $200 000
and received a commission of 1.5%.
What was her commission?

6. The bill for dinner at a restaurant
was $80.
If you want to leave a tip of 15%, how
much money should you leave?

NUMBERS AS PERCENTS

Example. Denise scored 184 out of 200 on a driving test. What is this score as a percent?

Solution: $\frac{184}{200} \times 100\% = 0.92 \times 100\%$
$$= 92\%$$

Denise scored 92%.

EXERCISE 6

1. (a) What percent of 80 is 20?
(b) What percent of 180 is 45?
(c) What percent of 200 is 10?
(d) What percent of 75 is 15?
(e) What percent of 120 is 6?

2. The football team won 10 of the 16 games played.
What percentage of the games did they win?

3. A jacket that cost $150.00 was reduced in price by $30.00.
What percentage reduction is this?

4. John received 70 out of 90 on a math test.
What is his mark as a percent to the nearest tenth?

5. For the play-offs, ticket prices increased from $20 to $60.
What percentage increase is this?

6. We use karats to indicate the amount of gold in an item. Each karat is one twenty-fourth part gold. Thus 24 karat gold is pure gold.
(a) A bracelet is marked as being 12 karat gold.
What percent gold is this?
(b) Ken has an 18 karat gold necklace.
What percent gold is it?

CALCULATING 100%

Example. Nine of the radios tested were found to be defective. If this represents 5% of the radios tested, how many radios were tested?

Solution: Let n represent the number of radios tested.

$$5\% \text{ of } n = 9$$
$$0.05n = 9$$
$$n = \frac{9}{0.05}$$
$$n = 180$$

∴ 180 radios were tested.

EXERCISE 7

1. (a) 15 is 20% of what number?
(b) 12 is 60% of what number?
(c) 8 is 10% of what number?
(d) 24 is 16% of what number?
(e) 35 is 40% of what number?

2. At a concert, 12 000 people bought souvenir programs. This represents 60% of the people who attended the concert.
How many people were at the concert?

3. Five hundred students bought yearbooks. This is 40% of the students in the school.
How many students are there?

4. Blood was donated by 132 mall employees. This represents 22% of the employees.
How many employees are there?

5. Tickets for 61 200 seats were sold for the game. This represents 72% of the seats available.
How many seats does the stadium have?

ROUNDING RULES AND SIGNIFICANT DIGITS

ROUNDING RULES

We round numbers when we want to simplify them. The following table illustrates the rounding rules for numbers. The first digit to be discarded is called the key digit.

Number	Required Place	Rule	Key Digit	Rounded Number
12 345 0.1214	1000 0.01	If the key digit is less than 5, we round down.	12 345 0.1214	12 000 0.12
375 0.8352 65 003	100 0.01 10 000	If the key digit is greater than 5, or if it is a 5 followed by digits other than zero, we round up.	375 0.8352 65 003	400 0.84 70 000
3500 2500 4.35 4.25	1000 1000 0.1 0.1	If the key digit is 5 followed only by zeros, we round to the nearest even digit.	3500 2500 4.35 4.25	4000 2000 4.4 4.2

SIGNIFICANT DIGITS

If someone reports that there are 700 cars in a parking lot, it is not clear if 700 is an exact count or an estimate. Are there 700 cars, or are there 703 cars? To resolve this problem we use significant digits when recording numbers.

A significant digit is any non-zero digit, or any zero that serves a purpose other than being a placeholder. In the number 700 it is not clear whether the zeros are significant, other than to indicate where the decimal point is. We show significant digits using scientific notation.

If 700 is exactly 700 and the zeros are significant, we write 7.00×10^2.

If 700 is an approximation to the nearest hundred and the two zeros are not significant, we write 7×10^2.

Measurement	Number of Significant Digits	Rule
7.83 cm	3	The digits 1, 2, 3, ..., 9 are significant.
18.07 km	4	Zeros between the non-zero digits are significant.
0.034 m	2	Zeros to the left of the first non-zero digit are not significant.
7000 km	1	The zeros are placeholders. If the zeros were not just placeholders but significant, we would write 7000 as 7.000×10^3.

Our rules for rounding to a stated place value extend to rounding to a given number of significant digits or precision.

When numbers are added or subtracted, we round the answer to a number as precise as the least precise of the numbers used. For example,

$$2.738 + 0.4761 + 5.21 = 8.4241$$

We round the answer to 8.42 because the least precise number used is 5.21, which is accurate to the nearest hundredth.

When numbers are multiplied or divided, the answer is rounded to as many significant digits as are contained in the number with the fewest significant digits in the computation. For example,

$$53.789 \times 4.52 = 243.126\,28$$

We round the answer to 243 because 4.52 has 3 significant digits.

EXERCISE 8

1. Round to the nearest ten.
(a) 32.75   (b) 45   (c) 143.04

2. Round to the nearest tenth.
(a) 14.17   (b) 0.752   (c) 0.95

3. Round to the nearest hundredth.
(a) 3.125   (b) 5.144   (c) 72.866

4. Round to the indicated place.
(a) 35 714   (nearest thousand) *36 000*
(b) 36 500   (nearest thousand) *36 000*
(c) 2312   (nearest hundred) *2300*
(d) 0.56   (nearest tenth) *0.6*
(e) 0.45   (nearest tenth) *0.4*
(f) 0.382   (nearest hundredth) *0.38*
(g) 3.475   (nearest hundredth) *3.48*
(h) 7.486   (nearest hundredth) *7.49*
(i) 876 310   (nearest ten thousand) *880 000*
(j) 946   (nearest hundred) *900*
(k) 73.65   (nearest tenth) *73.6*
(l) 8.723   (nearest hundredth) *8.72*
(m) 53 571   (nearest thousand) *54 000*
(n) 745.3   (nearest ten) *745.3*
                                  750

5. Calculate and round answers to the appropriate number of significant digits.
(a) 3.75 + 461.392 + 0.8473
(b) 5.687 − 3.4
(c) 56.555 × 4.8
(d) 816.2 ÷ 11
(e) 409 × 0.24
(f) 2134 + 47.9 + 0.66 + 88.88
(g) 9.761 − 3.8

MIND BENDER

Fill in the boxes to make a correct multiplication.

1.1 WORKING WITH WHOLE NUMBERS AND DECIMALS

The following map gives the driving distances, in kilometres, between several cities. The map is not drawn to scale.

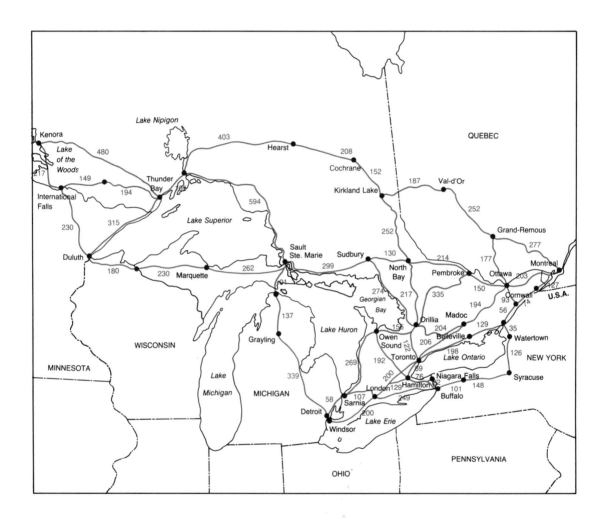

EXERCISE 1.1

B

1. What is the shortest distance from Ottawa to Sault Ste. Marie if you must travel through Orillia?

2. What is the shortest distance from Montreal to Thunder Bay?

3. What is the shortest distance from Toronto to Hearst and return?

4. A company pays its salespeople $0.27/km for travel expenses.
How much would be paid for a trip from Windsor to Hamilton and return?

5. (a) What is the shortest distance from Kirkland Lake to Owen Sound?
(b) Approximately how long would it take to complete the trip at an average speed of 80 km/h? Express your answer to the nearest tenth of an hour.

6. How long would it take to drive from Windsor to Montreal at an average speed of 95 km/h, allowing 1.5 h for stops for refreshments and gasoline?

7. (a) What is the shortest distance from Niagara Falls to Sarnia if you must travel through Hamilton?
(b) If your car uses fuel at a rate of 12 L/100 km, how many litres of fuel will you use?
(c) What is the cost of the fuel?

8. You can travel from Kirkland Lake to Montreal in two ways: through North Bay, or through Val-d'Or.
Which way is the shortest and by how much?

9. A car rally was organized to start at Duluth, go around Lake Superior, and finish at Duluth.
(a) How many kilometres was the rally?
(b) If cars must average 75 km/h, how long should the rally take? (To the nearest tenth of an hour.)

(c) If the winning car's gasoline consumption was 9 L/100 km, how many litres of gasoline were used?
(d) If the winning car used regular unleaded gasoline, what was the approximate cost of the fuel?

10. Frank left a service centre in Belleville at 08:30. He drove to Toronto at 95 km/h and from Toronto to Sudbury at 90 km/h.

If he stopped for 45 min during the trip, at approximately what time did he arrive in Sudbury?

11. Susan travelled for 2.5 h at 80 km/h and 1.25 h at 60 km/h.
How far did she travel?

12. Corrine lives in Toronto and works in Hamilton. She commutes 230 d each year.
(a) How many kilometres does she drive each year?
(b) Because of the traffic she averages 40 km/h.
How many hours does she spend commuting each year?
(c) Her car uses gasoline at the rate of 10 L/100 km.
How many litres of gasoline does her car use each year?
(d) Her car uses regular unleaded gasoline. How much does she spend for gasoline each year?

1.2 EVALUATING NUMERICAL EXPRESSIONS

The expression $2 + 4 \times 5$ can be evaluated in two ways.

$$2 + 4 \times 5 = 6 \times 5 \quad \text{or} \quad 2 + 4 \times 5 = 2 + 20$$
$$= 30 \qquad\qquad\qquad = 22$$

To eliminate this situation, the following order of operations has been agreed upon.

B	E	DM	AS
Do the computations in brackets first.	Simplify numbers with exponents and "of."	Divide or multiply in the order in which ÷ and × appear from left to right.	Add or subtract in the order in which + and − appear from left to right.

The acronym BEDMAS helps us to remember the order.

It is helpful to know if a calculator respects the order of operations. To determine this, evaluate $2 + 8 \times 9$.

Press **2** **+** **8** **×** **9** **=**

If the display is 74, the calculator performs ÷ and × before + and −.

If the display is 90, the above order of operations is not respected by the calculator. In this case, to evaluate $2 + 8 \times 9$,

press **8** **×** **9** **+** **2** **=**

The display is 74.

15.3

Spreadsheet activities related to this topic are found in section 15.3.

Example 1. Simplify. $32 \div 2 + 11 - (5 + 1)$

Solution:
$$\begin{aligned} & 32 \div 2 + 11 - (5 + 1) && \text{B} && \text{(brackets)} \\ = & 32 \div 2 + 11 - 6 && \text{D} && \text{(divide)} \\ = & 16 + 11 - 6 && \text{AS} && \text{(add and subtract)} \\ = & 21 \end{aligned}$$

Example 2. Evaluate $5x + (y + x)^2 - x^3$ for $x = 3$, $y = 5$.

Solution:
$$\begin{aligned} & 5x + (y + x)^2 - x^3 \\ = & 5(3) + (5 + 3)^2 - (3)^3 \\ = & 5(3) + 8^2 - (3)^2 && \text{B} && \text{(brackets)} \\ = & 5(3) + 64 - 9 && \text{E} && \text{(exponents)} \\ = & 15 + 64 - 9 && \text{M} && \text{(multiply)} \\ = & 70 && \text{AS} && \text{(add and subtract)} \end{aligned}$$

EXERCISE 1.2

B

1. Evaluate.
(a) 123 + 234 − 406
(b) 810 ÷ 10 + 37
(c) 99 × 7 − 46
(d) 23 × 7 + 13 × 6
(e) 7(5 + 9) + 18 ÷ 2

2. Evaluate.
(a) $9(87 + 12) + 13^2$
(b) 789 − 610 − 12 + 456
(c) 1000 − 43 × 8
(d) 468 ÷ 52 + 9 − 11
(e) 567 − 324 + 102 − 21 ÷ 3

3. If x = 4, y = 2, and z = 3, evaluate each of the following.
(a) 5x + 6y + 12z
(b) $x^2 + y^2 + z^2$
(c) 5xy − 2yz + 39
(d) $2(3x − y) + z^2$
(e) 7xyz − 2xy + 3yz − 4

4. Evaluate for t = 9.
(a) $t^2 + 3t − 12$
(b) (t − 1)(t + 7)
(c) 6t(3t + 19)
(d) t(4 + 5t) − (t − 2)
(e) $2t^2 − 4t + 21$

5. Evaluate for m = 4.5.
(a) $m^2 + 7m + 23$
(b) (2m + 9)(m − 2)
(c) $3m^2 − 2m − 1$
(d) m(5m − 4) + 6(2m − 1)
(e) 6m(5m − 13)

6. The area of a trapezoid is given by the formula

$$A = \frac{h}{2}(a + b)$$

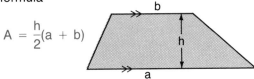

Calculate the value of A for each of the following to the correct number of significant digits.
(a) h = 22 cm, a = 14 cm, b = 9 cm
(b) h = 9.8 m, a = 4.3 m, b = 4.1 m
(c) h = 5.67 m, a = 11.23 m, b = 7.45 m
(d) h = 1986 m, a = 2345 m, b = 1011 m

EXTRA

INVESTIGATING SEQUENCES

Numbers such as

3, 5, 9, 7, 4, 12

are called terms of a sequence. Some sequences follow a pattern such as

3, 5, 7, 9, 11, 13,

or   2, 6, 18, 54, 162,

The following is an interesting sequence building problem.

Pick any number to start a sequence, for example 13.

If the last number in the sequence is odd, the next number is found by tripling it and adding 1.

If the last number in the sequence is even, the next number is found by halving it.

Since we chose 13 to start our sequence, the sequence becomes

13, 40, 20, 10, 5, 16, 8, 4, 2, 1

EXERCISE

1. Use the above rules to build sequences starting with the numbers
(a) 17   (b) 7   (c) 30

2. What conjecture can you draw about sequences that are built using the above rules?

1.3 INTEGERS

Nov.   Temp.

Dawson   −17°C
Halifax   +3°C
Regina   −5°C
Ottawa   +1°C

Whenever we record temperatures, we are using integers.

Whenever we record the elevation of a place on the earth, we are using integers.

Place   Elevation

Dead Sea   −400 m
Death Valley   −86 m
Mt. Everest   +8853 m
Lake Erie   +174 m

The set of integers consists of the positive integers, the negative integers, and zero.

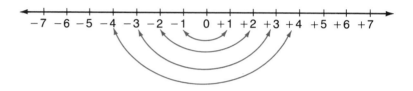

On the integer line, integers increase to the right. For any two integers, the one to the right is greater, and the one to the left is less.

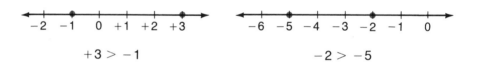

$+3 > -1$ $-2 > -5$

This section will review arithmetic operations with integers.

The following charts provide a summary of the rules for multiplying and dividing integers.

Multiplying

×	positive	negative
positive	+	−
negative	−	+

Dividing

÷	positive	negative
positive	+	−
negative	−	+

Example. Simplify.
        (a) $-3 + 5 - 7$ (b) $(-3)(-6)$ (c) $(-18) \div 3$

Solution:

(a) $-3 + 5 - 7$ (b) $(-3)(-6)$ (c) $(-18) \div 3$
      $= 2 - 7$ $= 18$ $= -6$
      $= -5$

EXERCISE 1.3

B

1. Simplify.
(a) $3 + 7 - 4$
(b) $-15 + 9 - 6$
(c) $-1 - 3 - 5$
(d) $8 - 14 - 3$
(e) $6 - 2 - 11$
(f) $-16 - 17 + 18$

2. Simplify.
(a) $6 - (-4) + 3$
(b) $-3 - (+7) - (-2)$
(c) $-9 - (+7) - 6$ (d) $27 - (-3) + 16$
(e) $-24 + (-5) + 8$ (f) $-9 - 3 - (-14)$

3. Simplify.
(a) $(-4)(-5)$ (b) $(-7)(+6)$
(c) $8 \times (-8)$ (d) $(-9) \times (-8)$
(e) $16 \div (-2)$ (f) $-30 \div 6$
(g) -7×4 (h) $-56 \div (-8)$

4. Simplify.
(a) $-3 + (-4)(-5)$
(b) $-5 \times (-2) + 7$
(c) $-12 \div 3 + 6$
(d) $7 - (-2)(-5)$
(e) $-6 \times (-5)(-4)$
(f) $21 \div (-7) - 4$
(g) $13 - (-4) + 6(-2)$
(h) $-30 - (-40) \div 4$
(i) $9 \div 3 - 4 - 5$
(j) $-2 \times 8 - 6 - 7$

5. Find the value of $2a + 3b - 4c$ for each of the following.
(a) $a = 1, b = 2, c = 1$
(b) $a = -1, b = -2, c = 0$
(c) $a = -3, b = 4, c = -2$

6. If $x = 2, y = -2,$ and $z = -1$, evaluate each of the following.
(a) $2x + 3y + 4z$
(b) $5x - 2y - 3z$
(c) $4x - y - z$
(d) $-3x + 5y - 2z$

7. Calculate.
(a) $(-3)^2$ (b) -3^2 (c) $(-4)^2$
(d) -4^2 (e) -1^2 (f) $(-1)^2$

THE +/– KEY

The +/– key on a calculator allows us to perform calculations involving integers.

When we enter a number into a calculator, the calculator assumes that the number is positive. To enter a negative number, we first enter the positive equivalent and then press the +/– key. A negative sign will then appear in front of the number and we proceed with the arithmetic operations as before.

To add -12 and -11, press

[1] [2] [+/–] [+] [1] [1] [+/–] [=]

The display is -23.

To subtract -6 from -7, press

[7] [+/–] [–] [6] [+/–] [=]

The display is -1.

To multiply -155 by -234, press

[1] [5] [5] [+/–] [×] [2] [3] [4] [+/–] [=]

The display is 36270.

To divide -875 by 7, press

[8] [7] [5] [+/–] [÷] [7] [=]

The display is -125.

Use your calculator to simplify each of the following.
1. -1043×86
2. $-3645 \div (-81)$
3. $(-407)(-309)$
4. $5016 \div (-11)$

1.4 APPLYING FRACTIONS

The following stock quotations are from the Toronto Stock Exchange.

Tuesday, September 15								
52-week								
High	Low	Stock	Div.	High	Low	Close	Ch'ge	Vol.
$26\frac{1}{4}$	$20\frac{1}{2}$	Southam	.56	$24	$23\frac{1}{4}$	$23\frac{1}{4}$	$-\frac{1}{8}$	30 432
$26\frac{1}{2}$	$17\frac{5}{8}$	Spar Aero	.40	$18\frac{3}{8}$	$18\frac{1}{8}$	$18\frac{1}{4}$	$+\frac{3}{8}$	4300
$8\frac{1}{8}$	$5\frac{1}{4}$	Tmedia A		$6	6	6	$-\frac{1}{4}$	2000
$23\frac{3}{4}$	$13\frac{5}{8}$	Tor Sun	.10	$21\frac{7}{8}$	$21\frac{3}{8}$	$21\frac{1}{2}$	$+\frac{1}{8}$	990
18	$16\frac{1}{4}$	Ux Corp	1.50	$18	18	18	$+\frac{7}{8}$	100
$28\frac{3}{4}$	$21\frac{3}{8}$	Xerox Can	.72	$21\frac{5}{8}$	$21\frac{3}{8}$	$21\frac{3}{8}$	$-\frac{1}{4}$	32 600
195	50	Zing		$175	130	155	$+15$	5000

EXERCISE 1.4

B

1. What is the difference in price between Spar Aero's 52-week high and low?

2. Sam owns 500 shares of Ux Corp.
(a) What was the closing price of Ux Corp on Tuesday, September 15?
(b) What was the closing price of Ux Corp on Monday, September 14?
(c) How much did Sam's stock increase in value on Tuesday?

3. Janet bought 3000 shares of Xerox at the high price for the day and sold it at the low price for the day.
How much money did she lose?

4. (a) What is the difference in the Tor Sun high and low for the day?
(b) What is the difference in the Tor Sun high and close for the day?

5. You own 750 shares of Southam. What is the total value of your dividend?

6. (a) John bought 3000 shares of Zing at its high for the day.
How much did he pay for the shares?
(b) What was the closing price for Zing on Monday, September 14?

7. What is the difference between Southam's low for the day and Tor Sun's low for the day?

8. Carl bought 500 shares of Spar Aero at the high for the day and 1500 shares of Tor Sun at the high for the day.
What was the total cost of his purchases?

9. Sue bought 600 shares of Spar Aero at the high for the day. Sandra bought 525 shares of Xerox at the high for the day. Who paid the most?

10. Holly has the following shares in her stock portfolio.

Tmedia A	450
Ux Corp	200
Southam	50
Zing	1000

(a) What was the total value of her portfolio at the end the day's trading on September 15?

(b) What was the total value of her portfolio at the end of the day's trading on September 14?

11. If you had bought 1200 shares of Tor Sun at its lowest 52-week price and sold them at the highest 52-week price, how much of a profit would you have made?

In the following questions be sure to follow the order of operations.

12. Simplify.

(a) $\frac{1}{5} + \frac{3}{5} - \frac{2}{5}$ (b) $1\frac{1}{2} + 3\frac{3}{4}$

(c) $3\frac{1}{3} + 2\frac{1}{4}$ (d) $4\frac{5}{6} + 2\frac{1}{12}$

(e) $\frac{1}{4} \times \frac{1}{3}$ (f) $1\frac{1}{2} \times 1\frac{1}{8}$

(g) $1\frac{1}{3} \div \frac{1}{2}$ (h) $\frac{2}{3} \div \frac{1}{3}$

(i) $1\frac{1}{2} + 1\frac{3}{4} \times 2$ (j) $2\frac{1}{3} \div \frac{1}{4} \times \frac{1}{2}$

(k) $2\frac{1}{2} - 1\frac{1}{4} \times \frac{1}{8}$ (l) $10 - 1\frac{1}{3} \div \frac{1}{2}$

13. Carlie's job pays $10.50/h for the first 40 h in a week, time and a half for the first 5 h of overtime, and double time and a half for all other overtime.
Complete the table to find her earnings for four weeks.

Week	Hours Worked	Earnings
1	39.5	
2	43	
3	46.5	
4	51.5	

CALCULATOR MATH

THE a b/c KEY

Some calculators have an a b/c key, which allows us to perform operations with fractions.

To enter $8\frac{3}{4}$, press

8 **a b/c** **3** **a b/c** **4**

The display is $8 \lrcorner 3 \lrcorner 4$

To simplify $2\frac{3}{8} \div 1\frac{1}{4}$, press

2 **a b/c** **3** **a b/c** **8** **÷** **1** **a b/c** **1** **a b/c** **4** **=**

The display is $1 \lrcorner 9 \lrcorner 10$

∴ $2\frac{3}{8} \div 1\frac{1}{4} = 1\frac{9}{10}$

Some calculators can express fractions in lowest terms.

To simplify $\frac{104}{117}$, press

1 **0** **4** **a b/c** **1** **1** **7** **=**

The display is $8 \lrcorner 9$

∴ $\frac{104}{117} = \frac{8}{9}$

EXERCISE

1. Simplify.

(a) $2\frac{1}{2} + 3\frac{5}{8}$ (b) $4\frac{1}{4} - 2\frac{3}{5}$

(c) $6\frac{7}{8} \times \frac{5}{6}$ (d) $\frac{7}{10} \div 1\frac{7}{12}$

(e) $\frac{4}{7} + \frac{3}{11} + 5$ (f) $17 \times 3\frac{3}{4}$

2. Express each fraction in lowest terms.

(a) $\frac{119}{153}$ (b) $\frac{209}{228}$ (c) $\frac{138}{161}$ (d) $\frac{145}{232}$

1.5 RULES OF EXPONENTS

The term 2^6 means $2 \times 2 \times 2 \times 2 \times 2 \times 2 = 64$.
2 is the base and 6 is the exponent.

Using the exponent key on a calculator, press $\boxed{2}\ \boxed{y^x}\ \boxed{6}\ \boxed{=}$

The display is $\boxed{64.}$

The following are the rules for simplifying expressions with exponents.

Multiplication

Rule for Multiplication
$a^m \times a^n = a^{m+n}$

Example 1. Multiply. $t^3 \times t^2$

Solution: Not using the rule,

$$t^3 \times t^2 = (t \times t \times t) \times (t \times t)$$
$$= t^5$$

Using the rule,

$$t^3 \times t^2 = t^{3+2}$$
$$= t^5$$

Division

Rule for Division
$a^m \div a^n = a^{m-n}$

Example 2. Divide. $y^5 \div y^3, \quad y \neq 0$

Solution: Not using the rule,

$$\frac{y^5}{y^3} = \frac{y \times y \times y \times y \times y}{y \times y \times y}$$
$$= y^2$$

Using the rule,

$$\frac{y^5}{y^3} = y^{5-3}$$
$$= y^2$$

Powers

Rule for Powers
$(a^m)^n = a^{m \times n} = a^{mn}$

Example 3. Simplify. $(z^2)^3$

Solution: Not using the rule,

$$(z^2)^3 = z^2 \times z^2 \times z^2$$
$$= z^6$$

Using the rule,

$$(z^2)^3 = z^{2 \times 3}$$
$$= z^6$$

Power of a Product

Power of a Product
$(a^m b^n)^p = a^{m \times p} b^{n \times p} = a^{mp} b^{np}$

Example 4. Simplify. $(-2s^5t^4)^3$

Solution:

Not using the rule,

$(-2s^5t^4)^3 = (-2s^5t^4)(-2s^5t^4)(-2s^5t^4)$
$\qquad\qquad = -8s^{15}t^{12}$

Using the rule,

$(-2s^5t^4)^3 = (-2)^{1 \times 3}s^{5 \times 3}t^{4 \times 3}$
$\qquad\qquad = (-2)^3s^{15}t^{12}$
$\qquad\qquad = -8s^{15}t^{12}$

Power of a Quotient
$\left(\dfrac{a^m}{b^n}\right)^p = \dfrac{a^{m \times p}}{b^{n \times p}} = \dfrac{a^{mp}}{b^{np}}, \quad b \neq 0$

Example 5. Simplify. $\left(\dfrac{3r^2}{s^3}\right)^4$

Solution:

Not using the rule,

$\left(\dfrac{3r^2}{s^3}\right)^4 = \dfrac{3r^2}{s^3} \times \dfrac{3r^2}{s^3} \times \dfrac{3r^2}{s^3} \times \dfrac{3r^2}{s^3}$

$\qquad\qquad = \dfrac{81r^8}{s^{12}}$

Using the rule,

$\left(\dfrac{3r^2}{s^3}\right)^4 = \dfrac{3^{1 \times 4}r^{2 \times 4}}{s^{3 \times 4}}$

$\qquad\qquad = \dfrac{81r^8}{s^{12}}$

EXERCISE 1.5

A

1. Simplify.
(a) 3^4 (b) 2^5 (c) 5^2
(d) $(-2)^3$ (e) $(-1)^7$ (f) $2^2 \times 3^2$
(g) $(3 \times 2)^2$ (h) $(-4)^2$ (i) -4^2

2. Simplify.
(a) $x^4 \times x^7$ (b) $b^8 \div b^7$ (c) $(m^3)^2$
(d) $s^3 \times s^4$ (e) $t^9 \div t^4$ (f) $(r^2)^5$
(g) $b^3 \times b^5 \times b$ (h) $(m^4)^5$
(i) $r^{11} \div r^9$ (j) $(a^2b^3)^2$

(k) $\left(\dfrac{a^6}{b^7}\right)^2$ (l) $\left(\dfrac{m^3}{n^2}\right)^3$

B

3. Simplify.
(a) $3m^3 \times 4m^5$ (b) $(7x^2)(-3x^4)$
(c) $(-2t^3)(-3t)(4t^2)$ (d) $7a^2 \times 8a^2 \times a$
(e) $(-24b^4) \div (6b^2)$ (f) $(18s^5) \div (-9s)$
(g) $(6x^2y^3)^2$ (h) $(2a^2bc^4)^3$

(i) $\left(\dfrac{4m^2}{3n^3}\right)^2$ (j) $\left(\dfrac{2x^2y}{3z^3}\right)^3$

4. Simplify.
(a) $(4x^2y^3)(5x^4y)$
(b) $6m^3n^4 \times 3mn^3$
(c) $(36a^3b^4) \div (9a^2b^2)$
(d) $(50x^3yz) \div (-10xy)$
(e) $(-6x^2y^4) \times (7x^3y^2)$

5. Simplify.
(a) $\dfrac{(2a^3b^2)(-3a^4b^3)}{6ab}$

(b) $\dfrac{(-3r^2s^2t^4)^3}{9r^2s}$

(c) $\dfrac{(-6x^2yz^3)(-3xyz)}{2x^2yz}$

(d) $\dfrac{(-2a^2b^2)^2(-3ab)}{(-6a^2b^2)}$

C

6. Simplify.
(a) $3^a \times 3^b \times 3^c$ (b) $2^{x+y} \div 2^{x-y}$

1.6 RATIONAL EXPONENTS

For the multiplication rule, $a^m \times a^n = a^{m+n}$, to be true for a zero exponent, we must define a^0 so that

$$a^0 \times a^m = a^{0+m}$$
$$= a^m$$

Since $1 \times a^m = a^m$, it is reasonable to make the following definition for a^0.

$$\boxed{a^0 = 1, \quad a \neq 0}$$

Example 1. Simplify.

(a) $3^0 + 5^0$

(b) $\dfrac{m^0}{4y^0}$

Solution: (a) $3^0 + 5^0 = 1 + 1$
$\qquad\qquad\quad = 2$

(b) $\dfrac{m^0}{4y^0} = \dfrac{1}{4 \times 1}$
$\qquad\qquad = \frac{1}{4}$

For the multiplication rule to be true for negative exponents, we must define a^{-m} so that

$$a^m \times a^{-m} = a^{m+(-m)}$$
$$= a^0$$
$$= 1$$

Since $a^m \times \dfrac{1}{a^m} = 1$, it is reasonable to define a^{-m} as the reciprocal of a^m.

$$\boxed{a^{-m} = \dfrac{1}{a^m}, \quad a \neq 0}$$

Example 2. Simplify.

(a) 3^{-2}

(b) $\dfrac{1}{2^{-4}}$

Solution: (a) $3^{-2} = \dfrac{1}{3^2}$
$\qquad\qquad = \dfrac{1}{9}$

(b) $\dfrac{1}{2^{-4}} = \dfrac{1}{\frac{1}{2^4}} = \dfrac{1}{\frac{1}{16}}$
$\qquad\qquad = 1 \times \dfrac{16}{1}$
$\qquad\qquad = 16$

For the multiplication rule to be true for fractional exponents, we must define $4^{\frac{1}{2}}$ so that

$$4^{\frac{1}{2}} \times 4^{\frac{1}{2}} = 4^{\frac{1}{2}+\frac{1}{2}} = 4$$

but
$$\sqrt{4} \times \sqrt{4} = 2 \times 2 = 4$$

Therefore
$$4^{\frac{1}{2}} = \sqrt{4}$$

Fractional Exponents

In general,

$$a^{\frac{1}{n}} = \sqrt[n]{a}$$

Further
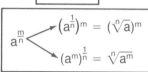
$$a^{\frac{m}{n}} \begin{cases} \left(a^{\frac{1}{n}}\right)^m = \left(\sqrt[n]{a}\right)^m \\ \left(a^m\right)^{\frac{1}{n}} = \sqrt[n]{a^m} \end{cases}$$

Example 3. Simplify.

$$\text{(a) } 36^{\frac{1}{2}} \qquad \text{(b) } 27^{-\frac{1}{3}} \qquad \text{(c) } 16^{\frac{3}{4}}$$

Solution:

(a) $36^{\frac{1}{2}} = \sqrt{36}$
$= 6$

(b) $27^{-\frac{1}{3}} = \dfrac{1}{27^{\frac{1}{3}}}$
$= \dfrac{1}{\sqrt[3]{27}}$
$= \dfrac{1}{3}$

(c) $16^{\frac{3}{4}} = (\sqrt[4]{16})^3$
$= (2)^3$
$= 8$

EXERCISE 1.6

B

1. Simplify.

(a) 7^0 (b) $4^0 + 5^0$ (c) 2^{-2}

(d) $\dfrac{1}{4^{-2}}$ (e) $\dfrac{1}{3^0}$ (f) $\dfrac{3^{-2}}{2^{-3}}$

(g) 10^{-4} (h) $(-5)^0$ (i) -9^0

(j) $(-2)^3$ (k) $(-3)^{-2}$ (l) $(-1)^{-5}$

2. Simplify.

(a) $9^{\frac{1}{2}}$ (b) $16^{\frac{1}{2}}$ (c) $8^{\frac{1}{3}}$

(d) $16^{\frac{1}{4}}$ (e) $8^{\frac{2}{3}}$ (f) $27^{\frac{2}{3}}$

(g) $81^{\frac{3}{4}}$ (h) $32^{\frac{3}{5}}$ (i) $32^{\frac{2}{5}}$

(j) $-16^{\frac{1}{4}}$ (k) $-81^{\frac{1}{4}}$ (l) $-125^{\frac{2}{3}}$

3. Simplify.

(a) $4^{-\frac{1}{2}}$ (b) $36^{-\frac{1}{2}}$ (c) $27^{-\frac{2}{3}}$

(d) $8^{-\frac{2}{3}}$ (e) $16^{-\frac{3}{4}}$ (f) $32^{-\frac{2}{5}}$

(g) $100^{-\frac{1}{2}}$ (h) $-8^{-\frac{1}{3}}$ (i) $-(-8)^{-\frac{1}{3}}$

(j) $125^{-\frac{2}{3}}$ (k) $-32^{-\frac{4}{5}}$ (l) $(-32)^{-\frac{4}{5}}$

4. Simplify.

(a) $\left(\dfrac{4}{9}\right)^{\frac{3}{2}}$ (b) $\left(\dfrac{27}{125}\right)^{\frac{2}{3}}$ (c) $\left(\dfrac{1}{16}\right)^{-\frac{1}{2}}$

(d) $\left(\dfrac{27}{64}\right)^{-\frac{4}{3}}$ (e) $\left(\dfrac{25x^4}{m^{16}}\right)^{\frac{1}{2}}$ (f) $\left(\dfrac{9a^4}{b^8}\right)^{\frac{1}{2}}$

(g) $b^{\frac{1}{4}} \times b^{\frac{1}{2}}$ (h) $a^{\frac{2}{3}} \times a^{\frac{1}{2}}$ (i) $b^{\frac{1}{2}} \div b^{\frac{1}{4}}$

5. Simplify. Show only positive exponents in the solution.

(a) $\dfrac{a^{-6}}{a^{-7}}$ (b) $b^{-3} \times b^{-7}$ (c) $(x^{-2})^4$

(d) $\left(\dfrac{x^2}{y}\right)^{-1}$ (e) $(a^{-2}b^{-1})^{-1}$ (f) $b^{-5} \div b^2$

(g) $\dfrac{4a^{-2}b}{8a^{-3}b}$ (h) $\dfrac{9x^{-3}y^5}{12x^{-4}y^{-5}}$ (i) $\left(\dfrac{x^{-2}}{y^3}\right)^{-3}$

(j) $\dfrac{2^0 + 3}{1 - 2^{-1}}$ (k) $\dfrac{3 + 5^0}{1 - 3^{-1}}$ (l) $\dfrac{1}{2^{-2}} + \dfrac{1}{3^{-1}}$

1.7 THE y^x AND $y^{\frac{1}{x}}$ KEYS

Many calculators have a y^x key and a $y^{\frac{1}{x}}$ key.

The y^x key evaluates expressions involving exponents such as 8^3.

Press 8 y^x 3 =

The display is $512.$

To evaluate expressions with negative exponents such as 5^{-2},

press 5 y^x 2 +/− =

The display is 0.04

which is the fraction $\frac{1}{25}$.

The $y^{\frac{1}{x}}$ key evaluates expressions with fractional exponents such as $32^{\frac{1}{5}}$.

Press 3 2 $y^{\frac{1}{x}}$ 5 =

The display is $2.$

For negative exponents such as $100^{-\frac{1}{2}}$, proceed as before.

Press 1 0 0 $y^{\frac{1}{x}}$ 2 +/− =

The display is 0.1

which is the fraction $\frac{1}{10}$.

To evaluate expressions such as $16^{\frac{3}{4}}$, we can proceed in two ways since $16^{\frac{3}{4}}$ can be rewritten as $(16^3)^{\frac{1}{4}}$ or $(16^{\frac{1}{4}})^3$.

For $(16^3)^{\frac{1}{4}}$,

press 1 6 y^x 3 $y^{\frac{1}{x}}$ 4 =

The display is $8.$

For $(16^{\frac{1}{4}})^3$,

press 1 6 $y^{\frac{1}{x}}$ 4 y^x 3 =

The display is $8.$

For negative exponents such as $100^{-\frac{3}{2}}$, we can rewrite the expression in four different ways:

$(100^{\frac{1}{2}})^{-3}$, $(100^{-\frac{1}{2}})^3$, $(100^3)^{-\frac{1}{2}}$, and $(100^{-3})^{\frac{1}{2}}$.

Each expression will give the same result.

For $(100^{\frac{1}{2}})^{-3}$,

press 1 0 0 $y^{\frac{1}{x}}$ 2 y^x 3 +/− =

The display is 0.001

For $(100^{-3})^{\frac{1}{2}}$,

press 1 0 0 y^x 3 +/− $y^{\frac{1}{x}}$ 2 =

The display is 0.001

EXERCISE 1.7

1. Estimate, then calculate.
(a) 32.5^4 (b) 0.592^6 (c) 817^3
(d) $202^{\frac{1}{2}}$ (e) $61.3^{\frac{1}{3}}$ (f) $99^{\frac{1}{4}}$
(g) 8.7^{-2} (h) 14.3^{-3} (i) 106^{-4}
(j) $33^{-\frac{1}{2}}$ (k) $42.8^{-\frac{1}{3}}$ (l) $1605^{-\frac{1}{4}}$
(m) $41^{\frac{2}{3}}$ (n) $66^{\frac{2}{5}}$ (o) $19.7^{\frac{3}{4}}$
(p) $151^{-\frac{2}{3}}$ (q) $88.7^{-\frac{3}{5}}$ (r) $6.3^{-\frac{3}{4}}$

1.8 RATIO, PROPORTION, AND RATE

A fraction can be used to compare a football team's 5 wins to 9 games played as shown.

$$\text{wins} \longrightarrow \frac{5}{9} \longleftarrow \text{games played}$$

wins $\longrightarrow$ 5

games played $\longrightarrow$ 9

We say that the ratio of wins to games played is "5 to 9."

> A ratio is a comparison of two or more quantities by division. The quantities must be expressed in the same units.

The above ratio of wins to games played may be expressed in one of three forms:

$$5 \text{ to } 9, \quad 5:9, \quad \text{or} \quad \frac{5}{9}$$

An equation such as $\frac{a}{b} = \frac{c}{d}$ states that two ratios are equal.

Such an equation is called a proportion. Since proportions are equations, we can use equation-solving rules to solve them.

Example 1. One out of six people in the town of Stevensville listen to CHIP radio. If there are 5400 radio listeners, how many listen to CHIP?

Solution: Let x represent the number of CHIP listeners in Stevensville. Then

$$\frac{x}{5400} = \frac{1}{6}$$

$$5400 \times \left(\frac{x}{5400}\right) = \left(\tfrac{1}{6}\right) \times 5400$$

$$x = 900$$

Approximately 900 people in Stevensville listen to CHIP.

A ratio can have more than two terms. If you have 15 LPs, 25 tapes, and 20 CDs, the ratio of LPs to tapes to CDs is

$$15:25:20 \quad \text{or} \quad 3:5:4$$

The ratio of CDs to LPs to tapes is

$$20:15:25 \quad \text{or} \quad 4:3:5$$

These are examples of three-term ratios.

Example 2. Solve the following for x and y.

$$2 : x : 9 = 5 : 7 : y$$

Solution:

Rewrite $2 : x : 9 = 5 : 7 : y$ in the form $\dfrac{2}{5} = \dfrac{x}{7} = \dfrac{9}{y}$.

Now

$$\dfrac{2}{5} = \dfrac{x}{7} \qquad \text{and} \qquad \dfrac{2}{5} = \dfrac{9}{y}$$

$$35 \times \left(\dfrac{2}{5}\right) = \left(\dfrac{x}{7}\right) \times 35 \qquad\qquad 5y \times \left(\dfrac{2}{5}\right) = \left(\dfrac{9}{y}\right) \times 5y$$

$$14 = 10x \qquad\qquad\qquad 2y = 45$$

$$x = 1.4 \qquad\qquad\qquad\quad y = 22.5$$

$\therefore x = 1.4$ and $y = 22.5$.

Example 3. In order to satisfy customer demand, a rental agency has cars, vans, and trucks in the ratio of $9 : 4 : 2$.
If there are a total of 570 vehicles, how many of each are there?

Solution: If there were 15 vehicles, there would be 9 cars, 4 vans, and 2 trucks.
If there were 30 vehicles, there would be 9×2 cars, 4×2 vans, and 2×2 trucks.
For 570 vehicles, there are $9 \times k$ cars, $4 \times k$ vans, and $2 \times k$ trucks

or

$$9k + 4k + 2k = 570$$
$$15k = 570$$
$$k = 38$$

$$9k = 342, \quad 4k = 152, \quad 2k = 76$$

There are 342 cars, 152 vans, and 76 trucks.

A rate is also a comparison of two quantities by division. In a rate the quantities are expressed in different units such as 50 km/h, $1.28/kg, $26/person, and 45 words/min.

To solve problems involving rate, we use the Rule of Three.

Example 4. Andrea drove 332 km in 4 h.
How far can she drive in 7 h at the same rate?

Solution:

1. Statement.   In 4 h Andrea drove 332 km.

2. Reduce to 1.   In 1 h Andrea drove $\frac{332}{4}$.

3. Multiply.   In 7 h she can drive $7 \times \frac{332}{4} = 581$

Andrea can drive 581 km in 7 h at the same rate.

EXERCISE 1.8

A

1. Express in lowest terms.

(a) $\frac{15}{20}$ (b) $21 : 28$

(c) 18 to 9   (d) $15 : 21 : 9$

(e) $\frac{32}{8}$ (f) 35 to 40

(g) $30 : 10$ (h) $12 : 24 : 18$

(i) $\frac{100}{50}$ (j) $3\frac{1}{2} : 2\frac{3}{4}$

B

2. Solve for the variables.

(a) $\frac{x}{12} = \frac{15}{30}$ (b) $\frac{10}{m} = \frac{16}{20}$

(c) $\frac{5}{8} = \frac{t}{13}$ (d) $\frac{20}{14} = \frac{7}{y}$

(e) $3 : x : y = 12 : 10 : 8$

(f) $9 : 7 : m = t : 12 : 6$

3. The ratio of motels to fast-food restaurants on a highway is $3 : 5$.
If there are 18 motels, how many fast-food restaurants are there?

4. Cheryl and Brian invested money in a rock group in the ratio of $2 : 3$.
If they invested a total of $9500, how much did each invest?

5. The scale on a map reads

$$1 : 100\ 000$$

where 1 cm represents 100 000 cm or 1 km.
If two towns on the map are 5.7 cm apart, what is the actual distance between the towns?

6. Rod, Dean, and Barbara sold seats for the charity cruise in the ratio of $3 : 4 : 6$.
If Dean sold 100 seats, how many did each of the others sell?

7. The ratio of sailboats to power boats to fishing boats in the harbour was $4 : 2 : 5$.
If there was a total of 209 boats in the harbour, how many of each kind were there?

8. If 8 notebooks cost $25.52, how much will 12 notebooks cost?

9. The owner of Ace Car Wash can purchase Presto Car Wax for $6.55 for 5 L.
Magic Car Wax costs $11.61 for 9 L.
If the quality is the same, which car wax is the better buy?

10. Tanya drove 315 km in 3.5 h.
(a) What was her rate in km/h?
(b) At this rate, how long will it take her to drive 495 km?
(c) At this rate, how far can she drive in 1.25 h?

11. A set of drums costs $3500.
What is the total cost of the drums if the rate of sales tax is
(a) 6%   (b) 7%   (c) 9%

12. Lou earned $225 in 18 h washing skyscraper windows.
At this rate of pay, how much can he earn in 43 h?

13. Terry typed 252 words in six minutes without making any errors.
What is his rate of typing in words/min?

14. Seventeen concert tickets cost $527.
How much will 7 tickets cost?

15. During the season Jenny pitched 216 innings and struck out 120 batters.
At this rate, how many batters would she strike out in a 9 inning game?

16. John's batting average is 0.260.
How many hits can he expect to get in 150 times at bat?

1.9 SIMPLIFYING RADICALS

Numbers such as $\sqrt{2}$, $\sqrt{3}$, $\sqrt{5}$, and $\sqrt{8}$ are called radicals.

In our previous work we used the following method to simplify radicals.

Since
$$\sqrt{9} \times \sqrt{4} = 3 \times 2$$
$$= 6$$
$$= \sqrt{36}$$
$$\sqrt{9} \times \sqrt{4} = \sqrt{36}$$

In general,

$$\boxed{\sqrt{a} \times \sqrt{b} = \sqrt{ab}, \quad \text{where } a, b \geq 0}$$

$\sqrt{20}$ is an entire radical.

$2\sqrt{5}$ is a mixed radical.

Example 1. Simplify. $\sqrt{20}$

Solution: $\sqrt{20} = \sqrt{4 \times 5}$
$$= \sqrt{4} \times \sqrt{5}$$
$$= 2\sqrt{5}$$

Example 2. Evaluate $\sqrt{7} \times \sqrt{5}$ to the nearest tenth.

Solution: $\sqrt{7} \times \sqrt{5} = \sqrt{35}$ Press **3** **5** $\boxed{\sqrt{}}$

$$\doteq 5.9$$ Display `5.916079783`

Example 3. Write $3\sqrt{5}$ as an entire radical.

Solution: $3\sqrt{5} = \sqrt{9} \times \sqrt{5}$
$$= \sqrt{45}$$

Example 4. Simplify.
      (a) $3\sqrt{2} \times 2\sqrt{7}$ (b) $2\sqrt{5} \times 3\sqrt{15}$

Solution:
(a) $3\sqrt{2} \times 2\sqrt{7} = 3 \times 2 \times \sqrt{2} \times \sqrt{7}$
$$= 6\sqrt{14}$$

(b) $2\sqrt{5} \times 3\sqrt{15} = 6\sqrt{75}$
$$= 6 \times \sqrt{25} \times \sqrt{3}$$
$$= 6 \times 5\sqrt{3}$$
$$= 30\sqrt{3}$$

Like terms such as 2a and 5a can be added using the distributive property.

$$2a + 5a = (2 + 5)a$$
$$= 7a$$

Radicals such as $5\sqrt{2}$ and $3\sqrt{2}$ are called *like radicals* and can be added the same way.

$$5\sqrt{2} + 3\sqrt{2} = (5 + 3)\sqrt{2}$$
$$= 8\sqrt{2}$$

Example 5. Simplify.

(a) $5\sqrt{7} + 4\sqrt{7} - 3\sqrt{7}$ (b) $4\sqrt{5} + 7\sqrt{13} + 3\sqrt{5} - 2\sqrt{13}$

Solution:

(a) $5\sqrt{7} + 4\sqrt{7} - 3\sqrt{7} = (5 + 4 - 3)\sqrt{7}$
$$= 6\sqrt{7}$$

(b) $4\sqrt{5} + 7\sqrt{13} + 3\sqrt{5} - 2\sqrt{13} = 4\sqrt{5} + 3\sqrt{5} + 7\sqrt{13} - 2\sqrt{13}$
$$= 7\sqrt{5} + 5\sqrt{13}$$

Note that $7\sqrt{5}$ and $5\sqrt{13}$ are not added because they are not like radicals.

Example 6. Simplify. $\sqrt{45} + \sqrt{5} - \sqrt{20}$

Solution: $\sqrt{45} + \sqrt{5} - \sqrt{20} = \sqrt{9} \times \sqrt{5} + \sqrt{5} - \sqrt{4} \times \sqrt{5}$
$$= 3\sqrt{5} + \sqrt{5} - 2\sqrt{5}$$
$$= 2\sqrt{5}$$

It is necessary to change all radicals to mixed radicals in simplest form before adding and subtracting.

Example 7. Simplify. $\sqrt{75} + 3\sqrt{27} - 2\sqrt{48}$

Solution: $\sqrt{75} + 3\sqrt{27} - 2\sqrt{48} = \sqrt{25} \times \sqrt{3} + 3 \times \sqrt{9} \times \sqrt{3} - 2 \times \sqrt{16} \times \sqrt{3}$
$$= 5 \times \sqrt{3} + 3 \times 3 \times \sqrt{3} - 2 \times 4 \times \sqrt{3}$$
$$= 5\sqrt{3} + 9\sqrt{3} - 8\sqrt{3}$$
$$= 6\sqrt{3}$$

EXERCISE 1.9

A

1. Express as mixed radicals.

(a) $\sqrt{8}$ (b) $\sqrt{12}$ (c) $\sqrt{18}$
(d) $\sqrt{20}$ (e) $\sqrt{32}$ (f) $\sqrt{50}$
(g) $\sqrt{28}$ (h) $\sqrt{27}$ (i) $\sqrt{200}$
(j) $\sqrt{45}$ (k) $\sqrt{54}$ (l) $\sqrt{72}$

2. Express as entire radicals.

(a) $3\sqrt{2}$ (b) $2\sqrt{5}$ (c) $3\sqrt{3}$
(d) $4\sqrt{2}$ (e) $4\sqrt{6}$ (f) $5\sqrt{10}$
(g) $5\sqrt{7}$ (h) $2\sqrt{11}$ (i) $3\sqrt{5}$

B

3. Simplify.

(a) $\sqrt{7} \times \sqrt{3}$ (b) $\sqrt{6} \times \sqrt{10}$
(c) $\sqrt{5} \times \sqrt{2}$ (d) $\sqrt{11} \times \sqrt{3}$
(e) $\sqrt{6} \times \sqrt{13}$ (f) $\sqrt{2} \times \sqrt{15}$
(g) $\sqrt{14} \times \sqrt{2}$ (h) $\sqrt{3} \times \sqrt{6}$

4. Simplify.

(a) $2\sqrt{2} \times 3\sqrt{7}$ (b) $6\sqrt{3} \times \sqrt{5}$
(c) $4\sqrt{6} \times 2\sqrt{2}$ (d) $5\sqrt{7} \times 3\sqrt{7}$
(e) $8\sqrt{2} \times \sqrt{10}$ (f) $3\sqrt{3} \times 4\sqrt{2}$

5. Simplify.
(a) $\sqrt{2} \times \sqrt{20}$ (b) $\sqrt{18} \times \sqrt{3}$
(c) $\sqrt{5} \times \sqrt{12}$ (d) $\sqrt{8} \times \sqrt{6}$
(e) $\sqrt{27} \times \sqrt{3}$ (f) $\sqrt{32} \times \sqrt{5}$
(g) $\sqrt{54} \times \sqrt{5}$ (h) $\sqrt{28} \times \sqrt{7}$

6. Simplify.
(a) $3\sqrt{7} + 5\sqrt{7}$ (b) $6\sqrt{3} - 2\sqrt{3}$
(c) $8\sqrt{13} - 7\sqrt{13}$ (d) $3\sqrt{5} + 2\sqrt{5}$
(e) $2\sqrt{11} + 12\sqrt{11}$ (f) $12\sqrt{3} - 7\sqrt{3}$
(g) $3\sqrt{7} + \sqrt{7}$ (h) $8\sqrt{15} - 7\sqrt{15}$
(i) $7\sqrt{5} - \sqrt{5}$ (j) $8\sqrt{3} + 4\sqrt{3}$
(k) $\sqrt{5} + \sqrt{5}$ (l) $3\sqrt{3} - \sqrt{3}$
(m) $\sqrt{3} + 4\sqrt{3} + 7\sqrt{3}$
(n) $2\sqrt{7} - 5\sqrt{7} + 6\sqrt{7}$

7. Simplify.
(a) $6\sqrt{3} - 2\sqrt{3} + 7\sqrt{11} - 9\sqrt{11}$
(b) $3\sqrt{17} + 8\sqrt{17} - 6\sqrt{15} + 3\sqrt{15}$
(c) $5\sqrt{2} + 3\sqrt{2} + 6\sqrt{3} - 2\sqrt{3}$
(d) $3\sqrt{5} + 7\sqrt{5} - 2\sqrt{7} + 5\sqrt{7}$
(e) $7\sqrt{3} + 2\sqrt{5} + 3\sqrt{3} + 4\sqrt{5}$
(f) $5\sqrt{7} - 3\sqrt{12} + 2\sqrt{7} - 5\sqrt{12}$

8. Simplify.
(a) $3\sqrt{2} + 5 + 2\sqrt{2} + 3$
(b) $6\sqrt{3} - 3 + 2\sqrt{3} + 7$
(c) $12 - 5\sqrt{2} - 3\sqrt{2} + 4$
(d) $3\sqrt{3} + 2\sqrt{5} + 2\sqrt{5} + \sqrt{3}$
(e) $5\sqrt{7} + 3 - 2\sqrt{7} - 3$
(f) $6\sqrt{2} - 2 - 3 - 7\sqrt{2}$

9. Simplify.
(a) $\sqrt{8} + \sqrt{18}$
(b) $\sqrt{12} + \sqrt{27}$
(c) $\sqrt{50} + \sqrt{18}$
(d) $\sqrt{98} - \sqrt{32}$
(e) $\sqrt{20} + \sqrt{45}$
(f) $\sqrt{75} - \sqrt{48}$
(g) $2\sqrt{18} + \sqrt{8} + 3\sqrt{2}$
(h) $5\sqrt{12} + 3\sqrt{12} - 3\sqrt{3}$
(i) $\sqrt{8} - 5\sqrt{2} + \sqrt{24}$
(j) $\sqrt{50} + 2\sqrt{18} - 10\sqrt{2}$
(k) $2\sqrt{48} + 5\sqrt{27}$
(l) $\sqrt{98} - 8\sqrt{2}$
(m) $\sqrt{50} + 2\sqrt{18}$
(n) $3\sqrt{8} - 2\sqrt{2}$
(o) $6\sqrt{32} + 2\sqrt{18} - 3\sqrt{50}$
(p) $3\sqrt{72} + \sqrt{75} - 3\sqrt{3}$

CALCULATOR MATH

THE $\sqrt{}$ AND $y^{\frac{1}{x}}$ KEYS

To determine $\sqrt{72}$ using the $\sqrt{}$ key,
press 7 2 $\sqrt{}$

The display is 8.4852814

Using the $y^{\frac{1}{x}}$ key,
press 7 2 $y^{\frac{1}{x}}$ 2

The display is 8.4852814

The $y^{\frac{1}{x}}$ key gives an approximation of any root of a number. For $\sqrt[3]{72}$,

press 7 2 $y^{\frac{1}{x}}$ 3

The display is 4.1601676

EXERCISE

1. Calculate each of the following to the nearest hundredth.
(a) $\sqrt{55}$ (b) $\sqrt[3]{89}$ (c) $\sqrt{158}$
(d) $\sqrt[3]{101}$ (e) $\sqrt[4]{76}$ (f) $\sqrt[3]{1072}$
(g) $\sqrt{5815}$ (h) $\sqrt[3]{1939}$ (i) $\sqrt[5]{253}$

MIND BENDER

How many jumps will it take a frog to move 10 m up an incline if every jump is 1 m long and the frog slides back 0.5 m after each jump?

1.10 DIVIDING RADICAL EXPRESSIONS

Division is the inverse operation of multiplication.

Since $7 \times 3 = 21$, then $\frac{21}{3} = 7$

Since $\sqrt{7} \times \sqrt{3} = \sqrt{21}$, then $\dfrac{\sqrt{21}}{\sqrt{3}} = \sqrt{\dfrac{21}{3}}$

$$= \sqrt{7}$$

Example 1. Simplify. $\dfrac{\sqrt{42}}{\sqrt{6}}$

Solution:

METHOD I

$\dfrac{\sqrt{42}}{\sqrt{6}} = \sqrt{\dfrac{42}{6}}$

$\qquad = \sqrt{7}$

METHOD II

$\dfrac{\sqrt{42}}{\sqrt{6}} = \dfrac{\sqrt{6} \times \sqrt{7}}{\sqrt{6}}$

$\qquad = \sqrt{7}$

Example 2. Evaluate $\dfrac{\sqrt{15}}{\sqrt{3}}$ to the nearest tenth.

Solution:

METHOD I

$\dfrac{\sqrt{15}}{\sqrt{3}} = \sqrt{\dfrac{15}{3}}$

$\qquad = \sqrt{5}$

Press **5** $\sqrt{}$

The display is `2.2360658`

$\dfrac{\sqrt{15}}{\sqrt{3}} \doteq 2.2$

METHOD II

$\dfrac{\sqrt{15}}{\sqrt{3}}$

Press **1** **5** $\sqrt{}$ ÷ **3** $\sqrt{}$ =

The display is `2.2360658`

$\dfrac{\sqrt{15}}{\sqrt{3}} \doteq 2.2$

EXERCISE 1.10

B

1. Simplify.

(a) $\dfrac{\sqrt{30}}{\sqrt{6}}$

(b) $\dfrac{\sqrt{75}}{\sqrt{3}}$

(c) $\dfrac{36\sqrt{18}}{9\sqrt{6}}$

(d) $\dfrac{\sqrt{24}}{\sqrt{6}}$

(e) $\dfrac{\sqrt{54}}{\sqrt{24}}$

(f) $\dfrac{2\sqrt{27}}{\sqrt{3}}$

2. Evaluate to the nearest tenth.

(a) $\dfrac{\sqrt{35}}{\sqrt{5}}$

(b) $\dfrac{\sqrt{18}}{\sqrt{3}}$

(c) $\dfrac{\sqrt{42}}{\sqrt{6}}$

(d) $\dfrac{15\sqrt{15}}{\sqrt{3}}$

(e) $\dfrac{20\sqrt{10}}{\sqrt{5}}$

(f) $\dfrac{8}{\sqrt{12}}$

(g) $\dfrac{\sqrt{21}}{\sqrt{3}}$

(h) $\dfrac{3\sqrt{50}}{\sqrt{2}}$

(i) $\dfrac{3\sqrt{75}}{\sqrt{15}}$

1.11 MULTIPLYING RADICALS

Radicals can be multiplied using the distributive property.

Example 1. Simplify.

       (a) $\sqrt{3}(\sqrt{5} - 2)$ (b) $2\sqrt{2}(\sqrt{6} + 3\sqrt{2})$

Solution:

(a) $\sqrt{3}(\sqrt{5} - 2) = \sqrt{3}(\sqrt{5} - 2)$

                $= \sqrt{15} - 2\sqrt{3}$

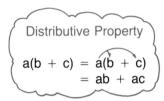

Distributive Property

$$a(b + c) = a(b + c)$$
$$= ab + ac$$

(b) $2\sqrt{2}(\sqrt{6} + 3\sqrt{2}) = 2\sqrt{2}(\sqrt{6} + 3\sqrt{2})$

                      $= 2\sqrt{12} + 6\sqrt{4}$

                      $= 2 \times 2\sqrt{3} + 6 \times 2$

                      $= 4\sqrt{3} + 12$

Recall that to multiply two binomials we proceed as follows:

       $(x + 3)(x + 4) = (x + 3)(x + 4)$

                  $= x^2 + 4x + 3x + 12$

                  $= x^2 + 7x + 12$

We multiply binomial radicals in the same way.

Example 2. Simplify. $(\sqrt{7} + 2)(\sqrt{3} - 1)$

Solution:

$(\sqrt{7} + 2)(\sqrt{3} - 1) = (\sqrt{7} + 2)(\sqrt{3} - 1)$

                $= \sqrt{21} - \sqrt{7} + 2\sqrt{3} - 2$

Example 3. Simplify. $(5\sqrt{2} - 4\sqrt{3})(3\sqrt{2} + 2\sqrt{3})$

Solution:

$(5\sqrt{2} - 4\sqrt{3})(3\sqrt{2} + 2\sqrt{3}) = (5\sqrt{2} - 4\sqrt{3})(3\sqrt{2} + 2\sqrt{3})$

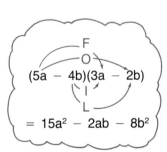

$$(5a - 4b)(3a - 2b)$$
$$= 15a^2 - 2ab - 8b^2$$

                         $= 15\sqrt{4} + 10\sqrt{6} - 12\sqrt{6} - 8\sqrt{9}$

                         $= 30 - 2\sqrt{6} - 24$

                         $= 6 - 2\sqrt{6}$

Example 4. Simplify. $(3\sqrt{5} - 2\sqrt{3})^2$

Solution:

$(3\sqrt{5} - 2\sqrt{3})^2 = (3\sqrt{5} - 2\sqrt{3})(3\sqrt{5} - 2\sqrt{3})$

                    $= 9(5) - 6\sqrt{15} - 6\sqrt{15} + 4(3)$

                    $= 45 - 12\sqrt{15} + 12$

                    $= 57 - 12\sqrt{15}$

$$(a + b)^2$$
$$= (a + b)(a + b)$$

Example 5. Simplify. $(2\sqrt{7} - \sqrt{5})(2\sqrt{7} + \sqrt{5})$

Solution:

$(2\sqrt{7} - \sqrt{5})(2\sqrt{7} + \sqrt{5}) = (2\sqrt{7} - \sqrt{5})(2\sqrt{7} + \sqrt{5})$

$$= 4\sqrt{49} + 2\sqrt{35} - 2\sqrt{35} - \sqrt{25}$$
$$= 28 - 5$$
$$= 23$$

$(a - b)(a + b)$
$= a^2 + ab - ab + b^2$
$= a^2 - b^2$

EXERCISE 1.11

B

1. Simplify using the distributive property.
(a) $\sqrt{2}(\sqrt{3} + \sqrt{5})$
(b) $\sqrt{3}(5 + \sqrt{7})$
(c) $3(2\sqrt{5} - 3\sqrt{2})$
(d) $5(\sqrt{3} - 2\sqrt{5})$
(e) $\sqrt{3}(\sqrt{3} + 1)$
(f) $\sqrt{2}(2\sqrt{2} - \sqrt{6})$
(g) $\sqrt{2}(\sqrt{6} - 2\sqrt{3})$
(h) $3\sqrt{5}(\sqrt{2} + \sqrt{6})$
(i) $\sqrt{3}(2 + 3\sqrt{2})$
(j) $2\sqrt{3}(\sqrt{6} + \sqrt{18})$

2. Simplify.
(a) $(\sqrt{5} + 3)(\sqrt{5} + 4)$
(b) $(2\sqrt{3} + \sqrt{7})(\sqrt{3} + 3\sqrt{7})$
(c) $(\sqrt{3} + \sqrt{2})(2\sqrt{3} + \sqrt{2})$
(d) $(3\sqrt{2} - 2)(\sqrt{2} - 5)$
(e) $(2\sqrt{7} + 4\sqrt{3})(5\sqrt{7} + 6\sqrt{3})$
(f) $(8\sqrt{3} + 2\sqrt{5})(2\sqrt{3} - 7\sqrt{5})$
(g) $(3\sqrt{5} + \sqrt{3})(7\sqrt{5} + \sqrt{3})$
(h) $(5 + 3\sqrt{11})(7 - 6\sqrt{11})$
(i) $(4\sqrt{5} + 2\sqrt{2})(3\sqrt{5} - 6\sqrt{2})$
(j) $(5\sqrt{2} + 4\sqrt{3})(3\sqrt{7} - 2\sqrt{5})$

3. Simplify.
(a) $(\sqrt{5} + \sqrt{3})^2$
(b) $(\sqrt{7} - \sqrt{2})^2$
(c) $(\sqrt{6} - \sqrt{2})^2$
(d) $(\sqrt{7} - \sqrt{6})^2$
(e) $(3\sqrt{2} + 1)^2$
(f) $(1 - \sqrt{2})^2$
(g) $(4\sqrt{5} - \sqrt{2})^2$
(h) $(8\sqrt{3} + 5\sqrt{6})^2$
(i) $(6\sqrt{10} + 2\sqrt{3})^2$
(j) $2(\sqrt{3} + 1)^2$
(k) $3(2\sqrt{2} + \sqrt{6})^2$
(l) $4(2\sqrt{5} - 3)^2$

4. Simplify.
(a) $(\sqrt{5} + \sqrt{2})(\sqrt{5} - \sqrt{2})$
(b) $(\sqrt{2} + 1)(\sqrt{2} - 1)$
(c) $(3\sqrt{2} - 4)(3\sqrt{2} + 4)$
(d) $(2\sqrt{3} + 2)(2\sqrt{3} - 2)$
(e) $(\sqrt{7} + 2\sqrt{3})(\sqrt{7} - 2\sqrt{3})$
(f) $(4\sqrt{5} - \sqrt{2})(4\sqrt{5} + \sqrt{2})$
(g) $(5\sqrt{6} + 2)(5\sqrt{6} - 2)$
(h) $(5\sqrt{6} + \sqrt{2})(5\sqrt{6} - \sqrt{2})$
(i) $(8\sqrt{3} + 7\sqrt{2})(8\sqrt{3} - 7\sqrt{2})$
(j) $(3\sqrt{7} - 4\sqrt{2})(3\sqrt{7} + 4\sqrt{2})$

C

5. Simplify the following.
(a) $(\sqrt{3} + \sqrt{2})(2\sqrt{3} + 5\sqrt{2})$
    $+ (3\sqrt{2} - 4\sqrt{3})^2$
(b) $(5 + \sqrt{3})(2 - 4\sqrt{3})$
    $- (6\sqrt{3} + 7)(2\sqrt{3} + 5)$
(c) $(\sqrt{7} + \sqrt{3})(\sqrt{7} - \sqrt{3})$
    $- (\sqrt{11} + 5)(\sqrt{11} - 5)$

MIND BENDER

There were 18 people invited to participate in a wrestling tournament. Each was assigned a number from 1 to 18. After everyone was paired for the first match, the organizer noticed that the sum of each pair's numbers was a perfect square.
What were the pairings?

1.12 PRINCIPLES OF PROBLEM SOLVING

Spreadsheet activities related to this topic are found in section 15.4.

Problem solving is a creative activity that requires strategies. Although there are no rules that we can use to solve problems, there are some steps to follow that will prove helpful. These steps are summarized in the

READ — PLAN — SOLVE — ANSWER

model for solving problems.

Example 1. The seats in one row of an airplane are labelled A, B, and C.
How many ways can three people be seated?

READ

Read the problem carefully and devote sufficient time to understanding the problem before trying to solve it. Note key words. Put the problem in your own words. Know what you are asked to find. Be aware of what is given.

PLAN

Think of a plan. Find a connection between the given information and the unknown which will enable you to calculate the unknown.

1. Classify information. Study the information carefully to determine what is needed to solve the problem. Identify the relevant and irrelevant information. Some information may be extraneous or redundant.
   You may find it helpful to summarize the information or make lists.

2. Search for a pattern. Try to recognize patterns. Some problems are solved by recognizing that some kind of pattern is occurring. The pattern could be geometric, numerical, or algebraic. If you can see there is some sort of regularity or repetition in a problem, then you might be able to guess what the continuing pattern is, and then prove it.

3. Draw a diagram or flow chart. For many problems it is useful to draw a diagram and identify the given and required quantities on the diagram. A flow chart can be used to organize a series of steps that must be performed in a definite order.

4. Estimate, guess, and check. This is a valid method to solve a problem where a direct method is not apparent. You may find it necessary to improve your guess and "zero in" on the correct answer.

5. Sequence operations. To solve some problems, several operations performed in a definite order are needed.

6. Work backwards. Sometimes it is useful to imagine that your problem is solved and work backwards step by step until you arrive at the given data. Then, you may be able to reverse your steps to solve the original problem.

7. Use a formula or an equation. In some problems, after analyzing the data, the problem can be written as an equation, or the data can be substituted into a formula.

8. Solve a simpler problem. A problem can sometimes be broken into smaller problems that can be solved more easily.

9. Account for all possibilities. List all of the cases. Your solution must account for all of these cases. You may sometimes be able to solve your problem using a process of elimination.

10. Make a table. In some problems, it is helpful to organize the data in a table, chart, or grid.

11. Check for hidden assumptions. In some problems, the information concerning what is given is presented in a subtle manner that may not attract your attention. Re-read the problem carefully and look for the implied information.

12. Conclude from assumptions. In some problems, it will be necessary to make assumptions. The conclusions that you draw from these assumptions should be those that you have made in the past, from the same types of information.

13. Introduce something extra. Sometimes it may be necessary to introduce something new, an auxiliary aid, to help make the connection between the given and the unknown. For instance in geometry, the auxiliary could be a new line drawn in the diagram. In algebra, it could be a new unknown which is related to the original unknown.

SOLVE

Before solving the problem, look at the reasons for selecting your strategy. If you have more than one strategy available, you should consider familiarity, efficiency, and ease, in making your choice. In carrying out your strategy, work with care and check each step as you proceed. Remember to present your ideas clearly.

ANSWER

State the answer in a clear and concise manner. Check your answer in the original problem and use estimation to decide if your answer is reasonable. In checking your answer, you may discover an easier way to solve the problem. You may wish to generalize your method of solution so that it can be applied to similar problems.

Solution: Call the people x, y, and z.
Use a table to list all the possibilities.

Seat A	Seat B	Seat C
x	y	z
x	z	y
y	x	z
y	z	x
z	x	y
z	y	x

There are 6 different ways to seat the three people.

READ

Example 2. The enclosure for a motorcycle competition is in the shape of a rectangle as shown. Two sides must be barricaded by sandbags. The supporting posts for the bags are 3 m apart. The dimensions of the enclosure are shown in the diagram.
How many support posts are required?

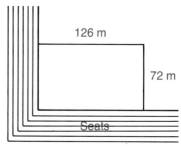

126 m

72 m

Seats

PLAN

Solution: Use diagrams and start with smaller rectangles.

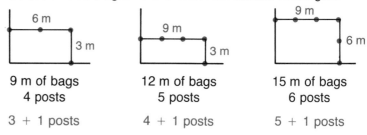

9 m of bags	12 m of bags	15 m of bags
4 posts	5 posts	6 posts
3 + 1 posts	4 + 1 posts	5 + 1 posts

SOLVE

The pattern indicates that we need 1 post for every 3 m of sandbags plus another endpost.
The enclosure for the motorcycle competition has 126 + 72 or 198 m of sandbags.

$$\frac{198}{3} = 66 \quad \text{and} \quad 66 + 1 = 67$$

ANSWER

∴ 67 support posts are required.

B

1. Eleven fence posts are spaced 2.5 m apart in a row.
What is the distance from the first to the last post?

2. A pirate found a treasure chest containing Spanish doubloons. He buried half of the doubloons and gave half of the remaining doubloons to his crew.
If he was left with 2589 doubloons, how many were in the treasure chest that he found?

3. The sum of the first two numbers in a list of seven consecutive odd numbers is 44.
What is the sum of the last three numbers?

4. How can you place fourteen chairs in a square room so that the chairs have their backs to a wall and there are the same number of chairs along each wall?

5. There are eleven ways to add eight odd numbers and get twenty. The following are three of the ways:

$1 + 1 + 1 + 1 + 3 + 3 + 5 + 5 \ = 20$

$1 + 1 + 1 + 1 + 1 + 1 + 3 + 11 = 20$

$1 + 1 + 1 + 1 + 1 + 1 + 5 + 9 \ = 20$

Find the other eight ways.

6. Name the wheels that are turning counter-clockwise.

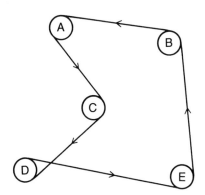

7. February 14th is a Tuesday.
How many other Tuesdays are there in the year?

8. Copy the following diagram in your notebook.

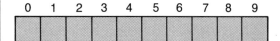

In each square write a digit such that the digit in the first block states the total number of 0s in the ten-digit number, the digit in the second block states the total number of 1s in the number, and so on. The last block states the total number of 9s in the number.

9. Hrotsvitha lived in a Benedictine abbey in Saxony in the year 1000. She was one of the first mathematicians to write about perfect numbers. A perfect number is equal to the sum of all its factors including 1 but not including the number itself. The number 6 is a perfect number because

$$6 = 1 + 2 + 3$$

Hrotsvitha wrote about three perfect numbers: 28, 496, and 8128.
Verify that 28, 496, and 8128 are perfect numbers.

10. How old will you be in seconds on your next birthday?

11. Ken has thirteen rare stamps to give to his friends George, Paul, and Jamie.
How many ways can he distribute the stamps so that each one of his friends gets an odd number of stamps?

12. Three friends plan to drive from Halifax to Vancouver in six days.
If they must drive at the speed limit, is it possible to make the trip in six days?

1.13 REVIEW EXERCISE

1. Round each of the following to the required place.
(a) 4.125   (hundredth)
(b) 36 732   (hundred)
(c) 15.18   (tenth)
(d) 6500   (thousand)
(e) 7500   (thousand)
(f) 0.0506   (thousandth)

2. Calculate.
(a) 314 + 4567 + 54
(b) 3450 − 789
(c) 23 × 89
(d) 405 ÷ 45
(e)   1234
      982
      3487
    + 134
(f)   3001
    − 987

(g) 703 × 18
(h) $32\sqrt{544}$

3. Calculate.
(a) 0.345 + 7.5 + 0.05
(b) 5.007 − 0.777
(c) 0.57 × 1.6
(d) 2.852 ÷ 0.31
(e)   1.567
      0.78
    +0.019
(f)   2.87
    −0.12

(g) 0.31 × 1.5
(h) $0.52\sqrt{98.8}$

4. Calculate the lengths of A, B, C, and D.

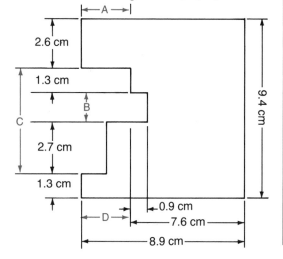

5. Evaluate.
(a) 407 + 45 − 154
(b) 56 × 9 − 35
(c) 5(13 − 7) − 56 ÷ 8
(d) 5^2 − 4 × 4 + 121
(e) 697 ÷ 17 + 3 − 66
(f) $6^2 + 7^2 − 9^2 + 11$
(g) 2000 − 76 × 9
(h) 2401 ÷ 7 ÷ 7

6. If x = 2, y = 3, and z = 5, evaluate each of the following.
(a) 6x + 7y − 2z
(b) $x^2 + z^2 − y^2$
(c) 7xy + 3yz + 2xz
(d) 9xyz − 61
(e) 3(4xy − 7) + xyz

7. Evaluate for x = 8.
(a) x^2 − 2x + 4
(b) (x + 7)(x − 5)
(c) 3(x − 6) + 5(x + 1)
(d) $3x^2$ + 5x + 9

8. Simplify.
(a) 7 + 11 − 19
(b) (−4)(−7)
(c) 66 ÷ (−3)
(d) (−8)(+7)
(e) −24 ÷ (−8)
(f) −16 + 9 − 2

9. If a = −1, b = 2, and c = −4, evaluate each of the following.
(a) 3a + 4b + 3c
(b) $a^2 + b^2 + c^2$
(c) 3ab − 7c + 9
(d) 6b − 7c − 9a
(e) −2bc + 5ab − 4ac

10. Simplify.
(a) $\frac{1}{3} + \frac{1}{5} - \frac{1}{4}$
(b) $3\frac{4}{5} - 2\frac{3}{4}$
(c) $2\frac{1}{2} \times 5$
(d) $4 \div 1\frac{1}{2}$
(e) $16 - 8\frac{7}{8}$
(f) $\frac{4}{5} \div 6$
(g) $3\frac{3}{10} + 4\frac{1}{5} + 7\frac{17}{20}$
(h) $2\frac{3}{4} \times 3\frac{2}{3}$

11. Simplify.
(a) $4x^2 \times 7x^3$
(b) $8y^2 \times (-2y)$
(c) $12xy \div 4x$
(d) $(2x^2y^3)^3$
(e) $24x^4y^2 \div 8xy$
(f) $(-36a^3b^4c) \div (-2abc)$
(g) $(9a^3bc^2)(-6ab)$
(h) $(-5m^3n^2)(-4m^4n^3)$

12. Simplify.
(a) $16^{\frac{1}{2}}$
(b) $27^{\frac{1}{3}}$
(c) $-8^{\frac{1}{3}}$
(d) $25^{-\frac{1}{2}}$
(e) $(-5)^{-2}$
(f) $-8^{\frac{2}{3}}$
(g) 10^{-3}
(h) $-16^{-\frac{3}{4}}$
(i) 27^0
(j) $(\frac{4}{25})^{\frac{1}{2}}$
(k) $(\frac{27}{8})^{-\frac{1}{3}}$
(l) $a^{\frac{1}{2}} \times a^{\frac{1}{3}}$

13. Solve for the variables.
(a) $x : 3 = 7 : 25$
(b) $2 : x : y = 16 : 10 : 4$

14. Fifteen train tickets cost \$480.
How much will 23 tickets cost?

15. A sweater costs \$66.00.
If the rate of sales tax is 8%, what is the total cost of the sweater?

16. Express as mixed radicals.
(a) $\sqrt{50}$
(b) $\sqrt{32}$
(c) $\sqrt{27}$
(d) $\sqrt{20}$
(e) $\sqrt{24}$
(f) $\sqrt{48}$

17. Express as entire radicals.
(a) $3\sqrt{5}$
(b) $2\sqrt{7}$
(c) $3\sqrt{6}$
(d) $4\sqrt{2}$
(e) $5\sqrt{3}$
(f) $10\sqrt{10}$

18. Simplify.
(a) $6\sqrt{2} \times 2\sqrt{6}$
(b) $\sqrt{10} \times \sqrt{2}$
(c) $5\sqrt{3} \times 3\sqrt{6}$
(d) $6\sqrt{12} \times 10\sqrt{2}$
(e) $\dfrac{\sqrt{18}}{\sqrt{2}}$
(f) $\dfrac{\sqrt{60}}{\sqrt{20}}$

19. Simplify.
(a) $4\sqrt{3} - 2\sqrt{3} + 5\sqrt{3}$
(b) $7\sqrt{2} + 5\sqrt{2} + 4\sqrt{5} - 3\sqrt{5}$
(c) $6\sqrt{7} + 4\sqrt{10} + 5\sqrt{7} - 6\sqrt{10}$
(d) $8\sqrt{3} + 3\sqrt{75}$
(e) $3\sqrt{7} - 5\sqrt{28}$
(f) $5\sqrt{20} + \sqrt{24} - \sqrt{180} + 7\sqrt{54}$
(g) $6\sqrt{5} + 8\sqrt{5} - \sqrt{80}$
(h) $3 + 4\sqrt{2} - 5\sqrt{50}$
(i) $3\sqrt{50} + 4\sqrt{18} - 2\sqrt{32} - \sqrt{8}$

20. Simplify.
(a) $\dfrac{\sqrt{50}}{\sqrt{2}}$
(b) $\dfrac{\sqrt{24}}{\sqrt{6}}$
(c) $\dfrac{\sqrt{27}}{\sqrt{3}}$

21. Simplify.
(a) $\sqrt{2}(\sqrt{5} - 2\sqrt{2})$
(b) $\sqrt{3}(2\sqrt{3} + \sqrt{6})$
(c) $3\sqrt{5}(2 + 5\sqrt{2})$
(d) $(\sqrt{2} - \sqrt{3})(\sqrt{5} + \sqrt{2})$
(e) $(3\sqrt{5} - 2\sqrt{7})(\sqrt{5} + \sqrt{7})$
(f) $(\sqrt{7} - \sqrt{3})(\sqrt{7} + \sqrt{3})$
(g) $(\sqrt{2} + \sqrt{3})^2$
(h) $(2 - \sqrt{5})^2$

22. The sum of two numbers is 50 and their product is 609.
What are the numbers?

23. What is the maximum number of times that four straight lines can intersect?

24. Draw five lines to divide the clock face into six parts so that each part contains two numbers and the six sums of the two numbers are equal.

MIND BENDER

Place the numbers from 1 to 8 in the boxes so that no two consecutive numbers are side by side.

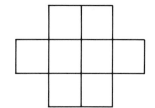

1.14 CHAPTER 1 TEST

1. Evaluate.
(a) $5.6 \times 79 + 100$
(b) $8^2 + 5(9 + 4)$
(c) $368 \div 16 - 4^2 + 12 \times 9$
(d) $0.6 \times 12 + 1.44 \div 1.2$

2. If $x = -2$, $y = 3$, and $z = -4$, evaluate the following.
(a) $3x + 4y - 5z$
(b) $x^2 + y^2 + z^2$
(c) $3x^2 - 4x - 7$
(d) $4yx - 3xy - xz$

3. Simplify.
(a) $(4x^2y^2)(-5x^3y^4)$
(b) $(3m^3s^2t^4)^3$
(c) $(-36a^3b^2c) \div (-9a^2bc)$

4. Simplify.
(a) $27^{\frac{2}{3}}$ (b) $16^{-\frac{3}{4}}$ (c) 9^0

(d) $-32^{\frac{2}{5}}$ (e) $(-32)^{\frac{3}{5}}$ (f) $(\frac{9}{4})^{\frac{3}{2}}$

5. Solve the following for x and y.

$$3 : x : y = 8 : 7 : 6$$

6. Carol taught sailing for 9 h and earned $132.75. How much will she earn in 16 h at this rate?

7. Simplify.
(a) $2\sqrt{8} + \sqrt{18} + 4\sqrt{2}$
(b) $2\sqrt{20} + 3\sqrt{80} - 3\sqrt{125}$

POLYNOMIALS AND RATIONAL EXPRESSIONS

2

REVIEW AND PREVIEW TO CHAPTER ②

FRACTIONS

EXERCISE 1

1. Add.

(a) $\frac{1}{5} + \frac{3}{5}$ (b) $\frac{3}{8} + \frac{1}{4}$ (c) $\frac{1}{4} + \frac{3}{5}$

(d) $2\frac{1}{3} + 3\frac{1}{6}$ (e) $4\frac{4}{5} + \frac{3}{10}$ (f) $4\frac{1}{9} + \frac{2}{3}$

(g) $\frac{7}{8} + \frac{3}{16}$ (h) $1\frac{7}{10} + \frac{2}{5}$ (i) $\frac{2}{3} + \frac{1}{4}$

2. Subtract.

(a) $\frac{7}{8} - \frac{5}{8}$ (b) $\frac{3}{4} - \frac{1}{8}$ (c) $\frac{2}{3} - \frac{1}{6}$

(d) $\frac{3}{5} - \frac{1}{10}$ (e) $\frac{1}{3} - \frac{1}{4}$ (f) $1\frac{1}{2} - \frac{7}{8}$

(g) $4 - 1\frac{3}{5}$ (h) $2\frac{5}{8} - 1\frac{1}{2}$ (i) $\frac{3}{4} - \frac{1}{3}$

3. Multiply.

(a) $\frac{1}{2} \times \frac{1}{3}$ (b) $\frac{3}{4} \times \frac{1}{5}$ (c) $\frac{5}{8} \times \frac{4}{5}$

(d) $\frac{2}{3} \times \frac{3}{7}$ (e) $\frac{4}{5} \times \frac{1}{3}$ (f) $1\frac{1}{2} \times \frac{2}{3}$

(g) $1\frac{1}{4} \times 1\frac{1}{8}$ (h) $3 \times 1\frac{3}{4}$ (i) $5\frac{1}{2} \times 10$

4. Divide.

(a) $\frac{3}{4} \div \frac{1}{4}$ (b) $\frac{3}{8} \div \frac{1}{3}$ (c) $\frac{5}{12} \div \frac{1}{6}$

(d) $\frac{5}{6} \div \frac{3}{2}$ (e) $\frac{1}{4} \div \frac{1}{2}$ (f) $1\frac{1}{2} \div \frac{1}{2}$

(g) $2\frac{2}{3} \div 2$ (h) $1\frac{1}{3} \div 1\frac{1}{4}$ (i) $6 \div \frac{2}{3}$

RATIONAL NUMBERS

EXERCISE 2

1. Simplify.

(a) $-\frac{3}{8} + \frac{5}{8}$ (b) $\frac{1}{3} - \frac{2}{3}$

(c) $\frac{3}{4} + \left(-\frac{1}{2}\right)$ (d) $1\frac{3}{5} - 2\frac{7}{10}$

(e) $-\frac{3}{5} - \frac{7}{10}$ (f) $-1\frac{1}{10} + 3\frac{4}{5}$

(g) $-2\frac{3}{4} - 4\frac{1}{8}$ (h) $\frac{3}{5} - 1\frac{3}{4}$

2. Simplify.

(a) $-\frac{3}{4} \times \frac{1}{2}$ (b) $-\frac{3}{4} \div \frac{1}{2}$

(c) $\frac{2}{3} \times \left(-\frac{3}{5}\right)$ (d) $\frac{2}{3} \div \left(-\frac{1}{5}\right)$

(e) $-\frac{1}{3} \times \left(-\frac{1}{2}\right)$ (f) $-\frac{1}{3} \div \left(-\frac{1}{2}\right)$

(g) $1\frac{1}{2} \times \left(-\frac{1}{4}\right)$ (h) $\frac{3}{5} \div \left(-1\frac{1}{2}\right)$

(i) $-3\frac{1}{3} \times (-2)$ (j) $-1\frac{1}{2} \div (-3)$

(k) $2\frac{2}{3} \times \left(-1\frac{1}{3}\right)$ (l) $-1\frac{3}{4} \div \left(-1\frac{2}{3}\right)$

(m) $4 \times \left(-1\frac{3}{5}\right)$ (n) $2 \div \left(-1\frac{1}{3}\right)$

3. Calculate the missing dimensions in the following diagram.

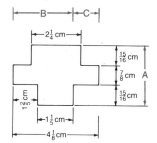

POLYNOMIALS

A polynomial is an algebraic expression of the form $7x^2 + 4x - 5$, $2m - 7$, or $a^2 - 2ab + b^2$.

In the polynomial $7x^2 + 4x - 5$ the quantities $7x^2$, $4x$, and -5 are called terms. To simplify polynomials, we collect like terms. Like terms have the same literal coefficients. $5x$ and $7x$ are like terms.

EXERCISE 3

1. Simplify.
(a) $3x + 4 + 7x - 2$
(b) $4a + 3b - 2a - b$

(c) $-2m + 3n + 5m - 4n$
(d) $7x - 6y - 4 - 3x + 2y - 3$
(e) $x^2 - 3x + 4x^2 + 5x$
(f) $2a^2 - 3a - 4 - a^2 - a - 1$
(g) $6t^2 - 5t^2 - 4 + 3t - 2t - 6$
(h) $3ab - 4bc + 5ac - 2ab + 6ac$
(i) $9x^2 - 13 + 5x - 6x^2 - 11$
(j) $6t - 4t^2 - 3 - 2t^2 - t - 1$
(k) $2m^2 - n^2 + 3mn - 4m^2 - 7n^2$
(l) $a^2 + 2ab + b^2 - 3a^2 - 5ab$
(m) $11 - x - x^2 - 10 - x - x^2$

2. Find an expression for the perimeter of each of the following.

(a)

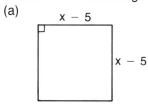

(b)

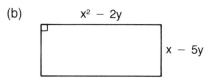

MULTIPLYING MONOMIALS

EXERCISE 4

1. Multiply.
(a) $3x \times 5y$
(b) $6m \times 3m$
(c) $(-2t)(-3t)$
(d) $4b(-8b)$
(e) $-5y \times 11y^2$
(f) $5ab \times 9cd$
(g) $6t^2 \times 3t^4$
(h) $(-7a)(-12a^2)$
(i) $10mn \times 14mn$
(j) $(-6a^4)(5a^3)$
(k) $(12cd)(-8c)$
(l) $(15x^2y^2)(10xy^3)$
(m) $(-2mnt)(3m)$
(n) $(4r^2s)(-11r^3s^2)$

THE DISTRIBUTIVE PROPERTY

We use the distributive property to simplify algebraic expressions.

$$2(x - 3) = 2(x - 3)$$
$$= 2x - 6$$

EXERCISE 5

1. Expand.
(a) $3(x - 4)$
(b) $4(2x - 3y)$
(c) $-2(x^2 - x - 1)$
(d) $-(3a - 4b - c)$
(e) $8(1 - 3y - y^2)$
(f) $7(12x - 3xy + 4y)$

2. Expand and simplify.
(a) $3(x + 4) + 4(x - 2)$
(b) $5(x - 3) - 2(x - 6)$
(c) $6(2x + 1) - 3(2x - 3)$
(d) $4(x - y) - 5(y - x)$
(e) $-5(2x - 4) - 2(3x - 2)$
(f) $-6x^2 - 2(2x^2 - x - 1) + 7x$
(g) $5(a - 3b) - 4 - 2(a + b)$
(h) $7r^2 - 2r - 1 - 3(5r^2 - 6r + 7)$
(i) $-2(a - 3ab + b) - 4(3a - 7b)$
(j) $2(x^2 - y^2) - (x^2 + y^2) + 2x^2$
(k) $6(m^2 - m - 3) - (m^2 - 6m - 4)$
(l) $2(3a - 4b) - (a - b) - 2(a - 5b)$
(m) $-(3x - y) - 7 - 2(x + y)$
(n) $7 - (x - y) + 3(x - y) - (x + y)$

3. Find an expression for the area of each of the following.

(a)

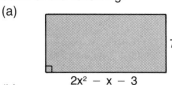

(b)

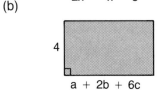

2.1 MULTIPLYING POLYNOMIALS

We use the distributive property to multiply a polynomial by a monomial. For example,

$$2x^2(3xy + 5y) = 2x^2(3xy + 5y)$$
$$= 6x^3y + 10x^2y$$

Binomial by Monomial

Example 1. Expand and simplify. $3x(2x^2 - 4x + 1)$

Solution: Use the distributive property and multiply each term in the bracket by the monomial.

Trinomial by Monomial

$$3x(2x^2 - 4x + 1) = 3x(2x^2 - 4x + 1)$$
$$= 6x^3 - 12x^2 + 3x$$

The distributive property is also used to multiply two binomials.

Example 2. Expand and simplify. $(2x + 3)(4x + 5)$

Solution: Let $(2x + 3) = m$

Binomial by Binomial

$$(2x + 3)(4x + 5) = m(4x + 5)$$
$$= 4xm + 5m$$

$$= 4x(2x + 3) + 5(2x + 3)$$
$$= 8x^2 + 12x + 10x + 15$$
$$= 8x^2 + 22x + 15$$

The multiplication of two binomials can also be accomplished by multiplying each term in the first bracket by each term in the second bracket.

$(2x + 3)(4x + 5)$

$$(2x + 3)(4x + 5) = (2x + 3)(4x + 5)$$

$$= 8x^2 + 10x + 12x + 15$$
$$= 8x^2 + 22x + 15$$

Example 3. Expand and simplify. $(3t - 2s)^2$

Squaring Binomials

Solution: $(3t - 2s)^2 = (3t - 2s)(3t - 2s)$

$$= 9t^2 - 6st - 6st + 4s^2$$
$$= 9t^2 - 12st + 4s^2$$

This technique can also be used to multiply a trinomial by a binomial.

Example 4. Expand and simplify. $(3a - 7)(2a^2 - a - 9)$

Trinomial
  by
Binomial

Solution:
$(3a - 7)(2a^2 - a - 9) = (3a - 7)(2a^2 - a - 9)$

$= 6a^3 - 3a^2 - 27a - 14a^2 + 7a + 63$
$= 6a^3 - 17a^2 - 20a + 63$

EXERCISE 2.1

B

1. Expand and simplify.
(a) $3x(4x + 1)$ (b) $2t(3t - 5)$
(c) $6m(1 - 3m)$ (d) $2x^2(xy - y)$
(e) $4xy(x + 3y)$ (f) $6st(1 - 3st)$

2. Expand and simplify.
(a) $2x(x - 3) + 4(3x + 5)$
(b) $5y(3y + 4) - 3y(2y + 7)$
(c) $6t(4t - 3s) - t(3t - s)$
(d) $9ab(a - 2b) - ab(2a + 3b)$

3. Simplify.
(a) $4x(x^2 - x - 1)$
(b) $3a(2a^2 - 2a - 5)$
(c) $5t^2(t^2 - t + 4)$
(d) $6a^2(1 + 5a + 6a^2)$
(e) $2xy(1 - 3y + 4x)$
(f) $7m(-2m^2 + 3m + 1)$

4. Simplify.
(a) $(2x - 7)(x - 4)$
(b) $(4a + 2b)(a - b)$
(c) $(3m + 7n)(2m - n)$
(d) $(x - 3y)(x - 4y)$
(e) $(5t - 3s)(7t + 2s)$
(f) $(1 - 9b)(1 + 9a)$

5. Simplify.
(a) $(x - 3)^2$ (b) $(x + 7)^2$
(c) $(4a - 5b)^2$ (d) $(2t + 1)^2$
(e) $(5m - 6n)^2$ (f) $(8x + 3y)^2$

6. Expand and simplify.
(a) $(x - 3)(x^2 + 3x + 5)$
(b) $(2y + 1)(3y^2 + 4y - 7)$
(c) $(3t - 4)(2t^2 - t - 2)$
(d) $(2a - 5)(4a^2 - 5a + 6)$
(e) $(t^2 - 3t + 3)(3t + 5)$

7. Write simplified polynomials for the volume of each of the following figures.
(a)

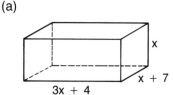

$3x + 4$, $x + 7$, x

(b)

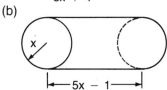

x, $5x - 1$

C

8. The diagram below shows the pattern for a box. To make the box, we fold the sides up and the corners in.

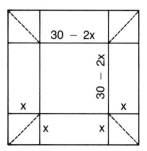

$30 - 2x$, $30 - 2x$, x, x, x, x

An expression for the volume of the box is
$$x(30 - 2x)^2$$
(a) What is the volume of the box when $x = 5$ cm?
    What are the dimensions of the box?
(b) What are the volume and dimensions of the box when $x = 6$ cm?

2.2 DIVIDING A POLYNOMIAL BY A MONOMIAL

Using the distributive property, we have seen how multiplication distributes over addition and subtraction.

$$3x(x - y) = 3x(x - y)$$
$$= 3x^2 - 3xy$$

Division also distributes over addition and subtraction.

$$\frac{2x + 7y}{3} = \frac{2x}{3} + \frac{7y}{3}$$

We use this property to divide a polynomial by a monomial.

Example. Simplify. $\dfrac{4x^3 - 8x^2 + 6x}{2x}$

Solution: $\dfrac{4x^3 - 8x^2 + 6x}{2x} = \dfrac{4x^3}{2x} - \dfrac{8x^2}{2x} + \dfrac{6x}{2x}$

$$= 2x^2 - 4x + 3, \quad x \neq 0$$

We state the restriction $x \neq 0$ because division by zero is not defined.

To divide a polynomial by a monomial, divide each term of the polynomial by the monomial.

EXERCISE 2.2

A

1. Simplify.

(a) $\dfrac{15x^2}{5x}$

(b) $\dfrac{12rst}{-4rs}$

(c) $\dfrac{-20x^7}{-5x^4}$

(d) $\dfrac{-16a^2b^2c}{4abc}$

(e) $\dfrac{-36x^4y^6}{-9x^2y^5}$

(f) $\dfrac{18m^2t^4}{-2t^3}$

2. Simplify.

(a) $\dfrac{8a + 16}{4}$

(b) $\dfrac{9x - 27}{3}$

(c) $\dfrac{10t - 20}{5}$

(d) $\dfrac{30 - 20r}{-10}$

(e) $\dfrac{36x - 24y}{12}$

(f) $\dfrac{x - y}{1}$

B

3. Simplify. State restrictions on the variables.

(a) $\dfrac{10xy + 5x^2}{5x}$

(b) $\dfrac{30a^3 - 20a^2}{10a}$

(c) $\dfrac{-18xy + 15y^2}{-3y}$

(d) $\dfrac{24x^3 - 12x^2}{-6x^2}$

4. Simplify. State restrictions on the variables.

(a) $\dfrac{6x^3 - 2x^2 + 8x}{-2x}$

(b) $\dfrac{15y^4 + 10y^3 - 20y^2}{-5y^2}$

(c) $\dfrac{16a^2b^2 - 8ab^2 + 4a^2b}{2ab}$

(d) $\dfrac{-24m^3n^3 + 16m^2n^3 - 8m^3n^2}{-4mn^2}$

(e) $\dfrac{5xt^3 - 10x^2t^4 - 25x^3t^5}{5xt^3}$

C

5. Divide.
(a) $(12x^8 - 9x^6 + 6x^4) \div (-3x^2)$
(b) $(8a^9 + 10a^7 - 12a^4) \div (2a^4)$
(c) $(t^7 - t^6 - t^5 - t^4) \div (-t^3)$
(d) $(x^3y^2 - x^2y^2 + xy^3) \div (xy)$

2.3 COMMON FACTORING

The distributive property was used to multiply a polynomial by a monomial. It can also be used to write a polynomial in factored form.

Multiplying	Factoring
$2x(3x - 5) = 6x^2 - 10x$	$6x^2 - 10x = 2x(3x - 5)$
$a(b + c) = ab + ac$	$ab + ac = a(b + c)$

Example 1. Factor. $18a^2b - 30ab^2$

Solution:
Find the greatest common factor (GCF) of $18a^2b$ and $30ab^2$, then use the distributive property.

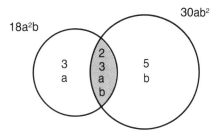

$18a^2b = 2 \times 3 \times 3 \times a \times a \times b$

$30ab^2 = 2 \times 3 \times 5 \times a \times b \times b$

GCF $= 2 \times 3 \times a \times b = 6ab$

$$18a^2b - 30ab^2 = (6ab)(3a) - (6ab)(5b) \quad \text{or} \quad 18a^2b - 30ab^2 = 6ab\left(\frac{18a^2b}{6ab} - \frac{30ab^2}{6ab}\right)$$
$$= 6ab(3a - 5b) \qquad\qquad\qquad = 6ab(3a - 5b)$$

Example 2. Factor.
(a) $x(x + 3) - 2(x + 3)$ (b) $2x(x - 1) - (x - 1)$

Solution:

(a)　　$x(x + 3) - 2(x + 3)$
　　$= x(x + 3) - 2(x + 3)$
　　$= (x + 3)(x - 2)$

(b)　　$2x(x - 1) - (x - 1)$
　　$= 2x(x - 1) - 1(x - 1)$
　　$= (x - 1)(2x - 1)$

EXERCISE 2.3

A

1. Factor.
(a) $3x + 6$ (b) $3x^2 + 5x$
(c) $x^3 + 7x$ (d) $x^4 + 7x^3 + 5x^2$
(e) $p^2m^2 - pmn$ (f) $6y^2 - 3y$

B

2. Factor.
(a) $31xy - 3x$
(b) $6a^2 - 9ab + 24a^2b^2$
(c) $x^5 + 5x^4 + 3x^2 + 2x$
(d) $3x^3y + 9xy^2 + 36xy$
(e) $42rst - 12r^2s^2 + 3r^2t^2$
(f) $14a^3x + 21a^3y + 7a^3z$
(g) $24abx + 12ax^2 + 6x^3$
(h) $80r^2t^3 - 24r^3t^2 + 36r^3t^4$

3. Factor.
(a) $3x(x + 3) + 4(x + 3)$
(b) $2a(a - 7) - 3(a - 7)$
(c) $3x^2(x - 1) - 4(x - 1)$
(d) $5a(a + 3) + (a + 3)$
(e) $5(t + 7) + 6t(t + 7)$
(f) $2x(x + 5) - (x + 5)$

C

4. Factor.
(a) $x^2 + 2x + xy + 2y$
(b) $x^2 + 5x + xt + 5t$
(c) $2x^2 - 5x + 2xy - 5y$
(d) $5at + 4t + 5a + 4$
(e) $x^2 + 3x - xy - 3y$
(f) $3xy - 2x - 3y + 2$

2.4 FACTORING TRINOMIALS: $x^2 + bx + c$

The product of two binomials is often a trinomial. It follows that the factors of such a trinomial are in the form of two binomials.

$$\underbrace{(x + 1)(x + 3)}_{\text{Binomials}} = \underbrace{x^2 + 4x + 3}_{\text{Trinomial}}$$

To factor a trinomial, we reverse the expanding procedure.

$$\begin{aligned}(x + 5)(x + 6) &= x^2 + 6x + 5x + 30 \\ &= x^2 + (6 + 5)x + 30 \\ &= x^2 + 11x + 30\end{aligned} \qquad \begin{aligned}(x + r)(x + s) &= x^2 + sx + rx + rs \\ &= x^2 + (s + r)x + rs\end{aligned}$$

We see that $s + r = 11$ and $rs = 30$.

To factor $x^2 + 11x + 30$, we find two integers, r and s, such that $s + r = 11$ and $r \times s = 30$. Since r and s are 5 and 6,

$$x^2 + 11x + 30 = (x + 5)(x + 6)$$

Example. Factor.

(a) $x^2 - 9x + 20$

(b) $x^2 - 7x - 18$

Solution:

(a) $x^2 - 9x + 20$
$\quad x^2 + (s + r)x + rs$

$\quad s + r = -9$, $rs = 20$

$\quad$ s and r are -4 and -5.

$\quad x^2 - 9x + 20 = (x - 4)(x - 5)$

(b) $x^2 - 7x - 18$
$\quad x^2 + (s + r)x + rs$

$\quad s + r = -7$, $rs = -18$

$\quad$ s and r are -9 and 2.

$\quad x^2 - 7x - 18 = (x - 9)(x + 2)$

EXERCISE 2.4

B

1. Factor.

(a) $x^2 + 7x + 12$ (b) $t^2 + 6t + 8$
(c) $a^2 - 5a + 6$ (d) $x^2 + 2x - 8$
(e) $y^2 - 3y - 10$ (f) $x^2 + 12x + 36$
(g) $x^2 - x - 2$ (h) $s^2 - s - 12$
(i) $x^2 + x - 12$ (j) $x^2 + 12x + 20$

2. Factor and check by expanding your answer.

(a) $a^2 + 8a + 12$ (b) $x^2 - 13x + 36$
(c) $x^2 + 5x - 36$ (d) $t^2 + 10t + 16$
(e) $x^2 - x - 30$ (f) $x^2 + 6x - 27$
(g) $b^2 + 17b + 70$ (h) $m^2 - 10m - 200$
(i) $x^2 - 14x + 48$ (j) $t^2 + 4t - 45$

3. Factor.

(a) $x^2 + 7xy + 12y^2$ (b) $x^2 - xy - 12y^2$
(c) $a^2 - 3ab - 4b^2$ (d) $p^2 - 8pq - 9q^2$

(e) $s^2 + 3st + 2t^2$ (f) $c^2 + cd - 12d^2$
(g) $x^2 - 7xy + 12y^2$ (h) $a^2b^2 - 2ab + 1$

4. Find three factors of each of the following by first finding a common factor.

$$\begin{aligned}2x^2 - 8x - 24 &= 2(x^2 - 4x - 12) \\ &= 2(x - 6)(x + 2)\end{aligned}$$

(a) $4a^2 - 8a - 60$ (b) $3b^2 + 15b - 42$
(c) $6c^2 - 12c + 6$ (d) $5d^2 - 50d + 125$
(e) $2e^2 + 10e - 48$ (f) $x - 5x^2 + 6x^3$
(g) $3x^2 + 6x + 3$ (h) $2x^2 + 24x + 72$
(i) $4t^2 - 8t - 60$ (j) $ax^2 + ax - 30a$

C

5. Factor.

(a) $x^2 + x + \frac{1}{4}$ (b) $x^2 - x + \frac{1}{4}$

(c) $x^2 + \frac{1}{2}x + \frac{1}{16}$ (d) $x^2 - \frac{1}{4}x - \frac{1}{8}$

2.5 FACTORING SPECIAL QUADRATICS

A perfect square trinomial is a trinomial that is the square of a binomial; therefore a perfect square trinomial has two equal binomial factors.

$(x + 3)^2 = x^2 + 6x + 9$

Factoring Perfect Squares
$a^2 + 2ab + b^2 = (a + b)(a + b) = (a + b)^2$
$a^2 - 2ab + b^2 = (a - b)(a - b) = (a - b)^2$

To factor the difference of two squares, we take the square root of each square. We then write the product of their difference and their sum.

$$(x - 2)(x + 2) = x^2 + 2x - 2x - 4$$
$$= x^2 - 4$$

Factoring the Difference of Squares
$a^2 - b^2 = (a - b)(a + b)$

Example. Factor.
    (a) $x^2 - 16x + 64$ (b) $25a^2 - 49b^2$

Solution:

(a) $x^2 - 16x + 64 = x^2 - 2(x)(8) + 8^2$
$$= (x - 8)^2$$

(b) $25a^2 - 49b^2 = (5a)^2 - (7b)^2$
$$= (5a - 7b)(5a + 7b)$$

EXERCISE 2.5

B

1. Factor.
(a) $t^2 + 12t + 36$ (b) $y^2 + 14y + 49$
(c) $x^2 - 18x + 81$ (d) $p^2 - 12p + 36$
(e) $s^2 - 20s + 100$ (f) $a^2 + 10a + 25$
(g) $4x^2 + 12x + 9$ (h) $9a^2 - 6a + 1$

2. Factor.
(a) $9x^2 + 24xy + 16y^2$
(b) $4a^2 - 12ab + 9b^2$
(c) $4c^2 - 20cd + 25d^2$
(d) $25p^2 + 30pq + 9q^2$
(e) $25s^2 + 20st + 4t^2$
(f) $64x^2 - 80xy + 25y^2$

3. Factor.
(a) $x^2 - 9$ (b) $x^2 - 25$
(c) $t^2 - 16$ (d) $a^2 - 100$

(e) $m^2 - 64n^2$ (f) $a^2 - 36b^2$
(g) $49t^2 - s^2$ (h) $121x^2 - y^2$
(i) $9x^2 - 4y^2$ (j) $25p^2 - 16q^2$

MIND BENDER

Determine the pattern and find the missing numbers.

8	5	7	6		3	
11	7	11		9		17
24	10	28		20	21	
3	2	4	3			9

2.6 FACTORING TRINOMIALS: ax² + bx + c

In the trinomial $x^2 + 7x + 12$, the coefficient of x^2 is 1. To factor this trinomial, we must find two integers whose product is 12 and whose sum is 7. Since $3 \times 4 = 12$ and $3 + 4 = 7$,

$$x^2 + 7x + 12 = (x + 3)(x + 4)$$

In the trinomial $6x^2 + 23x + 20$, the coefficient of x^2 is not 1. To factor trinomials like these, another method is used. We will see a pattern if we expand $(3x + 4)(2x + 5)$.

$$(3x + 4)(2x + 5) = (3x + 4)(2x + 5)$$

$$= 6x^2 + 15x + 8x + 20$$
$$= 6x^2 + (15 + 8)x + 20$$

$$15 \times 8 = 120$$
$$6 \times 20 = 120$$

Notice that the product of 6 and 20 is the same as the product of 15 and 8. We use this pattern to factor trinomials of the form $ax^2 + bx + c$.

Example 1. Factor. $6x^2 + 17x + 12$

Solution:

$$\begin{array}{l} 6 \times 12 = 72 \\ 6x^2 + 17x + 12 \\ = 6x^2 + (\blacksquare + \blacksquare)x + 12 \\ = 6x^2 + (9 + 8)x + 12 \\ = 6x^2 + 9x + 8x + 12 \\ = (6x^2 + 9x) + (8x + 12) \\ = 3x(2x + 3) + 4(2x + 3) \\ = (2x + 3)(3x + 4) \end{array}$$

The product of 6 and 12 is 72. We need to replace the ■ with two integers whose sum is 17 and whose product is 72.

Use the factors 9 and 8.

Group pairs that have a common factor.

Factor.

$\therefore 6x^2 + 17x + 12 = (2x + 3)(3x + 4)$

Check: $(2x + 3)(3x + 4) = 6x^2 + 8x + 9x + 12$
$= 6x^2 + 17x + 12$

Example 2. Factor. $4x^2 - 5x - 6$

Solution:
The product of 4 and -6 is -24. We need to replace the ■ with two integers whose sum is -5 and whose product is -24.

$$\begin{array}{l} 4x^2 - 5x - 6 = 4x^2 + (\blacksquare + \blacksquare)x - 6 \\ \quad = 4x^2 + (-8 + 3)x - 6 \\ \quad = 4x^2 - 8x + 3x - 6 \\ \quad = (4x^2 - 8x) + (3x - 6) \\ \quad = 4x(x - 2) + 3(x - 2) \\ \quad = (x - 2)(4x + 3) \end{array}$$

Factors of -24	Sum of factors
-24, 1	-23
24, -1	23
-12, 2	-10
12, -2	10
-8, 3	-5

$\therefore 4x^2 - 5x - 6 = (x - 2)(4x + 3)$

Example 3. Factor. $6x^2 - 7x + 2$

Solution:
The product of 6 and 2 is 12.
The required sum is -7.

$$6x^2 - 7x + 2 = 6x^2 - 4x - 3x + 2$$
$$= (6x^2 - 4x) - (3x - 2)$$
$$= 2x(3x - 2) - 1(3x - 2)$$
$$= (3x - 2)(2x - 1)$$

$\therefore 6x^2 - 7x + 2 = (3x - 2)(2x - 1)$

Factors of 12	Sum of factors
12, 1	13
$-12, -1$	-13
6, 2	8
$-6, -2$	-8
4, 3	7
$-4, -3$	-7

EXERCISE 2.6

A

1. Complete the factoring.
(a) $x(x + 7) - 3(x + 7)$
(b) $3t(2t + 1) + 2(2t + 1)$
(c) $2m(3m - 1) - 4(3m - 1)$
(d) $5y(y - 3) - 1(y - 3)$
(e) $4x(5x + 4) + 3(5x + 4)$
(f) $3m(4m - 5) + 6(4m - 5)$

B

2. Factor.
(a) $2x^2 + 7x + 5$ (b) $3x^2 + 7x + 2$
(c) $6x^2 + 19x + 10$ (d) $2x^2 + 5x - 3$
(e) $5x^2 - 17x + 6$ (f) $2x^2 - 3x - 14$
(g) $6x^2 + 19x + 15$ (h) $6x^2 + 13x + 6$
(i) $8x^2 + x - 9$ (j) $10x^2 - 21x - 10$

3. Factor.
(a) $2x^2 + 5x - 3$
(b) $5m^2 - 17m + 6$
(c) $6x^2 - 13x - 5$
(d) $9a^2 - 18ab + 8b^2$
(e) $15r^2 - 31r + 14$
(f) $4x^2 + 8xy + 3y^2$
(g) $28y^2 - 39xy + 8x^2$
(h) $12x^2 - 5xy - 2y^2$
(i) $3m^2 - 19mn - 14n^2$
(j) $10a^2 - 13ab - 30b^2$

MICRO MATH

The following program checks your factoring by multiplication. Use the program to check your answers.

```
NEW
  5 PRINT"QUADRATIC FACTOR CHECKER"
 10 PRINT"(PX + M) (QX + N)"
 15 PRINT"ENTER P,Q,M,N, IN ORDER."
 20 INPUT "P = ";P
 25 INPUT "Q = ";Q
 30 INPUT "M = ";M
 35 INPUT "N = ";N
 40 IF P*N+M*Q>0 AND M+N>0 THEN 65
 45 IF P*N+M*Q>0 AND M+N<0 THEN 75
 50 IF P*N+M*Q<0 AND M+N>0 THEN 85
 55 IF P*N+M*Q<0 AND M+N<0 THEN 95
 60 PRINT "THE POLYNOMIAL IS"
 65 PRINT P*Q;"X^2";"+";P*N+M*Q;"X";
    "+";M*N
 70 GOTO 110
 75 PRINT P*Q;"X^2";"+";P*N+M*Q;"X";M*N
 80 GOTO 110
 85 PRINT P*Q;"X^2";P*N+M*Q;"X";"+";M*N
 90 GOTO 110
 95 PRINT P*Q;"X^2";P*N+M*Q;"X";M*N
100 GOTO 110
105 END
110 INPUT"ANOTHER QUESTION Y/N";Z$
115 IF Z$="Y" THEN 15
120 END
RUN
```

2.7 SIMPLIFYING RATIONAL EXPRESSIONS

Rational numbers are numbers such as $\frac{3}{4}$, $-\frac{7}{11}$, and $\frac{21}{5}$. In general, a rational number is a number of the form $\frac{a}{b}$, where $a, b \in I$, and $b \neq 0$.

To simplify a rational number such as $\frac{21}{28}$, we first factor the numerator and denominator; then we eliminate common factors.

$$\frac{21}{28} = \frac{3 \times 7}{4 \times 7}$$

$$= \frac{3 \times \cancel{7}^{1}}{4 \times \cancel{7}_{1}}$$

$$= \frac{3}{4}$$

The same procedure can be used to simplify rational expressions or algebraic fractions. As with rational numbers, the denominator of a rational expression cannot be equal to zero. To prevent this, we place restrictions on the variables.

Example 1. Simplify. $\dfrac{35xy}{25y^2}$

Solution: $\dfrac{35xy}{25y^2} = \dfrac{7 \times 5 \times x \times y}{5 \times 5 \times y \times y}$

$$= \frac{7 \times \cancel{5}^{1} \times x \times \cancel{y}^{1}}{5 \times \cancel{5}_{1} \times y \times \cancel{y}_{1}}$$

$$= \frac{7x}{5y}, \quad y \neq 0$$

> $y \neq 0$ is the restriction so that we do not divide by zero.

Example 2. Simplify. $\dfrac{3x^2 + 6x}{2x + 4}$

Solution: $\dfrac{3x^2 + 6x}{2x + 4} = \dfrac{3x(x + 2)}{2(x + 2)}$

$$= \frac{3x\cancel{(x + 2)}^{1}}{2\cancel{(x + 2)}_{1}}$$

$$= \frac{3x}{2}, \quad x \neq -2$$

> $x \neq -2$ is the restriction so that we do not divide by zero.

Example 3. Simplify. $\dfrac{t^2 + 4t + 3}{t^2 - t - 12}$

Solution: $\dfrac{t^2 + 4t + 3}{t^2 - t - 12} = \dfrac{(t + 1)(t + 3)}{(t + 3)(t - 4)}$

1. Factor.

$$= \dfrac{(t + 1)\cancel{(t + 3)}^{\,1}}{\cancel{(t + 3)}_{\,1}(t - 4)}$$

2. Divide.

$$= \dfrac{t + 1}{t - 4}, \quad t \ne -3, 4$$

3. State restrictions.

EXERCISE 2.7

A

1. State the restrictions on the variables in each of the following.

(a) $\dfrac{5}{x}$

(b) $\dfrac{3a}{mn}$

(c) $\dfrac{6rst}{5w}$

(d) $\dfrac{x + 4}{x + 5}$

(e) $\dfrac{7}{t(t - 3)}$

(f) $\dfrac{m + 1}{m^2}$

(g) $\dfrac{x^2}{x + 1}$

(h) $\dfrac{x}{(x - 3)(x - 4)}$

(i) $\dfrac{2x}{(x + 1)(x + 2)}$

(j) $\dfrac{3x}{2x - 1}$

(k) $\dfrac{2x}{3 - x}$

(l) $\dfrac{x + 2}{(4 - x)(1 + x)}$

B

2. Simplify. State restrictions on the variables.

(a) $\dfrac{2a}{6a^2}$

(b) $\dfrac{-12xy}{-6x}$

(c) $\dfrac{36a^2b^2}{9ab}$

(d) $\dfrac{4x + 6y}{2}$

(e) $\dfrac{6ab - 9ac}{3a}$

(f) $\dfrac{2x}{2y - 8t}$

(g) $\dfrac{5ax}{10ay + 15at}$

(h) $\dfrac{3x + 6}{x + 2}$

(i) $\dfrac{2ab - ac}{6b - 3c}$

(j) $\dfrac{x^2 + 2x}{x^3 - 4x}$

(k) $\dfrac{x + 2}{x^2 - 4}$

(l) $\dfrac{a^2 + 7a}{a^2 - 49}$

3. Simplify. State restrictions on the variables.

(a) $\dfrac{t + 5}{t^2 + 7t + 10}$

(b) $\dfrac{m + 6}{m^2 + 7m + 6}$

(c) $\dfrac{x - 4}{x^2 - 9x + 20}$

(d) $\dfrac{r - 2}{r^2 + 5r - 14}$

(e) $\dfrac{s^2 + 7s + 12}{s^2 + 6s + 8}$

(f) $\dfrac{t^2 - 2t - 8}{t^2 - t - 6}$

(g) $\dfrac{y^2 + 8y + 15}{y + 3}$

(h) $\dfrac{x^2 + 8x - 20}{x^2 - 4}$

(i) $\dfrac{a^2 + a - 12}{a^2 + 2a - 15}$

(j) $\dfrac{6x^2 + 24x}{x^2 + 8x + 16}$

(k) $\dfrac{x^2 + 6x + 9}{x^2 + 4x + 3}$

(l) $\dfrac{m^2 - 3m + 2}{m^2 - 4m + 4}$

(m) $\dfrac{r^2 + 4r - 5}{r^2 + 3r - 10}$

(n) $\dfrac{x^2 - x - 6}{x^2 - 7x + 12}$

(o) $\dfrac{a^2 - 2a + 1}{a^2 - 5a + 4}$

(p) $\dfrac{x^2 - 9}{x^2 - 4x + 3}$

C

4. Simplify. State restrictions on the variables.

(a) $\dfrac{2t^2 - 5t + 3}{3t^2 - 5t + 2}$

(b) $\dfrac{3a^2 + 8a - 3}{6a^2 + 17a - 3}$

(c) $\dfrac{6m^2 + 5m - 4}{3m^2 - 8m - 16}$

(d) $\dfrac{6x^2 + 11x + 3}{4x^2 - 9}$

(e) $\dfrac{6k^2 - k - 12}{6k^2 - 17k + 12}$

(f) $\dfrac{3t^2 + 3t + 18}{5t^2 + 5t + 30}$

2.8 MULTIPLYING AND DIVIDING RATIONAL EXPRESSIONS

To multiply rational numbers in the form $\frac{a}{b}$, we multiply the numerators and the denominators.

$$\frac{3}{5} \times \frac{6}{7} = \frac{3 \times 6}{5 \times 7}$$
$$= \frac{18}{35}$$

This method can be generalized as follows:

$$\boxed{\frac{P}{Q} \times \frac{R}{S} = \frac{PR}{QS}, \quad Q, S \neq 0}$$

We use the same method to multiply rational expressions.

$$\frac{4a}{5b} \times \frac{6ab}{7a} = \frac{4a \times 6ab}{5b \times 7a}$$
$$= \frac{24a^2b}{35ab}$$
$$= \frac{24a \times ab}{35 \times ab}$$
$$= \frac{24a}{35}, \quad a, b \neq 0$$

To divide by a rational number, we multiply by the reciprocal.

$$\frac{2}{3} \div \frac{5}{7} = \frac{2}{3} \times \frac{7}{5}$$
$$= \frac{2 \times 7}{3 \times 5}$$
$$= \frac{14}{15}$$

This method can be generalized as follows:

$$\boxed{\frac{P}{Q} \div \frac{R}{S} = \frac{P}{Q} \times \frac{S}{R} = \frac{PS}{QR}, \quad Q, R, S \neq 0}$$

We use the same method to divide a rational expression by a rational expression.

$$\frac{3x}{2y} \div \frac{4xy}{5y^2} = \frac{3x}{2y} \times \frac{5y^2}{4xy}$$
$$= \frac{15xy^2}{8xy^2}$$
$$= \frac{15}{8}, \quad x, y \neq 0$$

Example. Simplify.

(a) $\dfrac{7a^2b}{3a} \times \dfrac{9a^3}{28b^2}$

(b) $\dfrac{x^2 - 1}{2x - 3} \div \dfrac{x + 1}{4x - 6}$

Solution:

(a) $\dfrac{7a^2b}{3a} \times \dfrac{9a^3}{28b^2} = \dfrac{7a^2b \times 9a^3}{3a \times 28b^2}$

$\qquad = \dfrac{7 \times 9 \times a^2b \times a^3}{3 \times 28 \times a \times b^2}$

$\qquad = \dfrac{3a^4}{4b}, \quad a, b \neq 0$

(b) $\dfrac{x^2 - 1}{2x - 3} \div \dfrac{x + 1}{4x - 6} = \dfrac{x^2 - 1}{2x - 3} \times \dfrac{4x - 6}{x + 1}$

$\qquad = \dfrac{(x - 1)(x + 1)2(2x - 3)}{(2x - 3)(x + 1)}$

$\qquad = 2(x - 1), \quad x \neq -1, \tfrac{3}{2}$

EXERCISE 2.8

B

1. Simplify.

(a) $\frac{2}{3} \times \frac{3}{5}$ (b) $\frac{4}{9} \times \frac{1}{3}$ (c) $5 \times \frac{2}{7}$

(d) $\left(\frac{1}{2}\right)^2$ (e) $\left(-\frac{1}{4}\right)\left(-\frac{8}{7}\right)$ (f) $\frac{2}{5} \times (-10)$

2. Simplify.

(a) $\frac{1}{2} \div \frac{1}{4}$ (b) $\frac{2}{3} \div \frac{3}{5}$

(c) $\frac{1}{5} \div 2$ (d) $3 \div \frac{1}{6}$

(e) $\left(-\frac{3}{4}\right) \div \left(-\frac{3}{8}\right)$ (f) $\left(\frac{6}{7}\right) \div \left(-\frac{2}{3}\right)$

3. Simplify.

(a) $\dfrac{2a}{3} \times \dfrac{b}{a}$ (b) $\dfrac{2x}{3y} \times \dfrac{5y}{x}$

(c) $\dfrac{-3a}{2b} \times \dfrac{2b}{3a}$ (d) $\dfrac{-4x}{m} \times \dfrac{-m}{2x}$

(e) $\dfrac{2a}{3} \div \dfrac{a}{b}$ (f) $\dfrac{-2m}{3t} \div \dfrac{2m}{3t}$

(g) $\dfrac{a^2b}{b^2c} \times \dfrac{c}{d}$ (h) $\dfrac{6s^2t}{8t^2} \times \dfrac{12t}{9s}$

4. Simplify.

(a) $\dfrac{10a^3}{6x^2} \times \dfrac{12a^2x^4}{25a^2x^2}$ (b) $\dfrac{6a^3b}{10s^2} \div \dfrac{9b^3}{4s^2a}$

(c) $\dfrac{44c^3}{21a^2b} \div \dfrac{11c^2}{7ab^3}$ (d) $\dfrac{2p^2s}{3qr} \times \dfrac{9q^2r}{16ps^2}$

5. Simplify.

(a) $\dfrac{x + 3}{6} \times \dfrac{12}{x + 3}$ (b) $\dfrac{8}{t - 1} \times \dfrac{5t - 5}{4}$

(c) $\dfrac{2m^3}{m + 1} \div \dfrac{m^2}{m + 1}$ (d) $\dfrac{x + 4}{x + 1} \div \dfrac{x + 4}{x + 2}$

6. Simplify.

(a) $\dfrac{x^2 + 2x + 1}{2} \times \dfrac{x - 1}{x + 1}$

(b) $\dfrac{1}{m^2 + m - 12} \times \dfrac{m - 3}{m + 5}$

(c) $\dfrac{x^2 + 4x - 12}{x^2 + 9x + 18} \div \dfrac{3x + 12}{6x + 18}$

(d) $\dfrac{a^2 - 6a + 8}{a^2 + 3a + 2} \div \dfrac{a^2 - 4a}{a^2 - 4}$

(e) $\dfrac{x^2 + 3x + 2}{x^2 - 5x + 6} \times \dfrac{x^2 + 3x - 10}{x^2 + 6x + 5}$

(f) $\dfrac{a^2 - 11a + 30}{a^2 - 6a + 9} \div \dfrac{a^2 - 5a}{a^2 - 3a}$

C

7. Simplify.

(a) $\dfrac{x^2 - x - 20}{x^2 - 25} \times \dfrac{x^2 - x - 2}{x^2 + 2x - 8} \div \dfrac{x^2 - 1}{x^2 + 5x}$

(b) $\dfrac{x^2 - 4x + 4}{x^2 + 6x + 9} \div \dfrac{x^2 - 3x + 2}{x^2 - 9}$

(c) $\dfrac{2a^2 + a - 1}{a^2 - 4a + 3} \div \dfrac{6a^2 + a - 2}{2a^2 - 5a + 3}$

$\quad \times \dfrac{3a^2 - 7a - 6}{2a^2 - 7a + 6}$

(d) $\dfrac{4x^2 - 1}{2x^2 + 7x + 3} \times \dfrac{3x^2 + 5x - 2}{2x^2 - x - 10}$

$\quad \div \dfrac{6x^2 - 5x + 1}{2x^2 + x - 15}$

2.9 ADDING AND SUBTRACTING RATIONAL EXPRESSIONS

To add or subtract rational numbers with the same denominator, we add or subtract the numerators. We then write the sum or difference over the common denominator.

$$\frac{2}{7} + \frac{3}{7} = \frac{2+3}{7} \qquad\qquad \frac{7}{9} - \frac{5}{9} = \frac{7-5}{9}$$
$$= \frac{5}{7} \qquad\qquad\qquad = \frac{2}{9}$$

This method can be generalized as follows:

$$\frac{P}{Q} + \frac{R}{Q} = \frac{P+R}{Q} \quad \text{and} \quad \frac{P}{Q} - \frac{R}{Q} = \frac{P-R}{Q}, \quad Q \neq 0$$

We use the same method to add or subtract rational expressions.

$$\frac{5}{x+2} + \frac{3}{x+2} = \frac{5+3}{x+2}$$
$$= \frac{8}{x+2}, \quad x \neq -2$$

$$\frac{3t+1}{t-3} - \frac{t-6}{t-3} = \frac{3t+1-(t-6)}{t-3}$$
$$= \frac{3t+1-t+6}{t-3}$$
$$= \frac{2t+7}{t-3}, \quad t \neq 3$$

To add or subtract rational numbers with different denominators, we use equivalent fractions to rewrite the numbers with the same denominators.

The Lowest Common Denominator of 8 and 6 is 24.

$$\frac{3}{8} + \frac{1}{6} = \frac{3}{8} \times \frac{3}{3} + \frac{1}{6} \times \frac{4}{4}$$
$$= \frac{9}{24} + \frac{4}{24}$$
$$= \frac{13}{24}$$

We use this method to add or subtract rational expressions with different denominators.

Example 1. Simplify. $\dfrac{2}{3ab} + \dfrac{5}{6bc}$

Solution: The LCD is 6abc.

$$\dfrac{2}{3ab} + \dfrac{5}{6bc} = \dfrac{2}{3ab} \times \dfrac{2c}{2c} + \dfrac{5}{6bc} \times \dfrac{a}{a}$$

$$= \dfrac{4c}{6abc} + \dfrac{5a}{6abc}$$

$$= \dfrac{4c + 5a}{6abc}, \quad a, b, c \neq 0$$

Example 2. Simplify. $\dfrac{7}{a + 6} - \dfrac{2}{a - 2}$

Solution: $\dfrac{7}{a + 6} - \dfrac{2}{a - 2} = \dfrac{7}{(a + 6)} \times \dfrac{(a - 2)}{(a - 2)} - \dfrac{2}{(a - 2)} \times \dfrac{(a + 6)}{(a + 6)}$ The LCD is $(a + 6)(a - 2)$.

$$= \dfrac{7(a - 2)}{(a + 6)(a - 2)} - \dfrac{2(a + 6)}{(a + 6)(a - 2)}$$

$$= \dfrac{7(a - 2) - 2(a + 6)}{(a + 6)(a - 2)}$$

$$= \dfrac{7a - 14 - 2a - 12}{(a + 6)(a - 2)}$$

$$= \dfrac{5a - 26}{(a + 6)(a - 2)}, \quad a \neq -6, 2$$

Example 3. Simplify. $\dfrac{3}{x^2 + x - 12} + \dfrac{2}{x + 4}$

Solution: $\dfrac{3}{x^2 + x - 12} + \dfrac{2}{x + 4} = \dfrac{3}{(x + 4)(x - 3)} + \dfrac{2}{(x + 4)}$ The LCD is $(x + 4)(x - 3)$.

$$= \dfrac{3}{(x + 4)(x - 3)} + \dfrac{2}{(x + 4)} \times \dfrac{(x - 3)}{(x - 3)}$$

$$= \dfrac{3}{(x + 4)(x - 3)} + \dfrac{2(x - 3)}{(x + 4)(x - 3)}$$

$$= \dfrac{3 + 2(x - 3)}{(x + 4)(x - 3)}$$

$$= \dfrac{3 + 2x - 6}{(x + 4)(x - 3)}$$

$$= \dfrac{2x - 3}{(x + 4)(x - 3)}, \quad x \neq -4, 3$$

EXERCISE 2.9

A

1. Simplify.

(a) $\dfrac{3}{7} + \dfrac{2}{7}$ (b) $\dfrac{7}{13} - \dfrac{4}{13}$

(c) $\dfrac{5x}{2} - \dfrac{x}{2}$ (d) $\dfrac{5}{x} - \dfrac{1}{x}$

(e) $\dfrac{9}{2a} - \dfrac{4}{2a}$ (f) $\dfrac{7m}{3} + \dfrac{3m}{3}$

(g) $\dfrac{8a}{5} - \dfrac{2a}{5}$ (h) $\dfrac{2}{y-1} + \dfrac{4}{y-1}$

(i) $\dfrac{9}{x+1} - \dfrac{5}{x+1}$ (j) $\dfrac{6}{a+3} + \dfrac{4}{a+3}$

(k) $\dfrac{11}{a+b} - \dfrac{7}{a+b}$ (l) $\dfrac{a}{x+y} - \dfrac{b}{x+y}$

B

2. Simplify.

(a) $\dfrac{3x}{7} + \dfrac{2x}{3}$ (b) $\dfrac{5a}{2} - \dfrac{3a}{5}$

(c) $\dfrac{3m}{6} + \dfrac{2m}{4}$ (d) $\dfrac{x}{8} - \dfrac{2x}{3}$

(e) $\dfrac{5x}{6} - \dfrac{2x}{5}$ (f) $\dfrac{2a}{11} - \dfrac{3b}{2}$

(g) $\dfrac{5d}{2} + \dfrac{3c}{7}$ (h) $\dfrac{3a}{4} + \dfrac{2b}{3} - \dfrac{5c}{6}$

3. Simplify.

(a) $\dfrac{3}{x} + \dfrac{4}{y}$ (b) $\dfrac{5}{a} + \dfrac{2}{b}$

(c) $\dfrac{7}{m} - \dfrac{3}{n}$ (d) $\dfrac{2}{3m} + \dfrac{5}{2n}$

(e) $\dfrac{3}{4a} - \dfrac{5}{3b}$ (f) $\dfrac{x}{y} + \dfrac{y}{x}$

(g) $\dfrac{a}{xy} + \dfrac{b}{yz}$ (h) $\dfrac{x}{a} + \dfrac{y}{b} - \dfrac{z}{c}$

4. Simplify.

(a) $\dfrac{x+3}{4} + \dfrac{x+5}{3}$ (b) $\dfrac{x-1}{2} + \dfrac{x+7}{5}$

(c) $\dfrac{a-3}{3} - \dfrac{a+4}{5}$ (d) $\dfrac{m+1}{6} - \dfrac{m-7}{5}$

(e) $\dfrac{b+4}{6} - \dfrac{b+2}{3}$ (f) $\dfrac{2a-1}{4} + \dfrac{3a+2}{5}$

(g) $\dfrac{2x+3y}{9} - \dfrac{x+4y}{2}$ (h) $\dfrac{2b+3c}{6} - \dfrac{b-2c}{2}$

5. Simplify.

(a) $\dfrac{3}{x+2} + \dfrac{4}{x}$ (b) $\dfrac{7}{m-1} - \dfrac{3}{m}$

(c) $\dfrac{6}{a} - \dfrac{5}{a+1}$ (d) $\dfrac{1}{r} + \dfrac{1}{r+5}$

(e) $\dfrac{m}{m+3} + \dfrac{5}{m}$ (f) $\dfrac{2x}{x-4} - \dfrac{3}{x}$

6. Simplify.

(a) $\dfrac{5}{x+3} + \dfrac{2}{x+2}$ (b) $\dfrac{3}{a-1} + \dfrac{5}{a+2}$

(c) $\dfrac{4}{m+3} - \dfrac{3}{m-1}$ (d) $\dfrac{5}{b+4} - \dfrac{2}{b-3}$

(e) $\dfrac{x+3}{x+1} + \dfrac{x-2}{x-1}$ (f) $\dfrac{m-5}{m+1} + \dfrac{m-3}{m-2}$

(g) $\dfrac{x-4}{x-2} - \dfrac{x-7}{x-5}$ (h) $\dfrac{a+2}{a-3} - \dfrac{a-4}{a+3}$

7. Simplify.

(a) $\dfrac{3}{x^2+5x+6} + \dfrac{2}{x+3}$

(b) $\dfrac{5}{a^2-7a+10} - \dfrac{3}{a-5}$

(c) $\dfrac{1}{m-7} + \dfrac{4}{m^2-6m-7}$

(d) $\dfrac{6}{t+5} - \dfrac{2}{t^2+11t+30}$

(e) $\dfrac{3}{x+4} - \dfrac{1}{x^2-x-20}$

(f) $\dfrac{2}{x^2-6x+9} + \dfrac{1}{x-3}$

8. Simplify.

(a) $\dfrac{2}{x^2-x-12} + \dfrac{3}{x^2-6x+8}$

(b) $\dfrac{4}{x^2+7x+10} - \dfrac{3}{x^2-x-6}$

(c) $\dfrac{5}{a^2+7a+12} - \dfrac{2}{a^2+6a+9}$

C

9. (a) If $\dfrac{1}{R} = \dfrac{1}{R_1} + \dfrac{1}{R_2}$, find R.

(b) If $\dfrac{1}{R} = \dfrac{1}{R_1} + \dfrac{1}{R_2} + \dfrac{1}{R_3}$, find R.

EXTRA

2.10 TELEPHONE AREA CODES AND RADIO STATION CALL LETTERS

The telephone area codes in Canada and the United States consist of three digits. The first digit is from 2 to 9, the second digit must be 0 or 1, and the third digit is from 1 to 9.

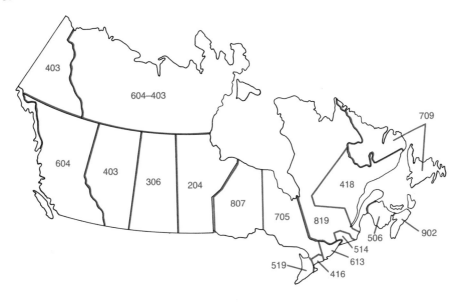

EXERCISE 2.10

1. How many different telephone area codes can begin with the digit 5?

2. How many different telephone area codes can end with the digit 7?

3. How many different telephone area codes are possible?

4. Why is the second digit of a telephone area code either 0 or 1?

5. To call overseas station-to-station you must dial 011 plus a country code, a routing code, and the local number. To call overseas person-to-person you start with 01 instead of 011. Why not start with 0?

6. The call letters of radio stations in Canada and the United States begin with either W, K, or C.
If you start a radio station somewhere in North America, what will determine the first call letter?

7. Some radio stations in Canada have 3 call letters.
How many sets of call letters having three letters are possible in Canada?

2.11 PROBLEM SOLVING

1. Two trains are 300 km apart on the same track. They start toward each other at the same time. One train travels at 60 km/h, and the other travels at 90 km/h. At the start, when the trains are 300 km apart, a swift travels from one train to the other at a speed of 200 km/h. When the swift reaches the second train, it immediately returns to the first train. This continues until the trains meet each other.

How many kilometres did the swift travel?

2. Find all the whole numbers less than 100 whose digits have a sum of 10.

3. Suppose the scoring in football is changed to 7 points for a touchdown and 3 points for a field goal. There are no other ways to score points.
What scores are impossible to achieve?

4. Two sides of a triangle have the same length. The third side is 3 m longer. The perimeter of the triangle is 27 m.
Find the lengths of the sides.

5. Paper cups can be bought in packages of 15 or 25. Justine bought 7 packages and got 125 cups.
How many packages of each did she buy?

6. In order to determine a grade point average for the courses taken at a college, four points are given for an A, three for a B, two for a C, one for a D, and zero for an F. If a student has a total of twelve points for five courses, what combinations of letter grades could she have?

7. How many triangles are in the diagram?

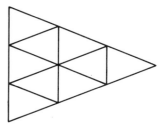

8. How many ways can you receive change for a quarter if one of the coins must be a nickel?

9. Which numbers between 0 and 100 are divisible by both 3 and 11?

10. Each circle in the figure below has a diameter of 4 cm.

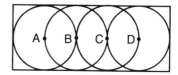

What is the area of the rectangle?

11. At the entrance to a bay a bell rings every thirteen minutes and a horn blasts every seven minutes. Assume that the bell and the horn start at the same time.
In how many minutes will they sound at the same time?

12. PQRS is a square. PQ = 6 cm. P is the centre of arc QS. R is the centre of arc QS.

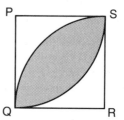

Find the area of the shaded region.

13. How many ways can a tennis game of mixed doubles be arranged from a group of four males and two females?

14. Smaller and smaller squares are formed as shown in the diagram.

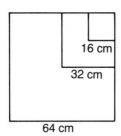

16 cm
32 cm
64 cm

The length of each side of the first square is 64 cm.
Find the sum of the perimeters of the first 8 squares.

15. Paul tore a sheet of paper in half. Then he tore both pieces in half. He then tore the resulting four pieces in half.
If he continued this process seven more times, how many pieces would he have?

16. Adams, Beam, Cliffe, and Dalton are an artist, a dentist, an editor, and a trucker.
(a) Adams and her husband went to dinner with the dentist and his wife.
(b) The editor said he bowled with Cliffe last week.
(c) The trucker congratulated Dalton on her golf score.
Find each person's job and sex.

17. How can you measure 6 L of water using a 7 L container and a 4 L container?

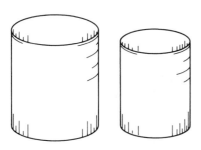

REGISTERED NURSE

A registered nurse provides care for the sick. This is done through activities such as administering medication, observing patients, recording changes in a patient's condition, and monitoring a patient with electronic life-saving equipment. Nurses work in schools, clinics, industry, private homes, and nursing homes, as well as in hospitals. The work of the nurse is demanding, both physically and emotionally. Because of the speed at which medical advances are occurring, many nurses upgrade their skills with extra courses throughout their careers.

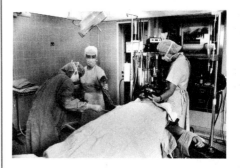

EXERCISE

1. A patient requires 3 mL of medication every 3 h.
How much medication is required in a 24 h period?

2. In a medical research project with 50 people, 20 people were given medication A, and 15 were given medication B. The others were given a placebo.
What percentage of people in the research project were given medication A or B?

2.12 REVIEW EXERCISE

1. Expand and simplify.
(a) $2x(x - 4) + 5(x - 7)$
(b) $5m(m - 1) - m(m + 3)$
(c) $2t(1 + 3t) - t(1 - t)$
(d) $6(x^2 - 2x - 4)$
(e) $3(2t^2 - 5t + 1)$
(f) $2x(x^2 - x - 1)$
(g) $-m(2m^2 - 3m - 3)$
(h) $-2t(1 - 3t - 2t^2)$

2. Expand and simplify.
(a) $(2x + 1)(x + 3)$
(b) $(5t - 4)(3t - 1)$
(c) $(2m - s)(3m + 4s)$
(d) $(x - 1)^2$
(e) $(x - 7)(x + 7)$
(f) $(3a - 2b)(a - 4b)$
(g) $(6a - 1)(6a + 1)$
(h) $(2m - n)^2$
(i) $(x - 3y)(x - 4y)$
(j) $(5s + 2t)(4s - 3t)$

3. Expand and simplify.
(a) $(x + 1)(x^2 + 2x + 3)$
(b) $(t - 2)(t^2 - 5t + 4)$
(c) $(3a - 1)(2a^2 + 3a + 5)$
(d) $(2m - 1)(m^2 - 6m - 7)$

4. Simplify.
(a) $\dfrac{20x^2y^2}{5xy}$

(b) $\dfrac{-36s^3t^4}{9st^2}$

(c) $\dfrac{8a - 16b - 4c}{4}$

(d) $\dfrac{5x^2 - 10x + 30}{-5}$

(e) $\dfrac{20a - 30a^2}{10a}$

(f) $\dfrac{36a^3 - 9a^2 + 18a}{-9a}$

(g) $\dfrac{24a^2b^3 - 20a^3b^4 - 32a^2b^5}{4ab^2}$

(h) $\dfrac{16a^3b^2c^4 - 40a^2b^2c^2 + 24a^2b^2c}{-8a^2b^2c}$

5. Factor each of the following.
(a) $4x^2 - 6x$
(b) $25xy^2 - 30x^2y$
(c) $18rst + 27r^2s^2t^2 - 9rs^2t$
(d) $5a^3b^2c^4 - 10a^2bc^3 - 5a^4b^3c^2$
(e) $4x(x - 1) - 3(x - 1)$
(f) $2t(t + 3) + 5(t + 3)$
(g) $5a(1 - 3a) - (1 - 3a)$
(h) $24a^2b - 6ab^2$
(i) $5mnt + 10m^2nt - 30m^2n^2t^2$
(j) $2ab - 3b - 2ax + 3x$
(k) $4mx^2 - 2mx + 2x - 1$

6. Factor.
(a) $x^2 - 7x + 12$
(b) $a^2 - a - 12$
(c) $x^2 + 5x - 36$
(d) $x^2 + 12x + 35$
(e) $t^2 + 12t + 35$
(f) $b^2 - 8b - 9$
(g) $x^2 - 144$
(h) $m^2 - 8m + 16$
(i) $t^2 - t - 42$
(j) $a^2 - 17a + 72$
(k) $x^2 - 15x + 54$
(l) $m^2 - 8m + 15$
(m) $s^2 - s - 30$
(n) $t^2 + 16t + 60$
(o) $p^2 - 10p + 16$
(p) $r^2 + 12r + 35$
(q) $x^2 + 3x - 40$
(r) $x^2 + 9xy + 18y^2$
(s) $a^2 - 2ab - 15b^2$
(t) $x^2 - \frac{1}{2}x - \frac{1}{2}$
(u) $x^2 - \frac{5}{6}x - \frac{1}{6}$

7. Factor.
(a) $x^2 - 25$
(b) $a^2 + 14a + 49$
(c) $m^2 - 22m + 121$
(d) $4t^2 + 20t + 25$
(e) $49y^2 - 100$
(f) $81b^2 - 36bc + 4c^2$
(g) $25t^2 + 20t + 4$
(h) $16m^2 - 24m + 9$

8. Factor.
(a) $3m^2 + 19m + 20$
(b) $3x^2 + 11x - 4$
(c) $6t^2 - 19t + 10$
(d) $7a^2 - 12a + 5$
(e) $6t^2 + 23t + 20$
(f) $9y^2 - 18y + 8$

9. Simplify. State restrictions on the variables.
(a) $\dfrac{36x^2y^2}{6x^2y}$
(b) $\dfrac{-40a^2b^3c}{-10abc}$
(c) $\dfrac{3a^2 - 6a}{3a}$
(d) $\dfrac{4x - 8y}{3x - 6y}$
(e) $\dfrac{x^2 + 6x + 8}{x^2 + 7x + 12}$
(f) $\dfrac{x^2 - 9}{x^2 - 6x + 9}$

10. Simplify. State restrictions on the variables.
(a) $\dfrac{3a^2}{4b^3} \times \dfrac{8b^2}{6a}$
(b) $\dfrac{36x^2y^3}{12xy} \times \dfrac{x^3y^3}{2xy^6}$
(c) $\dfrac{4a^2b}{3ab^2} \div \dfrac{2ab}{3b^2}$
(d) $\dfrac{x^2 - 8x + 16}{x^2 + 3x - 10} \times \dfrac{x^2 + 2x - 8}{x^2 - 16}$
(e) $\dfrac{x^2 + 11x + 30}{x^2 + x - 20} \div \dfrac{x^2 + 8x + 12}{x^2 - 8x + 16}$
(f) $\dfrac{x^2 - 25}{x^2 + 3x + 2} \div \dfrac{x^2 - 7x + 10}{5x + 10}$

11. Simplify. State restrictions on the variables.
(a) $\dfrac{3x}{2} + \dfrac{4y}{3}$
(b) $\dfrac{5a}{3} - \dfrac{2b}{4}$
(c) $\dfrac{3}{m} - \dfrac{2}{n}$

(d) $\dfrac{2}{a} + \dfrac{3}{b} - \dfrac{2}{c}$
(e) $\dfrac{3x + 1}{2} + \dfrac{5x - 1}{3}$
(f) $\dfrac{2a + 3b}{4} - \dfrac{3a - 2b}{6}$
(g) $\dfrac{1}{x + 1} + \dfrac{2}{x + 2} + \dfrac{3}{x + 3}$
(h) $\dfrac{3}{x - 1} - \dfrac{2}{x - 2}$
(i) $\dfrac{x + 2}{x + 3} + \dfrac{x + 1}{x + 2}$
(j) $\dfrac{3}{x^2 - x - 12} - \dfrac{2}{x^2 - 6x + 8}$
(k) $\dfrac{5}{(x - 5)^2} - \dfrac{x + 5}{x - 5}$
(l) $\dfrac{2x^2 + 7}{x^2 + x - 2} - \dfrac{x - 3}{x + 2}$

MIND BENDER

Place the numbers from 1 to 9 in the circles so that each side adds to 23.

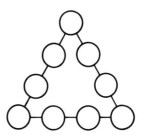

2.13 CHAPTER 2 TEST

1. Expand and simplify.
(a) $3x(x - 5) - 5(x - 4)$
(b) $(3t - 5)(2t - 1)$
(c) $(a - 4)^2$
(d) $(x - 1)(x^2 - 3x - 5)$

2. Simplify.
(a) $\dfrac{-30a^2b^2c}{-5abc}$

(b) $\dfrac{20x^2y - 10xy^2 + 5xy}{-5xy}$

3. Factor each of the following.
(a) $6x^2 - 9x$
(b) $a^2 - 7a + 12$
(c) $m^2 + 9x + 14$
(d) $2t^2 + 7t - 4$
(e) $4b^2 - 12b + 9$

4. Simplify and state the restrictions.
(a) $\dfrac{x^2 - 16}{x^2 - 8x + 16}$

(b) $\dfrac{3m^2}{2n^2} \times \dfrac{6n^3}{5n}$

(c) $\dfrac{4}{x} + \dfrac{3}{y}$

(d) $\dfrac{x^2 - x - 2}{x^2 + x - 6} \times \dfrac{x^2 + 8x + 15}{x^2 + x - 20}$

(e) $\dfrac{x^2 - 1}{x^2 + 2x - 3} \div \dfrac{x - 1}{x + 3}$

(f) $\dfrac{3}{x + 4} - \dfrac{3}{x - 4}$

(g) $\dfrac{x + 1}{x - 2} + \dfrac{x}{x + 2}$

EQUATIONS

3

REVIEW AND PREVIEW TO CHAPTER 3

SOLVING LINEAR EQUATIONS PART I

Solve. $3(x - 1) - 5(x - 2) = 9$

$$3(x - 1) - 5(x - 2) = 9$$
$$3x - 3 - 5x + 10 = 9$$
$$-2x + 7 = 9$$
$$-2x = 2$$
$$x = -1$$

Check:
$$\text{L.S.} = 3(x - 1) - 5(x - 2)$$
$$= 3(-1 - 1) - 5(-1 - 2)$$
$$= 3(-2) - 5(-3)$$
$$= -6 + 15$$
$$= 9$$
$$\text{R.S.} = 9$$

EXERCISE 1

1. Solve.
(a) $2x + 3 + 8x = 23$
(b) $11x + 5 = 9x - 7$
(c) $3x + 4 = 6x - 11$
(d) $5x + 4 - 2x = 7 + 4x - 5$
(e) $5a - 3a + 7 = 7a - 23$
(f) $3b + 13 - 5b + 8 = 0$
(g) $-3x + 14 = 2x + 7 - 3x + 2$

2. Solve.
(a) $2(x - 3) + 3 = -15$
(b) $3(x - 2) - 2(x + 3) = 0$
(c) $2(2a - 1) - (3a + 2) = 8$
(d) $5(2b - 3) - 7 = 4 - (b + 7)$
(e) $4 = 3m - 4(m - 2) + 6(2m + 3)$
(f) $4y + 7 - (3y - 4) = 2(1 - 2y) - 1$
(g) $-2 - (x - 7) - 3(4x - 2) = 17$
(h) $2(1 - 3a) - (2a - 3) + 5(a - 1)$
$\quad = 7$
(i) $2(3t - 4) + 2t - 5 = 5t$

SOLVING LINEAR EQUATIONS PART II

Solve. $\dfrac{2x + 1}{3} + \dfrac{x}{2} = \dfrac{x - 10}{6}$

Clear fractions.
The LCD is 6.

$$6\left(\frac{2x + 1}{3}\right) + 6\left(\frac{x}{2}\right) = 6\left(\frac{x - 10}{6}\right)$$
$$2(2x + 1) + 3x = x - 10$$
$$4x + 2 + 3x = x - 10$$
$$7x + 2 = x - 10$$
$$6x = -12$$
$$x = -2$$

Check:
$$\text{L.S.} = \frac{2x + 1}{3} + \frac{x}{2} \qquad \text{R.S.} = \frac{x - 10}{6}$$
$$= \frac{2(-2) + 1}{3} + \frac{(-2)}{2} \qquad = \frac{-2 - 10}{6}$$
$$= -1 - 1 \qquad = -2$$
$$= -2$$

EXERCISE 2

1. Solve.
(a) $\dfrac{x}{3} = 7$ (b) $\dfrac{x + 1}{2} = 5$

(c) $\dfrac{x}{2} + \dfrac{x}{3} = 4$ (d) $\dfrac{2x}{5} - \dfrac{3x}{2} = 7$

(e) $\dfrac{x + 1}{3} - \dfrac{x - 2}{4} = 1$

(f) $\dfrac{1 - 2x}{5} - \dfrac{3x + 2}{6} = \dfrac{1}{2}$

(g) $\dfrac{3x - 1}{4} - \dfrac{2x + 1}{3} = -2$

(h) $\dfrac{2x + 1}{5} = \dfrac{1 - x}{2} + 2$

POLYNOMIALS

EXERCISE 3

1. Expand and simplify.
(a) $2(x + 3) - 3(x + 4)$
(b) $5(2t + 6) - (3t - 5)$
(c) $4(t - 1) - 3(t + 6) + 2(1 - 3t)$
(d) $(x - 4)(x + 3)$
(e) $(2a - 7)(3a + 1)$
(f) $(4b - 3)(4b + 3)$
(g) $(7m - 5)(m - 7)$
(h) $(x - 3y)^2$
(i) $(x + 6)(x - 1) + (x + 7)(x - 4)$
(j) $(t - 3)(t + 5) - (t - 6)(t - 2)$
(k) $3(x - 4)(x + 6) + 5(x - 1)(x - 8)$
(l) $4(3t - 6)(t - 3) - (4t - 1)(t - 5)$
(m) $7(x - 6)(x + 1) + 5(x + 2)(x + 4)$
(n) $5(3a - 1)(a + 4) - (2a - 5)(a - 6)$
(o) $4(1 - 2x)(1 - x)$
$\quad - (1 - 3x)(1 + 3x)$

2. Solve.
(a) $(x - 2)(x + 3) = (x + 4)(x + 1)$
(b) $(2x - 1)(x - 3) = (2x + 1)(x + 4)$
(c) $(x + 2)(x + 3) - (x - 7)(x + 1) = 2$
(d) $3x^2 - (1 + 3x)(1 + x) - 6$
$\quad = 2(x - 1)$
(e) $2x(x - 1) - (x + 1)(x + 2) = x^2$
(f) $2(x - 1)^2 - (x - 3)^2 = x^2 + 7$
(g) $2(1 - 2x)(x + 1) - 2(x + 1)$
$\quad (x - 1) = 6x(1 - x)$
(h) $2(2x - 1)(x + 3) - 3 - 4x^2$
$\quad = 2(x - 1)$

3. Solve for x.
(a) $x + b = 7$
(b) $x - m = t$
(c) $ax = m$
(d) $-2x = a$
(e) $bx + t = m$
(f) $ax - m = w$
(g) $2bx = t$
(h) $3cx = 9$
(i) $x + a + b = c$
(j) $-ax = b$

POWERS AND ROOTS

EXERCISE 4

1. Evaluate the following to three figures.
(a) 3.75^2 (b) $\sqrt{28.6}$
(c) $\sqrt{55.3}$ (d) 5.25^2
(e) 67.3^2 (f) 0.475^2
(g) $\sqrt{3.65}$ (h) $\sqrt{75\,500}$
(i) 0.259^2 (j) 5.37^2
(k) $\sqrt{66.6}$ (l) $\sqrt{32\,700}$
(m) 0.215^2 (n) 0.137^2
(o) $\sqrt{28.7}$ (p) $\sqrt{3160}$

2. Evaluate the following.
(a) $(6.374)^2$
(b) $(0.8163)^3$
(c) $(81.44)^4$
(d) $(0.0816)^3$
(e) $(6.813)^2 + (4.761)^3$
(f) $(0.4167)^3 + (0.5843)^4$
(g) $(1.683)^2 + (2.418)^3 - (8.713)^2$
(h) $(2.481)^2(0.973)^3$
(i) $(56.81)^4(2.78)^2$
(j) $\dfrac{(1.813)^4}{(1.721)^3}$

3. Evaluate the following.
(a) $\sqrt{(31.65)^2 + (48.27)^2}$
(b) $\sqrt{(3.675)^2 + (2.163)^2}$
(c) $\sqrt{(0.0275)^2 + (0.0865)^2}$
(d) $\sqrt{(54.75)^2 - (29.61)^2}$
(e) $\sqrt{(3.025)^2 - (1.964)^2}$
(f) $\sqrt{\dfrac{(32.75)(55.63)}{(284.5)}}$
(g) $\sqrt{\dfrac{(39.65)^2}{(5.645)(21.85)}}$
(h) $\sqrt{\dfrac{(5.675)^2 - (2.635)^2}{(4.285)}}$
(i) $\sqrt{(54.65)^2 + (21.35)^2 - (42.65)^2}$

3.1 EQUATIONS AND FORMULAS

Formulas have many important uses in business, technology, sports, medicine, and many other fields. Formulas are equations that use symbols which we replace with numbers.

The equation or formula for the area of a rectangle is
$$A = \ell \times w$$
If we replace ℓ by 10 m and w by 3 m, the area of the rectangle is

$$A = \ell \times w$$
$$A = 10\,m \times 3\,m$$
$$= 30\,m^2$$

Sometimes it is useful to solve the formula for one of the symbols or variables. For example, if there are 200 m of fence available, it would be useful to know the dimensions of the possible rectangles that could be contained by 200 m of fence.

Example 1. The formula for the perimeter of a rectangle is
$$P = 2(\ell + w)$$
(a) Solve the formula for w.
(b) If $P = 200$ m, find w when $\ell = 85$ m, 77 m, and 66 m.

Solution: (a)
$$P = 2(\ell + w)$$
$$P = 2\ell + 2w$$
$$P - 2\ell = 2w$$
$$\frac{P - 2\ell}{2} = w \quad or \quad w = \frac{P - 2\ell}{2}$$

(b) When $\ell = 85$, $w = \dfrac{200 - 2(85)}{2}$
$$= 15\,m$$

When $\ell = 77$, $w = \dfrac{200 - 2(77)}{2}$
$$= 23\,m$$

When $\ell = 66$, $w = \dfrac{200 - 2(66)}{2}$
$$= 34\,m$$

E=mc²

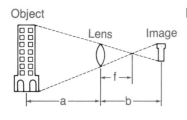

Object
Lens   Image

Example 2. The formula $\dfrac{1}{f} = \dfrac{1}{a} + \dfrac{1}{b}$

applies to cameras. f is the focal length of the lens, a is the distance from the object to the lens, and b is the distance from the image to the lens.
Solve for f.

Solution:

$$\frac{1}{f} = \frac{1}{a} + \frac{1}{b}$$

$$abf\left(\frac{1}{f}\right) = abf\left(\frac{1}{a}\right) + abf\left(\frac{1}{b}\right) \qquad \text{The LCD is abf.}$$

$$ab = bf + af$$

$$ab = f(b + a) \qquad \text{Common factor.}$$

$$\frac{ab}{(b + a)} = f$$

EXERCISE 3.1

B

1. The formula for the descent speed of a person wearing a parachute is

$$S = \frac{50M}{A}$$

where S is the speed in m/s,
  M is the mass of the person in kg,
  A is the area of the parachute in m².

(a) Solve the formula for A.
(b) Find A when S = 20 m/s and
  M = 90 kg.
(c) Find A when S = 20 m/s and
  M = 70 kg.

2. The formula for the area of a trapezoid is

$$A = \frac{h}{2}(a + b)$$

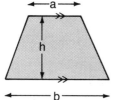

(a) Solve for b.
(b) Find b when
  (i) A = 140 m², h = 20 m, a = 6 m
  (ii) A = 576 cm², h = 36 cm,
    a = 19 cm

3. (a) If E = IR, find I when E = 220 and R = 4.

(b) If $P = \frac{r + 2}{d}$, find r when P = 7 and d = 9.

4. The mass of fuel carried by a jetliner is given by the formula

$$F = bT + r$$

where F is the mass of fuel carried,
    b is the mass of fuel burned per hour,
    T is the flying time in hours,
    r is the mass of the reserve fuel.

(a) Solve for b.
(b) Find b when F = 45.9 t, T = 4.5 h, and
  r = 9 t.
(c) If r = 8.5 t and b = 6 t/h, how much
  fuel should a plane carry for a 6.5 h
  flight?

5. Solve each of the following formulas for the variable indicated.
(a) p = 4t, for t
(b) V = ℓwh, for w
(c) d = vt, for v
(d) pv = Rt, for R

3.2 SOLVING SYSTEMS OF EQUATIONS

Sunset Rentals charges a $5 fee plus $1 per hour to rent a sailboard.

Action Rentals charges a $7 fee plus $0.50 per hour to rent a sailboard.

Which is the cheapest rental plan?
When are the costs the same?

If we let h represent the number of hours rented and C the total cost, then the formula for Sunset Rentals is

$$C = h + 5$$

The formula for Action Rentals is

$$C = 0.5h + 7$$

To compare the costs, we draw a graph of the cost of each rental plan for several periods of time.

Sunset C = h + 5		Action C = 0.5h + 7	
h	C	h	C
0	5	0	7
1	6	1	7.5
2	7	2	8
3	8	3	8.5
4	9	4	9
5	10	5	9.5
6	11	6	10

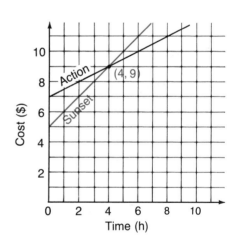

Up to four hours, it is cheaper to rent from Sunset Rentals.
For four hours, both costs are the same, $9.
Over four hours, it is cheaper to rent from Action Rentals.
The point of intersection is (4, 9).

In the example above, the system of equations was solved graphically.
In the following examples, two algebraic methods of solution are shown.

Example 1. Solve using substitution.
$$2x - y = 1 \quad ①$$
$$x + y = 5 \quad ②$$

Solution:
Solve one of the equations for one of the variables.

From ② $x + y = 5$ ②
and $x = 5 - y$
Substitute for x $2x - y = 1$ ①
in ①. $2(5 - y) - y = 1$
                           $10 - 2y - y = 1$
                                   $-3y = -9$
                                     $y = 3$

                               $x + y = 5$ ②
Substitute in ②. $x + 3 = 5$
                                   $x = 2$

Verify in ①.   L.S. $= 2x - y$ R.S. $= 1$
                     $= 2(2) - 3$
                     $= 1$

To solve a system of equations by elimination, we eliminate one of the variables by addition or subtraction.

Example 2. Solve using elimination.
$$3x - 2y = -7 \quad ①$$
$$2x - 5y = 10 \quad ②$$

Solution:
Multiply ① by 5 and ② by 2 to make the coefficients of y the same.

                              $3x - 2y = -7$ ①
                              $2x - 5y = 10$ ②

$5 \times$ ① $15x - 10y = -35$
$2 \times$ ② $4x - 10y = 20$
Subtract. $11x = -55$
                              $x = -5$

Substitute in ①. $3x - 2y = -7$
                            $3(-5) - 2y = -7$
                             $-15 - 2y = -7$
                                   $-2y = 8$
                                     $y = -4$
Verify in ②.   L.S. $= 2x - 5y$ R.S. $= 10$
                     $= 2(-5) - 5(-4)$
                     $= -10 + 20$
                     $= 10$

Example 3. Solve.
$$\tfrac{2}{3}x - \tfrac{3}{2}y = -4 \quad ①$$
$$\tfrac{3}{2}x - \tfrac{1}{8}y = 4 \quad ②$$

Solution:

First, clear the fractions.

$$\tfrac{2}{3}x - \tfrac{3}{2}y = -4 \quad \text{①}$$

$$\tfrac{3}{2}x - \tfrac{1}{8}y = 4 \quad \text{②}$$

| ① × 6 | $4x - 9y = -24$ |
| ② × 8 | $12x - y = 32$ |

Multiply ② by 9.

①	$4x - 9y = -24$
② × 9	$\underline{108x - 9y = 288}$
Subtract.	$-104x = -312$
	$x = 3$

Substitute in ①.

$$\tfrac{2}{3}x - \tfrac{3}{2}y = -4$$

$$\tfrac{2}{3}(3) - \tfrac{3}{2}y = -4$$

$$2 - \tfrac{3}{2}y = -4$$

$$-\tfrac{3}{2}y = -6$$

$$y = 4$$

Verify in ②.   L.S. $= \tfrac{3}{2}x - \tfrac{1}{8}y$ | R.S. $= 4$

$$= \tfrac{3}{2}(3) - \tfrac{1}{8}(4)$$

$$= \tfrac{9}{2} - \tfrac{1}{2}$$

$$= 4$$

∴ the solution is (3, 4).

EXERCISE 3.2

B 1. Solve each of the following systems graphically.

(a) $2x - y = 5$
$x - y = 3$

(b) $x - y = 4$
$x + y = 4$

(c) $x + 2y = 5$
$2x + y = 1$

(d) $3x - 2y = 10$
$x + y = 0$

(e) $5x - y = 32$
$x - 2y = 19$

(f) $2x + y = -5$
$x + 3y = 10$

(g) $5x - 3y = 12$
$2x - 3y = 3$

2. Solve each of the following by substitution.

(a) $5x + y = -15$
$x - y = 3$

(b) $x + y = 7$
$2x - 3y = 4$

(c) $2m - n = 7$
$5m + 2n = 4$

(d) $-3s + t = -4$
$7s + t = 11$

(e) $2x + 3y = 5$
$4x + y = 5$

(f) $3s + 4t = 2$
$4s - t = 9$

(g) $x + 3y = 5$
$3x - 2y = 7$

3. Solve each of the following by elimination.
(a) $x + 2y = 7$
    $x + 8y = 37$
(b) $5a - 8b = 8$
    $10a + 4b = 1$
(c) $2x + 3y = -2$
    $2x - 3y = 0$
(d) $2x + 3y = 13$
    $3x + 2y = 12$
(e) $2m + 5n = 4$
    $6m - 2n = -5$
(f) $3x + y = 16$
    $-2x + 3y = -7$

4. Solve each of the following.
(a) $\frac{1}{4}x - 2y = -3$
    $4x + 3y = 22$
(b) $\frac{1}{2}m + \frac{1}{3}n = 3$
    $\frac{1}{4}m + \frac{2}{3}n = -3$
(c) $\frac{1}{2}x + \frac{1}{2}y = 2$
    $\frac{2}{5}x - \frac{2}{3}y = 8$
(d) $0.3m + 0.2n = 0.5$
    $0.5m - 0.3n = 0.2$
(e) $2x - y + 1 = 0$
    $3x - 5y + 1 = 0$

EXTRA

SYSTEMS WITH THREE VARIABLES

To solve a system of three equations with three variables, we use elimination.

Example. Solve.
$$x + y + z = 6 \quad ①$$
$$2x - 3y - z = -7 \quad ②$$
$$x + 2y - z = 2 \quad ③$$

Solution:
Eliminate z from ① and ②.

$$\begin{array}{ll} x + y + z = 6 & ① \\ 2x - 3y - z = -7 & ② \\ \hline 3x - 2y = -1 & ④ \end{array}$$
Add.

Eliminate z from ② and ③.

$$\begin{array}{ll} 2x - 3y - z = -7 & ② \\ x + 2y - z = 2 & ③ \\ \hline x - 5y = -9 & ⑤ \end{array}$$
Subtract.

Solve equations ④ and ⑤.

$$\begin{array}{ll} 3x - 2y = -1 & ④ \\ x - 5y = -9 & ⑤ \end{array}$$

$$\begin{array}{l} ④ \\ ⑤ \times 3 \\ \text{Subtract.} \end{array} \quad \begin{array}{l} 3x - 2y = -1 \\ 3x - 15y = -27 \\ \hline 13y = 26 \\ y = 2 \end{array}$$

Substitute in ④.
$$3x - 2y = -1$$
$$3x - 2(2) = -1$$
$$3x - 4 = -1$$
$$3x = 3$$
$$x = 1$$

Substitute in ①.
$$x + y + z = 6$$
$$1 + 2 + z = 6$$
$$z = 3$$

The solution is $x = 1$, $y = 2$, and $z = 3$.

EXERCISE

1. Solve the following systems of equations.
(a) $4x + y - 2z = 12$
    $x - y + z = 5$
    $2x + y + z = 13$
(b) $5a + 3b + c = -4$
    $3a + 2b - c = -4$
    $a - 3b + 5c = 4$

3.3 SOLVING QUADRATIC EQUATIONS BY FACTORING

If we equate the expression $3x - 6$ to 0, we have a linear equation that we can solve.

$$3x - 6 = 0$$
$$3x - 6 + 6 = 0 + 6$$
$$3x = 6$$
$$x = 2$$

If we equate the expression $x^2 - 7x + 12$ to 0, we have the quadratic equation

$$x^2 - 7x + 12 = 0$$

Some quadratic equations can be solved by factoring. Solving equations by this method depends on the zero-product property.

> For any two numbers a and b,
> if $a \times b = 0$, then $a = 0$ or $b = 0$.

For $x^2 - 7x + 12 = 0$, $s + r = -7$
$$s \times r = +12$$
s and r are -3 and -4.

$$(x - 3)(x - 4) = 0$$

$x - 3 = 0$	$x - 4 = 0$
$x = 3$	or $x = 4$

Check:
L.S. $= x^2 - 7x + 12$	L.S. $= x^2 - 7x + 12$
$= (3)^2 - 7(3) + 12$	$= (4)^2 - 7(4) + 12$
$= 9 - 21 + 12$	$= 16 - 28 + 12$
$= 0$	$= 0$
R.S. $= 0$	R.S. $= 0$

The roots are 3 and 4.

Example. Solve by factoring. $6x^2 + 11x - 10 = 0$

Solution:

$$6x^2 + 11x - 10 = 0$$

$$6x(-10) = -60$$

$$6x^2 + (\blacksquare\ \blacksquare)x - 10 = 0$$
$$6x^2 + (15 - 4)x - 10 = 0$$
$$6x^2 + 15x - 4x - 10 = 0$$
$$(6x^2 + 15x) - (4x + 10) = 0$$
$$3x(2x + 5) - 2(2x + 5) = 0$$
$$(2x + 5)(3x - 2) = 0$$

Factors of -60	Sum of Factors
60, -1	59
-60, 1	-59
30, -2	28
-30, 2	-28
20, -3	17
-20, 3	-17
15, -4	11

$$2x + 5 = 0$$
$$2x = -5$$
$$x = \tfrac{2}{3}$$

or

$$3x - 2 = 0$$
$$3x = 2$$
$$x = \tfrac{2}{3}$$

Check: L.S. $= 6x^2 + 11x - 10$
$$= 6(-\tfrac{5}{2})^2 + 11(-\tfrac{5}{2}) - 10$$
$$= \tfrac{75}{2} - \tfrac{55}{2} - \tfrac{20}{2}$$
$$= 0$$

R.S. $= 0$

L.S. $= 6x^2 + 11x - 10$
$$= 6(\tfrac{2}{3})^2 + 11(\tfrac{2}{3}) - 10$$
$$= \tfrac{8}{3} + \tfrac{22}{3} - \tfrac{30}{3}$$
$$= 0$$

R.S. $= 0$

The roots are $-\tfrac{5}{2}$ and $\tfrac{2}{3}$.

EXERCISE 3.3

A

1. Solve.
(a) $(x - 2)(x + 3) = 0$
(b) $(t + 1)(t + 2) = 0$
(c) $(a - 3)(a - 4) = 0$
(d) $(x + 5)(x - 4) = 0$
(e) $x(x + 4) = 0$
(f) $2x(x - 3) = 0$

B

2. Solve and check.
(a) $x^2 + 7x + 12 = 0$
(b) $c^2 - c - 6 = 0$
(c) $t^2 + 4t + 3 = 0$
(d) $x^2 + 3x - 10 = 0$
(e) $b^2 - 2b - 15 = 0$
(f) $x^2 + 6x + 9 = 0$
(g) $m^2 - 9m + 20 = 0$
(h) $r^2 - 8r + 16 = 0$
(i) $x^2 + 4x - 21 = 0$
(j) $x^2 + x - 30 = 0$

3. Solve and check.
(a) $t^2 - 4 = 0$ (b) $x^2 - 49 = 0$
(c) $x^2 - 64 = 0$ (d) $b^2 - 100 = 0$
(e) $2x^2 - 72 = 0$ (f) $4x^2 - 36 = 0$

4. Solve and check.
(a) $3t^2 - 14t + 8 = 0$
(b) $6a^2 + 13a + 6 = 0$
(c) $2m^2 + 9m + 4 = 0$
(d) $6x^2 + 7x - 3 = 0$
(e) $2y^2 + 9y - 35 = 0$
(f) $3a^2 - 5a - 28 = 0$

M I C R O   M A T H

The following BASIC program solves linear systems in two variables in the form

$$Ax + By = C$$
$$Dx + Ey = F$$

NEW
```
10 PRINT"LINEAR SYSTEMS"
20 INPUT"A=";A
30 INPUT"B=";B
40 INPUT"C=";C
50 INPUT"D=";D
60 INPUT"E=";E
70 INPUT"F=";F
80 IF A*E<>B*D THEN 90
81 IF A*F=C*D THEN PRINT"INFINITELY
   MANY SOLUTIONS":GOTO 99
82 PRINT"NO SOLUTION":GOTO 99
90 X=(C*E-B*F)/(A*E-B*D)
91 Y=(C*D-A*F)/(B*D-A*E)
95 PRINT"X = ";X;"Y = ";Y
99 END
```
RUN

EXERCISE

1. Solve the following systems.
(a) $4x - 5y = 3$
   $3x + 2y = 4$
(b) $3x - 2y = 6$
   $3x - y = 3$
(c) $9x + 4y = 7$
   $3x + 3y = 8$

3.4 THE QUADRATIC FORMULA

A quadratic equation can be written in many forms. For example, $x^2 + 3x + 2 = 0$, $2x^2 + 7x + 3 = 0$, and $4t^2 - 9 = 0$. The standard form of a quadratic equation is $ax^2 + bx + c = 0$, $a \neq 0$.

> A quadratic equation has 2 roots. The formulas for solving a quadratic equation are
> $$x = \frac{-b + \sqrt{b^2 - 4ac}}{2a} \quad \text{and} \quad x = \frac{-b - \sqrt{b^2 - 4ac}}{2a}$$

Example 1. Solve. $x^2 - 3x - 28 = 0$

Solution:
Compare $x^2 - 3x - 28 = 0$ and $ax^2 + bx + c = 0$.
We have $a = 1$, $b = -3$, and $c = -28$.
Substitute.

$$x = \frac{-b + \sqrt{b^2 - 4ac}}{2a}$$
$$x = \frac{-(-3) + \sqrt{(-3)^2 - 4(1)(-28)}}{2(1)}$$
$$= \frac{3 + \sqrt{9 + 112}}{2}$$
$$= \frac{3 + \sqrt{121}}{2}$$
$$= \frac{3 + 11}{2}$$
$$= 7$$

or

$$x = \frac{-b - \sqrt{b^2 - 4ac}}{2a}$$
$$x = \frac{-(-3) - \sqrt{(-3)^2 - 4(1)(-28)}}{2(1)}$$
$$= \frac{3 - \sqrt{9 + 112}}{2}$$
$$= \frac{3 + \sqrt{121}}{2}$$
$$= \frac{3 - 11}{2}$$
$$= -4$$

$\therefore$ the roots are 7 and -4.

Example 2. Solve. $2x^2 - 7x + 6 = 0$

Solution:
By comparison with $ax^2 + bx + c = 0$, $a = 2$, $b = -7$, and $c = 6$.
Substitute into the formulas.

$$x = \frac{-b + \sqrt{b^2 - 4ac}}{2a}$$
$$x = \frac{-(-7) + \sqrt{(-7)^2 - 4(2)(6)}}{2(2)}$$
$$= \frac{7 + \sqrt{49 - 48}}{4}$$
$$= \frac{7 + 1}{4}$$
$$= 2$$

or

$$x = \frac{-b - \sqrt{b^2 - 4ac}}{2a}$$
$$x = \frac{-(-7) - \sqrt{(-7)^2 - 4(2)(6)}}{2(2)}$$
$$= \frac{7 - \sqrt{49 - 48}}{4}$$
$$= \frac{7 - 1}{4}$$
$$= \frac{3}{2}$$

$\therefore$ the roots are 2 and $\frac{3}{2}$.

Example 3. Solve. $4x^2 - 7x + 2 = 0$

Solution:

Here $a = 4$, $b = -7$, and $c = 2$.

$$x = \frac{-b + \sqrt{b^2 - 4ac}}{2a}$$

$$x = \frac{7 + \sqrt{49 - 32}}{8}$$

$$= \frac{7 + \sqrt{17}}{8}$$

or

$$x = \frac{-b - \sqrt{b^2 - 4ac}}{2a}$$

$$x = \frac{7 - \sqrt{49 - 32}}{8}$$

$$= \frac{7 - \sqrt{17}}{8}$$

∴ the roots are $\dfrac{7 + \sqrt{17}}{8}$ and $\dfrac{7 - \sqrt{17}}{8}$

It should be noted that $\dfrac{7 + \sqrt{17}}{8}$ and $\dfrac{7 - \sqrt{17}}{8}$ are the exact roots of $4x^2 - 7x + 2 = 0$.
Once they have been found, $4x^2 - 7x + 2 = 0$ has been solved. In practice, decimal approximations for the roots may be required.

On a calculator,

press $\boxed{7}\ \boxed{x^2}\ \boxed{-}\ \boxed{4}\ \boxed{\times}\ \boxed{4}\ \boxed{\times}\ \boxed{2}\ \boxed{=}\ \boxed{\sqrt{}}\ \boxed{\text{STO}}$ The display is `4.123`

Press $\boxed{7}\ \boxed{+}\ \boxed{\text{RCL}}\ \boxed{=}\ \boxed{\div}\ \boxed{(}\ \boxed{2}\ \boxed{\times}\ \boxed{4}\ \boxed{)}\ \boxed{=}$ The display is `1.390388203`

Press $\boxed{7}\ \boxed{-}\ \boxed{\text{RCL}}\ \boxed{=}\ \boxed{\div}\ \boxed{(}\ \boxed{2}\ \boxed{\times}\ \boxed{4}\ \boxed{)}\ \boxed{=}$ The display is `0.359611796`

∴ the roots are 1.39 and 0.36.

Example 4. Find the roots of $3x^2 + 5x + 1 = 0$ to the nearest hundredth.

Solution:

$a = 3$, $b = 5$, and $c = 1$.

$$x = \frac{-b + \sqrt{b^2 - 4ac}}{2a}$$

$$x = \frac{-5 + \sqrt{25 - 12}}{6}$$

$$= \frac{-5 + \sqrt{13}}{6}$$

$$\doteq \frac{-5 + 3.606}{6}$$

$$= \frac{-1.39}{6}$$

$$= -0.232$$

or

$$x = \frac{-b - \sqrt{b^2 - 4ac}}{2a}$$

$$x = \frac{-5 - \sqrt{25 - 12}}{6}$$

$$= \frac{-5 - \sqrt{13}}{6}$$

$$\doteq \frac{-5 - 3.606}{6}$$

$$= \frac{-8.606}{6}$$

$$= -1.434$$

On a calculator,

press $\boxed{5}\ \boxed{x^2}\ \boxed{-}\ \boxed{4}\ \boxed{\times}\ \boxed{3}\ \boxed{\times}\ \boxed{1}\ \boxed{=}\ \boxed{\sqrt{}}\ \boxed{\text{STO}}$ The display is `3.605551275`

Press $\boxed{5}\ \boxed{+/-}\ \boxed{+}\ \boxed{\text{RCL}}\ \boxed{=}\ \boxed{\div}\ \boxed{(}\ \boxed{2}\ \boxed{\times}\ \boxed{3}\ \boxed{)}\ \boxed{=}$ The display is `-0.23240812`

Press $\boxed{5}\ \boxed{+/-}\ \boxed{-}\ \boxed{\text{RCL}}\ \boxed{=}\ \boxed{\div}\ \boxed{(}\ \boxed{2}\ \boxed{\times}\ \boxed{3}\ \boxed{)}\ \boxed{=}$ The display is `-1.434258546`

∴ the roots are -0.23 and -1.43 correct to two decimal places.

When a quadratic equation is expressed in the form $ax^2 + bx + c = 0$, it may be solved by factoring if the factors are readily obtainable. If not, use the formulas, which always produce an answer.

The solutions of a quadratic equation of the form $ax^2 + bx + c = 0$, $a \neq 0$ are

$$x = \frac{-b \pm \sqrt{b^2 - 4ac}}{2a}$$

EXERCISE 3.4

A

1. State the values of a, b, and c for each of the following.
(a) $2x^2 + 3x + 4 = 0$
(b) $3x^2 - 5x + 2 = 0$
(c) $x^2 + 7x - 1 = 0$
(d) $4x^2 - x - 3 = 0$
(e) $5x^2 - 3x = 0$
(f) $x^2 - 25 = 0$
(g) $x^2 + 5x = 16$
(h) $2x^2 = 3x + 4$
(i) $2x^2 + 3 = 5x$
(j) $3x^2 + 17 = 0$

B

2. Solve.
(a) $x^2 - 7x + 12 = 0$
(b) $3x^2 - 6x + 1 = 0$
(c) $x^2 - 6x - 7 = 0$
(d) $x^2 - 3x - 88 = 0$
(e) $3x^2 - 5x + 2 = 0$
(f) $2x^2 - 6x = 1$
(g) $3x^2 + 6x - 2 = 0$
(h) $7x^2 = 2x + 1$
(i) $2x^2 + 5x + 1 = 0$
(j) $x^2 = 2x - 1$
(k) $3x^2 + 2x - 7 = 0$
(l) $2x^2 - 25x + 77 = 0$
(m) $x^2 - 9 = 0$
(n) $x^2 - 5x = 0$

3. Solve the following to the nearest hundredth.
(a) $x^2 + 3x + 1 = 0$ (b) $x^2 - 3x - 5 = 0$
(c) $x^2 - 5x + 1 = 0$ (d) $2x^2 = 3x + 4$
(e) $2x^2 = 5$ (f) $3x^2 = 5x + 3$
(g) $5x^2 + 3 = 11x$ (h) $6x^2 - 7x + 1 = 0$

4. Solve.
(a) $x^2 - 5x + 6 = 0$
(b) $x^2 = 2x + 3$
(c) $x^2 = 2x + 2$
(d) $20x^2 + x - 15 = 0$
(e) $2x^2 - 7x - 15 = 0$
(f) $x^2 - 11x + 28 = 0$
(g) $3x^2 + 6x - 10 = 0$
(h) $4x^2 - 4x - 1 = 0$
(i) $2x^2 - 4x = 5$
(j) $5x^2 - 15x + 9 = 0$
(k) $2x^2 + 7x = 0$
(l) $x^2 = 5$
(m) $2x^2 + 6x - 20 = 0$
(n) $2x^2 + 8x + 2 = 0$

C

5. Solve.
(a) $2(x^2 - 1) = 3x$
(b) $4x(x + 3) + 5 = 0$
(c) $(x - 1)(x + 3) - 6 = 0$
(d) $\dfrac{1}{x} = 2x + 1$

3.5 NON-REAL ROOTS

If we use the quadratic formula to solve the equation

$$x^2 - 2x + 5 = 0$$

we have

$$x = \frac{-b + \sqrt{b^2 - 4ac}}{2a} \qquad \text{or} \qquad x = \frac{-b - \sqrt{b^2 - 4ac}}{2a}$$

$$x = \frac{-(-2) + \sqrt{(-2)^2 - 4(1)(5)}}{2(1)} \qquad = \frac{-(-2) - \sqrt{(-2)^2 - 4(1)(5)}}{2(1)}$$

$$= \frac{2 + \sqrt{4 - 20}}{2} \qquad = \frac{2 - \sqrt{4 - 20}}{2}$$

$$= \frac{2 + \sqrt{-16}}{2} \qquad = \frac{2 - \sqrt{-16}}{2}$$

We cannot determine the value of $\sqrt{-16}$ because negative numbers do not have square roots. We say that the roots of the equation $x^2 - 2x + 5 = 0$ are non-real.

There is a way of simplifying numbers such as $\sqrt{-16}$. We use the letter i to represent $\sqrt{-1}$. Therefore $\sqrt{-16}$ becomes $\sqrt{-1} \times \sqrt{16}$, which becomes $i \times 4$ or $4i$. This is called the i-form of $\sqrt{-16}$.

The roots of the original equation can be written as $\frac{2 + 4i}{2}$ and $\frac{2 - 4i}{2}$, which become $1 + 2i$ and $1 - 2i$. They are still non-real roots, however.

15.3

Spreadsheet activities related to this topic are found in section 15.3.

EXERCISE 3.5

A
1. Write each of the following in i-form.
(a) $\sqrt{-100}$ (b) $\sqrt{-121}$
(c) $\sqrt{-169}$ (d) $-\sqrt{-36}$
(e) $-\sqrt{-64}$ (f) $\sqrt{-9}$
(g) $-\sqrt{-25}$ (h) $-\sqrt{-144}$
(i) $-\sqrt{-1}$ (j) $2 - \sqrt{-4}$

B
2. Solve the following equations. Express the solutions in the form $a + bi$.
(a) $x^2 + 2x + 2 = 0$
(b) $2x^2 + 2x + 5 = 0$
(c) $x^2 + 16 = 0$

MIND BENDER

If $\begin{vmatrix} a & b \\ c & d \end{vmatrix} = ad - bc,$

find the value of

$$\begin{vmatrix} 2 & -3 \\ 5 & 7 \end{vmatrix} + \begin{vmatrix} -5 & 3 \\ 7 & -2 \end{vmatrix}$$

3.6 SOLVING PROBLEMS USING QUADRATIC EQUATIONS

In this section we solve problems using quadratic equations. When a problem is solved by a quadratic equation it does not necessarily mean that both roots of the equation will be solutions to the problem. For example, a length cannot be negative, and the number of seats in a room cannot be a fraction. A root of an equation that is excluded by the conditions of the problem is called an inadmissible solution.

Example 1. The boat slips at the marina are numbered using consecutive numbers. The sum of the squares of three consecutive slip numbers is 77. Find the slip numbers.

Solution: Let x, $x + 1$, and $x + 2$ represent the slip numbers.
$$\therefore x^2 + (x + 1)^2 + (x + 2)^2 = 77$$
$$x^2 + (x^2 + 2x + 1) + (x^2 + 4x + 4) = 77$$
$$x^2 + x^2 + 2x + 1 + x^2 + 4x + 4 = 77 \longleftarrow \text{Remove the brackets.}$$
$$3x^2 + 6x + 5 = 77 \longleftarrow \text{Collect like terms.}$$
$$3x^2 + 6x - 72 = 0$$
$$x^2 + 2x - 24 = 0 \longleftarrow \text{Divide by 3.}$$
$$(x + 6)(x - 4) = 0 \longleftarrow \text{Factor.}$$
$$\therefore x = -6 \quad \text{or} \quad x = 4$$

-6 is inadmissible. Slips are not numbered with negative numbers.

$\therefore x = 4$ and the slip numbers are 4, 5, and 6.

Example 2. Astro Supply has two square pieces of artificial grass. The total area is 52 m². The side of one square is 2 m longer than the side of the other square. Find the dimensions of each piece.

Solution:

Let x and $x + 2$ represent the lengths of the sides of the squares in metres.
$\therefore$ the areas of the squares are x^2 and $(x + 2)^2$ respectively.

$A = x^2$, x, x

$$x^2 + (x + 2)^2 = 52$$
$$x^2 + x^2 + 4x + 4 = 52$$
$$2x^2 + 4x - 48 = 0 \longleftarrow \text{Divide by 2.}$$
$$x^2 + 2x - 24 = 0$$
$$(x + 6)(x - 4) = 0$$
$$x = -6 \quad \text{or} \quad x = 4$$

The solution -6 is inadmissible since a length must be positive. Therefore the lengths of the sides of the squares are 4 m and 6 m.

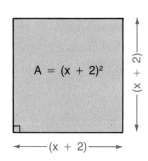

$A = (x + 2)^2$, $(x + 2)$, $(x + 2)$

EXERCISE 3.6

A

1. State algebraic expressions for each of the following.
(a) the sum of three consecutive integers
(b) a number plus its square
(c) the square of a number less twice the number
(d) the sum of the squares of two consecutive numbers

B

2. The sum of the squares of two consecutive integers is 113.
Find the integers.

3. The sum of the squares of three consecutive integers is 302.
Find the integers.

4. The sum of the squares of four consecutive integers is 966.
Find the integers.

5. A right triangle is made up of a hypotenuse and two legs.

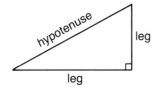

If one leg is 2 m longer than the other leg and the hypotenuse is 10 m long, find the length of each leg.

6. In a right triangle the hypotenuse is 8 m longer than one leg and 4 m longer than the other leg.
Find the lengths of the three sides.

7. A rectangle is 4 m longer than it is wide. The area is 192 m².
Find the dimensions of the rectangle.

8. The base of a triangle is 6 cm longer than its height. The area of the triangle is 56 cm².
Find the length of the base.

9. A square and a rectangle have the same width. The length of the rectangle is four times its width. The sum of the two areas is 45 m².
Find the area of the rectangle.

10. Two integers differ by 8 and the sum of their squares is 130.
Find the integers.

11. Three times the square of a number equals 21 times the number.
Find the number.

12. A rectangular label on a book has an area of 44 cm² and a perimeter of 27 cm.
Find the dimensions of the label.

C

13. A rectangular sheet of tin is 15 cm long and 9 cm wide. A uniform strip is to be cut off around the sheet. The remaining area is to be 112 cm².

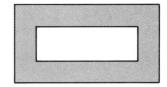

Calculate the width of the strip to be cut off.

14. A rectangular orchard measures 25 m by 50 m. The dimensions of the orchard are increased on all sides by the same amount. As a result the area of the orchard increased by 400 m².
By how much did each dimension of the original orchard increase?

15. A rug measuring 9 m by 12 m was installed in the recreation hall. A strip of floor of equal width was left uncovered along all edges of the hall. The area of the uncovered floor is 270 m².
How wide is the uncovered strip?

3.7 RADICAL EQUATIONS

Equations that contain radicals with variables in the radicand are called radical equations. Examples of radical equations are $\sqrt{x} + 3 = 0$ and $\sqrt{x + 1} + \sqrt{x - 1} = 3$.

To solve radical equations, isolate the radical on one side of the equation; then square both sides of the equation to eliminate the radical.

Example 1. Solve and check. $\sqrt{x} = 9$

    Solution: $\sqrt{x} = 9$
             $(\sqrt{x})^2 = 9^2$ ⟵————————— Square both sides.
             $x = 81$

    Check: L.S. $= \sqrt{x}$ | R.S. $= 9$
              $= \sqrt{81}$
              $= 9$
    The solution is 9.

Example 2. Solve and check. $\sqrt{3x + 1} - 4 = 0$

    Solution: $\sqrt{3x + 1} - 4 = 0$
                 $\sqrt{3x + 1} = 4$ ⟵——— Isolate the radical.
                  $3x + 1 = 16$ ⟵——— Square both sides.
                     $3x = 15$
                      $x = 5$

    Check: L.S. $= \sqrt{3x + 1} - 4$ | R.S. $= 0$
                $= \sqrt{3(5) + 1} - 4$
                $= \sqrt{16} - 4$
                $= 4 - 4$
                $= 0$
    The solution is 5.

Example 3. Solve and check. $\sqrt{7 - x} + 2 = 0$

    Solution: $\sqrt{7 - x} + 2 = 0$
                  $\sqrt{7 - x} = -2$ ⟵——— Isolate the radical.
                  $7 - x = 4$ ⟵——— Square both sides.
                    $-x = -3$
                     $x = 3$

    Check: L.S. $= \sqrt{7 - x} + 2$ | R.S. $= 0$
                $= \sqrt{7 - (3)} + 2$
                $= \sqrt{4} + 2$
                $= 2 + 2$
                $= 4$
    The equation has no solution.

Sometimes squaring both sides of an equation produces numbers that are not solutions of the original equation. Therefore we must check all solutions when solving radical equations.

Example 4. Solve and check. $4 + \sqrt{y - 2} = y$

Solution: $4 + \sqrt{y - 2} = y$

$\sqrt{y - 2} = y - 4$ ⟵——————— Isolate the radical.

$(\sqrt{y - 2})^2 = (y - 4)^2$ ⟵——————— Square both sides.

$y - 2 = y^2 - 8y + 16$

$0 = y^2 - 9y + 18$

$0 = (y - 3)(y - 6)$

$y - 3 = 0$ or $y - 6 = 0$

$y = 3$ $y = 6$

Check:

L.S. $= 4 + \sqrt{y - 2}$	L.S. $= 4 + \sqrt{y - 2}$
$= 4 + \sqrt{3 - 2}$	$= 4 + \sqrt{6 - 2}$
$= 4 + 1$	$= 4 + 2$
$= 5$	$= 6$
R.S. $= y$	R.S. $= y$
$= 3$	$= 6$

3 does not satisfy the original equation. 6 does. The solution is 6.

EXERCISE 3.7

B

1. Solve.
(a) $\sqrt{x} = 3$
(b) $\sqrt{y} = 1$
(c) $\sqrt{x + 1} = 4$
(d) $\sqrt{y - 1} = 1$
(e) $\sqrt{x} = 0$
(f) $\sqrt{2x + 1} = 3$
(g) $\sqrt{2x - 1} = 1$
(h) $\sqrt{3x + 1} = 2$

2. Solve.
(a) $\sqrt{x} - 1 = 3$
(b) $\sqrt{x} - 2 = 1$
(c) $\sqrt{x + 3} - 5 = 0$
(d) $\sqrt{x + 3} - 2 = 4$
(e) $\sqrt{3x - 6} = 0$
(f) $\sqrt{2x} - 3 = 0$
(g) $\sqrt{x} + 2 = 5$
(h) $3 - \sqrt{x} = 5$

3. Solve.
(a) $\sqrt{5x - 1} = \sqrt{4x + 12}$
(b) $\sqrt{3x - 2} = \sqrt{3 - 2x}$
(c) $\sqrt{2x + 3} = \sqrt{3x}$
(d) $\sqrt{4x - 3} = \sqrt{2x}$

4. Solve.
(a) $\sqrt{x + 2} = x - 4$
(b) $\sqrt{1 - 2y} = 1 + y$
(c) $\sqrt{m + 4} + 7 = 2m$
(d) $\sqrt{2t + 3} - t = 0$
(e) $\sqrt{5x - 4} - x = 0$
(f) $r = 4 + \sqrt{r + 8}$
(g) $\sqrt{2x + 11} + 2 = x$

C

5. Solve.
(a) $\sqrt{x + 1} = 5 - \sqrt{x - 3}$
(b) $\sqrt{y + 11} = 3 + \sqrt{y - 4}$
(c) $\sqrt{x} + \sqrt{x + 1} = 3$

3.8 PROBLEM SOLVING

1. Copy the figure below into your notebook.

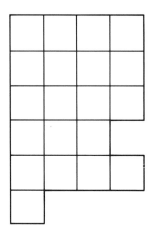

Divide the figure into five parts, each containing four squares, and with no two parts having the same shape. (Shapes that can be made the same by reflections or rotations are not allowed.)

2. The perimeter of the triangle below is 13 m.

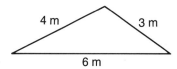

How many other triangles are there with a perimeter of 13 m if the length of each side is a whole number?

3. The sum of four consecutive whole numbers is 274.
What are the numbers?

4. A bus left the terminal at 07:00 and travelled south at 80 km/h. A second bus left the same terminal at 08:30 and travelled north at 90 km/h.
At what time were the buses 460 km apart?

5. The figure below is made up of two rectangles.

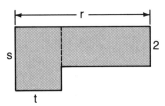

Determine the area of the figure in terms of r, s, and t.

6. A rectangular piece of cardboard is 80 cm long and 60 cm wide. A 10 cm square is cut from each corner. The four flaps are then folded up to make an open box.
What is the volume of the box?

7. Peter, Bob, Marie, Shelly, and Kim are sitting in a row of seats. Neither Peter nor Bob is sitting next to Shelly. Neither Peter nor Bob is sitting next to Marie. Neither Shelly nor Bob is sitting next to Kim. Kim is sitting just to the right of Marie.
Find the seating arrangement.

8. Your plane is scheduled to leave for Halifax at 08:30. You are to pick up your tickets at the boarding gate thirty minutes before departure. It takes you forty minutes to drive to the airport, fifteen minutes to check your car into the overnight lot, and ten minutes to get to the boarding gate from there.
On the way to the airport you need to pick up a package at your office. This will take ten minutes.
It takes you one hour to get up and get ready to leave your apartment.
For what time should you set your alarm?

9. Complete the division. All the missing digits are odd.

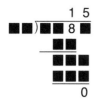

10. Determine the pattern and find the missing numbers.

$$4 \times 6 = 24$$
$$14 \times 16 = 224$$
$$24 \times 26 = 624$$
$$34 \times 36 = 1224$$
$$44 \times 46 = \blacksquare$$
$$54 \times 56 = \blacksquare$$
$$64 \times 66 = \blacksquare$$

11. Without evaluating 2^{300} or 3^{200}, determine which is larger.

12. How many times will your heart beat this month?

13. In the following figure find six points such that no two points lie on the same line segment.

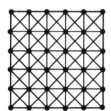

14. A sunken boat is filled with 200 000 L of water. A salvage crew is pumping out the water at the rate of 30 L/min. Water is leaking back in at the rate of 10 L/min. The boat will float when the water level drops to 20 000 L.
How long will it take to float the boat?

CAREER

FOOD SCIENCE TECHNOLOGIST

A food science technologist is an expert in the processing and grading of food. The broad range of work in this career depends on one's educational background. For some, the interest of food science technology could be in the scientific aspects of testing food products and developing new foods. Others could find interest in applications connected with food processing. Most of the work of the food science technologist takes place in the laboratory. A high level of precision and care in working within government regulations and standards is required.

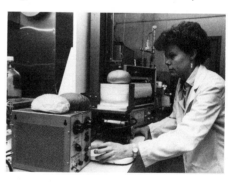

EXERCISE

1. An apple contains 240 kJ of energy. A T-bone steak contains 2600 kJ of energy.
How many apples could you eat before you consume the amount of energy equivalent to 3 T-bone steaks?

2. A boiled egg contains 350 kJ of energy. A hot dog contains 650 kJ of energy.
How many boiled eggs could you eat before you consume the amount of energy equivalent to 5 hot dogs?

3.9 REVIEW EXERCISE

1. Solve and check.
(a) $3x + 7 = 2x - 4$
(b) $5b = 7b - 4$
(c) $2(x - 1) = x + 6$
(d) $3(m + 1) + 4 = 2(m - 1)$
(e) $2(x + 3) = 3(x - 1) - 3(x - 2) + 1$
(f) $5 + 2(b - 3) - (b - 7) + 6 = 11$
(g) $3 + 2(2x - 1) + 6 = 5(x - 3)$
(h) $3a - 2(a - 3) + 7 = 4a - (a - 1)$
(i) $4x - (3x - 1) - 3 + 6(x - 2) = 0$

2. Solve.
(a) $\dfrac{2x}{3} = \dfrac{3}{2}$
(b) $\dfrac{a}{2} + 1 = \dfrac{a}{3}$
(c) $\dfrac{b + 1}{2} = 4$
(d) $\dfrac{2m - 1}{3} = 5$
(e) $\dfrac{a + 3}{2} - 1 = 0$
(f) $\dfrac{x + 2}{2} = \dfrac{x - 1}{3}$
(g) $\dfrac{b + 7}{4} = \dfrac{2b - 1}{3}$
(h) $\frac{1}{2}(x + 1) + \frac{1}{3}(x + 1) = 5$

3. (a) If $A = \ell w$, find A when $\ell = 5$ and $w = 3$.
(b) If $A = \ell w$, find ℓ when $A = 40$ and $w = 4$.
(c) If $P = 2(\ell + w)$, find ℓ when $P = 30$ and $w = 5$.
(d) If $A = \frac{1}{2}(a + b)h$, find b when $A = 40$, $h = 10$, and $a = 3$.
(e) If $A = \frac{1}{2}bh$, find h when $A = 50$ and $b = 10$.
(f) If $I = prt$, find p when $I = 400$, $r = \frac{7}{100}$, and $t = 20$.
(g) If $A = \frac{1}{2}bh$, solve for h.
(h) If $\dfrac{1}{x} = \dfrac{1}{y} + \dfrac{1}{z}$, solve for y.
(i) If $V = \pi r^2 h$, solve for r.

4. Solve each of the following systems of equations graphically.
(a) $2x + y = 3$
     $x - y = 3$
(b) $4x - y = -3$
     $x - y = 0$
(c) $x - 2y = 7$
     $x + y = -2$
(d) $x + y = 9$
     $x - y = 3$
(e) $2x + y = 3$
     $3x - 4y = 10$

5. Solve.
(a) $2x + y = 3$
     $5x - 2y = 3$
(b) $x + 2y = 13$
     $3x - y = 5$
(c) $2x - y = -2$
     $x - 2y = 2$
(d) $3x + 2y = 4$
     $5x - 3y = 13$
(e) $3m - n = 3$
     $3m - 5n = 3$
(f) $y = 2x - 7$
     $y = 3 - 3x$
(g) $\frac{1}{5}x + \frac{1}{2}y = 5$
     $x - y = 4$
(h) $5x + y = 14$
     $2x + y = 5$
(i) $2x + 5y = 0$
     $3x - 2y = -19$
(j) $2x - 3y = -7$
     $4x - 5y = -9$

6. Solve.
(a) $\dfrac{x}{3} + \dfrac{y}{5} = -\dfrac{1}{5}$
     $\frac{2}{3}x - \frac{3}{4}y = -5$
(b) $2x - y = 1.5$
     $3x - 2y = 0.5$
(c) $2x - 3y = 0.1$
     $3x - 5y = -0.3$

7. Solve by factoring.
(a) $x^2 + 6x + 8 = 0$
(b) $t^2 - 9t + 20 = 0$
(c) $y^2 - 4y - 21 = 0$
(d) $s^2 + 3s - 40 = 0$
(e) $x^2 + 4x + 4 = 0$

(f) $b^2 - 12b + 36 = 0$
(g) $m^2 + 6m - 27 = 0$
(h) $x^2 + 7x + 12 = 0$
(i) $x^2 - 4x - 21 = 0$
(j) $x^2 - 6x + 9 = 0$

8. Solve by factoring.
(a) $2x^2 + 5x + 3 = 0$
(b) $2t^2 - 3t - 9 = 0$
(c) $4s^2 - 11s - 3 = 0$
(d) $3x^2 + 13x - 10 = 0$
(e) $4a^2 - 17a + 4 = 0$
(f) $6m^2 + 7m - 3 = 0$
(g) $2x^2 - 14x - 36 = 0$
(h) $x^2 - 36 = 0$
(i) $x^2 - x - 42 = 0$
(j) $2x^2 - 3x - 2 = 0$
(k) $2x^2 + 11x + 12 = 0$
(l) $3x^2 - 5x + 2 = 0$
(m) $6x^2 + 5x - 4 = 0$
(n) $10x^2 + 13x - 3 = 0$
(o) $6x^2 + 37x + 6 = 0$

9. Solve.
(a) $x^2 - 3x - 28 = 0$
(b) $2t^2 + 3t - 7 = 0$
(c) $3n^2 - 7n - 20 = 0$
(d) $2x^2 + 6x + 3 = 0$
(e) $4x^2 + x - 2 = 0$
(f) $t^2 - 5t + 3 = 0$
(g) $3x^2 - x - 4 = 0$
(h) $5t^2 + 3t - 1 = 0$
(i) $m^2 - 6m + 1 = 0$
(j) $y^2 + 5y + 2 = 0$
(k) $4r^2 + 2r - 3 = 0$

10. Solve the following equations. Express the solutions in i-form.
(a) $x^2 + 2x + 6 = 0$
(b) $x^2 - 3x + 5 = 0$
(c) $x^2 + 4 = 0$

11. Find two consecutive integers whose product is 756.

12. A park is 30 m long and 20 m wide. The area of the park is to be doubled by adding a strip across one end and a strip the same width along one side. Find the width of the strips.

13. Solve.
(a) $\sqrt{x} = 5$
(b) $\sqrt{t - 2} = 7$
(c) $\sqrt{2x - 6} = 6$
(d) $\sqrt{r - 1} = 4$
(e) $\sqrt{2r - 5} = 3$
(f) $\sqrt{x - 4} = \sqrt{2x - 3}$
(g) $\sqrt{2t - 3} = \sqrt{t + 5}$
(h) $3 + \sqrt{3x + 1} = x$
(i) $6 + \sqrt{3t} = t$
(j) $\sqrt{3a - 1} - \sqrt{a - 4} = 3$
(k) $\sqrt{b + 4} = \sqrt{b + 20} - 2$

MICRO MATH

The following BASIC program solves quadratic equations. If the roots are complex, the real part and the imaginary part are calculated separately.

NEW
```
100 REM SOLVING QUADRATICS OF THE FORM
110 REM A*X*X+B*X+C=0
120 INPUT A
130 INPUT B
140 INPUT C
150 D=B*B-4*A*C
160 IF D=0 THEN 220
170 IF D<0 THEN 250
180 X1=(-B+SQR(D))/(2*A)
190 X2=(-B-SQR(D))/(2*A)
200 PRINT"THE TWO ROOTS ARE";X1;"AND"
    ;X2
210 GOTO 280
220 X=-B/(2*A)
230 PRINT"THE ROOTS ARE BOTH";X
240 GOTO 280
250 R=-B/(2*A)
260 I=SQR(-D)/(2*A)
270 PRINT"THE COMPLEX ROOTS ARE ";R;
    "+";I;"I AND ";R;"-";I;"I"
280 END
```
RUN

Solve the following equations.
(a) $3x^2 + 8x - 3 = 0$
(b) $x^2 - x - 6 = 0$
(c) $2x^2 + x - 1 = 0$
(d) $x^2 + x + 7 = 0$

3.10 CHAPTER 3 TEST

1. If $I = prt$, find I when $p = 2000$, $r = 0.07$, and $t = 5$.

2. If $y = mx + b$, solve for m.

3. If $S = ut + \frac{1}{2}gt^2$, solve for g.

4. Solve and check your solution.
(a) $2x + 3y = -6$
   $3x + 2y = 1$
(b) $0.04s + 0.05t = 44$
   $s + t = 1000$
(c) $\frac{3}{2}x + \frac{y}{4} = 7$

   $\frac{x}{5} - \frac{2}{3}y = \frac{7}{3}$

5. Solve by factoring.
(a) $x^2 - 8x + 15 = 0$
(b) $t^2 - 9 = 0$
(c) $2x^2 + 5x - 3 = 0$

6. Solve.
(a) $2x^2 + 5x + 1 = 0$
(b) $x^2 - 3x - 6 = 0$

7. The sum of the squares of four consecutive integers is 366.
Find the integers.

8. Solve.
(a) $\sqrt{x + 1} = 3$
(b) $\sqrt{y - 1} = y - 3$

ANALYTIC GEOMETRY

REVIEW AND PREVIEW TO CHAPTER 4

SLOPE OF A LINE

The slope of a line is a measure of the steepness or slant of the line. Slope is expressed as a ratio of

$$\frac{\text{vertical change}}{\text{horizontal change}}$$

The slope, m, of a non-vertical line that contains the points $P_1(x_1, y_1)$ and $P_2(x_2, y_2)$ is

$$m = \frac{y_2 - y_1}{x_2 - x_1}$$

or

$$m = \frac{\triangle y}{\triangle x}$$

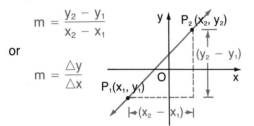

Positive Slope
Negative Slope

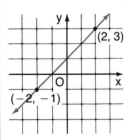
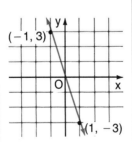

The line rises from left to right.

$$m = \frac{\triangle y}{\triangle x}$$

$$m = \frac{3 - (-1)}{2 - (-2)}$$

$$= \frac{4}{4}$$

$$= 1$$

The line falls from left to right.

$$m = \frac{\triangle y}{\triangle x}$$

$$m = \frac{3 - (-3)}{-1 - 1}$$

$$= \frac{6}{-2}$$

$$= -3$$

Zero Slope
Not Defined

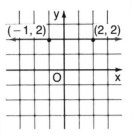
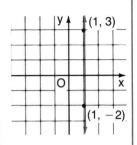

The line is horizontal.

$$m = \frac{\triangle y}{\triangle x}$$

$$m = \frac{2 - 2}{2 - (-1)}$$

$$= \frac{0}{3}$$

$$= 0$$

The line is vertical.

$$m = \frac{\triangle y}{\triangle x}$$

$$m = \frac{3 - (-2)}{1 - 1}$$

$$= \frac{5}{0}$$

Division by zero is not defined. Thus the slope is not defined.

EXERCISE 1

1. Determine the slope of the line passing through each pair of points.
(a) (4, 5) and (1, 1)
(b) (8, 7) and (−1, 4)
(c) (2, 3) and (−6, 3)
(d) (−4, 7) and (−4, 9)
(e) (7, 6) and (−3, −2)
(f) (0, 9) and (−8, 0)
(g) (−3, 8) and (6, −2)
(h) (5, −11) and (5, 13)
(i) (7, 1) and (−6, −2)
(j) (−4, −6) and (−1, −1)
(k) (0, 0) and (−9, −6)
(l) (5, 5) and (−5, −5)

THE PYTHAGOREAN THEOREM

$c^2 = a^2 + b^2$

THE CIRCLE

$A = \pi r^2$
$C = 2\pi r$

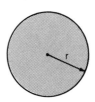

EXERCISE 2

1. Calculate the length of the unknown side to the nearest tenth.

(a)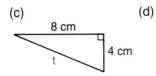

(b)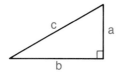
10 m, 9 m, y

(c)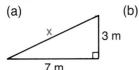
8 cm, 4 cm, t

(d)
11 cm, y, 7 cm

PROPORTIONS AND POWERS OF 10

EXERCISE 3

1. Complete the following to form true statements.

(a) $\dfrac{2}{5} = \dfrac{\blacksquare}{20} = \dfrac{10}{\blacksquare}$

(b) $\dfrac{5}{8} = \dfrac{\blacksquare}{16} = \dfrac{40}{\blacksquare}$

(c) $\dfrac{\blacksquare}{8} = \dfrac{21}{24} = \dfrac{\blacksquare}{40}$

(d) $\dfrac{3}{7} = \dfrac{9}{\blacksquare} = \dfrac{24}{\blacksquare}$

(e) $\dfrac{\blacksquare}{6} = \dfrac{4}{24} = \dfrac{\blacksquare}{30}$

(f) $\dfrac{\blacksquare}{2} = 2 = \dfrac{14}{\blacksquare}$

(g) $3 = \dfrac{\blacksquare}{2} = \dfrac{\blacksquare}{8}$

(h) $2 = \dfrac{8}{\blacksquare} = \dfrac{\blacksquare}{9}$

2. Simplify.
(a) $10^5 \times 10^7$
(b) $10^3 \times 10^0$
(c) $10^{-5} \times 10^{-3}$
(d) 1000×10^5
(e) $10^4 \times 10^{21}$
(f) $(10^5)^3$
(g) $10^9 \div 10^7$
(h) $10^2 \div 10^{-5}$
(i) $(10^3)^5$
(j) $(10^{-3})^2$
(k) $(10^{-3})^2$
(l) $(10^6)^{-2}$

EXERCISE 4

1. Calculate the perimeter and area of the following to the nearest tenth.

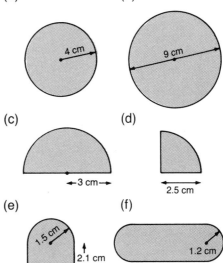

(a) 4 cm
(b) 9 cm
(c) 3 cm
(d) 2.5 cm
(e) 1.5 cm, 2.1 cm
(f) 1.2 cm, 5.2 cm

EQUATIONS

EXERCISE 5

1. Solve the following equations.
(a) $7.813x = 8.143$
(b) $21.44x + 53.75 = 81.46$
(c) $7.816x - 7.213 = 1.473$
(d) $0.9873x + 0.4182 = 0.6376$
(e) $-83.42x = -162.43$
(f) $3.814 - 1.753x = 8.593$
(g) $82.43x - 66.31x = 97.43$
(h) $9.417x + 1.763 = 6.431x - 9.743$
(i) $(16.43 - 12.77)x = 81.44$
(j) $53.75x + 48.17 = 77.59 - 16.34x$

4.1 THE STRAIGHT LINE

Equations such as $3x + 5y = 45$ and $y = 2x - 4$ are equations in two variables. Each of these equations has many ordered pairs, (x, y), that satisfy them (make the equation true). The graph of each equation is the set of points whose coordinates are solutions of the equation.

Example 1. Graph. $3x + 5y = 45$

Solution:
Solve the equation for y.

$$3x + 5y = 45$$
$$5y = -3x + 45$$
$$y = -\tfrac{3}{5}x + 9$$

Find three ordered pairs that satisfy the equation.

x	$-\tfrac{3}{5}x + 9$	y	(x, y)
0	$-\tfrac{3}{5}(0) + 9$	9	(0, 9)
5	$-\tfrac{3}{5}(5) + 9$	6	(5, 6)
10	$-\tfrac{3}{5}(10) + 9$	3	(10, 3)

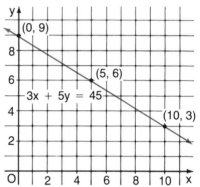

Graph the ordered pairs and join the points with a straight line.
Using any two points on the line, we can determine the slope.
For (5, 6) and (10, 3),

$$m = \frac{\triangle y}{\triangle x}$$
$$m = \frac{6 - 3}{5 - 10}$$
$$= -\tfrac{3}{5}$$

Equations in two variables can also be graphed using the intercepts. The intercepts are the points where the graph of the line crosses the x- and y-axes.

Example 2. Graph. $2x - 3y = 6$

Solution:

On the y-axis, $x = 0$.

To find the y-intercept, let $x = 0$.

$$2x - 3y = 6$$
$$2(0) - 3y = 6$$
$$-3y = 6$$
$$y = -2$$

Point: $(0, -2)$

On the x-axis, $y = 0$.

To find the x-intercept, let $y = 0$.

$$2x - 3y = 6$$
$$2x - 3(0) = 6$$
$$2x = 6$$
$$x = 3$$

Point: $(3, 0)$

To determine the slope, use (3, 0) and (0, −2).

$$m = \frac{\triangle y}{\triangle x}$$

$$m = \frac{0 - (-2)}{3 - 0}$$

$$= \frac{2}{3}$$

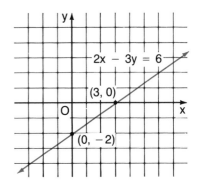

Solving 2x − 3y = 6 for y, we have

$$2x - 3y = 6$$
$$-3y = -2x + 6$$
$$y = \tfrac{2}{3}x - 2$$

From the examples, we see that solving equations for y gives the following patterns.

Equation	Solve for y	Coefficient of x	Constant
3x + 5y = 45	$y = -\tfrac{3}{5}x + 9$	$-\tfrac{3}{5}$	9
2x − 3y = 6	$y = \tfrac{2}{3}x - 2$	$\tfrac{2}{3}$	−2

Recall that the coefficient of x is the slope of the line and the constant term is the y-intercept.

> The slope y-intercept form of an equation of a line is
> y = mx + b. The slope is m. The y-intercept is b.

EXERCISE 4.1

B

1. Sketch the graph of each.
(a) y = 3x + 2   (b) y = 2x − 5
(c) y = −4x + 5   (d) y = −2x − 6
(e) y = ½x + 7   (f) y = −⅔x − 5
(g) x = 5   (h) y = 4
(i) x = −2   (j) y = −1
(k) x = 0   (l) y = 0
(m) y = x   (n) y = −x

2. Solve for y, then graph each.
(a) 2x + 3y = 9
(b) x + y = 7
(c) x − y = −3
(d) 4x − 2y = 3
(e) 2x + y + 1 = 0
(f) x + 4y + 4 = 0

3. Use the intercepts to graph each.
(a) 2x + 3y = 12
(b) x − 4y = 8
(c) 5x − y = 10
(d) 4x + 3y = −12
(e) x + y = 6
(f) x − 2y = −2
(g) 4x + 5y − 20 = 0
(h) 2x − 7y + 14 = 0

4. State the slope, x-intercept, and
y-intercept of each of the following.
(a) y = 7x + 6   (b) y = −2x + 1
(c) 2y − 3x = 8   (d) 2y = −x + 6
(e) y = −x − 4   (f) −6x + 4y = 7

4.2 DETERMINING EQUATIONS OF LINES

To determine the equation of a line, we use
(i) a point on the line, which gives the location of the line, and
(ii) the slope of the line, which gives the direction of the line.

Let $P_1(x_1, y_1)$ be any point on the line with slope m. Choose
any other point, $P(x, y)$, on the line. The slope of the line is

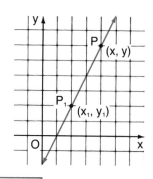

$$m = \frac{\triangle y}{\triangle x}$$

$$m = \frac{(y - y_1)}{(x - x_1)}$$

Multiply by $(x - x_1)$. $m(x - x_1) = (y - y_1)$
$$y - y_1 = m(x - x_1)$$

Point-Slope Form of a Linear Equation

If the slope of a non-vertical line is m, and the point
$P_1(x_1, y_1)$ lies on the line, then the equation of the line is

$$y - y_1 = m(x - x_1)$$

Example 1. (a) Find an equation of the line through
$(3, -2)$ with slope m = 4.
(b) Write the equation in standard form,
$Ax + By + C = 0$.

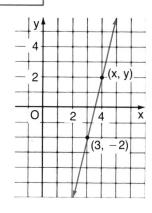

Solution:
(a) $(x_1, y_1) = (3, -2)$ and m = 4.

$$y - y_1 = m(x - x_1)$$
$$y - (-2) = 4(x - 3)$$
$$y + 2 = 4x - 12$$
$$y = 4x - 14$$

(b) $y = 4x - 14$
$4x - y - 14 = 0$

Example 2. Find an equation of the line through
$(-2, 5)$ and $(3, 0)$.

Solution:
Since we know two points on the line, we can
determine the slope.

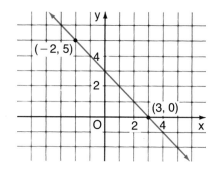

$$m = \frac{\triangle y}{\triangle x}$$

$$m = \frac{5 - 0}{-2 - 3}$$

$$= \frac{5}{-5}$$

$$= -1$$

We now have the slope of the line, m = -1, and a point on the line, $(-2, 5)$ or $(3, 0)$.

Using $(-2, 5)$,

$$y - y_1 = m(x - x_1)$$
$$y - 5 = -1(x - (-2))$$
$$y - 5 = -1(x + 2)$$
$$y - 5 = -x - 2$$
$$x + y - 3 = 0$$

Example 3. Given the graph of a line, determine the equation of the line.

Solution:
From the graph, two points on the line are $(-3, 4)$ and $(2, -2)$.

$$m = \frac{\triangle y}{\triangle x}$$

$$m = \frac{4 - (-2)}{-3 - 2}$$

$$m = -\frac{6}{5}$$

Using $(2, -2)$,

$$y - y_1 = m(x - x_1)$$
$$y - (-2) = -\tfrac{6}{5}(x - 2)$$
$$y + 2 = -\tfrac{6}{5}(x - 2)$$
$$5y + 10 = -6(x - 2)$$
$$5y + 10 = -6x + 12$$
$$6x + 5y - 2 = 0$$

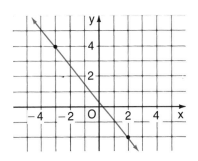

E=mc²

EXERCISE 4.2

B

1. Find an equation of the line through the given point with the given slope.
Express the equation in standard form.
(a) $(5, 6)$, m = 3   (b) $(-2, -4)$, m = -2

(c) $(0, 4)$, m = $\tfrac{1}{2}$ (d) $(-6, 0)$, m = $-\tfrac{1}{3}$

(e) $(6, -2)$, m = $\tfrac{2}{3}$ (f) $(2, -3)$, m = $-\tfrac{4}{5}$

(g) $(8, -1)$, m = $\tfrac{3}{4}$ (h) $(6, 4)$, m = -1

(i) $(2, 0)$, m = 0   (j) $(5, -2)$, m = $\tfrac{1}{2}$

2. Find an equation of the line through the given points.
Express the equation in standard form.
(a) $(6, 1)$ and $(8, -4)$
(b) $(-3, 0)$ and $(8, 2)$
(c) $(5, 7)$ and $(4, -6)$
(d) $(-6, -3)$ and $(4, 1)$
(e) $(-8, -2)$ and $(-4, 8)$
(f) $(2, 4)$ and $(-1, 8)$
(g) $(3, -4)$ and $(\tfrac{1}{2}, 2)$

4.3 DISTANCE BETWEEN TWO POINTS

To calculate the distance between two points, we need to use the concept of absolute value. The symbol for absolute value is two vertical bars, $|\ |$. The absolute value of a number is the magnitude of the number.

$$|5| = 5 \quad \text{and} \quad |-5| = 5$$

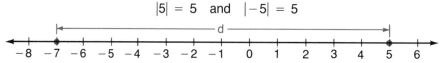

On a number line the distance between -7 and 5 is

$$d = |-7 - 5| \qquad \qquad \qquad d = |5 - (-7)|$$
$$= |-12| \qquad \qquad \text{or} \qquad \qquad = |5 + 7|$$
$$= 12 \qquad \qquad \qquad \qquad = |12|$$
$$\qquad \qquad \qquad \qquad \qquad \qquad = 12$$

Length of a Horizontal Line Segment

Calculate $|\Delta x|$ for the line segment graphed at the right.

$$AB = |\Delta x|$$
$$= |4 - (-3)|$$
$$= |7|$$
$$= 7$$

Length of a Vertical Line Segment

Calculate $|\Delta y|$ for the line segment graphed at the right.

$$PQ = |\Delta y|$$
$$= |4 - (-1)|$$
$$= |5|$$
$$= 5$$

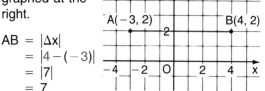
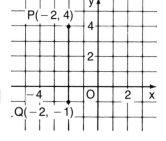

When the line is neither horizontal nor vertical, we use the Pythagorean theorem.

Example 1. Calculate the length of the line segment joining $S(2, 3)$ to $T(-3, -5)$.

Solution:
Draw line segment ST.
Construct the right triangle RST.

Length of $SR = |\Delta y|$
$$= |3 - (-5)|$$
$$= 8$$

Length of $TR = |\Delta x|$
$$= |2 - (-3)|$$
$$= 5$$

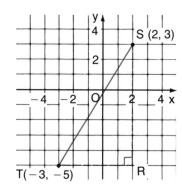

Using the Pythagorean theorem,

$$(ST)^2 = (SR)^2 + (TR)^2$$
$$ST = \sqrt{(SR)^2 + (TR)^2}$$
$$= \sqrt{8^2 + 5^2}$$
$$= \sqrt{64 + 25}$$
$$= \sqrt{89}$$

Since $(TR)^2 = (\Delta x)^2$ and $(SR)^2 = (\Delta y)^2$, the formula for length is generalized as follows:

$$\ell = \sqrt{(\Delta x)^2 + (\Delta y)^2}$$
$$= \sqrt{(x_2 - x_1)^2 + (y_2 - y_1)^2}$$

Example 2. Find the length of the line segment joining A(2, 5) to B(−1, −1) to the nearest tenth.

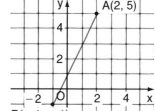

Solution:

$AB = \sqrt{(\Delta x)^2 + (\Delta y)^2}$

$AB = \sqrt{(-1 - 2)^2 + (-1 - 5)^2}$

$\quad = \sqrt{(-3)^2 + (-6)^2}$

$\quad = \sqrt{9 + 36}$

$\quad = \sqrt{45}$

$\quad \doteq 6.7$

Example 3. Find the length of the line segment joining E(21.5, 26.3) to F(−18.1, 12.7) to the nearest tenth.

Solution:

Using a calculator, press ﹝2﹞﹝1﹞﹝·﹞﹝5﹞﹝−﹞﹝1﹞﹝8﹞﹝·﹞﹝1﹞﹝+/−﹞﹝=﹞﹝x²﹞﹝M+﹞﹝2﹞﹝6﹞﹝·﹞﹝3﹞ ﹝−﹞﹝1﹞﹝2﹞﹝·﹞﹝7﹞﹝=﹞﹝x²﹞﹝+﹞﹝MR﹞﹝=﹞﹝√﹞

The display is ᴨ1.870276

∴ EF = 41.9

EXERCISE 4.3

A

1. Determine the lengths of the line segments joining the given points.
(a) A(5, 1) to C(5, 8)
(b) B(2, 9) to D(7, 9)
(c) R(0, 8) to T(0, −3)
(d) M(−3, 6) to N(7, 6)

B

2. Calculate the lengths of the line segments joining the given points to the nearest tenth.
(a) A(7, 4) and B(2, 3)
(b) C(−1, 6) and D(5, −2)
(c) E(−3, −5) and F(−4, 9)
(d) G(−7, 0) and H(0, −8)
(e) I(9, −6) and J(−10, −11)
(f) K(−1, −2) and L(−5, −9)
(g) M(4, −4) and N(0, 0)
(h) P(11, −6) and Q(13, −1)

MICRO MATH

The following program will calculate the length of a line segment.

```
NEW
10 REM LENGTH
20 PRINT"(X1,Y1)";
30 INPUT X1,Y1
40 PRINT"(X2,Y2)";
50 INPUT X2,Y2
60 L=SQR((X2-X1)*(X2-X1)+(Y2-Y1)*
   (Y2-Y1))
70 PRINT"THE LENGTH OF THE SEGMENT
   IS"; L
80 END
RUN
```

Calculate the lengths of the line segments to the nearest tenth.
(a) A(56, 84) and B(89, 104)
(b) C(21.8, 25.6) and D(−24.2, 19.9)
(c) E(562, 841) and F(701, 594)

4.4 THE CIRCLE WITH CENTRE AT THE ORIGIN

The circle, parabola, ellipse, and hyperbola are called the conic sections. Conic sections are formed by the intersection of a plane and double right circular cones in different directions.

Circle   Ellipse   Parabola   Hyperbola

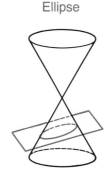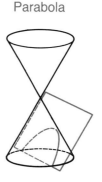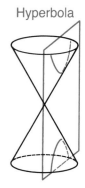

A circle is the conic section formed by the intersection of a right circular cone and a plane perpendicular to the axis of the cone.

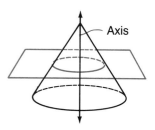

Axis

A circle can also be defined as a set of points.

> A circle is a set of points in the plane that are a given distance from a given point in the plane.
> The given distance is the radius of the circle.
> The given point is the centre of the circle.

Example 1. Find an equation of the circle with centre at the origin and radius 5 units.

Solution:
Let P(x, y) be any point on the circle.
Since the radius is 5 units, OP = 5.
By the distance between two points formula,

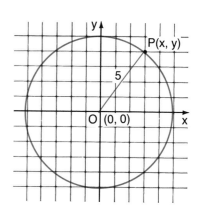

$$OP = \sqrt{(\Delta x)^2 + (\Delta y)^2}$$
$$5 = \sqrt{(x - 0)^2 + (y - 0)^2}$$
$$5 = \sqrt{x^2 + y^2}$$

Square both sides.

$$25 = x^2 + y^2$$
or $\quad x^2 + y^2 = 25$

The equation of the circle is $x^2 + y^2 = 25$.

To find an equation of the circle with radius r and centre at the origin, we proceed as follows:

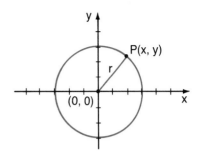

Let P(x, y) be any point on the circle.
Using the distance formula, we have

$$\ell = \sqrt{(\Delta x)^2 + (\Delta y)^2}$$
$$r = \sqrt{(x - 0)^2 + (y - 0)^2}$$
$$r = \sqrt{x^2 + y^2}$$

Square both sides.

$$r^2 = x^2 + y^2$$

> An equation of the circle with centre (0, 0) and radius r is
> $$x^2 + y^2 = r^2$$

Example 2. Find an equation of the circle, centre (0, 0), that passes through the point $(-4, 3)$.

Solution:
Draw a diagram.
Use the distance formula to determine the radius of the circle.

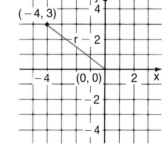

$$r = \sqrt{(\Delta x)^2 + (\Delta y)^2}$$
$$r = \sqrt{(-4 - 0)^2 + (3 - 0)^2}$$
$$= \sqrt{16 + 9}$$
$$= \sqrt{25}$$
$$= 5$$

The radius is 5 and the equation of the circle is $x^2 + y^2 = 25$.

Example 3. Sketch the graph of $x^2 + y^2 = 9$.

Solution:
The general equation of a circle is

$$x^2 + y^2 = r^2$$

But

$$x^2 + y^2 = 9$$
$$\therefore r^2 = 9$$

and

$$r = 3$$

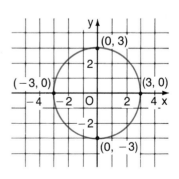

Now plot points 3 units from the origin as shown on the grid.
Draw the circle.

Example 4. Sketch the graph of $x^2 + y^2 = 20$.

Solution:
Comparing $x^2 + y^2 = 20$ to $x^2 + y^2 = r^2$, we have

$$r^2 = 20$$
$$r = \sqrt{20}$$
and $\quad r \doteq 4.5$

Plot points 4.5 units from the origin.
Draw the circle.

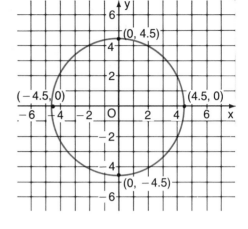

EXERCISE 4.4

A

1. State an equation of the following circles.
(a) centre (0, 0), radius 5
(b) centre (0, 0), radius 9
(c) centre (0, 0), radius 4
(d) centre (0, 0), radius 12
(e) centre (0, 0), radius 7
(f) centre (0, 0), radius 8
(g) centre (0, 0), radius $\sqrt{3}$
(h) centre (0, 0), radius $\sqrt{2}$
(i) centre (0, 0), radius a
(j) centre (0, 0), radius r

2. State the radius of each circle.
(a) $x^2 + y^2 = 16$
(b) $x^2 + y^2 = 100$
(c) $x^2 + y^2 = 25$
(d) $x^2 + y^2 = 5$
(e) $x^2 + y^2 = 36$
(f) $x^2 + y^2 = 49$
(g) $x^2 + y^2 = 12$
(h) $x^2 + y^2 = r^2$

B

3. (a) Find the radius of a circle, centre (0, 0), that passes through the point (4, 0).
(b) Find an equation of the circle, centre (0, 0), that passes through (4, 0).

4. (a) What is the radius of the circle, centre (0, 0), that passes through the point (5, 12)?
(b) Find an equation of the circle, centre (0, 0), that passes through (5, 12).

5. Find an equation of these circles.
(a) centre (0, 0) passing through (3, 4)
(b) centre (0, 0) passing through (24, −7)
(c) centre (0, 0) passing through (3, 1)
(d) centre (0, 0), y-intercept 7

6. Sketch the graph of each circle.
(a) $x^2 + y^2 = 36$
(b) $x^2 + y^2 = 12$
(c) $x^2 + y^2 = 29$

7. Match each of the following equations of circles with the coordinates of the point that lies on it.
(a) $x^2 + y^2 = 10$ (i) (2, 5)
(b) $x^2 + y^2 = 32$ (ii) (1, −3)
(c) $x^2 + y^2 = 29$ (iii) (4, 0)
(d) $x^2 + y^2 = 16$ (iv) (−2, −3)
(e) $x^2 + y^2 = 13$ (v) (−4, −4)

8. Give the coordinates of two points that lie on each of the following circles.
(a) $x^2 + y^2 = 17$ (b) $x^2 + y^2 = 50$
(c) $x^2 + y^2 = 20$ (d) $x^2 + y^2 = 81$

MIND BENDER

There are two different ways to look at the object at the right. Describe them.

4.5 THE CIRCLE WITH CENTRE NOT AT THE ORIGIN

We will use the same method as shown in section 4.4 to find an equation of the circle with the centre not at the origin.

Example 1. Find an equation of the circle with centre C(h, k) and radius r.

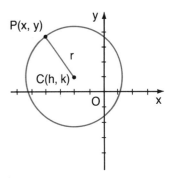

Solution:
Let P(x, y) be any point on the circle.
Using the distance formula, we have

$$\ell = \sqrt{(\Delta x)^2 + (\Delta y)^2}$$
$$r = \sqrt{(x - h)^2 + (y - k)^2}$$

Square both sides.

$$r^2 = (x - h)^2 + (y - k)^2$$

> The equation of a circle with centre (h, k) and radius r is
> $$(x - h)^2 + (y - k)^2 = r^2$$

Example 2. Write an equation for the circle with radius 4 and centre $(-2, 3)$.

Solution: $(x - h)^2 + (y - k)^2 = r^2$
$(x - (-2))^2 + (y - 3)^2 = 4^2$
$(x + 2)^2 + (y - 3)^2 = 16$

An equation is $(x + 2)^2 + (y - 3)^2 = 16$.

EXERCISE 4.5

A
1. State the centre and radius of the circle whose equation is
(a) $(x - 4)^2 + (y - 7)^2 = 121$
(b) $(x + 5)^2 + (y - 2)^2 = 25$
(c) $(x - 2)^2 + (y - 3)^2 = 36$
(d) $(x - 2)^2 + (y + 3)^2 = 49$

B
2. Write the equation of these circles.
(a) centre (0, 3), radius 4
(b) centre (1, 2), radius 8
(c) centre (4, 0), radius 6
(d) centre (3, 6), radius 7
(e) centre (2, 4), radius 9
(f) centre (5, 2), radius 12
(g) centre (5, 2), radius $\sqrt{5}$

3. Find the equation of the following circles.
(a) centre (4, 5), radius 3
(b) centre $(-1, 4)$, radius 5
(c) centre $(3, -4)$, radius 7
(d) centre (6, 0), radius 8

4. Find an equation of the circle having centre (3, 3) and passing through the point $(-1, 4)$.

5. Find an equation of the circle having centre $(-4, -5)$ and passing through the point (1, 1).

6. Find an equation of the circle having centre $(0, -6)$ and passing through the point $(-7, 0)$.

4.6 THE PARABOLA

The parabola is another one of the conic sections we saw in section 4.4. The graphs of two parabolas are shown at the right.

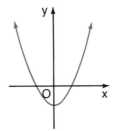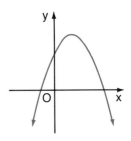

The equations of parabolas can take many forms. Some examples are

$$y = x^2, \qquad\qquad y = -2x^2 + 3, \qquad\qquad y = x^2 - 3x, \qquad\qquad y = -x^2 - 2x + 3$$

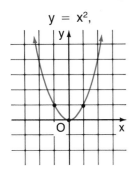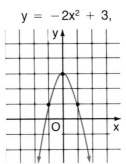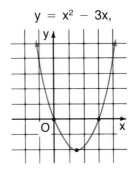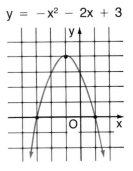

The general form of the equation of a parabola is $y = ax^2 + bx + c$.
The x^2 term gives the parabola its curved shape.
If $a = 0$, then $ax^2 = 0$, and the equation becomes $y = bx + c$, which is a straight line.
For this reason, the defining equation of the parabola is $y = ax^2 + bx + c$, $a \neq 0$.

Investigation 1. $y = ax^2$

1. (a) Complete the table in your notebook and graph the results on the same axes.

x	$y = x^2$	$y = 2x^2$	$y = 3x^2$	$y = \frac{1}{2}x^2$	$y = \frac{1}{3}x^2$
-3	9	18	27	$\frac{9}{2}$	3
-2	4		12	2	
-1		2			
0					
1					
2					
3					

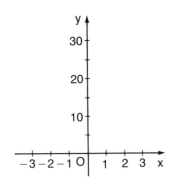

(b) Each of the curves opens upward or is concave upward.
   Is a positive or negative in each case?
(c) Are there any points on the curves below the x-axis?
(d) What is the minimum point for each curve?
(e) Fold the graph along the y-axis.
   What do you observe?

(f) Notice that for every point (a, b) that satisfies $y = x^2$, there is a corresponding point $(-a, b)$ also satisfying $y = x^2$. This is because the curve is symmetric about a line, in this case the y-axis.
Are the other four curves symmetric about the y-axis?

(g) The point of intersection of a parabola with its axis of symmetry is called its vertex.
What are the coordinates of the vertex of each of these parabolas?

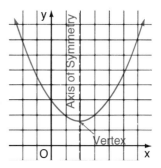

(h) Which parabola is flattest?
(i) Which parabola is sharpest?
(j) What happens to the graph of a parabola as a increases in value?
(k) What happens to the graph of a parabola as a decreases in value?

2. (a) Using a table similar to the one in question 1(a), graph the following on the same set of axes for $-3 \leq x \leq 3$.

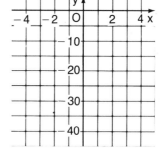

(i) $y = -x^2$
(ii) $y = -2x^2$
(iii) $y = -4x^2$
(iv) $y = -\frac{1}{2}x^2$
(v) $y = -\frac{1}{4}x^2$

(b) Each of these curves opens downward or is concave downward.
Is a positive or negative in each case?
(c) Are there any points on the curves above the x-axis?
(d) Does each curve have a maximum point? If so, what is it?
(e) What is the equation of the axis of symmetry of these curves?
(f) What are the coordinates of the vertex of each of these parabolas?
(g) Which parabola is flattest?
(h) Which parabola is sharpest?

3. Without making a table of values, sketch the following on the same set of axes.

(a) $y = 2x^2$ (b) $y = -3x^2$ (c) $y = \frac{2}{3}x^2$

(d) $y = -\frac{1}{5}x^2$ (e) $y = \frac{1}{4}x^2$ (f) $y = -6x^2$

Investigation 2. $y = ax^2 + c$

1. (a) Using the same set of axes, graph the following for $-3 \leq x \leq 3$.
(i) $y = x^2 - 3$ (ii) $y = x^2$ (iii) $y = x^2 + 3$
(b) What is the direction of opening of each parabola?
(c) What is the equation of the axis of symmetry of each parabola?
(d) What are the coordinates of the vertex of each parabola?
(e) Is the vertex a maximum point or a minimum point?
(f) How do the three graphs seem to be related?

2. (a) Using the same set of axes, graph the following for $-3 \leqslant x \leqslant 3$.
(i) $y = -x^2 - 2$ (ii) $y = -x^2$ (iii) $y = -x^2 + 2$
(b) What is the direction of opening of each parabola?
(c) What is the equation of the axis of symmetry of each parabola?
(d) What are the coordinates of the vertex of each parabola?
(e) Is the vertex a maximum point or a minimum point?
(f) How do these graphs seem to be related?

3. (a) Using the same set of axes, graph $y = 3x^2$, $y = 3x^2 + 2$, and $y = 3x^2 - 1$
for $-2 \leqslant x \leqslant 2$.
(b) What is the direction of opening of each parabola?
(c) What is the equation of the axis of symmetry of each parabola?
(d) What are the coordinates of the vertex of each parabola?
(e) Is the vertex a maximum point or a minimum point?
(f) How do these graphs seem to be related?

4. Without making a table of values, sketch $y = x^2$, $y = x^2 + 2$, $y = x^2 - 3$, $y = x^2 + 6$, and $y = x^2 - 5$ on the same set of axes.

5. Sketch the following on the same set of axes.
(a) $y = -2x^2$ (b) $y = -2x^2 - 3$ (c) $y = 2x^2 - 2$ (d) $y = 2x^2 + 4$

Investigation 3. $y = ax^2 + bx + c$

As soon as the x-term is included in the equation of the parabola, we use intercepts to determine points on the graph. This is necessary because the x-term moves the graph to the left or right of the y-axis.

Example. Sketch the graph of $y = x^2 - 8x + 12$.

Solution:

Since $a = +1$, the parabola opens upward.
To find the y-intercept, let $x = 0$.

$$y = x^2 - 8x + 12$$
$$y = (0)^2 - 8(0) + 12$$
$$y = 12$$

One point on the parabola is $(0, 12)$.

To find the x-intercepts, if they exist, let $y = 0$.

$$y = x^2 - 8x + 12$$
$$0 = x^2 - 8x + 12$$
or $x^2 - 8x + 12 = 0$

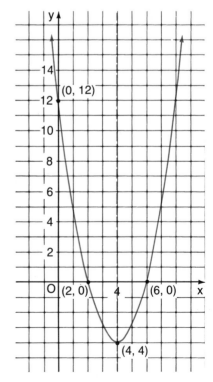

This is a quadratic equation that can be solved by using the quadratic formula or by factoring.

$$x^2 - 8x + 12 = 0$$
$$(x - 6)(x - 2) = 0$$
$$x - 6 = 0 \quad \text{or} \quad x - 2 = 0$$
$$x = 6 \quad \text{or} \quad x = 2$$

Two other points on the parabola are $(6, 0)$ and $(2, 0)$.

From the graph, we see that the axis of symmetry of the parabola is the line $x = 4$.
Substituting $x = 4$ in $y = x^2 - 8x + 12$, we have

$$y = (4)^2 - 8(4) + 12$$
$$= 16 - 32 + 12$$
$$= 4$$

The coordinates of the vertex of the parabola are $(4, 4)$.

1. Sketch the graphs of the parabolas indicating
(a) the y-intercept, (b) the x-intercepts, and (c) the vertex.
 (i) $y = x^2 - 8x + 15$ (ii) $y = x^2 - 2x - 8$
(iii) $y = x^2 + 8x + 7$ (iv) $y = x^2 - 4x - 12$

Investigation 4.

Using a series of algebraic operations collectively, called completing the square, we can transform the equation $y = ax^2 + bx + c$ into a form that allows us to easily sketch the parabola. The steps of completing the square are outlined in the following example.

Example.   Complete the square. $y = 2x^2 - 12x + 14$

Solution: $y = 2x^2 - 12x + 14$

Group the first two terms. $y = [2x^2 - 12x] + 14$

Common factor the two terms. $y = 2[x^2 - 6x] + 14$

Take half the coefficient of x.
Square it.
Add and subtract the 9 in the square
brackets. $y = 2[x^2 - 6x + 9 - 9] + 14$

Group the first three terms in the square
brackets. $y = 2[(x^2 - 6x + 9) - 9] + 14$

Write the three terms as a perfect square. $y = 2[(x - 3)^2 - 9] + 14$

Multiply to remove the square brackets. $y = 2(x - 3)^2 - 18 + 14$

Simplify the last two terms. $y = 2(x - 3)^2 - 4$

Starting with $x = 3$, construct a table of values to find the coordinates of the vertex of the parabola and the points around it.

x	y
3	-4
2	-2
4	-2
1	4
5	4

The equation of the axis of symmetry
is $x - 3 = 0$ or $x = 3$.
The coordinates of the vertex are $(3, -4)$.

Completing the square put the equation of the parabola in the form

$$y = 2(x - 3)^2 - 4$$

The general form is $y = a(x - m)^2 + d$

where a gives the opening of the parabola;
. $x - m = 0$ gives the axis of symmetry, $x = m$; and
   d gives the distance the parabola is moved vertically.

1. Sketch the graphs of the following parabolas indicating the vertex and y-intercept.
(a) $y = 2(x - 3)^2 + 4$ (b) $y = 3(x + 2)^2 - 1$
(c) $y = -2(x + 4)^2 + 5$ (d) $y = -2(x - 1)^2 - 2$

Investigation 5.

We have found that the equation of the parabola in the form $y = a(x - m)^2 + d$ enables us to sketch the graph very quickly. If we expand and simplify this equation, the results are as follows:

$$\begin{aligned} y &= a(x - m)^2 + d \\ &= a(x^2 - 2mx + m^2) + d \\ &= ax^2 - 2amx + (am^2 + d) \end{aligned}$$

This is compared to $Y = AX\hat{}2 + BX + C$

This comparison is used in the following BASIC program to provide information to sketch the graph.

```
NEW
10 PRINT"THE PARABOLA"
20 PRINT"Y = AX^2 + BX + C"
30 INPUT"ENTER A:";A
31 INPUT"ENTER B:";B
32 INPUT"ENTER C:";C
33 PRINT
34 PRINT"Y =";A"X^2 + ("B")X + ("C")"
35 PRINT
40 IF A>0 THEN 43
41 PRINT"OPENING DOWNWARD"
42 GOTO 44
43 PRINT"OPENING UPWARD"
44 PRINT
45 PRINT"THE VERTEX IS"
46 PRINT"(";-B/2/A;",";(4*A*C-B*B)/4/A;")"
47 PRINT
50 PRINT"THE AXIS OF SYMMETRY IS"
51 PRINT"X = ";-B/2/A
52 PRINT
53 PRINT"THE Y-INTERCEPT IS ";C
54 PRINT
55 IF B*B-4*A*C<0 THEN 61
56 PRINT
57 PRINT"THE X-INTERCEPTS ARE"
58 PRINT(-B+SQR(B*B-4*A*C))/2/A
59 PRINT(-B-SQR(B*B-4*A*C))/2/A
60 GOTO 99
61 PRINT"NO X-INTERCEPTS"
99 END
RUN
```

1. Sketch the graphs of the following parabolas using the BASIC program.
(a) $y = 2x^2 - 16x + 37$
(b) $y = -3x^2 - 6x - 5$
(c) $y = 3x^2 + 24x + 46$
(d) $y = -2x^2 - 20x - 57$
(e) $y = x^2 + x + 1$
(f) $y = -2x^2 + 5x + 7$
(g) $y = 3x^2 - 7x + 2$
(h) $y = 5x^2 - 7x + 2$
(i) $y = 3x^2 - 12$
(j) $y = x^2 - 6x$
(k) $y = -2x^2 + 10x$

4.7 LINEAR-QUADRATIC SYSTEMS

In Chapter 3 we solved systems of equations that contained two linear equations, which are straight lines. In this section we will solve systems of linear-quadratic equations.

As shown in the diagrams below, a system of one quadratic equation and one linear equation may have no solution, one solution, or two solutions.

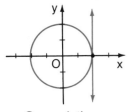

One solution

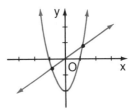

No solution   Two solutions

Example 1. Solve the linear-quadratic system and illustrate with a graph.

$$x + y = 15 \quad ①$$
$$x^2 + y^2 = 125 \quad ②$$

Solution:
From the linear equation, ①, $y = 15 - x$.
Substitute ① in the quadratic equation, ②.

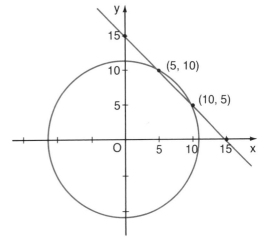

$$x^2 + (15 - x)^2 = 125$$
$$x^2 + 225 - 30x + x^2 = 125 \qquad \text{Simplify.}$$
$$2x^2 - 30x + 100 = 0$$
$$x^2 - 15x + 50 = 0$$
$$(x - 5)(x - 10) = 0 \qquad \text{Factor.}$$
$$x - 5 = 0 \quad \text{or} \quad x - 10 = 0$$
$$x = 5 \qquad\qquad x = 10$$

Substitute the values of x in the linear equation.

If x = 5, then   If x = 10, then
$$y = 15 - 5$$ $$y = 15 - 10$$
$$= 10$$ $$= 5$$
$$\therefore (x, y) = (5, 10)$$ $$\therefore (x, y) = (10, 5)$$

Note that here there are two solutions.

1·2·3

Steps in Solving a Linear-Quadratic System

1. Express the linear equation in the form $y = mx + b$.
2. Substitute the expression $mx + b$ for y in the quadratic equation.
3. Solve the resulting quadratic equation in x by factoring or using the quadratic formula.
4. Substitute both values of x in $y = mx + b$ to find all solutions.

Example 2. Solve.

$$2x + y + 1 = 0 \quad ①$$
$$y = x^2 - 4 \quad ②$$

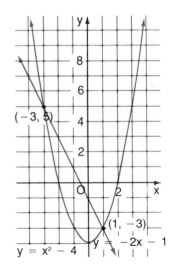

Solution:

Step 1. $2x + y - 1 = 0$
$$y = -2x - 1$$

Step 2. $y = x^2 - 4$
$$-2x - 1 = x^2 - 4$$
$$0 = x^2 + 2x - 3$$
$$x^2 + 2x - 3 = 0$$

Step 3. $(x + 3)(x - 1) = 0$
$$x + 3 = 0 \quad \text{or} \quad x - 1 = 0$$
$$x = -3 \qquad\qquad x = 1$$

Step 4.   For $x = -3$,   For $x = 1$,
$$y = -2x - 1 \qquad\quad y = -2x - 1$$
$$= -2(-3) - 1 \qquad = -2(1) - 1$$
$$= 5 \qquad\qquad\qquad = -3$$
$$\therefore (x, y) = (-3, 5) \qquad \therefore (x, y) = (1, -3)$$

There are two solutions.

EXERCISE 4.7

B

1. Solve the linear-quadratic systems.
(a) $x - y = -2$
$y = x^2$
(b) $y = x^2 - 4$
$3x - y = 0$
(c) $x^2 + y^2 = 25$
$x - y = 1$
(d) $x + y = 5$
$2x^2 + 3y^2 = 35$
(e) $x + y = 2$
$3x^2 - y^2 = 2$
(f) $y = -x^2$
$x + y + 2 = 0$
(g) $x^2 + 3y = 16$
$x + 3y = 10$
(h) $y - 3x + 9 = 0$
$2y = x^2 - 10$
(i) $xy = 8$
$x - y + 2 = 0$
(j) $y = 2x - 5$
$x^2 + y^2 = 25$
(k) $x^2 + y^2 = 5$
$2x - y = 0$

2. Solve and graph the systems.
(a) $4x + 3y = 0$
$x^2 + y^2 = 25$
(b) $4x + 3y = 25$
$x^2 + y^2 = 25$
(c) $4x + 3y = 30$
$x^2 + y^2 = 25$

C

3. Solve.
(a) $x^2 - y^2 = 3$
$x - y = 1$
(b) $x^2 + xy + y^2 = 49$
$x + y = 8$
(c) $3x + 2y = -2$
$xy + 8x = 4$
(d) $y^2 + 2x = 17$
$x + 4y = -8$

4. The sum of two numbers is 9 and their product is 14.
Find the numbers.

5. The perimeter of a rectangle is 28 m and the area is 45 m².
Find the dimensions of the rectangle.

4.8 GRAPHING EXPONENTIAL FUNCTIONS

An equation such as $y = 2^x$ is called an exponential equation because the variable appears in the exponent.

A graph of $y = 2^x$ is drawn using the table of values below.

x	2^x	y
4	2^4	16
3	2^3	8
2	2^2	4
1	2^1	2
0	2^0	1
-1	2^{-1}	$\frac{1}{2}$
-2	2^{-2}	$\frac{1}{4}$
-3	2^{-3}	$\frac{1}{8}$
-4	2^{-4}	$\frac{1}{16}$

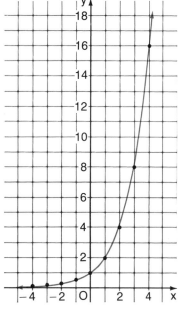

Integers were used to determine the ordered pairs for $y = 2^x$. However, any number could have been used. A calculator simplifies the calculation.

For $x = 3.6$, press $\boxed{2}$ $\boxed{y^x}$ $\boxed{3}$ $\boxed{\cdot}$ $\boxed{6}$ $\boxed{=}$

The display is $\boxed{12.12573253}$

$y \doteq 12.1$

EXERCISE 4.8

A

1. Complete the tables.
(a) $y = 10^x$

x	-3	-2	-1	0	1	2	3
y	0.001						

(b) $y = 3^x$

x	-3	-2	-1	0	1	2	3
y	$\frac{1}{27}$						

B

2. Sketch the graphs of the following.
(a) $y = 3^x$ (b) $y = 10^x$ (c) $y = 4^x$
(d) $y = (\frac{1}{2})^x$ (e) $y = (\frac{1}{3})^x$ (f) $y = (\frac{1}{10})^x$

3. Use the graphs in question 2 to answer the following.
(a) What point do the graphs have in common? Explain.
(b) Will any of the graphs intersect the x-axis?
Why or why not?

4.9 EXPONENTIAL GROWTH AND DECAY

$2^0 = 1$
$2^1 = 2$
$2^2 = 4$
$2^3 = 8$
$2^4 = 16$
$2^5 = 32$
$2^6 = 64$
$2^7 = 128$
$2^8 = 256$
$2^9 = 512$
$2^{10} = 1024$
$2^{11} = 2048$
$2^{12} = 4096$

The main characteristic of exponential functions is the rapid way they grow in value as the value of the exponent increases. Exponential growth is demonstrated by small single-celled animals called amoebas, which reproduce by splitting in half. After a period of growth, they split again so that two become four. If y represents the number of amoebas and x the number of times division has taken place, the number of amoebas is given by the equation

$$y = 2^x$$

This is called an exponential function, since the variable x is an exponent. Under the most favourable conditions of food and temperature, the amoeba can split every 2 h. If one amoeba is placed in a bottle of water, at the end of one day it is theoretically possible to have 2^{12} or 4096 amoebas.

Example 1. How many great-great-great grandparents does a person have?

Solution: This represents a span of five generations. Since each individual has two parents, the number of great-great-great grandparents is given by $n = 2^5$.

A person has 32 great-great-great grandparents.

Exponents can be used to describe the decay of radioactive metals. These metals give off radiation in the form of sub-atomic particles. This eventually results in the original metal changing to a different one. For instance, uranium gradually changes to lead. The rate at which the change takes place depends on the amount of the original material left at any given time. One gram of radium will decay to $\frac{1}{2}$ g of radium plus other elements in 1600 a. It will take an additional 1600 a for the $\frac{1}{2}$ g to be reduced to $\frac{1}{4}$ g, and so on. We describe this process by saying that radium has a half-life of 1600 a.

READ

PLAN

SOLVE

ANSWER

Example 2. How long will it take for 16 g of radium to decay to 1 g of radium?

Solution: Let the number of half-lives required be n.

Since we are reducing 16 g to 1 g, $16(\frac{1}{2})^n = 1$.

Therefore $(\frac{1}{2})^n = \frac{1}{16}$

$(\frac{1}{2})^4 = \frac{1}{16}$

$n = 4$

It will take four half-lives or 6400 a.

Example 3. A free-swinging pendulum is held 36 cm to one side and released. Because of air resistance and friction, the bob of the pendulum returns to a position with 80% of the previous displacement.
Find the amplitude after four swings.

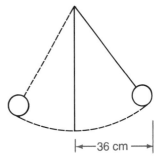

$\leftarrow$ 36 cm $\rightarrow$

Solution:
Let the maximum displacement for each swing be A.
Then

$A_0 = 36.0$

$A_1 = 80\% \times 36.0$
$\quad = (0.8)^1 \times 36.0$

$A_2 = 80\%(80\% \times 36.0)$
$\quad = (0.8)^2 \times 36.0$

$A_4 = (0.8)^4(36.0)$
$\quad \doteq 0.410(36.0)$
$\quad \doteq 14.8$

After four swings the amplitude would be 14.8 cm.

EXERCISE 4.9

B

1. A civil defence warning system works on a "fan-out" phone network where the commander phones five subordinates, these five each phone five others, each of whom phone five more, and so on.
How many people would have been called after the fourth level had completed their calls? (Consider the commander to be the first level.)

2. A bouncing ball rebounds to half its previous height on each bounce.
If the ball is dropped from 4 m, how high will it rebound after it has hit the ground for the fifth time?

3. If a "superball" rebounds to 90% of its previous height on each bounce and is dropped from a balcony 12 m above the sidewalk, how far will it rebound after it has hit the ground for the third time?

4. A radioactive element, actinium, has a half-life of 4 s.
What fraction of an original mass of actinium is left after 20 s?

5. A radioactive metal, "geigerite," is found to have a half-life of 8 a. Ore containing 10% "geigerite" is mined and stockpiled for 16 a.
Approximately what percentage of "geigerite" will remain?

6. A bacteria culture doubles in number every hour.
If there are 11 bacteria in the original culture, how many will there be after 8h?

7. A bacteria culture doubles in number every 90 min.
If there are n bacteria in the original culture, how many will there be after 6 h?

8. The sales manager of Forest Wood Products Ltd. is in charge of sales for four departments. Each department has four area supervisors, each area supervisor has four branch managers, and each branch manager has four sales representatives. How many sales representatives are there?

4.10 PROBLEM SOLVING

1. The number 1 can be written using four 4s as follows:

$$(4 + 4 - 4) \div 4 = 1$$

Write expressions for 0, 1, 2, 3, 4, 5, 6, 7, 8, 9, and 12 using four 4s.

2. We can write 25 as the sum of two perfect squares.

$$25 = 9 + 16$$

Find the whole numbers less than 50 that can be written as the sum of two non-zero perfect squares.

3. Find the number of ways we can make change for a quarter if one coin must be a dime.

4. How many rectangles are there in each of the following diagrams?

(a)

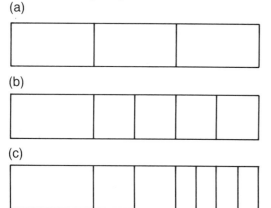

(b)

(c)

5. The following is a sample of a MAN 72A seven-segment display, which is used with computers. This display forms the digits from 0 to 9 as shown.

How many new digits could be formed if all digits must be the same height and all lines must be continuous or connected?

6. If St. Valentine's Day is on a Monday, on what day of the week will St. Patrick's Day fall?

7. What is the degree measure of the acute angle formed by the hands of a clock when the time reads 11:45?

8. The length of the base of an isosceles triangle is 24 cm and the perimeter is 144 cm.
What is the length of each of the other two sides?

9. In a cash register there are 24 more nickels than dimes. The total value of the nickels and dimes is $3.90.
How many nickels are there?

10. The gas tank of a truck is half full. When 15 L of gasoline are removed, the tank is only one-eighth full.
What is the capacity of the tank?

11. At 9:00 there were 20 000 cases of canned goods on the shipping dock. Every half hour, one quarter of the remaining cases were shipped to stores.
How many cases were on the shipping dock at 10:45?

12. Eric's average for the last six tests is 72%.
What mark must Eric receive on his next test in order to raise his average to 75%?

13. Tara averages three sales for every five calls. So far, she has thirty-five sales in the last sixty calls.
How many sales does Tara need in her next thirty calls in order to maintain her average?

14. Supply the missing information and solve the problem.
George William's restaurant has advertised for a short-order cook, paying $2.75 above the minimum wage required by law.
How much would you expect as a weekly wage if you worked 36.5 h per week?

15. Virginia is the chief shipper and takes 4 h to process 100 orders for building materials. Lois is a trainee and takes 6 h to complete the same job.
How long will it take Virginia and Lois to complete the job working together?

16. It takes Terry 3 h to plough a field using a small tractor.
How long will it take Terry to plough a field twice as long and twice as wide?

17. A recipe for chocolate cake makes two cakes in 20 cm square cake pans. The batter fills the pans to a depth of 2.5 cm. What size of square cake pan is required if the recipe is doubled and the depth of the batter remains at 2.5 cm?

18. Karl and Ricki drove from Calgary to Edmonton at an average speed of 80 km/h. They returned by the same route at an average speed of 90 km/h.

Edmonton
Calgary

What was the average speed for the trip?

19. A radioactive material has a half-life of 2 h; that is, every 2 h the amount of material is reduced by $\frac{1}{2}$.
How many units of material are left if there were 64 units 6 h ago?

EXTRA

SEISMOLOGY

Seismology is the study of earthquakes and other movements of the earth's crust. A scale called the Richter scale is used to measure the strength of an earthquake. Each increase of one on the Richter scale corresponds to an increase in intensity of ten times. In other words, an earthquake that measures 5 on the Richter scale is ten times as intense as an earthquake that measures 4 and one hundred times as intense as an earthquake that measures 3. The table below gives the effects of earthquakes of several intensities.

Richter Magnitude	Intensity	Effect
1	10^1	Only detectable by a seismograph.
2	10^2	Hanging lamps sway.
3	10^3	Can be felt.
4	10^4	Buildings shake.
5	10^5	Furniture collapses.
6	10^6	Wood buildings damaged.
7	10^7	Buildings collapse.
8	10^8	A catastrophe.

EXERCISE

1. How much stronger is an earthquake with a rating of 6 than an earthquake with a rating of 3?

2. How much stronger is an earthquake that measures 6.8 than an earthquake that measures 5.9?

CAREER

PARAMEDIC

Jim Cameron is a paramedic. Jim travels with the ambulance to an accident scene where a victim may be in trauma, a form of shock. In many of these cases, it is important to examine the patient and to begin treatment immediately. Once treatment has begun, the patient must be monitored to determine if the treatment is working and if there are any changes in the condition of the patient. Improvement in the patient is often an indication to continue the same treatment.

One of the indicators of a patient's condition is the Glasgow Coma Scale. This is a number from 3 to 15, calculated from observations of eye opening, verbal response, and motor response. The paramedic also takes readings of respiratory rate and effort, as well as blood pressure through pulse and capillary refill. These readings and observations can be combined using weighted code values to produce a number called the Trauma Score. By calculating a trauma score at regular intervals, changes in a patient's condition can be monitored. An increase in the trauma score number indicates that the patient is getting better. The computer program on the following page calculates the Glasgow Coma Scale and the Trauma Score at any given time.

The following chart shows the readings taken over a period of time for one patient.

Time	8:15	8:40	9:15	9:30	10:00
Respiratory Rate	8	10	12	16	20
Respiratory Effort	shallow	shallow	shallow	shallow	shallow
Systolic Blood Pressure	64	72	72	80	84
Capillary Refill	delay	delay	delay	normal	normal
Eye Opening	to pain	to voice	to voice	to voice	spontaneous
Verbal Response	none	inappropriate words	confused	confused	oriented
Motor Response	extension (pain)	withdraw (pain)	withdraw (pain)	purposeful movements	obeys commands

1. Compute a Glasgow Coma Score and a Trauma Score number for each time.
2. Draw a graph to show changes in the patient's condition.
3. Determine whether the patient is getting better.

```
NEW
10 PRINT"GLASGOW SCALE AND TRAUMA SCORE"
11 PRINT
20 PRINT"RESPIRATORY RATE"
21 PRINT"NUMBER OF RESPIRATIONS PER MINUTE","CODE"
23 PRINT,"10-24","","4"
24 PRINT,"25-35","","3"
25 PRINT,">36","","2"
26 PRINT,"1-9","","1"
27 PRINT,"0","","0"
28 INPUT"ENTER CODE";A
29 PRINT
30 PRINT"RESPIRATORY EFFORT","","CODE"
32 PRINT,"NORMAL","","1"
33 PRINT,"SHALLOW","","0"
34 INPUT"ENTER CODE";B
39 PRINT
40 PRINT"SYSTOLIC BLOOD PRESSURE","","CODE"
42 PRINT,">=90","","4"
43 PRINT,"70-89","","3"
44 PRINT,"50-69","","2"
45 PRINT,"1-49","","1"
46 PRINT,"NO PULSE","","0"
47 INPUT"ENTER CODE";C
49 PRINT
50 PRINT"CAPILLARY REFILL","","CODE"
51 PRINT,"NORMAL","","2"
52 PRINT,"DELAYED","","1"
53 PRINT,"NONE","","0"
54 INPUT"ENTER CODE";D
59 PRINT
60 PRINT"EYE OPENING","","","CODE"
61 PRINT,"SPONTANEOUS","","4"
62 PRINT,"TO VOICE","","3"
63 PRINT,"TO PAIN","","2"
64 PRINT,"NONE","","1"
65 INPUT"ENTER CODE";E1
69 PRINT
70 PRINT"VERBAL RESPONSE","","CODE"
71 PRINT,"ORIENTED","","5"
72 PRINT,"CONFUSED","","4"
73 PRINT"INAPPROPRIATE WORDS","","3"
74 PRINT"INCOMPREHENSIBLE SOUNDS","","2"
75 PRINT,"NONE","","1"
76 INPUT"ENTER CODE";E2
79 PRINT
80 PRINT"MOTOR RESPONSE","","CODE"
81 PRINT,"OBEYS COMMANDS","6"
82 PRINT"PURPOSEFUL MOVEMENTS(PAIN)","5"
83 PRINT,"WITHDRAW(PAIN)","4"
84 PRINT,"FLEXION(PAIN)","","3"
85 PRINT,"EXTENSION(PAIN)","2"
86 PRINT,"NONE","","1"
87 INPUT"ENTER CODE";E3
88 E=E1+E2+E3
89 PRINT
90 PRINT"GLASGOW COMA SCALE";E
91 G=INT((E+1)/3)
99 PRINT
100 PRINT"TRAUMA SCORE";A+B+C+D+G
110 END
RUN
```

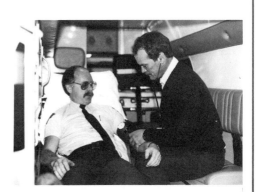

4.11 REVIEW EXERCISE

1. Determine the slope of the line passing through each pair of points.
(a) (5, 10) and (8, 6)
(b) (16, 1) and (10, −2)
(c) (2, 1) and (5, −6)
(d) (−4, −2) and (−1, 7)
(e) (−1, 4) and (−3, −5)
(f) (6, −5) and (2, −7)

2. Determine whether the following sets of points are collinear.
(a) A(−2, −2), B(1, 1), C(4, 4)
(b) D(3, 3), C(4, 5), E(7, 7)
(c) G(1, 3), F(2, 5), H(3, 7)
(d) R(−1, 4), S(2, −6), T(0, 1)
(e) M(1, 1), N(3, 0), R(5, −2)

3. Find an equation of each line in the form $Ax + By + C = 0$.

(a) passing through (−4, 3) with slope $\frac{1}{2}$
(b) passing through (0, 5) with slope −2
(c) passing through (2, 0) with slope $\frac{3}{4}$
(d) passing through (−1, −3) with slope $-\frac{2}{3}$

(e) passing through (2, −5) with slope $\frac{2}{5}$

4. Write an equation of the line with the same y-intercept as $y = 3x + 4$ and slope −1.

5. Determine an equation of the line through (1, 2) with slope $-\frac{1}{4}$.

6. Determine an equation of the line through (−2, −3) parallel to $5x + 3y = 2$.

7. Write an equation of the line whose x- and y-intercepts are 5 and −3 respectively.

8. Find the slope and y-intercept of $3x + 2y = 7$.

9. Determine the value of k so that
(a) $4x − ky = 7$ has slope 3.
(b) $kx − y = −15$ has x-intercept 5.

10. What is the value of m if the line $y = mx + 7$ passes through (−2, 5)?

11. Find an equation of the straight line parallel to $6x − 7y = 13$, which passes through (−2, −5).

12. Determine the lengths of the line segments joining the given points.
(a) D(0, 3) to E(4, 2)
(b) A(−1, −1) to B(6, −3)
(c) G(9, 8) to H(3, 4)
(d) D(−1, −2) to E(3, −2)
(e) R(4, −3) to T(−2, 4)
(f) M(6, 6) to N(2, 2)
(g) Q(−3, 0) to R(0, −3)
(h) A(3, 0) to B(9, 0)

13. The sides of a triangle are represented by $3x + y + 4 = 0$, $x − y = 4$, and $x − 5y − 4 = 0$.
Find
(a) the vertices of the triangle,
(b) the length of the sides,
(c) the slopes of the sides.

14. Find an equation of the circle having centre (0, 0) and
(a) radius 6.
(b) radius 9.
(c) passing through (−4, −3).
(d) y-intercept 5.
(e) x-intercept 7.
(f) passing through (1, 1).

15. Find an equation of the following circles.
(a) centre (1, 2), radius 3
(b) centre (2, 3), radius 5
(c) centre (0, 4) passing through (1, −2)
(d) centre (0, 1), y-intercept 5
(e) centre (7, −2) passing through the origin
(f) centre (4, 0), y-intercept 3

16. Find an equation of the circle having its centre at the origin and passing through the point (1, 2).

17. Find an equation of the circle whose diameter has endpoints A(3, −2) and B(−3, 2).

18. (a) Graph the parabola represented by y = $\frac{1}{4}$x².
(b) Using the result of (a), sketch graphs of the following parabolas on one set of axes.
   (i) y = −$\frac{1}{4}$x²
   (ii) y = $\frac{1}{4}$x² + 2

19. Sketch the graphs of each of the following.
Indicate the vertex, y-intercept, and x-intercept in each case.
(a) y = x² + 3
(b) y = −2x² + 8
(c) y = $\frac{1}{2}$x² − 4

20. On the same set of axes sketch the following graphs.
(a) y = 2^x
(b) y = 3^x
(c) y = 10^x
(d) y = ($\frac{1}{2}$)^x

21. (a) Sketch the graphs of y = 2^x and y = ($\frac{1}{2}$)^x on the same set of axes.
(b) Is there an axis of symmetry for the graphs?

22. Find an equation of the circle having its centre at the point of intersection of the lines represented by x − y = 4 and x − 2y = 7 and passing through the point (4, 3).

23. Find an equation of the circle having a diameter with endpoints (5, −6) and (1, −4).

24. (a) Find the radius of the circle having centre (3, 2) and passing through (6, −2).
(b) State an equation of the circle having centre (3, 2) and passing through (6, −2).

25. Find an equation of each of the following lines.
(a)

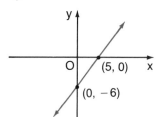

(b)

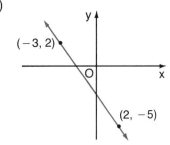

26. Solve.
(a) x² + y² = 100
   x − y = 2
(b) x² + 4y² = 25
   2y = 1 − x

27. The accompanying graph illustrates the height to which a ball returns after being released at a height of 4 m.

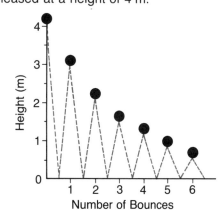

(a) To what height does the ball rebound after
   (i) the second bounce?
   (ii) the fifth bounce?
(b) What fraction of the height is lost after each bounce?

4.12 CHAPTER 4 TEST

1. Find an equation of the line passing through $A(-2, -4)$ with slope $\frac{2}{3}$.

2. Find an equation of the line passing through $C(-4, -5)$ and $D(0, 6)$.

3. Sketch the following graphs.

(a) $2x - 3y = 6$ (b) $y = \frac{1}{2}x - 4$

(c) $y = 2^x$ (d) $y = x^2 - 4$

(e) $x^2 + y^2 = 36$ (f) $y = 2x^2 + 5$

(g) $y = -x^2 + 4$ (h) $x^2 + y^2 = \frac{9}{4}$

4. Find the distance between each of the following points.
(a) $(-1, -4)$ and $(-3, 2)$
(b) $(5, 6)$ and $(7, -2)$
(c) $(0, 6)$ and $(8, 6)$

5. Find an equation of the following lines.
(a)   (b)

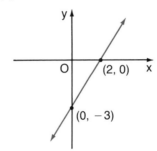
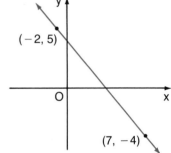

6. Solve.
(a) $y = x^2$
$\quad y - 2 = x$

(b) $x^2 + y^2 = 25$
$\quad x + y = -7$

PROPERTIES OF GEOMETRIC FIGURES

REVIEW AND PREVIEW TO CHAPTER 5

PYTHAGOREAN THEOREM

$c^2 = a^2 + b^2$
$a^2 = c^2 - b^2$
$b^2 = c^2 - a^2$

EXERCISE 1

1. Calculate the value of x to the nearest tenth.

(a)

(b)

(c)

(d)

(e) 8 cm

(f)

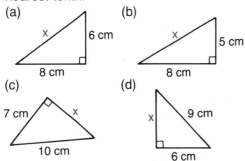

2. Calculate the length of the unknown side to the nearest tenth.

(a)

(b)

(c)

(d)

(e)

(f)

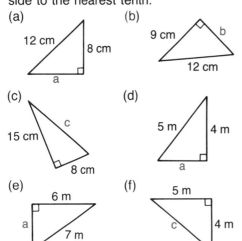

3. A 6 m ladder leans against a wall. The foot of the ladder is 1.7 m from the base of the wall.

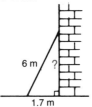

To what height does the ladder reach on the wall?

4. Joey takes shortcut across the corner of a field as shown.

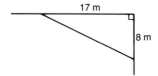

How much shorter is the shortcut?

5. How long is the wire that supports the following sign?

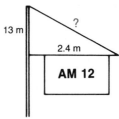

6. Calculate the length of the airplane strut in the following diagram.

7. A ship sails 120 km east and 90 km north.
How far is the ship from its starting point?

SUBSTITUTION AND EVALUATION

EXERCISE 2

1. Evaluate for $x = 3$.
(a) $x^2 - 5x + 3$
(b) $2x^2 + 3x - 1$
(c) $4x^3 + 2x - 5$
(d) $4x^2 - 2x + 5$
(e) $6x(x - 5) + 3$

2. Evaluate for $x = -3$.
(a) $x^2 + 5x + 3$
(b) $x^2 - 3x + 5$
(c) $2x^2 + 4x - 1$
(d) $5x^2 - 2x + 3$
(e) $6x^3 - 2x + 4$

3. Evaluate for $x = 2$ and $y = 5$.
(a) $x^2 + y^2$
(b) $(x + y)^2$
(c) $x^3 + y^3$
(d) $(x + y)(x^2 - xy + y^2)$
(e) $6x^2 - 3xy + 5y^2$

4. Evaluate for $x = -2$ and $y = 3$.
(a) $x^2 - y^2$
(b) $(x - y)^2$
(c) $x^2 - 2xy - 3y^2$
(d) $4(x - 2) + 3(y + 4)$
(e) $(2x - 3y)(5x + 2y)$

5. Evaluate for $x = \frac{1}{2}$ and $y = \frac{1}{3}$.
(a) $x + y$
(b) $x^2 + y^2$
(c) $(x + y)^2$
(d) $x^2 - xy + y^2$
(e) $\dfrac{x}{y} + \dfrac{y}{x}$
(f) $\dfrac{1}{x} + \dfrac{1}{y}$
(g) $x^2 + y^2 - 2xy$
(h) $y + \dfrac{x}{y}$
(i) $3x - 2y + 4$
(j) $2x^2 - (2x)^2 + y$

DRAWING THREE-DIMENSIONAL FIGURES ON A GRID

A square is one unit.

A diagonal is two units.

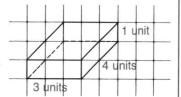

1 unit
4 units
3 units

EXERCISE 3

1. Draw the following three-dimensional figures on grids. These figures are not drawn to scale.

(a)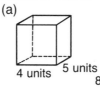
4 units 5 units

(b)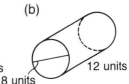
8 units 12 units

(c)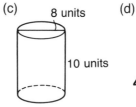
8 units
10 units

(d)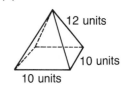
12 units
10 units
10 units

(e)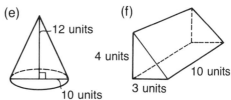
12 units
10 units

(f)
4 units
3 units
10 units

2. Make a rough sketch of each of the following.
Draw each figure on a grid.
(a) a cube with sides 8 units long
(b) a rectangular solid with sides 5 units, 7 units, and 12 units long
(c) a cylinder with a diameter of 10 units and a height of 12 units
(d) a rectangular solid with sides 4 units, 8 units, and 16 units long
(e) a cone with a diameter of 8 units at its base and a height of 10 units

5.1 PERIMETER OF POLYGONS

The distance around any region is called its perimeter. The word perimeter comes from the Greek words *peri* meaning around and *metron* meaning measure. We can find the perimeter of a figure by measuring each side and finding the sum. For any polygon, it is often convenient to write a formula for perimeter.

Triangle

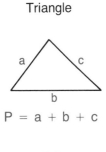

$P = a + b + c$

Square

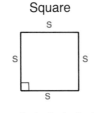

$P = s + s + s + s$
$P = 4s$

Rectangle

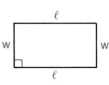

$P = \ell + w + \ell + w$
$P = 2(\ell + w)$

Parallelogram

$P = a + b + a + b$
$P = 2(a + b)$

Trapezoid

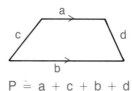

$P = a + c + b + d$

Pentagon

$P = a + b + c + d + e$

A regular polygon has equal sides and equal angles. For a regular polygon, the perimeter is

$P = ns$

where n is the number of sides, and
s is the length of each side.

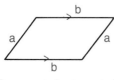

n sides

Example. Find the perimeter of △ABC, where a = 20.3 cm, c = 25.7 cm, and ∠C = 90°.

Solution: Find the third side using the Pythagorean theorem.

$c^2 = a^2 + b^2$
$b^2 = c^2 - b^2$
$b = \sqrt{c^2 + a^2}$
$b = \sqrt{25.7^2 - 20.3^2}$
$ = \sqrt{660.49 - 412.09}$
$ = \sqrt{248.40}$
$ \doteq 15.8$

$P = a + b + c$
$P = 20.3 + 15.8 + 25.7$
$ = 61.8$

The perimeter is 61.8 cm.

EXERCISE 5.1

A

1. Find the perimeter of each polygon.

(a)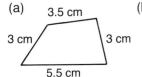
3.5 cm
3 cm   3 cm
5.5 cm

(b)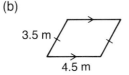
3.5 m
4.5 m

(c)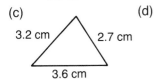
3.2 cm   2.7 cm
3.6 cm

(d)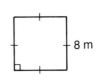
8 m

(e)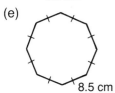
8.5 cm

(f)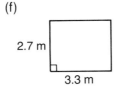
2.7 m
3.3 m

2. Find the length of the indicated side.

(a)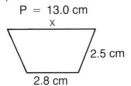
P = 12.7 cm
x   3.4 cm
4.1 cm

(b)
P = 13.0 cm
x
2.5 cm
2.8 cm

(c)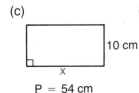
10 cm
x
P = 54 cm

(d)
x   x
x   x
x
P = 3.5 m

B

3. Write a formula for the perimeter of each of the following polygons.

(a)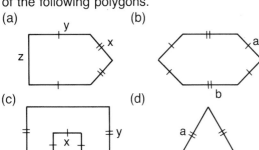
y
x
z

(b)
a
b

(c)
x
y

(d)
a
b

4. What is the length of each side of a square if the perimeter is 37 cm?

5. How many sides does a regular polygon have if the perimeter is 109.8 cm and the sides are 18.3 cm long?

6. What is the width of a rectangle whose perimeter is 52.4 cm if the length is 16.5 cm?

7. Find the perimeter of the following parallelogram.

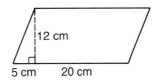
12 cm
5 cm   20 cm

8. Find the perimeter of the following octagon.

17.5 cm

9. Find a formula for the length of the indicated side in each figure.

(a)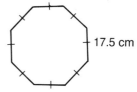
b   b ?
P
a

(b)
ℓ
P
w ?

(c)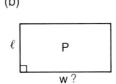
a
c   P   d ?
b

(d)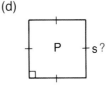
P   s ?

10. What is the effect on the perimeter of the following polygons if the dimensions are doubled?
(a) a square
(b) a rectangle

5.2 AREA OF POLYGONS

The amount of surface covered by a region is called its area. Although a region of any shape can be used to measure area, square units are commonly used because they are the easiest. In order to find the area of a polygon, we need to know the height of the polygon. The height of a triangle is the length of a segment from a vertex to the opposite side. In quadrilaterals such as rectangles, parallelograms, and trapezoids, the height is the distance between the base of the polygon and the opposite side. As in the case of perimeter, it is often convenient to write a formula for area.

| Triangle | Square | Rectangle | Parallelogram | Trapezoid |

 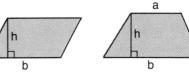

$A = \frac{1}{2}bh$ $\qquad$ $A = s^2$ $\qquad$ $A = \ell w$ $\qquad$ $A = bh$ $\qquad$ $A = \frac{1}{2}(a + b)h$

For a regular polygon, the area is

$$A = \frac{1}{2}aP$$

where a is the apothem (height of the triangle), and
$\qquad$ P is the perimeter.

Example. Find, to the nearest tenth, the area of a regular octagon of side 2.00 cm and apothem 2.41 cm.

Solution: The apothem is 2.41 cm; a = 2.41.

$\qquad$ P = ns
$\qquad$ P = 8 × 2
$\qquad\qquad$ = 16

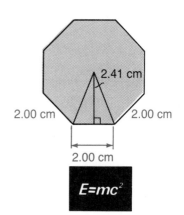
2.41 cm
2.00 cm $\qquad$ 2.00 cm
2.00 cm

Substitute in the formula for area.

$\qquad$ $A = \frac{1}{2}aP$

$\qquad$ $A = \frac{1}{2} × 2.41 × 16$

$\qquad\qquad$ = 19.28

$E=mc^2$

The area of the octagon is 19.3 cm².

EXERCISE 5.2

B

1. Find the area of each polygon to the nearest tenth.

(a)

3.8 cm
4.4 cm

(b)

5.3 cm
4.8 cm

(c)

4.1 cm
4.1 cm

(d)

6.2 m
5.8 m
8.4 m

(e)

4.2 m
3.5 m

(f)

12.1 cm

2. Find the length of the indicated side to the nearest tenth.

(a) A = 25.42 cm²

w
6.2 cm

(b) A = 31.8 cm²

5.3 cm
5.3 cm
b

(c) A = 5.44 cm²

3.4 cm
b

(d) A = 6 cm²

5 cm
a
4 cm

3. Write a formula for the area of each of the following polygons.

(a)

x²y
2xy²

(b)

(x − y)
xy
(x + y)

(c)

2xy
3xy²

(d)

2x²

4. What is the length of each side of a square if the area is 13.69 cm²?

5. Find the area of the following hexagon to the nearest tenth.

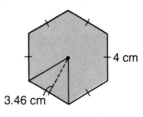

4 cm
3.46 cm

6. What is the width of a rectangle whose area is 100.8 cm² if the length is 12.0 cm?

7. Find the area of the following trapezoid.

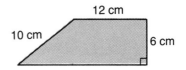

12 cm
10 cm
6 cm

8. Find the area of the following pentagon.

4.25 cm
5 cm
3.44 cm

C

9. Find a formula for the length of the indicated side in each figure.

(a) A = 16x⁸

s?

(b) A = 15x²y³

w?
3xy²

(c) A = 12x²y

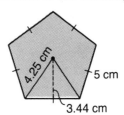

xy
b?

(d) A = 2x² + 3xy

x + y
x
b?

5.3 CIRCLES

When a dog is tied to a stake and allowed to move freely within the limits of the rope, the region traced out by the dog is circular. This idea leads to the following definition of a circle:

> A circle is a set of points equidistant from a fixed point. The constant distance is called the radius.

In our earlier work, we used the formulas for circumference and area of a circle.

Circumference

$C = 2\pi r$
$C = \pi d$

Area

$A = \pi r^2$

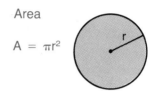

A sector of a circle is a region bounded by an arc and two radii. The top of a piece of cake and a wedge of cheese are examples of a sector. The angle formed by the two radii is called the sector angle. For a sector angle, θ, we can find the arc length and the area of the sector using the fraction $\dfrac{\theta}{360}$.

Example. Find the perimeter and area of the given sector.

24 cm
45°
24 cm

Solution:

Perimeter

The arc length is

$$a = \frac{\theta}{360} \times 2\pi r$$
$$a = \frac{45}{360} \times 2 \times \pi \times 24$$

Using a calculator, press

4 5 ÷ 3 6 0 × 2 × π × 2 4 =

The display is 18.84955592

The arc length is 19 cm.

$$P = r + r + a$$
$$P = 24 + 24 + 19$$
$$= 67$$

∴ the perimeter of the sector is 67 cm.

Area

The area of the sector is

$$A = \frac{\theta}{360} \times \pi r^2$$
$$A = \frac{45}{360} \times \pi \times 24^2$$

Using a calculator, press

4 5 ÷ 3 6 0 × π × 2 4 x² =

The display is 226.1946711

∴ the area of the sector is 226 cm².

B

1. Find the circumference and area of each of the given circles to the nearest tenth.

(a)   (b)

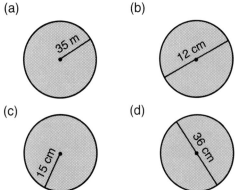

(c)   (d)

2. Find the perimeter and area of each of the following to the nearest tenth.

(a)   (b)

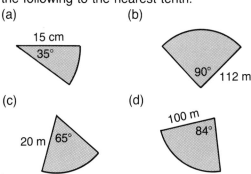

(c)   (d)

3. What is the radius of a circle whose circumference is 100 m?

4. What is the diameter of a circle whose area is 100 m?

5. The track around a playing field is 10 m wide.

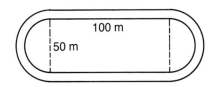

How much longer is the outer edge of the track than the inner edge?

6. Assume that the moon travels around the earth in a circular path at a distance of 384 000 km, to the nearest 1000 km.
(a) Find the distance travelled in one revolution. (The radius of the earth is approximately 6400 km.)
(b) What is the speed per hour if one revolution takes 28 d?

7. The hour hand of a wall clock is 8.5 cm long and the minute hand is 11.2 cm long. How far does the tip of each hand travel in a 12 h period?

MICRO MATH

The approximate distance a person can see to the horizon is given by the formula

$$D = \sqrt{2rh}$$

where r is the radius of the earth, and h is the height above the earth.

The variables D, r, and h represent distances in kilometres.

The following BASIC program computes the distance to the horizon when we enter the height above the earth.

```
NEW
10 PRINT"DISTANCE TO THE HORIZON"
20 INPUT"HEIGHT OF OBSERVER";H
30 D=SQR(12800*H)
40 PRINT"THE DISTANCE IS";D
50 END
RUN
```

EXERCISE

1. How far can you see from a plane flying at a height of 10 000 m?

2. From what height must you look in order to see 100 km?

5.4 RECTANGULAR PRISMS

A prism is a polyhedron with the same shape along its length.

The following are some examples of prisms.

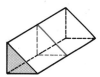 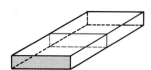 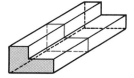

A rectangular prism has the shape of a rectangle along its length as shown.

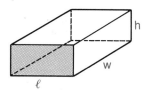

The figure at the right is a rectangular prism with length ℓ measuring 12 cm, width w measuring 8 cm, and height h measuring 5 cm.

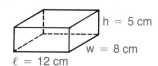

We can find the surface area using the formula

$A = 2(\ell w + \ell h + wh)$
$A = 2(12 \times 8 + 12 \times 5 + 8 \times 5)$
$\quad = 392$

The surface area is 392 cm².

We can find the volume using the formula

$V = \ell wh$
$V = 12 \times 8 \times 5$
$\quad = 480$

The volume is 480 cm³.

Example. Find the surface area of a rectangular prism whose volume is 2000 cm³ and whose length and width are 25 cm and 20 cm respectively.

Solution: To find the height, use $V = \ell wh$, where $\ell = 25$, $w = 20$, and $V = 2000$.

$V = \ell wh$
$2000 = 25 \times 20 \times h$
$2000 = 500h$
$\quad h = 4$

∴ the height is 4 cm.

To find the surface area, use

$A = 2(\ell w + \ell h + wh)$
$A = 2(25 \times 20 + 25 \times 4 + 20 \times 4)$
$\quad = 1360$

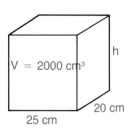

∴ the surface area is 1360 cm².

A cuboid is a rectangular prism with rectangles on all of its faces.

EXERCISE 5.4

B

1. Find the surface area and volume of each of the following rectangular prisms.

(a)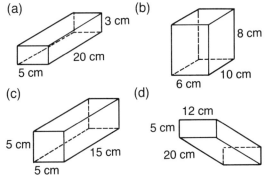

(b)

(c)

(d)

2. The surface area of a rectangular prism is 425 cm². The length and width of the base are 3.4 cm and 3.2 cm respectively. What is the height of the prism?

3. The volume of a rectangular prism is 170 cm³, and the height is 6.8 cm. What is the length of a side of the square base?

4. The area of the base of a rectangular prism is 35 cm², and the height is 7 cm. What is the volume of the prism?

5. The dimensions of a rectangular prism are 25 cm by 12 cm by 90 cm. Find the dimensions of the cube that has the same volume.

6. The dimensions of a rectangular prism are 6.0 cm by 4.0 cm by 8.4 cm. Find the dimensions of the cube that has the same surface area.

7. A bank vault is made out of concrete and steel. The interior dimensions of the vault are 2.4 m by 3.7 m by 2.4 m high. The walls, roof, and floor are 0.65 m thick. The door is made of steel 2.0 m by 0.9 m and is 0.38 m thick.
(a) Find the volume of the interior of the vault.
(b) Find the volume of material required to build the vault, excluding the door.

8. A storage room is 3.5 m by 2.6 m by 2.4 m high. A 12 L case of engine oil is approximately 32 cm by 42 cm by 18 cm high.
How many 12 L cases of engine oil can be stacked neatly in rows if we assume that we can stack right up to the roof at the door?

9. Two rectangular prisms have square bases with sides 6 cm and 8 cm respectively. Both prisms have the same height, namely 15 cm.

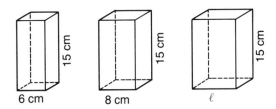

Find the length of the side of a square-based rectangular solid, also 15 cm high, so that it has the same volume as the other two prisms.

10. Complete the following table to investigate volume and total area of a rectangular prism.

Dimensions of Prism			Volume	Surface Area
ℓ	w	h		
4 cm	4 cm	3 cm		
4 cm	4 cm	4 cm		
5 cm	4 cm	3 cm		
5 cm	4 cm	4 cm		
7 cm	3 cm	3 cm		
9 cm	3 cm	2 cm		
10 cm	3 cm	2 cm		
12 cm	3 cm	2 cm		

5.5 CYLINDERS

A cylinder is a prism with the shape of a circle along its length.

The following are some examples of cylinders.

The figure at the right is a cylinder with a radius of 5 cm and a height of 15 cm. As with other solids, we can find the surface area and the volume.

r = 5 cm

h = 15 cm

Base

Surface Area = Area of Bases + Curved Area

Area of the curved part: $2\pi r \times h$

Area of circular ends: $2(\pi r^2)$

Surface Area: S.A. $= 2(\pi r^2) + 2\pi rh$
             S.A. $= 2\pi r(r + h)$

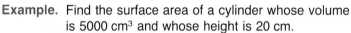

2πr

h

Volume = Area of base × height
    $V = A \times h$
    $V = \pi r^2 h$

Example. Find the surface area of a cylinder whose volume is 5000 cm³ and whose height is 20 cm.

V = 5000 cm³

Solution:

To find the radius, use $V = \pi r^2 h$, where h = 20 and V = 5000.

$$V = \pi r^2 h$$
$$5000 = \pi \times r^2 \times 20$$

Solve for r.

$$r^2 = \frac{5000}{\pi \times 20}$$

Using a calculator, press

The display is 8.920620581

∴ the radius is 8.92 cm.

To find the surface area, use

$$S.A. = 2\pi r(r + h)$$
$$S.A. = 2\pi 8.92(8.92 + 20)$$

Using a calculator, press

The display is 1620.850694

∴ the surface area is 1621 cm³.

EXERCISE 5.5

B 1. Find the surface area and volume of each of the following cylinders to the nearest tenth.

(a) (b)

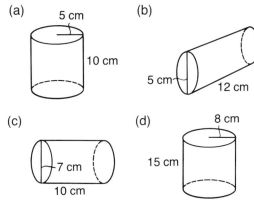

(c) (d)

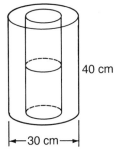

2. The surface area of a cylinder is 500 cm², and the height is 10 cm. What is the radius of the cylinder?

3. The volume of a cylinder is 1000 cm³, and the height is 10 cm. What is the radius of the cylinder?

4. A cylinder has a diameter of 12.4 cm, and the volume is 525 cm³. What is the height of the cylinder?

5. A container designed to carry radioactive materials is in the shape of two cylinders. The outer diameter is 30 cm, and the outer height is 40 cm. The walls and plug of the container are 8 cm thick.

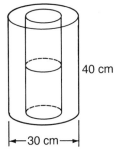

(a) Find the volume of the outer cylinder.
(b) Find the volume of the inner cylinder.
(c) How many cubic centimetres of material were required to make the entire container?

6. The surface area of a cylinder is 1600 cm², and the radius is 11.4 cm. What is the height of the cylinder?

7. An asphalt roller has a cylindrical wheel 2.4 m wide and 1.7 m in diameter. How much surface is rolled in one full turn?

C 8. A cylindrical tank is 8.5 m high and has a diameter of 3.0 m when measured inside.
(a) What is the total surface area of the inside of the tank?
(b) If 1 L of paint covers approximately 10 m², how many 3 L cans of paint are required to paint the inside of the tank?

9. The air flow in the pipes is to remain constant. In order to do this, when two smaller pipes join one larger pipe, the volume of air in the same lengths of pipe must be the same.

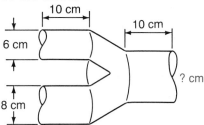

Find the diameter of the larger pipe so that the volume of air in the larger pipe is the same as the volume of air in the two smaller pipes.

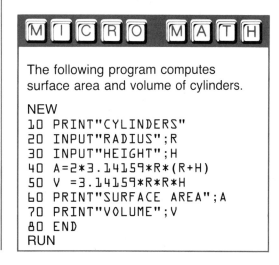

The following program computes surface area and volume of cylinders.

```
NEW
10 PRINT"CYLINDERS"
20 INPUT"RADIUS";R
30 INPUT"HEIGHT";H
40 A=2*3.14159*R*(R+H)
50 V =3.14159*R*R*H
60 PRINT"SURFACE AREA";A
70 PRINT"VOLUME";V
80 END
RUN
```

5.6 PYRAMIDS AND CONES

The following are examples of regular pyramids. A pyramid is called regular if its lateral faces are congruent isosceles triangles, and the base is a regular polygon.

The following are examples of regular pyramids.

Regular Triangular Pyramid   Regular Square Pyramid

For the regular pyramid with slant height ℓ,
perimeter of the base p,
area of the base B, and height h,

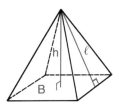

Lateral Area: L.A. $= \frac{1}{2}\ell p$

Surface Area: S.A. $= \frac{1}{2}\ell p + B$

Volume: V $= \frac{1}{3}Bh$

The following is an example of a right circular cone. A cone is said to be right circular if the line from the vertex to the centre of the circular base is perpendicular to the base.

For the right circular cone with slant
height ℓ, radius r, and height h,

Lateral Area: L.A. $= \pi r\ell$
Surface Area: S.A. $= \pi r\ell + \pi r^2$

Volume: V $= \frac{1}{3}\pi r^2 h$

Example. Find the radius of a cone whose height is 12 cm and volume is the same as a square-based pyramid whose sides are 8 cm long and height is 10 cm.

Solution: Volume of the pyramid

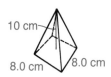

10 cm

8.0 cm   8.0 cm

V $= \frac{1}{3}Bh$

V $= \frac{1}{3} \times 8^2 \times 10$

$\doteq 213.33$

Volume of the cone

$$V = \frac{1}{3}\pi r^2 h$$

$$213.33 = \frac{1}{3}\pi \times r^2 \times 12$$

$$r^2 = \frac{213.33 \times 3}{\pi \times 12}$$

Using a calculator, press

`2` `1` `3` `·` `3` `3` `×` `3` `÷` `π` `÷` `1` `2` `=` `√`

The display is 4.120225965

The radius is 4.1 cm to the nearest tenth.

EXERCISE 5.6

B

1. Find the volume of each of the following to the nearest tenth.

(a)

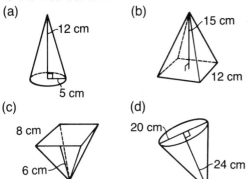

12 cm

5 cm

(b)

15 cm

12 cm

(c)

8 cm

6 cm

(d)

20 cm

24 cm

2. Find the lateral area to the nearest tenth.

(a)

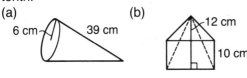

6 cm   39 cm

(b)

12 cm

10 cm

(c)

10 m

7.5 m

(d)

12 m

8 m

3. Find the surface area to the nearest tenth.

(a)

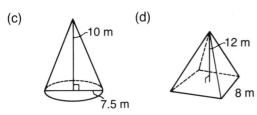

25 cm

14 cm

(b)

30 cm

40 cm

4. Find the radius of the base of a cone whose volume is 235 cm³ and height is 7.2 cm. Give your answer to the nearest tenth.

5. Find the slant height of the square-based pyramid whose surface area is 1000 cm². The sides of the base are 12 cm. Give your answer to the nearest tenth.

C

6. A square-based pyramid has a height of 12 cm and a slant height of 13 cm.
(a) Find the dimensions of the base.
(b) Find the surface area.
(c) Find the volume of the pyramid.
(d) Find the radius of the base of the cone with the same height and volume.

7. The square base of a pyramid has sides 20 cm long. The surface area of the pyramid is 960 cm².
What is the volume of the pyramid?

8. The radius of a cone is 6.0 cm and the surface area is 275 cm².
Find the volume of the cone.

These programs compute surface area and volume of square-based pyramids and cones.

```
NEW
10 PRINT"PYRAMIDS"
20 INPUT"SLANT HEIGHT";L
30 INPUT"SIDES OF BASE";S
40 INPUT"HEIGHT";H
50 A = 2*L*S+S*S
60 V = S*S*H/3
70 PRINT"SURFACE AREA";A
80 PRINT"VOLUME";V
90 END
RUN

NEW
10 PRINT"CONES"
20 INPUT"SLANT HEIGHT";L
30 INPUT"RADIUS";R
40 INPUT"HEIGHT";H
50 A = 3.14159*R*(L+R)
60 V = 3.14159*R*R*H/3
70 PRINT"SURFACE AREA";A
80 PRINT"VOLUME";V
90 END
RUN
```

5.7 PROBLEM SOLVING

1. There are two containers. One contains 1 L of gasoline, and the other contains 1 L of outboard motor oil.

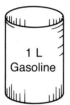

1 L Gasoline

10 mL

1 L Oil

Take 10 mL of gasoline from the first container and mix it with the oil in the second container. Then take 10 mL of the new mixture from the second container and mix it with the gasoline in the first container. Is there more gasoline in the oil, or more oil in the gasoline?

2. A, B, and C are 3 points on a wheel, where A is on the tread, B is on the rim, and C is the centre of the wheel.

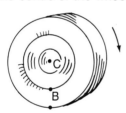

Make a diagram to show the paths made by A, B, and C during two revolutions of the wheel on level ground.

3. The Roman Pantheon is the largest dome built in ancient times. The diameter of the dome is 42.7 m. The diameter of the Houston Astrodome is 216.4 m.

How many times more area does the Astrodome cover than the Pantheon?

4. A warehouse is located in Notre Dame. Deliveries must be made to all the towns in the territory. The following is a map of the territory.

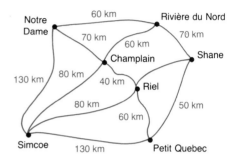

What is the shortest route that begins and ends in Notre Dame?

5. A fly and a spider are located on a wall and ceiling of a room as shown below.

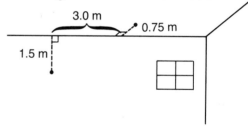

Find the length of the shortest route up the wall and along the ceiling from the spider to the fly?

6. The following diagram shows the locations of a fly and a spider on opposite walls of a room.

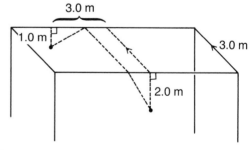

Find the length of the shortest path from the spider to the fly.

7. Pipelines are to be built from two oil wells, A and B, to a terminal, T, located on the shore of the gulf.

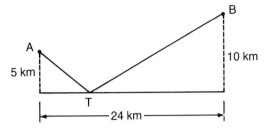

Where should the terminal, T, be located to have the shortest lengths of pipeline?

8. Sixty people ate lunch in an Italian restaurant. One half ordered minestrone and one third ordered veal. Three quarters of the people also had Caesar salad. How many orders of each were there?

9. The combined ages of two sisters is four times the difference of their ages. Three years ago, one sister was twice as old as the other.
How old are the sisters?

10. At what time between 11:00 and 12:00 will the two hands of a clock be in a straight line?

11. What is the real time if you see the face of a clock reflected in a mirror and the hands read 09:15?

12. What is the maximum number of pieces that a block of cheese can be cut into using exactly 5 cuts?

13. Find the square root of the nearest perfect square less than 6863.

14. Place the numbers from 1 to 23 into three groups so that no group contains a number that is the sum of two others in the same group.

CAREER

INDUSTRIAL PRODUCTS DESIGNER

Yves Longpre is an industrial products designer who draws plans for the fabrication of housewares and appliances. In designing these products, he is mainly concerned with their appearance and technical requirements. Most of Yves' projects fall into three categories: research, development, and presentation. In the research stage he gathers, studies, and organizes needed facts. Once design ideas are created, tested, and improved in the development phase, they must be finalized through drawings and model-making. Technical specifications and cost limitations are always important factors in design work. Materials and processes must be evaluated as well as any other factors affecting the design. Throughout all of this, the industrial products designer consults with fellow workers.

EXERCISE

1. A cake pan is in the shape of an open cylinder with a diameter of 25 cm. The sides are 3 cm high.
What are the dimensions of a square cake pan with the same height having the same volume?

2. It takes 425 g of material to make five small knives.
(a) How much material is required to produce 3000 knives?
(b) How many knives can be produced from 10 000 g of material?

5.8 REVIEW EXERCISE

1. Find the perimeter of each of the following polygons.

(a)

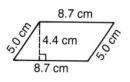

8.7 cm
4.4 cm
5.0 cm
5.0 cm
8.7 cm

(b)

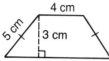

4 cm
5 cm
3 cm

(c)

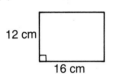

12 cm
16 cm

(d)

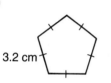

8 cm
6 cm

(e)

3.2 cm

(f)

5.7 cm

2. Find the area of each of the following polygons.

(a)

10 cm
6 cm

(b)

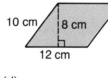

10 cm
8 cm
12 cm

(c)

2.5 cm

(d)

5 cm
13 cm
12 cm

(e)

6.5 cm
5 cm

(f)

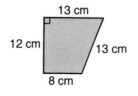

13 cm
12 cm
13 cm
8 cm

3. Find the value of the missing dimension.

(a)

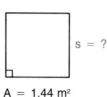

s = ?
A = 1.44 m²

(b)

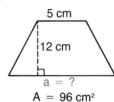

5 cm
12 cm
a = ?
A = 96 cm²

(c)

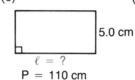

5.0 cm
ℓ = ?
P = 110 cm

(d)

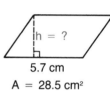

h = ?
5.7 cm
A = 28.5 cm²

(e)

A = 85 cm²
h = ?
8.5 cm

(f)

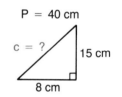

P = 40 cm
c = ?
15 cm
8 cm

4. Find the perimeter and area of each of the following figures to the nearest tenth.

(a)

3.5 m

(b)

3.5 cm

(c)

12 cm
30°

(d)

120°
5 cm

(e)

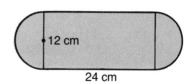

12 cm
24 cm

5. Find the surface area and volume of each of the following solids to the nearest tenth.

(a)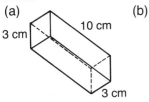
3 cm
10 cm
3 cm

(b)
12 cm
12 cm

(c)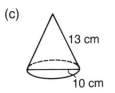
13 cm
10 cm

(d)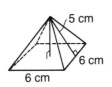
5 cm
6 cm
6 cm

(e)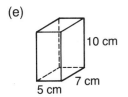
10 cm
7 cm
5 cm

(f)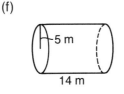
5 m
14 m

6. A cylinder has a volume of 1000 cm³ and a diameter of 13 cm.
What is the height of the cylinder?

7. A rectangular solid has a surface area of 1225 cm². The sides of the square base are 8.5 cm long.
Find the height of the solid.

8. A cone is inscribed in a pyramid with a height of 24 cm. The base is a square with 20 cm sides.

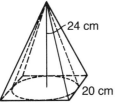
24 cm
20 cm

(a) Find the slant height and diameter of the cone.
(b) Find the surface area of the cone.
(c) Find the volume of the cone.
(d) Find the volume of the original pyramid.
(e) What is the difference in the volume of the pyramid and the volume of the cone?

9. The volume of a cube is 1000 cm³. What is the volume of the largest pyramid that can be inscribed in the cube?

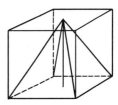

10. A rectangular solid has a base 12 cm by 18 cm and a height of 15 cm.
Find the volume of the cylinders that can be inscribed in the rectangular solid
(a) if the diameter is 12 cm.
(b) if the diameter is 15 cm.

11. A square tower 10 m by 10 m is 30 m high and is capped with a pyramid 12 m high.
(a) What is the surface area of the tower?
(b) What is the volume of the tower?

12. A seed hopper is in the shape of a cylinder with a diameter of 3.5 m and a height of 4.7 m. Both ends of the cylinder are capped with a cone 2.1 m high.
(a) Find the number of square metres of sheet metal required to build the hopper.
(b) Find the total volume of the hopper.

MIND BENDER

Any natural number can be written as the sum of at most 4 perfect squares.

$$46 = 5^2 + 4^2 + 2^2 + 1^2$$
$$182 = 10^2 + 9^2 + 1^2$$

Write 128, 213, and 318 as the sum of at most 4 perfect squares.

$$128 = \blacksquare^2 + \blacksquare^2 + \blacksquare^2 + \blacksquare^2$$
$$213 = \blacksquare^2 + \blacksquare^2 + \blacksquare^2 + \blacksquare^2$$
$$318 = \blacksquare^2 + \blacksquare^2 + \blacksquare^2 + \blacksquare^2$$

5.9 CHAPTER 5 TEST

1. Find the perimeter of each figure.

(a)

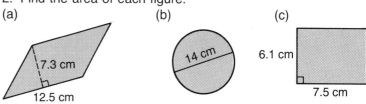

8.0 cm

10.0 cm 8.0 cm

14.0 cm

(b)

12 cm

(c)

5 cm

12 cm

2. Find the area of each figure.

(a)

7.3 cm

12.5 cm

(b)

14 cm

(c)

6.1 cm

7.5 cm

3. Find the perimeter and area of the sector shown at the right.

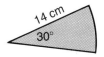

14 cm

30°

4. Find the surface area of the cone shown at the right.

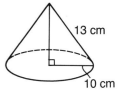

13 cm

10 cm

5. Find the volume of a pyramid with a square base whose sides are 15 cm long and height is 20 cm.

6. The length of a rectangle is 12 cm and the area is 96 cm². Find the perimeter of the rectangle.

7. What is the height of a square-based pyramid if the sides of the base are 12 cm long and the volume is 480 cm³?

TRIGONOMETRY

6

REVIEW AND PREVIEW TO CHAPTER **6**

ANGLES, TRIANGLES, AND PARALLEL LINES

EXERCISE 1

1. Calculate the values of x and y.

(a)

(b)

20°

x y

(c)

62.7° x

(d)

60°

50° x y

(e)

x

x + 20°   y

x + 40°

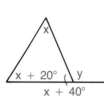

(f)

50°

x 2x

y

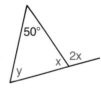

(g)

62°

x

y

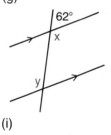

(h)

55° x y

(i)

x y

120°

25°

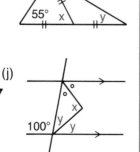

(j)

100°

y x

y

PYTHAGOREAN THEOREM

In any right triangle the square of the length of the hypotenuse is equal to the sum of the squares of the lengths of the other two sides.

$$c^2 = a^2 + b^2$$

c b

a

EXERCISE 2

1. Find the values of the variables.

(a)

c 3

4

(b)

c 5

12

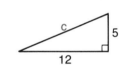

(c)

b 17

8

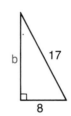

(d)

c 7

24

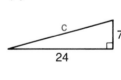

(e)

10 6

a

(f)

b 26

10

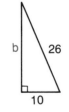

2. A ladder 4.3 m long is leaning against a wall. The foot of the ladder is 1.7 m from the wall.
How high up the wall will the ladder reach?

RATIO AND PROPORTION

A ratio is a comparison of two quantities in the same units. A ratio can be written

$$a : b, \quad \frac{a}{b}, \quad \text{or} \quad a \text{ to } b$$

A proportion is the equality of two ratios.

$$\frac{a}{b} = \frac{c}{d}$$

EXERCISE 3

1. Solve for x.

(a) $\frac{x}{5} = \frac{8}{20}$ (b) $\frac{3}{x} = \frac{12}{28}$

(c) $\frac{15}{45} = \frac{x}{60}$ (d) $\frac{27}{12} = \frac{36}{x}$

(e) $\frac{x}{48} = \frac{12}{x}$ (f) $\frac{5}{x} = \frac{x}{125}$

2. The ratio of seniors to juniors in the business club is 5 : 2. There are 133 students in the club.
How many seniors are in the business club?

3. The ratio of cars to trucks passing a survey point was 7 : 16. A total of 240 trucks passed the survey point and were counted.
What was the total number of cars and trucks that passed the survey point?

4. Solve for x.

(a) $\frac{x}{13.76} = \frac{18.51}{15.76}$ (b) $\frac{x}{57.29} = \frac{48.76}{33.54}$

(c) $\frac{58.72}{72.83} = \frac{x}{2.67}$ (d) $\frac{582.7}{633.5} = \frac{x}{104.6}$

(e) $\frac{85.76}{x} = \frac{95.43}{18.71}$ (f) $\frac{4.743}{x} = \frac{5.894}{6.382}$

(g) $\frac{21.73}{15.46} = \frac{77.81}{x}$ (h) $\frac{0.7134}{0.8123} = \frac{0.5812}{x}$

SIMILAR TRIANGLES

If two triangles are similar, then the corresponding angles are equal and the corresponding sides are proportional.

$\triangle ABC \sim \triangle DEF$

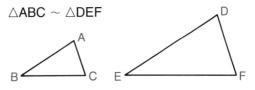

$$\angle A = \angle D, \angle B = \angle E, \angle C = \angle F,$$

and $\quad \dfrac{AB}{DE} = \dfrac{BC}{EF} = \dfrac{CA}{FD}$

EXERCISE 4

1. Find the indicated dimension in each of the following pairs of similar triangles.

(a)

(b)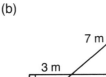

(c)

(d)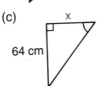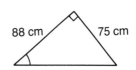

6.1 TRIGONOMETRIC RATIOS

In trigonometry the ratios of the sides of a right triangle are related to the measures of the acute angles of the triangle. These ratios depend solely on the measures of the angles and are independent of the lengths of the sides.

With reference to the indicated angle marked by the Greek letter θ (theta), we refer to the sides of the triangle as the opposite side, the adjacent side, and the hypotenuse, as shown in the diagram at the right.

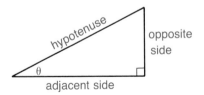

Each of the following triangles has one angle equal to 30°. The ratios of the opposite side to the adjacent side of the 30° angle in each triangle are equal.

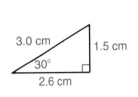

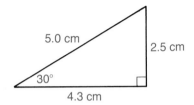

$$\frac{\text{opposite side}}{\text{adjacent side}} = \frac{1.5}{2.6}$$
$$\doteq 0.58$$

$$\frac{\text{opposite side}}{\text{adjacent side}} = \frac{2.5}{4.3}$$
$$\doteq 0.58$$

Since the ratios of the sides of a right triangle depend on the angle, we can define the trigonometric ratios as follows:

sine of θ	$= \dfrac{\text{opposite side}}{\text{hypotenuse}}$	cosecant of θ	$= \dfrac{\text{hypotenuse}}{\text{opposite side}}$	
cosine of θ	$= \dfrac{\text{adjacent side}}{\text{hypotenuse}}$	secant of θ	$= \dfrac{\text{hypotenuse}}{\text{adjacent side}}$	
tangent of θ	$= \dfrac{\text{opposite side}}{\text{adjacent side}}$	cotangent of θ	$= \dfrac{\text{adjacent side}}{\text{opposite side}}$	

We abbreviate our work using the following symbols:

$$\sin \theta = \frac{\text{opp}}{\text{hyp}} \qquad \cos \theta = \frac{\text{adj}}{\text{hyp}} \qquad \tan \theta = \frac{\text{opp}}{\text{adj}}$$

$$\csc \theta = \frac{\text{hyp}}{\text{opp}} \qquad \sec \theta = \frac{\text{hyp}}{\text{adj}} \qquad \cot \theta = \frac{\text{adj}}{\text{opp}}$$

Example 1. Find the six trigonometric ratios for the indicated 38° angle.

Solution:

$$\sin 38° = \frac{4.3}{7.0} \doteq 0.614 \qquad \csc 38° = \frac{7.0}{4.3} \doteq 1.627$$

$$\cos 38° = \frac{5.5}{7.0} \doteq 0.786 \qquad \sec 38° = \frac{7.0}{5.5} \doteq 1.273$$

$$\tan 38° = \frac{4.3}{5.5} \doteq 0.782 \qquad \cot 38° = \frac{5.5}{4.3} \doteq 1.279$$

We can use a calculator to check the results of Example 1.

To find	Press	The display is
sin 38°	3 8 sin	0.61566148
cos 38°	3 8 cos	0.78801075
tan 38°	3 8 tan	0.78128563

Discrepancy in the third decimal place is due to presenting angles to the nearest degree.

Since $\sin \theta = \dfrac{opp}{hyp}$ and $\csc \theta = \dfrac{hyp}{opp}$, we say that the cosecant ratio is the reciprocal of the sine ratio. We find the reciprocal ratios cosecant, secant, and cotangent on a calculator using the ¹⁄ₓ key.

To find	Press	The display is
csc 38°	3 8 sin ¹⁄ₓ	1.62426925
sec 38°	3 8 cos ¹⁄ₓ	1.26901822
cot 38°	3 8 tan ¹⁄ₓ	1.27994163

Example 2. Find the measures of the acute angles of the given triangle to the nearest degree.

Solution: From the diagram,

$$\sin A = \frac{6.3}{7.8}$$
$$\doteq 0.808$$

From the tables in the Appendix,
sin 54° = 0.8090
∴ ∠A ≐ 54°
and ∠B = 90° − 54°
= 36°

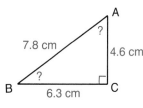

To find ∠A using a calculator,

press 6 . 3 ÷ 7 . 8 = INV sin

The display is 53.8710725

Spreadsheet activities related to this topic are found in section 15.5.

∴ ∠A ≐ 54° to the nearest degree.

EXERCISE 6.1

A

1. Identify each side of the following triangles as the hypotenuse, the opposite side, or the adjacent side to the indicated angle.

(a)   (b)

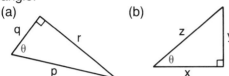

2. Using a calculator or tables, state the value of each of the following.
(a) sin 42°   (b) cos 25°   (c) tan 53°
(d) cos 75°   (e) sin 82°   (f) sin 21°
(g) tan 65°   (h) tan 75°   (i) cos 16°
(j) sin 74°   (k) tan 15°   (l) cos 74°

3. Using a calculator or tables, state the value of each of the following.
(a) csc 24°   (b) sec 56°   (c) cot 45°
(d) sec 75°   (e) cot 54°   (f) csc 72°
(g) cot 32°   (h) cot 58°   (i) csc 44°
(j) sec 80°   (k) csc 65°   (l) cot 15°

4. State the measure of each angle to the nearest degree.
(a) tan A = 0.6009   (b) sin B = 0.9903
(c) sin D = 0.250   (d) sin E = 0.695
(e) sin G = 0.707   (f) cos H = 0.809
(g) tan H = 0.250   (h) cos K = 0.707
(i) cos M = 0.309   (j) tan N = 11.400

B

5. Calculate the values of sin θ, cos θ, and tan θ in each of the following to the nearest thousandth.

(a)   (b)

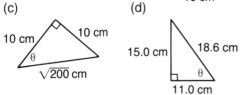

(c)   (d)

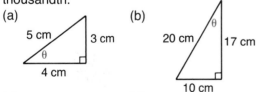

6. Calculate the value of csc θ, sec θ, and tan θ in each of the following to the nearest thousandth.

(a)   (b)

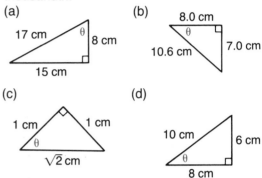

(c)   (d)

7. Find the value of the indicated angle, θ, to the nearest degree in each of the following.

(a)   (b)

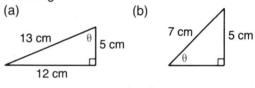

(c)   (d)

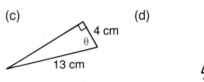

8. Find the measures of the acute angles to the nearest degree in each of the following right triangles.

(a)   (b)

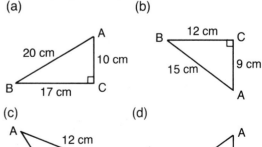

(c)   (d)

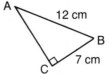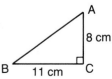

6.2 DEGREES, MINUTES, AND SECONDS

Angles measure the amount of rotation of a ray about the vertex. Angles can be expressed in decimal degrees such as 35.4°, or in degrees and minutes such as 35°24′. The following table shows the relationship between decimal degrees and minutes and seconds.

1 rotation = 360°	degree
1° = 60′	minute
1′ = 60″	second

This table gives us a method for changing decimal degrees into minutes and seconds.

Example 1. Express 35.28° in degrees, minutes, and seconds.

Solution: 35.28° = 35°(0.28 × 60)′
            = 35°16.8′
            = 35°16′(0.8 × 60)″
            = 35°16′48″

Example 2. Express 28°25′30″ in decimal degrees.

Solution: 28°25′30″ = 28°(25 + $\frac{30}{60}$)′
            = 28°25.5′
            = 28° + $\left(\frac{25.5}{60}\right)^{\circ}$
            = 28.475°

EXERCISE 6.2

B

1. Change each of the following to degrees, minutes, and seconds.
(a) 55.6°   (b) 21.75°
(c) 16.37°   (d) 9.17°
(e) 45.15°   (f) 24.84°
(g) 65.24°   (h) 18.65°
(i) 53.47°   (j) 45.45°
(k) 73.50°   (l) 20.85°

2. Change each of the following angle measures to decimal degrees.
(a) 25°36′   (b) 18°42′
(c) 63°48′   (d) 35°18′
(e) 31°54′   (f) 15°6′
(g) 75°12′   (h) 57°30′
(i) 49°21′   (j) 20°20′

3. Change each of the following angle measures to decimal degrees.
(a) 16°25′15″   (b) 24°24′24″
(c) 65°25′42″   (d) 66°21′34″
(e) 52°32′15″   (f) 64°39′43″
(g) 64°20′35″   (h) 56°16′5″
(i) 83°51′21″   (j) 71°28′3″

4. Show that
(a) sin 30° + sin 60° ≠ sin 90°
(b) (sin 30°)² + (sin 60°)² = (sin 90°)²

Change 24.568° (decimal degrees) to degrees, minutes, and seconds.

Enter 24.568° in your calculator.

Press	Display	Write
2 4 · 5 6 8	24.568	
− 2 4 =	0.568	24°
× 6 0 =	34.08	
− 3 4 =	0.08	24°34′
× 6 0 =	4.8	24°34′5″

6.3 SOLVING RIGHT TRIANGLES

In △ABC, the side opposite ∠A is a units long, the side opposite ∠B is b units long, and the side opposite ∠C is c units long. When the meaning is clear, A represents the measure of the angle at vertex A. The following chart summarizes the trigonometric relationships between the angles of the right triangle and the lengths of the sides.

$\sin A = \dfrac{a}{c}$	$\cos A = \dfrac{b}{c}$	$\tan A = \dfrac{a}{b}$
$\sin B = \dfrac{b}{c}$	$\cos B = \dfrac{a}{c}$	$\tan B = \dfrac{b}{a}$
$\csc A = \dfrac{c}{a}$	$\sec A = \dfrac{c}{b}$	$\cot A = \dfrac{b}{a}$
$\csc B = \dfrac{c}{b}$	$\sec B = \dfrac{c}{a}$	$\cot B = \dfrac{a}{b}$
where $c = \sqrt{a^2 + b^2}$		

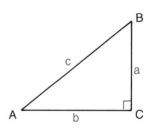

Example 1. In △ABC, ∠C = 90°, b = 2.5 cm, and
∠A = 42.4°.
Find a.

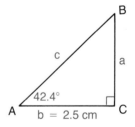

$E=mc^2$

Solution:

Using tables,

$\dfrac{a}{2.5} = \tan 42.4°$

$a = 2.5 \times \tan 42.4°$

$\doteq 2.5 \times 0.9131$

$\doteq 2.28$

∴ a = 2.3 cm

Using a calculator, press

[2] [.] [5] [×] [4] [2] [.] [4] [tan] [=]

The display is `2.2828137`

Example 2. In △ABC, ∠B = 90°, c = 3.2 cm, and
b = 5.3 cm.
Solve the triangle.

Solution:

Using tables,

$\sin C = \dfrac{3.2}{5.3}$

$\doteq 0.6038$

∴ ∠C ≐ 37.1°

∠A ≐ 90° − 37.1°

= 52.9°

Using a calculator, press

[3] [.] [2] [÷] [5] [.] [3] [=] [INV] [sin]

The display is `37.1406415`

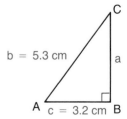

Using tables,

$\dfrac{a}{5.3} = \cos 37.1°$

$a = 5.3 \times \cos 37.1°$

$\doteq 5.3 \times 0.7976$

$a \doteq 4.23$

Using Pythagoras,

$a^2 = b^2 - c^2$

$a^2 = (5.3)^2 - (3.2)^2$

$= 28.09 - 10.24$

$= 17.85$

$a \doteq 4.23$

Using a calculator, press

The display is 4.2271948

$\therefore \angle C = 37.1°$, $\angle A = 52.9°$, and $a = 4.23$ cm.

EXERCISE 6.3

B 1. Find the length of the side labelled x in each of the following triangles.

(a)

155 cm
35°
x

(b)

x
52°
2.35 cm

(c)
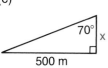
70°
x
500 m

(d)

5 m
40°
x

(e)

20 m
x
35°

(f)
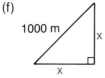
1000 m
x
x

2. Find $\angle \theta$ to the nearest tenth of a degree in each of the following.

(a)
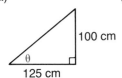
100 cm
θ
125 cm

(b)
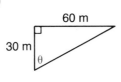
60 m
30 m
θ

(c)
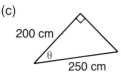
200 cm
θ
250 cm

(d)

60 cm
50 cm
θ

(e)
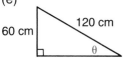
120 cm
60 cm
θ

(f)
200 cm
θ
150 cm

3. Solve the following triangles.

(a)
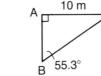
250 cm
A
B
35°
C

(b)
31 cm
C
B
A
65.7°

(c)
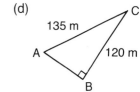
10 m
A
C
B
55.3°

(d)
135 m
C
A
120 m
B

4. Make reasonably accurate diagrams and solve the following triangles.

(a) △ABC, ∠B = 90°, c = 35 cm, a = 42 cm

(b) △DEF, ∠E = 90°, f = 48 cm, e = 61 cm

(c) △PQR, ∠P = 90°, r = 58 cm, p = 67 cm

(d) △ABC, ∠A = 90°, c = 675 cm, a = 857 cm

(e) △STU, ∠S = 90°, t = 487 cm, u = 518 cm

(f) △XYZ, x = 70 cm, y = 240 cm, z = 250 cm

C 5. Find x in each of the following.

(a)
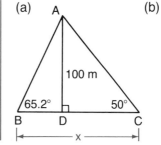
A
100 m
65.2°
50°
B
D
C
x

(b)
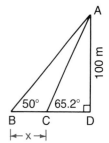
A
100 m
50°
65.2°
B
C
D
x

6.4 SOLVING PROBLEMS WITH TRIGONOMETRY

For more than two thousand years, astronomers, navigators, and surveyors have used trigonometry to find distances to inaccessible objects and to determine unmeasurable heights. Today, this branch of mathematics continues to grow in importance not only in the space program but also in the day-to-day work of technologists. The following diagrams illustrate some of the terms that are used in the problems in the exercise.

When the object is above the observer, the angle that the line of sight makes with the horizontal is called the angle of elevation. When the object is below the observer, the angle that the line of sight makes with the horizontal is called the angle of depression.

In solving these problems the length of a side is found using the relationship

$$\frac{\text{unknown}}{\text{known}} = \text{trigonometric ratio}$$

READ

Example 1. A guy line is attached to a radio tower at a point 75.5 m above the ground and makes an angle of 62.5° with the ground.
Calculate the length of cable required to the nearest 0.5 m and include an extra 1.5 m for each end connection.

PLAN

Solution: Let the length of the guy line be d m.

$$\frac{d}{75.5} = \csc 62.5°$$

$$d = 75.5 \times \csc 62.5°$$
$$\doteq 75.5 \times 1.1274$$
$$\doteq 85.1$$

SOLVE

Using a calculator, press

7 5 · 5 × 6 2 · 5 sin ¹/ₓ =

The display is 85.117337

E=mc²

∴ the length of cable required is 85.0 m plus 3.0 m for connections for a total of 88.0 m.

ANSWER

When working with theoretical examples, we usually assume that the data are exact. When working with real world problems, calculators often give us more accuracy than is reasonable to expect. In these cases it is necessary to consider the implied accuracy of the answers in comparison with the numbers used. If the context of the problem does not supply information about the precision of the numbers involved, then approximations made in the process of calculation should assume that the original data were exact. When working with angles in the degree system, the following guide is used in conjunction with our rounding rules.

Where lengths are rounded to	The accuracy of angles is to the nearest
1 significant digit	10°
2 significant digits	1°
3 significant digits	0.1° or 6′
4 significant digits	0.01° or 30″

Example 2. From the top of a 123 m cliff, two boats are observed in the same direction so that the angles of depression are 21.5° and 34.6°, as shown in the diagram. Find the distance between the two boats.

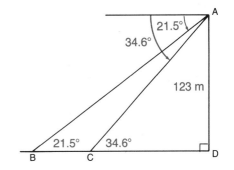

Solution:
BC = BD − CD

In △ABD, $\dfrac{BD}{123}$ = cot 21.5°

$\qquad$ BD = 123 × cot 21.5°
$\qquad\qquad \doteq$ 123 × 2.5386
$\qquad\qquad \doteq$ 312.2

Using a calculator to find BD, press

`1` `2` `3` `×` `2` `1` `·` `5` `tan` `¹/ₓ` `=`

The display is `312.25369`

In △ACD, $\dfrac{CD}{123}$ = cot 34.6°

$\qquad$ CD = 123 × cot 34.6°
$\qquad\qquad \doteq$ 123 × 1.4496
$\qquad\qquad \doteq$ 178.3

Using a calculator to find CD, press

`1` `2` `3` `×` `3` `4` `·` `6` `tan` `¹/ₓ` `=`

The display is `178.29865`

∴ BC $\doteq$ 312.2 − 178.3 = 133.9

The two boats are 134 m apart.

EXERCISE 6.4

B

1. The angle of elevation of the top of a building is 68.3° from a point 241 m from the foot of the building.
Find the height of the building.

2. From the top of a fire tower, the angle of depression of a cabin is observed to be 21.8°.
Find the distance from the cabin to the foot of the tower if the tower is 212 m high.

3. A building casts a shadow 57 m long when the angle of elevation of the sun is 35°.
(a) Find the height of the building.
(b) Find the length of the shadow when the angle of elevation of the sun is 60°.

4. A 324 m guy wire makes an angle of 36.8° at the top of a communications tower. Calculate the height of the tower.

5. Find the length of cable required to secure a radio tower 175 m high if the cable must make an angle of 28.3° at the top of the tower and 4 m of cable are required for fastening.

6. From a point 125 m from the foot of a building, the angles of elevation of the top and bottom of the building's flagpole are 40.0° and 38.1° respectively.

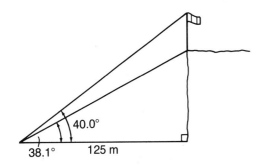

Calculate
(a) the height of the building,
(b) the height of the flagpole.

7. From the top of a cliff 109 m high, the angles of depression of two small boats on the water are 9.2° and 15.2°.

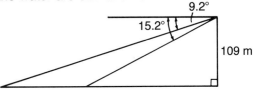

Calculate the distance
(a) from the foot of the cliff to the closer boat,
(b) between the boats if they are sighted in the same direction.

8. A ladder 7.4 m long is placed on level ground to reach a window 5.8 m above the ground.
(a) What angle does the ladder make with the ground?
(b) How far is the foot of the ladder from the foot of the building?

C 9. A ladder 15 m long is placed on a driveway between two buildings so that it reaches 12 m up on one building. If it is turned over, its foot being held in position, it will reach 8 m up the other building.

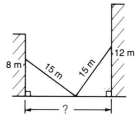

How wide is the driveway from building to building?

10. From an office window 42.5 m above level ground, a building 156 m tall at a distance of 104 m is observed across a courtyard.
(a) Find the angle of elevation of the top of the building.
(b) Find the angle of depression of the base of the building.

11. From two points A and B on the opposite sides of a bay, the distances to a point C were measured and found to be 1500 m and 2000 m respectively.

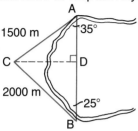

If $\angle A = 35°$ and $\angle B = 25°$, find the distance AB across the bay.

12. A surveyor wishes to find the height BC of an inaccessible cliff. To do this, she sets up her transit at A, and measures $\angle CAB = 32°$. She then lays off a baseline AD so that $\angle BAD = 90°$ and AD = 50 m. She measures $\angle ADB = 58°$.

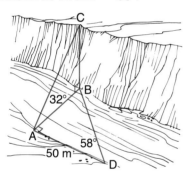

Calculate the height of the cliff.

13. A cylindrical tank with a diameter of 3 m is rolled up a 15° incline.

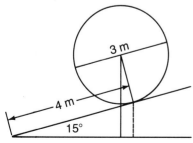

When the point of contact of the tank is 4 m from the start of the incline, what is the height of the centre of the tank from the base of the incline?

14. From the ends of a bridge the angles of depression of a marker buoy on the water are 45° and 37° respectively.

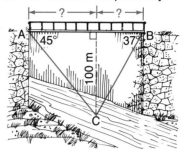

Find the length of the bridge if it is known that the bridge is 100 m above the water.

15. To determine the height of an inaccessible tower, readings as shown in the diagram were taken.

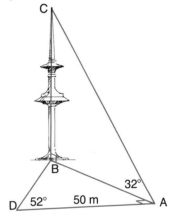

$\triangle ABC$ is in the vertical plane and $\angle A = 32°$. $\triangle ABD$ is in the horizontal plane, the baseline AD = 50 m, $\angle ADB = 52°$, and $\angle DAB = 90°$.
Calculate the height of the tower BC.

16. From two points A and B, in the same vertical plane as a tower, the angles of elevation are 21° and 30° respectively.

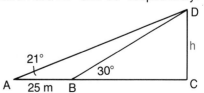

Calculate CD, the height of the tower, if A and B are 25 m apart.

6.5 APPLICATIONS OF TRIGONOMETRY

A machine technologist is responsible for setting up sophisticated equipment to process materials in manufacturing. Machine technologists work closely with design engineers and drafters so that the objects that are designed can be produced. In machining on a lathe, the machine technologist often has to work with tolerances as small as one thousandth of a millimetre. This work also requires a very high level of accuracy in calculation. Since both angles and lengths appear in the measurements, trigonometry is an important branch of mathematics to the machine technologist.

Example. A circular steel cover requires fifteen holes to be drilled in a circle having a diameter of 21 cm. This is often called a bolt circle, and the distance between the centres of the holes is called the chordal distance.
Calculate the distance between centres of adjacent holes.

Solution:
The diameter of the circle is 21 cm.
The radius of the circle is

$$21 \div 2 = 10.5 \text{ cm}$$

The angle at the centre can be found when the number of holes is known.

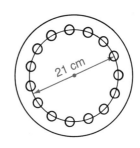

$$\text{Angle at the centre} = \frac{360°}{15}$$
$$= 24°$$

If x represents one half of the distance between centres (the chordal distance), then

$$\frac{x}{10.5} = \sin 12°$$
$$x = 10.5 \times \sin 12°$$
$$\doteq 10.5 \times 0.2079$$
$$\doteq 2.183$$
$$2x = 2 \times 2.183$$
$$= 4.366$$

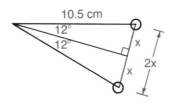

Using a calculator, press

```
1 0 . 5 × 1 2 sin = × 2 =
```

The display is   2.1830728   4.3661456

∴ the distance between centres is 4.36 cm.

EXERCISE 6.5

B

1. Calculate the depth of a sharp V-thread if the pitch of the thread is 0.500 cm.
A sharp V-thread is in the shape of an equilateral triangle.

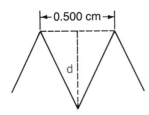

2. Calculate the distance between centres of two adjacent holes on a 30 cm bolt circle containing 9 holes.

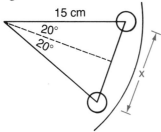

3. Three holes are to be located in a rectangular plate as shown.
Find the dimensions a and b.

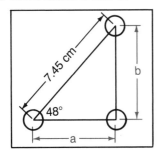

4. Find the indicated angle in the steel wedge as shown. Use a right triangle.

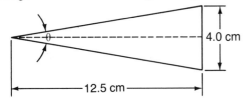

5. Calculations for tapers are similar to those for wedges.

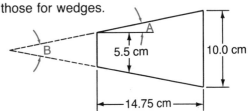

Calculate the angles marked A and B to the nearest degree for the conical taper to be turned on a lathe.

6. Calculate the length of the slot to be milled in the given plate.

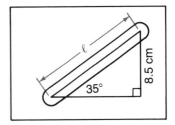

7. Calculate the chordal distance between centres of two adjacent holes on a five-hole bolt circle with a diameter of 34.0 cm.

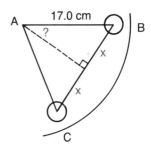

8. If the length of the hole MN is 5.0 cm and the hole is at an angle of 62°, calculate the thickness of the material AC.

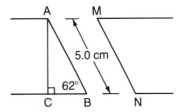

6.6 REFERENCE ANGLES

In some of the work that follows, we will need to use the trigonometric ratios of obtuse angles. We have defined the trigonometric ratios in terms of the ratios of the sides of a right triangle. In this section we will extend our definitions of the trigonometric ratios to angles greater than 90° and less than 180°.

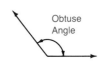
Obtuse Angle

If we relate a right triangle to a set of coordinate axes as shown, then the coordinates of vertex A are (a, b). Let △ABC be reflected about the y-axis, so that A falls on A′ and C falls on C′. The coordinates of A′ are (−a, b).

Since △ABC and △A′BC′ are congruent,

$$\triangle ABC \cong \triangle A'BC' \qquad \text{reflection}$$
$$\angle ABC = \angle A'BC'$$

Let $\angle ABC = \angle A'BC' = \theta$
∴ $\angle A'BC = 180° - \theta$

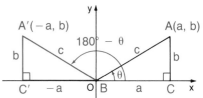

For ∠ABC	For ∠A′BC′	Conclusion
$\sin \theta = \dfrac{b}{c} = \dfrac{\text{y-coordinate of A}}{c}$	$\sin (180° - \theta) = \dfrac{\text{y-coordinate of A}'}{c} = \dfrac{b}{c}$	$\dfrac{b}{c} = \dfrac{b}{c}$ $\sin (180° - \theta) = \sin \theta$
$\cos \theta = \dfrac{a}{c} = \dfrac{\text{x-coordinate of A}}{c}$	$\cos (180° - \theta) = \dfrac{\text{x-coordinate of A}'}{c} = \dfrac{-a}{c}$	$\dfrac{a}{c} = -\left(\dfrac{-a}{c}\right)$ $\cos (180° - \theta) = -\cos \theta$
$\tan \theta = \dfrac{b}{a} = \dfrac{\text{y-coordinate of A}}{\text{x-coordinate of A}}$	$\tan (180° - \theta) = \dfrac{\text{y-coordinate of A}'}{\text{x-coordinate of A}'} = \dfrac{b}{-a}$	$\dfrac{b}{a} = -\left(\dfrac{b}{-a}\right)$ $\tan (180° - \theta) = -\tan \theta$

Example. Find sin 124.7°, cos 108.6°, tan 144.5°.

Solution:
Using the above relationships,

$$\sin 124.7° = \sin (180° - 124.7°)$$
$$= \sin 55.3°$$
$$= 0.8221$$

$$\cos 108.6° = -\cos (180° - 108.6°)$$
$$= -\cos 71.4°$$
$$= -0.3190$$

$$\tan 144.5° = -\tan (180° - 144.5°)$$
$$= -\tan 35.5°$$
$$= -0.7133$$

Calculator check:

Press [1] [2] [4] [·] [7] [sin]
The display is `0.82214404`

Press [1] [0] [8] [·] [6] [cos]
The display is `-0.31895931`

Press [1] [4] [4] [·] [5] [tan]
The display is `-0.7132931`

6.7 THE LAW OF SINES

Triangles that do not contain a right angle are called oblique triangles. In solving right triangles, three of the six parts (3 angles, 3 sides) of the triangle were given and the remaining three parts could be found using trigonometric ratios. In this section we will solve oblique triangles using a general formula — the Law of Sines.

Acute Triangle

Obtuse Triangle

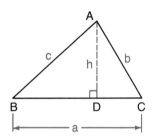

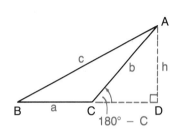

In $\triangle ACD$, $\dfrac{h}{b} = \sin C$

$h = b \sin C$

In $\triangle ABD$, $\dfrac{h}{c} = \sin B$

$h = c \sin B$

In $\triangle ACD$, $\dfrac{h}{b} = \sin (180° - C)$

$= \sin C$

$h = b \sin C$

In $\triangle ABD$, $\dfrac{h}{c} = \sin B$

$h = c \sin B$

For both the acute and obtuse triangles,

$$b \sin C = c \sin B$$
$$\frac{b}{\sin B} = \frac{c}{\sin C}$$

By drawing the altitude from C, we have

$$\frac{a}{\sin A} = \frac{b}{\sin B}$$

The results are the same for both the acute and obtuse triangles.

$$\frac{a}{\sin A} = \frac{b}{\sin B} = \frac{c}{\sin C} \quad \text{or} \quad \frac{\sin A}{a} = \frac{\sin B}{b} = \frac{\sin C}{c}$$

Example 1. In △ABC, ∠A = 78°, ∠B = 68°, and
a = 5.9 cm.
Find c.

Solution: $\angle C = 180° - (78° + 68°)$

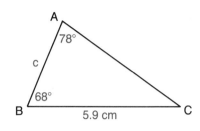

$$= 34°$$

$$\frac{c}{\sin C} = \frac{a}{\sin A}$$

$$c = \frac{a \sin C}{\sin A}$$

$$= \frac{5.9 \times \sin 34°}{\sin 78°}$$

$$\doteq \frac{5.9 \times 0.5592}{0.9782}$$

$$\doteq 3.4$$

Using a calculator, press

`5 . 9 × 3 4 sin ÷ 7 8 sin =`

The display is `3.3729451`

The length of c is 3.4 cm.

Example 2. In △ABC, c = 3.25 cm, ∠C = 36.5°, and a = 5.35 cm.
Find ∠A, given that △ABC is acute.

Solution: $\dfrac{\sin A}{a} = \dfrac{\sin C}{c}$

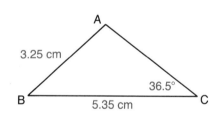

$$\sin A = \frac{a \sin C}{c}$$

$$\sin A \doteq \frac{5.35 \sin 36.5°}{3.25}$$

$$\doteq \frac{5.35 \times 0.5948}{3.25}$$

$$\doteq 0.9791$$

$$\angle A \doteq 78.3°$$

Using a calculator, press

`5 . 3 5 × 3 6 . 5 sin ÷ 3 . 2 5`

`= INV sin`

The display is `78.285031`
∴ ∠A is 78.3°.

If Example 2 had stated that the triangle was obtuse, then we would have used the
sin (180° − θ) = sin θ relationship, and

$$\angle A = 180° - 78.3°$$
$$= 101.7°$$

Example 3. In △ABC, ∠B = 28.3°, ∠C = 111.6°, and
a = 31.2 cm.
Find c.

Solution: ∠A = 180° − (28.3° − 111.6°)
= 40.1°

$$\frac{c}{\sin C} = \frac{a}{\sin A}$$

$$c = \frac{a \sin C}{\sin A}$$

$$= \frac{31.2 \sin 111.6°}{\sin 40.1}$$

$$\doteq \frac{31.2 \times 0.9298}{0.6441}$$

$$\doteq 45.0$$

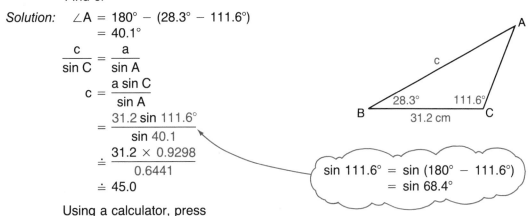

sin 111.6° = sin (180° − 111.6°)
= sin 68.4°

Using a calculator, press

3 1 · 2 × 1 1 1 · 6 sin
÷ 4 0 · 1 sin =

The display is 45.036426

The length of c is 45.0 cm.

EXERCISE 6.7

B 1. Find the indicated side.

(a)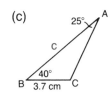

(b)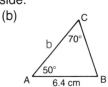

(c)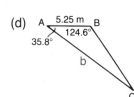

(d)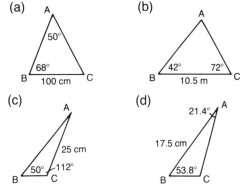

(c) In △ABC, ∠B = 70.0°, ∠C = 75.4°,
and a = 54.5 cm.
Find b.

(d) In △ABC, ∠A = 105.4°, ∠B = 24.8°,
and a = 49.2 m.
Find c.

2. In each of the following, make a
reasonably accurate diagram and use the
Law of Sines to find the required side.

(a) In △ABC, ∠A = 25.5°, ∠C = 84.6°,
and a = 15.8 cm.
Find b.

(b) In △ABC, ∠B = 40.8°, ∠C = 69.7°,
and b = 19.5 cm.
Find a.

C 3. Solve the following triangles.

(a)

(b)

(c)

(d)

(e) △ABC, c = 40 cm, ∠B = 48°,
∠C = 63°

6.8 THE LAW OF COSINES

When an oblique triangle with two sides and a contained angle (SAS) or three sides (SSS) is given, we use the Law of Cosines. We develop the Law of Cosines as follows:

Acute Triangle	Obtuse Triangle

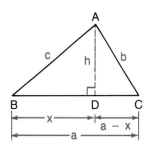 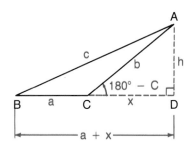

In △ABD, $\dfrac{x}{c} = \cos B$

$$x = c \cos B$$

and $\quad c^2 = h^2 + x^2$

In △ACD, $b^2 = h^2 + (a - x)^2$
$$= h^2 + a^2 - 2ax + x^2$$
$$= a^2 + (h^2 + x^2) - 2ax$$

$$\boxed{b^2 = a^2 + c^2 - 2ac \cos B}$$

Similarly $\boxed{\begin{array}{l} c^2 = a^2 + b^2 - 2ab \cos C \\ a^2 = b^2 + c^2 - 2bc \cos A \end{array}}$

In △ACD, $\dfrac{x}{b} = \cos (180° - C)$

$$x = b \cos (180° - C)$$
$$= -b \cos C$$

and $\quad b^2 = h^2 + x^2$

In △ABD, $c^2 = h^2 + (a + x)^2$
$$= h^2 + a^2 + 2ax + x^2$$
$$= a^2 + (h^2 + x^2) + 2ax$$
$$= a^2 + b^2 + 2a(-b \cos C)$$

$$\boxed{c^2 = a^2 + b^2 - 2ab \cos C}$$

Similarly $\boxed{\begin{array}{l} a^2 = b^2 + c^2 - 2bc \cos A \\ b^2 = a^2 + c^2 - 2ac \cos B \end{array}}$

Example 1. In △ABC, $a = 61.6$ cm, $\angle B = 36°$, and $c = 55.5$ cm. Find b.

Solution: $b^2 = a^2 + c^2 - 2ac \cos B$
$$b^2 \doteq (61.6)^2 + (55.5)^2 - 2(61.6)(55.5)(0.809)$$
$$\doteq 3795 + 3080 - 5532$$
$$\doteq 1343$$

SAS

$$b \doteq \sqrt{1343}$$
$$\doteq 36.6$$

∴ the length of b is 36.6 cm.

Example 2. In $\triangle ABC$, a = 49.8 cm, b = 36.3 cm, and c = 72.4 cm.
Find $\angle C$.

Solution: $\cos C = \dfrac{a^2 + b^2 - c^2}{2ab}$ because $c^2 = a^2 + b^2 - 2ab \cos C$

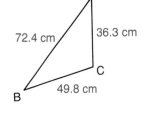

SSS $\cos C = \dfrac{(49.8)^2 + (36.3)^2 - (72.4)^2}{2(49.8)(36.3)}$

$\doteq \dfrac{2480 + 1318 - 5242}{3615.5}$

$\doteq -0.3994$

$\cos 66.5° \doteq 0.3987$

$\therefore \angle C \doteq 180° - 66.5°$

$\doteq 113.5°$

Using a calculator, press

| 4 | 9 | · | 8 | x² | + | 3 | 6 | · | 3 | x² | − | 7 | 2 | · | 4 | x² | = |

| ÷ | 2 | ÷ | 4 | 9 | · | 8 | ÷ | 3 | 6 | · | 3 | = |

inv cos

Display
-1444.03
-0.3994020
113.5408

$\therefore \angle C$ is 113.5°.

EXERCISE 6.8

B

1. Find the indicated side in each of the following.

(a)

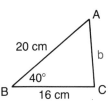

(b)

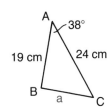

(c)

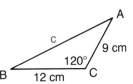

(d)

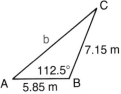

2. Find the indicated angle in each of the following.

(a)

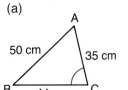

(b)

A 25 cm C
40 cm
55 cm
B

C

3. Make a reasonably accurate diagram and find the required value.

(a) In $\triangle ABC$, a = 55.5 cm, c = 50.5 cm, and $\angle B$ = 42.7°.
    Find b.

(b) In $\triangle ABC$, a = 65.5 cm, b = 44.8 cm, and c = 55.3 cm.
    Find $\angle A$.

(c) In $\triangle ABC$, a = 90.4 cm, c = 102.3 cm, and $\angle B$ = 127.2°.
    Find b.

6.9 PROBLEMS INVOLVING OBLIQUE TRIANGLES

The six trigonometric ratios cannot be applied directly to oblique triangles because there is no right angle. Formulas that have been developed in previous sections and the suggested approaches are summarized in the table below.

Given				Formula	You can calculate
ASA		Sine Law		$\dfrac{a}{\sin A} = \dfrac{b}{\sin B} = \dfrac{c}{\sin C}$	Side
SAS		Cosine Law		$a^2 = b^2 + c^2 - 2bc \cos A$ $b^2 = a^2 + c^2 - 2ac \cos B$ $c^2 = a^2 + b^2 - 2ab \cos C$	Side
SSS		Cosine Law		$\cos A = \dfrac{b^2 + c^2 - a^2}{2bc}$ $\cos B = \dfrac{a^2 + c^2 - b^2}{2ac}$ $\cos C = \dfrac{a^2 + b^2 - c^2}{2ab}$	Angle
SSA		Sine Law		$\dfrac{\sin A}{a} = \dfrac{\sin B}{b} = \dfrac{\sin C}{c}$	Angle*

*In the SSA case, additional information such as "the angle is acute" is often given where required to avoid having two solutions because $\sin(180° - θ) = \sin θ$ and $\cos(180° - θ) = -\cos θ$.

EXERCISE 6.9

For each of the following problems, complete a reasonably accurate diagram in your notebook marking all given data, then find the required dimensions.

B

1. A hockey net is 2 m wide. A player shoots from a point where the puck is 13 m from one goal post and 12 m from the other.

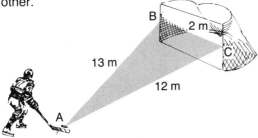

Within what angle must he make his shot to hit the net?

2. Football goal posts are measured and found to be 5.5 m apart. A player is to attempt a field goal from a point where the ball is 44 m and 43 m from the ends of the goal posts.

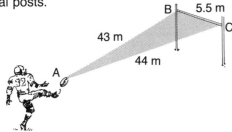

Within what angle must he kick the ball?

3. The vertical angle of a cone is 20°.

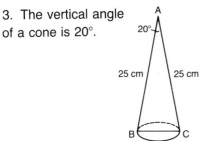

Find the diameter of the cone at a point on the face 25 cm from the vertex.

4. A greenhouse is 10 m wide and the rafters make angles of 25° and 60° with the joists.

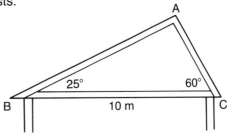

Find the length of each rafter.

5. Find the width of a small lake if from point B an angle of 61° is contained by the lengths 610 m and 560 m.

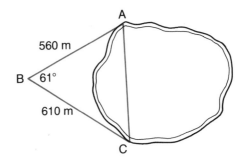

C

6. Town A is 80 km west of town B. The inclination of town C is 45° from A and 120° from B.

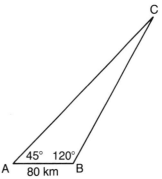

Find the distances from A to C and B to C.

6.10 SOLVING TRIANGLES WITH A COMPUTER

The following computer program solves oblique triangles. When we identify the case required as ASA, SAS, or SSS, the program prompts us to enter the appropriate information. When the entire program is not required, the following sections can be used.

Case	Program Lines
ASA	200 to 330
SAS	400 to 530
SSS	600 to 740

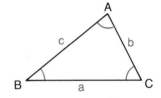

```
NEW
 10 PRINT"TRIANGLE SOLVER"
 20 PRINT"GIVEN: ASA, SAS, OR SSS"
 30 PRINT"WHICH CASE :";
 40 INPUT" ASA, SAS, OR SSS";C$
 50 IF C$="ASA" THEN 200
 60 IF C$="SAS" THEN 400
 70 IF C$="SSS" THEN 600
 80 PRINT"ENTER, SAS, OR SSS"
 90 GOTO 30

200 PRINT"LAW OF SINES CASE"
210 PRINT"GIVEN ASA"
220 PRINT"ENTER ANGLE - SIDE - ANGLE"
230 INPUT"ANGLE B = ";ANGB
240 INPUT"SIDE A = ";A
250 INPUT"ANGLE C = ";ANGC
260 ANGA=180-ANGB-ANGC
270 PRINT"ANGLE A =";ANGA
280 B1=A*SIN(ANGB*3.14159/180)
290 B=B1/SIN(ANGA*3.14159/180)
300 C1=A*SIN(ANGC*3.14159/180)
310 C=C1/SIN(ANGA*3.14159/180)
320 PRINT"SIDE B = ";B
330 PRINT"SIDE C = ";C
340 GOTO 800

400 PRINT"LAW OF COSINES CASE"
410 PRINT"GIVEN SAS"
420 PRINT"ENTER SIDE - ANGLE - SIDE "
430 INPUT"SIDE B = ";B
440 INPUT"ANGLE A = ";ANGA
450 INPUT"SIDE C = ";C
460 A1=COS(ANGA*3.14159/180)
470 A = (B*B+C*C-2*B*C*A1)^.5
480 PRINT"SIDE A = ";A
490 B1=(B*SIN(ANGA*3.14159/180)/A)
500 ANGB=ATN(B1/1-B1*B1)^.5)*180/3.14159
510 ANGC=180-ANGA-ANGB
520 PRINT"ANGLE B =";ANGB
530 PRINT"ANGLE C =";ANGC
540 GOTO 800
```

Continue at line 600.

```
600 PRINT" - GIVEN SSS"
610 PRINT"ENTER SIDE - SIDE - SIDE"
620 INPUT"SIDE A = ";A
630 INPUT"SIDE B = ";B
640 INPUT"SIDE C = ";C
650 N1=A+B-C:N2=A-B+C
660 D1=A+B+C:D2=B+C-A
670 A1=2*ATN((N1*N2/D1/D2)^.5)
680 ANGA=A1*180/3.14159
690 B1=(B*SIN(ANGA*3.14159/180)/A)
700 ANGB=ATN(B1/(1-B1*B1)^.5)*180/3.14159
710 ANGC=180-ANGB-ANGA
720 PRINT"ANGLE A =";ANGA
730 PRINT"ANGLE B =";ANGB
740 PRINT"ANGLE C =";ANGC

800 PRINT"ANOTHER QUESTION?"
810 INPUT"Y OR N";Z$
820 IF Z$="Y" THEN 30
830 END
RUN
```

Example. Solve △ABC, where
∠B = 33.9°, a = 10.2 m,
and ∠C = 104.1.

Solution: RUN the program.

```
RUN
TRIANGLE SOLVER
GIVEN: ASA, SAS, OR SSS
WHICH CASE: ASA, SAS, OR SSS? ASA
LAW OF SINES CASE
GIVEN ASA
ENTER ANGLE - SIDE - ANGLE
ANGLE B = ? 33.9
SIDE A = ? 10.2
ANGLE C = ? 104.1
ANGLE A = 42.00001
SIDE B = 8.502076
SIDE C = 14.78441
ANOTHER QUESTION?
Y OR N?
```

6.11 ALTITUDE OF A TRIANGLE

When we are given a side and two angles of a triangle, we can find the altitude of the triangle to the given side. The formula, which is derived below, is used to find the altitude of a triangle when given two angles and the common side (ASA).

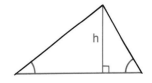

In △ABC, AD ⊥ BC
Let BD = x and DC = y

In △ABD, $\frac{x}{h}$ = cot B   In △ACD, $\frac{y}{h}$ = cot C

x = h cot B   y = h cot C

Add.   x + y = h cot B + h cot C
                    = h (cot B + cot C)
        h (cot B + cot C) = x + y = a

$$h = \frac{a}{\cot B + \cot C}$$

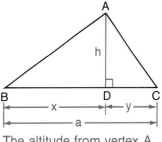

The altitude from vertex A to the base BC is AD.

EXERCISE 6.11

B 1. Find the height of a mountain if the angles of elevation of the summit from opposite ends of a 2.7 km tunnel are 48° and 62° (assume the tunnel is straight).

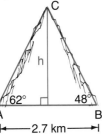

2. Two guy wires AC and BC secure a tower CD, making angles of 58° and 62° with the level ground.

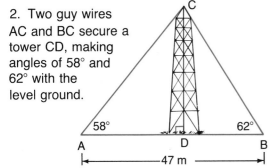

If A and B are 47 m apart, calculate the height of the tower.

3. From a 100 m baseline AB, the angles of sight to a point C on the opposite shore of a river are 71° and 43° as shown in the diagram.

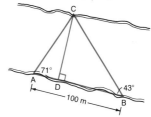

Calculate the width of the river.

4. Along one bank of a river with parallel banks, a surveyor lays off a baseline AB, 200 m long. From each end of the baseline, he sights an object C across the river. The lines of sight make angles of 60° and 80° with the baseline.

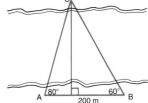

Find the width of the river.

6.12 PROBLEM SOLVING

1. On a compass SSW is how many degrees from due North?

2. At what temperature does the Fahrenheit temperature scale have the same reading as the Celsius temperature scale?

3. The latitude of any point, P, on the earth is determined by the angle formed at the centre of the earth as shown in the following diagram.

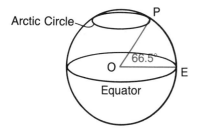

The radius of the earth is 6400 km, and the latitude of the Arctic Circle is 66.5°N. Find the circumference of the Arctic Circle.

4. There are eight hockey teams in a double-elimination tournament. (A team must lose twice before it is eliminated.) How many games are needed to determine a winner?

5. An aircraft is 300 m above the ground and 3000 m from the end of the runway during its descent.
What adjustments should be made to the approach if the angle of descent is to be 10°?

6. Find the smallest number with the property that division by 3, 4, and 5 yields a remainder of 1.

7. A baseball diamond is a square with sides 27.4 m. The pitcher's mound is 18.4 m from home plate on the diagonal from home plate to second base.

How long is the throw from the pitcher's mound to first base?

8. Two oil wells are 4 km and 6 km from a river. The points along the river are 8 km apart. Pipelines are to be laid from each well to a common loading point for tankers along the river.

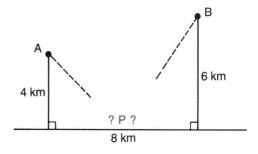

Where should the loading point be located in order to have the shortest amount of pipeline?

9. Which of the numerals 0 through 9 viewed as a geometric figure has a line of symmetry?

10.

A monorail travels from A to B, C, D, and E as shown in the following diagram.

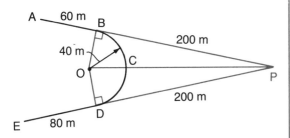

AB = 60 m and DE = 80 m. The radius of the turn is 40 m.
Find the total length of rail required for the ABCDE portion of the monorail with the given conditions.

11. Find the measure of ∠A in the cube as indicated below.

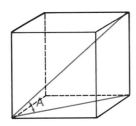

12. The number 1729 can be written as the sum of two cubes in two ways. One of them is

$$1^3 + 12^3$$

Find the other way.

TRACTOR-TRAILER DRIVER

Wanda and Newt Simms are tractor-trailer drivers. As tractor-trailer drivers, they are licensed to drive any straight truck plus any tractor-trailer or truck-trailer combination. The routes may vary in length from daily runs within an area to weekly cross-country runs. It may also be necessary to pick up and drop off goods along the route. Tractor-trailer drivers are hired by companies that transport large quantities of goods or produce. Many drivers purchase their own vehicles and work under contract for transport companies.

EXERCISE

1. A tractor-trailer with two drivers leaves Halifax and travels non-stop to Calgary, a distance of 5426 km.
How long will the trip take if they average 72 km/h?

2. A tractor-trailer leaves Winnipeg at 11:30 for Thunder Bay, a distance of 682 km.
What is the estimated time of arrival if the driver averages 68 km/h?

6.13 REVIEW EXERCISE

1. Find the length of the side labelled x.

(a)

120 cm
40°
x

(b)

14.5 cm
x
58°

(c)
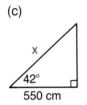
x
42°
550 cm

(d)
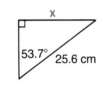
x
53.7° 25.6 cm

2. Find ∠θ to the nearest degree.

(a)

300 cm
250 cm
θ

(b)
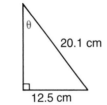
θ
20.1 cm
12.5 cm

(c)
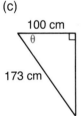
100 cm
θ
173 cm

(d)
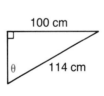
100 cm
θ 114 cm

3. From the top of a lighthouse CD, the angles of depression of two small boats A and B in the same vertical plane are 15° and 21°.

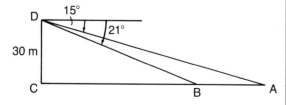
D
15°
21°
30 m
C   B   A

How far apart are the boats if the observer is 30 m above water level?

4. Make reasonably accurate diagrams, then solve the following triangles.
(a) △ABC, ∠A = 90°, c = 45 cm, a = 55 cm
(b) △DEF, ∠D = 90°, d = 65 cm, e = 48 cm
(c) △GHI, ∠I = 90°, ∠G = 52°, i = 55 cm
(d) △JKL, ∠K = 90°, ∠L = 60°, j = 200 cm

5. Solve the following triangles

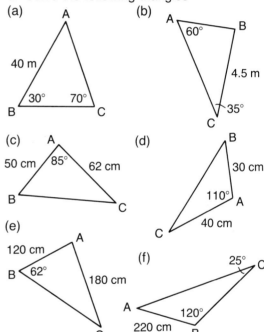

(a)
A
40 m
30° 70°
B   C

(b)
A
60°   B
4.5 m
35°
C

(c)
A
50 cm 85° 62 cm
B   C

(d)
B
30 cm
110° A
40 cm
C

(e)
120 cm
A
B 62°
180 cm
A
C

(f)
25° C
A
120°
220 cm B

6. Solve the following triangles.
(a) △ABC, a = 15.5 cm, ∠B = 25.6°, c = 12.7 cm
(b) △ABC, ∠A = 21.8°, b = 75.6 cm, ∠C = 105.2°
(c) △ABC, a = 31.6 cm, b = 45.7 cm, c = 38.2 cm
(d) △ABC, ∠A = 104.2°, ∠B = 34.6°, b = 12.8 cm

7. The string of a kite is 80 m long. The angle formed by the string and the ground is 50°.
Find the height of the kite.

8. A ladder extended to 30 m makes an angle of 75° with the ground when leaning against the wall.
How far up the wall does the ladder reach?

9. A cliff rises 42 m above the water. From a boat on the water, the angle of elevation of the top of the cliff is 20°.
How far is the boat from the cliff?

10. The angle of elevation of the sun is 53° and a tree casts a shadow 11.4 m long.
What is the height of the tree?

11. From the top of a building 80 m high, the angle of depression of a bus stop is 32°.
How far is the bus stop from the building?

12. During a storm, a tree was broken as shown.

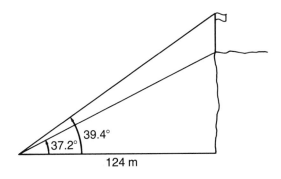

Find the original height of the tree.

13. From a point 124 m from the foot of a building, the angles of elevation of the top and bottom of a flagpole which is on top of the building are 39.4° and 37.2°.

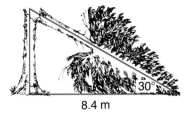

Find the height of the flagpole.

14. A triangular plate has one side 45 cm long and angles of 42° and 55° as in the diagram.

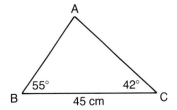

(a) Find the perimeter of the plate.
(b) Find the cost of grinding the edges at 8¢ for 3 cm.

15. From two hilltops A and B, 5.7 km apart, a third hill C is sighted making angles of 63° and 78° at A and B as in the diagram.

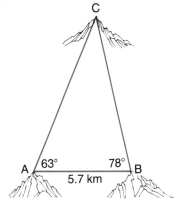

Find the distances from A to C and B to C.

16. Two highways diverge at 35° from point C. A third road, AB, is approximately 3.8 km long and joins the two highways as in the diagram, making an angle of 55° with one of the roads.

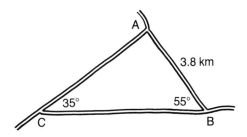

How far are intersections A and B from C?

6.14 CHAPTER 6 TEST

A scientific calculator or trigonometric tables are required to complete this test.

1. Find the length of the indicated side.

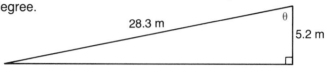

2. Find the measure of the indicated angle to a tenth of a degree.

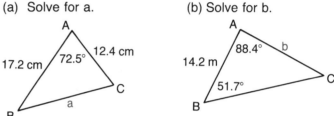

3. (a) Solve for a.   (b) Solve for b.

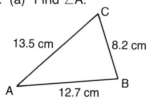 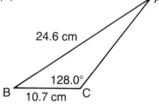

4. (a) Find ∠A.   (b) Find ∠B.

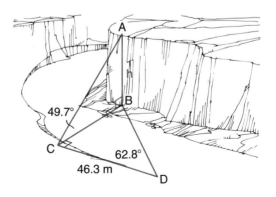

5. Use the information in the diagram to find the height of the cliff AB. △ABC lies in a vertical plane and △BCD lies in a horizontal plane.

TRIGONOMETRIC FUNCTIONS

7

REVIEW AND PREVIEW TO CHAPTER

CONGRUENCE

SAS   ASA

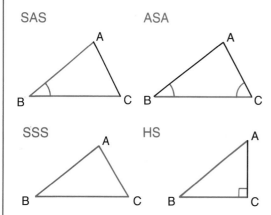

SSS   HS

EXERCISE 1

1. State with reasons, whether each of the following pairs of triangles is congruent.

(a)

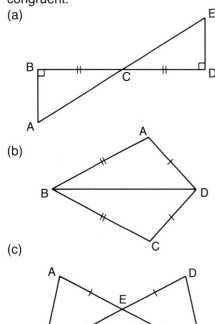

(b)

(c)

RIGHT TRIANGLE TRIGONOMETRY

$c^2 = a^2 + b^2$

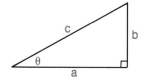

$\sin \theta = \dfrac{b}{c}$ $\csc \theta = \dfrac{c}{b}$

$\cos \theta = \dfrac{a}{c}$ $\sec \theta = \dfrac{c}{a}$

$\tan \theta = \dfrac{b}{a}$ $\cot \theta = \dfrac{a}{b}$

EXERCISE 2

1. Find the measure of the indicated angle to the nearest tenth of a degree.

(a)   (b)

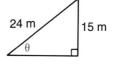

2. Find the length of the indicated side to three significant digits.

(a)   (b)

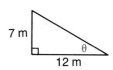

3. Solve the following triangles.

(a)   (b)

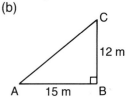

CIRCLE

The formulas for the circumference and area of a circle are as follows:

Circumference

$$C = 2\pi r$$
and $\quad C = \pi d$

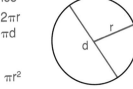

Area

$$A = \pi r^2$$

In a sector of a circle, the arc length and the area of the sector depend on the sector angle, θ.

Arc length of a sector

$$a = \frac{\theta}{360} \times 2\pi r$$

Area of a sector

$$A = \frac{\theta}{360} \times \pi r^2$$

EXERCISE 3

1. Find the circumference and area of each of the following circles.

(a)   5.6 m

(b) 4.8 m

2. Find the arc length and the area of each of the following sectors.

(a)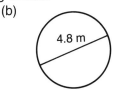
8 m
36°

(b) 16 cm

(c)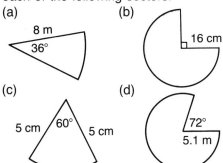
5 cm 60° 5 cm

(d)
72°
5.1 m

GRAPHING LINEAR EQUATIONS

The formulas for the equation of a straight line are as follows:

$$y = mx + b$$

$$y - y_1 = m(x - x_1)$$

EXERCISE 4

1. Find three points on each of the lines defined by the following equations and draw the graph.
(a) $y = 3x - 5$
(b) $y = -2x + 3$
(c) $y = -4x - 3$
(d) $x + y - 3 = 0$
(e) $2x + y = 6$
(f) $2x - 3y + 4 = 0$
(g) $-3x + 2y = 7$
(h) $x = 2y + 1$

2. Find the equation of each of the following lines.
(a) passing through $(2, 4)$ and $(6, 8)$
(b) passing through $(1, 5)$ with a slope of 3
(c) passing through $(-1, 2)$ with a slope of 4
(d) passing through $(-2, -3)$ and $(5, 4)$
(e) passing through the origin with a slope of 3
(f) passing through $(0, 5)$ and parallel to the x-axis

3. Find the point of intersection of the graphs of each pair of equations.
(a) $y = 2x + 5$
   $y = x + 1$
(b) $2x + 3y = 5$
   $x - 3y = 2$
(c) $4x + y = 7$
   $2x - 2y = -4$
(d) $5x + 2y = 7$
   $x = 1$

7.1 RADIAN MEASURE

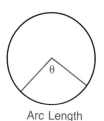

Arc Length

In our previous work angles were measured in degrees as an amount of rotation.

> One revolution equals 360°.
> $1r = 360°$

The measure of an angle can also be expressed as the arc length that subtends the angle at the centre of a circle.

> An angle subtended at the centre of a circle by an arc equal in length to the radius has a measure of one radian.

 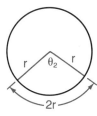 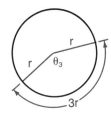

$\theta_1 = 1$ rad $\theta_2 = 2$ rad $\theta_3 = 3$ rad

From the above diagrams, the radian measures can be found as follows:

$$\theta_1 = \frac{r}{r} \qquad\qquad \theta_2 = \frac{2r}{r} \qquad\qquad \theta_3 = \frac{3r}{r}$$
$$= 1 \qquad\qquad\qquad = 2 \qquad\qquad\qquad = 3$$

This leads to the following generalizations.

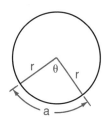

> Number of radians $= \dfrac{\text{arc length}}{\text{radius}}$ or $\theta = \dfrac{a}{r}$
>
> Arc length $=$ radius $\times \left(\begin{matrix} \text{radian measure} \\ \text{of angle} \end{matrix} \right)$ or $a = r\theta, \theta > 0$

It is often necessary to convert from degree measure to radian measure and vice versa. In order to do this, we first establish the relationship between degrees and radians. Since one revolution is 360°, we need to find the same angle in radian measure.

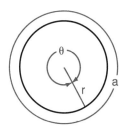

From the diagram on the left, the measure of θ is one revolution (360°), and the arc length is equal to the circumference of the circle ($2\pi r$). Hence the radian measure of θ, which would be one complete revolution, is given by

$$\frac{a}{r} = \frac{2\pi r}{r} = 2\pi$$

The relationship between radian measure and degree measure is given by 2π rad $= 360°$, which simplifies to the following.

$$\boxed{\pi \text{ rad } = 180°}$$

Example 1. Calculate degree measures of the angles whose radian measures are given.

(a) $\dfrac{\pi}{6}$
(b) $\dfrac{2\pi}{3}$

Solution:
We use the Rule of Three.

(a) π rad $= 180°$

1 rad $= \dfrac{180°}{\pi}$

$\dfrac{\pi}{6}$ rad $= \dfrac{\pi}{6} \times \dfrac{180°}{\pi}$

$= 30°$

(b) π rad $= 180°$

1 rad $= \dfrac{180°}{\pi}$

$\dfrac{2\pi}{3}$ rad $= \dfrac{2\pi}{3} \times \dfrac{180°}{\pi}$

$= 120°$

> Rule of Three
> 5 apples cost 60¢
> 1 apple costs 12¢
> 7 apples cost 84¢

Example 2. Calculate the radian measures of the following angles.

(a) $210°$
(b) $315°$

Solution:

(a) $180° = \pi$ rad

$1° = \dfrac{\pi}{180}$ rad

$210° = 210° \times \dfrac{\pi}{180°}$

$= \dfrac{7\pi}{6}$ rad

(b) $180° = \pi$ rad

$1° = \dfrac{\pi}{180}$ rad

$315° = 315° \times \dfrac{\pi}{180°}$

$= \dfrac{7\pi}{4}$ rad

EXERCISE 7.1

A 1. Convert the following radian measures to degree measure.

(a) 3π
(b) $\dfrac{3\pi}{4}$
(c) $\dfrac{4\pi}{3}$
(d) $\dfrac{5\pi}{6}$
(e) $\dfrac{3\pi}{2}$
(f) $\dfrac{5\pi}{4}$

2. Convert the following degree measures to radian measure.

(a) $120°$
(b) $330°$
(c) $90°$
(d) $225°$
(e) $30°$
(f) $240°$

B 3. Calculate the number of degrees in 1 rad.

4. Calculate the radian measure of an angle whose measure is $1°$.

5. Convert the following radian measures to degree measure.

(a) 3
(b) 2.45
(c) 5.2
(d) 11.5
(e) 0.147
(f) 457

6. Convert the following degree measures to radian measure.

(a) $40.8°$
(b) $70.4°$
(c) $160.6°$
(d) $200.5°$
(e) $410.1°$
(f) $325.3°$

7.2 LINEAR AND ANGULAR VELOCITY

A point, P, on the edge of a long-playing record is 15 cm from the centre of rotation. The record turns at a rate of $33\frac{1}{3}$ r/min. The measure of how fast the position of P is changing is called linear velocity.

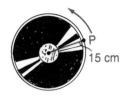

We can calculate the linear velocity for a point on the edge of a long-playing record using the formula $R = \dfrac{D}{T}$

where D is the arc length formed by the point, P, in a time, T.
For 1 min,

D = Circumference of record $\times\ 33\frac{1}{3}$

$D = 2 \times \pi \times 15.0 \times \frac{100}{3}$

$\doteq 3141.5926$

The point travels 3141.59 cm in 1 min.

On a calculator, press

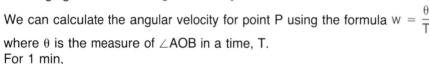

The display is 3141.592654

To find the linear velocity,

$R = \dfrac{D}{T}$

$R = \dfrac{3141.5926}{60}$

$\doteq 52.4$

The linear velocity of a point on the circumference of a long-playing record is 52.4 cm/s or 0.524 m/s.

As point P moves along the circumference of the circle, ray OP rotates around the centre O. If point P starts at A and moves along the arc AB, then the ray OP moves through $\angle AOB$. The measure of how fast $\angle AOB$ is changing is called the angular velocity.

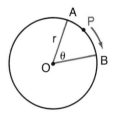

We can calculate the angular velocity for point P using the formula $w = \dfrac{\theta}{T}$

where θ is the measure of $\angle AOB$ in a time, T.
For 1 min,

θ = Number of revolutions $\times\ 2\pi$ rad

$\theta = 33\frac{1}{3} \times 2\pi$

$\doteq 209.4395$

The point P rotates through 209.4 rad in 1 min.

$w = \dfrac{\theta}{T}$

$w = \dfrac{209.4395}{60}$

$\doteq 3.49$

The angular velocity of a point P on a long-playing record is 3.49 rad/s.

To relate linear velocity to angular velocity, we substitute arc length, $r\theta$, for D and angular velocity, w, for $\dfrac{\theta}{T}$ in the formula $R = \dfrac{D}{T}$.

$$R = \frac{D}{T} = \frac{r\theta}{T} = r\left(\frac{\theta}{T}\right) = rw$$

$$R = rw$$

where R is the linear velocity,
r is the radius of the circle, and
w is the angular velocity.

Example. A V-belt runs a pulley with a radius of 11.5 cm at 240 r/min.
(a) Find the angular velocity of the pulley in rad/s.
(b) Find the linear velocity of the V-belt in cm/s.

Solution:
(a) Change revolutions to radians.
$$240 = 240 \times 2\pi$$
$$= 480\pi$$
Angular velocity
$$w = \frac{\theta}{T}$$
$$w = \frac{480\pi}{60}$$
$$= 8\pi$$

Using a calculator, press

2 4 0 × 2 × π =

The display is `1507.96447`

÷ 6 0 =

The display is `25.132741`

(b) To find the linear velocity, use
$$R = rw$$
$$R = 11.5 \times 8\pi$$
$$= 92\pi$$
$$\doteq 289$$

∴ the angular velocity is 8π rad/s, and the linear velocity of the V-belt is 289 cm/s.

EXERCISE 7.2

B

1. A wheel is turning at 8 rad/s. The radius of the wheel is 24 cm.
What is the linear velocity of a point on the rim of the wheel in cm/s?

2. Find the angular velocity, w, of a point on a circle, 20 cm from the centre of rotation, turning through an angle of 8π rad in 5 s.

3. Find the angular velocity for each of the following hands on a clock.
(a) the second hand
(b) the minute hand
(c) the hour hand

4. Find the angular velocity for a point on the circumference of a 45 r/min record.

5. A pulley 10 cm in diameter is rotating at 2500 r/min.
(a) Find the angular velocity.
(b) Find the linear velocity of a point on the circumference of the pulley to determine the belt speed.

6. Find the linear velocity for each of the following.
(a) the tip of a second hand on a clock if the hand is 12 cm long from the centre
(b) the tip of an aircraft propeller 2.4 m long rotating at 850 r/min
(c) a point on the edge of a bicycle wheel with a diameter of 65 cm turning at 25 r/min
(d) a point on a long-playing record, 6 cm from the centre

7.3 ANGLES IN STANDARD POSITION

An angle is in standard position if it is related to a pair of coordinate axes so that its vertex is at the origin and the initial arm lies along the positive x-axis. If P is a point on the terminal arm, then ∠POX is in standard position.

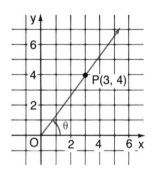

Example 1. The point P(3, 4) lies on the terminal arm of an angle, θ, that is in standard position.
Calculate the distance OP.

Solution: From the diagram,

$$OP^2 = 3^2 + 4^2$$
$$= 9 + 16$$
$$= 25$$
$$OP = 25$$

Consider a right triangle placed on a set of axes so that ∠θ is in standard position. The adjacent side is along the x-axis, and its length equals the x-coordinate. The length of the opposite side is the y-coordinate. The hypotenuse is $r = \sqrt{x^2 + y^2}$. The trigonometric functions can now be defined in terms of x, y, and r.

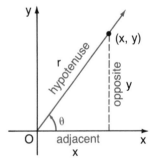

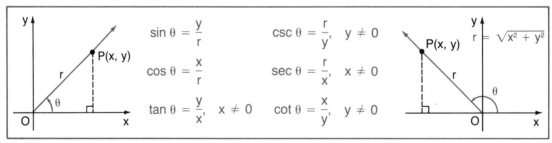

$$\sin \theta = \frac{y}{r} \qquad \csc \theta = \frac{r}{y}, \quad y \neq 0$$
$$\cos \theta = \frac{x}{r} \qquad \sec \theta = \frac{r}{x}, \quad x \neq 0$$
$$\tan \theta = \frac{y}{x}, \quad x \neq 0 \qquad \cot \theta = \frac{x}{y}, \quad y \neq 0$$

Note that while x and y can be positive or negative, r is always positive.

With these definitions, the trigonometric ratios for the angle in Example 1 are as follows:

$$\sin \theta = \frac{4}{5} \qquad\qquad \csc \theta = \frac{5}{4}$$

$$\cos \theta = \frac{3}{5} \qquad\qquad \sec \theta = \frac{5}{3}$$

$$\tan \theta = \frac{4}{3} \qquad\qquad \cot \theta = \frac{3}{4}$$

Example 2. If $(-12, 5)$ is a point on the terminal arm of $\angle\theta$ in standard position, find the values of the six trigonometric functions.

Solution: $r = \sqrt{x^2 + y^2}$

$$r = \sqrt{(-12)^2 + 5^2}$$
$$= \sqrt{169}$$
$$= 13$$

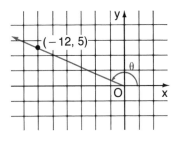

$\sin\theta = \frac{5}{13}$ $\qquad$ $\csc\theta = \frac{13}{5}$

$\cos\theta = -\frac{12}{13}$ $\qquad$ $\sec\theta = -\frac{13}{12}$

$\tan\theta = -\frac{5}{12}$ $\qquad$ $\cot\theta = -\frac{12}{5}$

In order to locate angles in standard position quickly, we identify each angle as being in one of four quadrants. Angles less than 90° are in the first quadrant, angles from 90° to 180° are in the second quadrant, angles from 180° to 270° are in the third quadrant, and angles from 270° to 360° are in the fourth quadrant.

In the figure on the right, $\angle POX$ is a third quadrant angle. Since $\angle POX$ can be the result of either a clockwise or counter-clockwise rotation, we eliminate confusion by agreeing to designate a counter-clockwise rotation as positive.

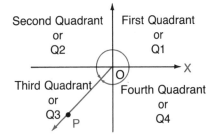

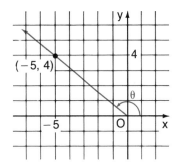

Example 3. If θ is a second quadrant angle and $\tan\theta = -\frac{4}{5}$, find the values of the other five trigonometric functions.

Solution: Since $\tan\theta = -\frac{4}{5}$ and θ is a second quadrant angle, $y = 4$ and $x = -5$ are one pair of values for x and y.

$r = \sqrt{x^2 + y^2}$
$$r = \sqrt{(-5)^2 + (4)^2}$$
$$= \sqrt{25 + 16}$$
$$= \sqrt{41}$$

$\sin\theta = \dfrac{4}{\sqrt{41}}$ $\qquad$ $\csc\theta = \dfrac{\sqrt{41}}{4}$

$\cos\theta = \dfrac{-5}{\sqrt{41}}$ $\qquad$ $\sec\theta = \dfrac{\sqrt{41}}{-5}$

$\tan\theta = \dfrac{4}{-5}$ $\qquad$ $\cot\theta = \dfrac{-5}{4}$

EXERCISE 7.3

A

1. State the measurement in degrees of each of the angles indicated.

(a)

(b)

(c)

(d)

(e)

(f)

(g)

(h)

(i)

(j)

(k)

(l)

B

2. For each of the diagrams below,
(a) calculate the value of r,
(b) state the six trigonometric ratios.

(i)
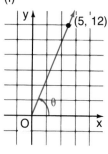

(ii)
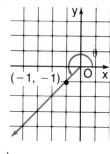

(iii)
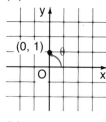

(iv)
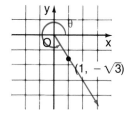

(v)
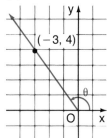

(vi)
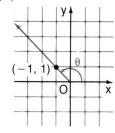

3. If θ is a second quadrant angle and $\cos \theta = -0.8$, state the coordinates of a point on the terminal arm and find $\sin \theta$.

4. If θ is a third quadrant angle and $\tan \theta = 1$, state the coordinates of a point on the terminal arm and find $\cos \theta$.

5. If $\sin \theta = \frac{5}{13}$, where θ is an angle in standard position,
(a) calculate two possible values for x,
(b) make a diagram for each possibility,
(c) state the other trigonometric ratios.

7.4 SPECIAL ANGLES

In trigonometry the 30°–60°–90° triangle and the 45°–45°–90° triangle contain special angles. In the following exercise we will find the trigonometric ratios associated with these right triangles and other special angles.

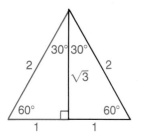

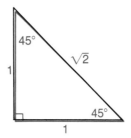

EXERCISE 7.4

B

1. Find the six trigonometric ratios for each of the following.
(a) 60°   (b) 150°

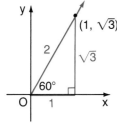   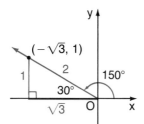

(c) 45°   (d) 225°

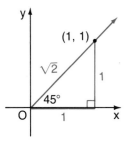   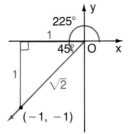

(e) 120°   (f) 30°   (g) 135°

(h) 315°   (i) 240°   (j) 210°
Draw diagrams for (e) to (j).

2. Find the six trigonometric ratios for each of the following.
(a) 0°   (b) 90°

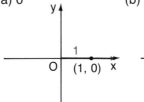

(c) 180°   (d) 270°

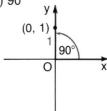

3. Find the six trigonometric ratios for each angle whose radian measure is given.
(π rad = 180°)

(a) $\dfrac{3\pi}{2}$ (b) $\dfrac{11\pi}{6}$ (c) $\dfrac{7\pi}{3}$

(d) $\dfrac{5\pi}{2}$ (e) $\dfrac{7\pi}{6}$ (f) $\dfrac{7\pi}{4}$

7.5 GRAPHING TRIGONOMETRIC FUNCTIONS

In business the fiscal year is divided into four quarters for the purpose of reporting profits and losses to shareholders. The pattern for reporting is repeated in the following year. We say that the fiscal year is cyclic or periodic, and the four quarters of the year make up one period. In mathematics there are many examples of functions that are periodic. From the following graph we see that the values for y are repeated and the period is 2.

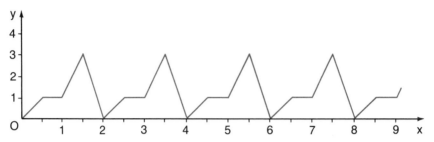

The cyclic nature of the values of the trigonometric functions can be investigated using a circle with a radius of 1, that is, a unit circle. If a circle with a radius of 1 is placed with its centre at the origin, then every angle in standard position determines a point on the unit circle. Angles θ and $\theta + 360°$ (θ and $\theta + 2\pi$) determine the same point P on the unit circle, so that the values of x and y are repeated.

In the exercise the unit circle is used to determine the values of sin θ, cos θ, and tan θ for $0° \le \theta \le 360°$.

EXERCISE 7.5

B 1. The following circle has a radius of 1.0 units and is placed with its centre at the origin of a pair of coordinate axes.
Find the coordinates for points A, B, C, ..., X.

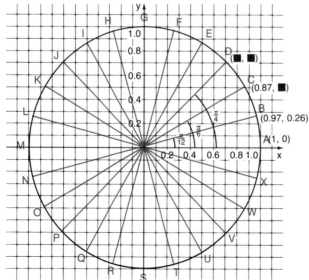

Since r = 1,

$$\sin \theta = \frac{y}{1}, \text{ and}$$

$$\cos \theta = \frac{x}{1}.$$

∴ the ordered pairs (x, y) are (cos θ, sin θ)

∴ for any point on this unit circle, the ordered pairs are (cos θ, sin θ).

2. The graph of y = sin θ

(a) Complete the following table using the results of question 1.

θ (radians)	0	$\dfrac{\pi}{12}$	$\dfrac{\pi}{6}$	$\dfrac{\pi}{4}$	$\dfrac{\pi}{3}$	$\dfrac{5\pi}{12}$	$\dfrac{\pi}{2}$	$\dfrac{7\pi}{12}$	$\dfrac{2\pi}{3}$	$\dfrac{3\pi}{4}$	$\dfrac{5\pi}{6}$	...	2π
θ (degrees)	0°	15°	30°	45°	60°	75°	90°	105°	120°	135°	150°	...	360°
sin θ													

(b) Using θ- and y-axes, plot the values of y = sin θ from the table above and draw a smooth curve through the points.

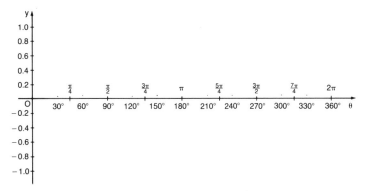

Using a calculator, we can prepare a table of values for ordered pairs (θ, sin θ), 0° ⩽ θ ⩽ 90°. Using these values, we can draw the graph of y = sin θ.

θ	sin θ	(θ, sin θ)
0°	0	(0°, 0)
5°	0.087 155 742	(5°, 0.09)
10°	0.173 648 177	(10°, 0.17)
15°	0.258 819 045	(15°, 0.26)
20°	0.342 020 143	(20°, 0.34)
25°	0.422 618 261	(25°, 0.42)
30°	0.5	(30°, 0.5)
35°	0.573 576 436	(35°, 0.57)
40°	0.642 787 609	(40°, 0.64)
45°	0.707 106 781	(45°, 0.71)
50°	0.766 044 443	(50°, 0.77)
55°	0.819 152 044	(55°, 0.82)
60°	0.866 025 403	(60°, 0.87)
65°	0.906 307 787	(65°, 0.91)
70°	0.939 692 62	(70°, 0.94)
75°	0.965 925 826	(75°, 0.97)
80°	0.984 807 753	(80°, 0.98)
85°	0.996 194 698	(85°, 0.996)
90°	1.0	(90°, 1)

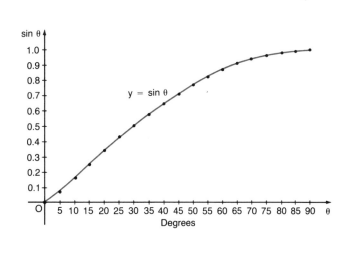

From the graph for 0° to 90°, we see that the graph of the sine function, y = sin θ, is a smooth curve. This enables us to sketch a reasonably accurate graph using the values derived from the unit circle.

3. The graph of $y = \cos \theta$
(a) Complete the following table using the results of question 1.

θ (radians)	0	$\dfrac{\pi}{12}$	$\dfrac{\pi}{6}$	$\dfrac{\pi}{4}$	$\dfrac{\pi}{3}$	$\dfrac{5\pi}{12}$	$\dfrac{\pi}{2}$	$\dfrac{7\pi}{12}$	$\dfrac{2\pi}{3}$	$\dfrac{3\pi}{4}$	$\dfrac{5\pi}{6}$	...	2π
θ (degrees)	0°	15°	30°	45°	60°	75°	90°	105°	120°	135°	150°	...	360°
$\cos \theta$													

(b) Using θ- and y-axes, plot the values of $y = \cos \theta$ from the table above and draw a smooth curve through the points.

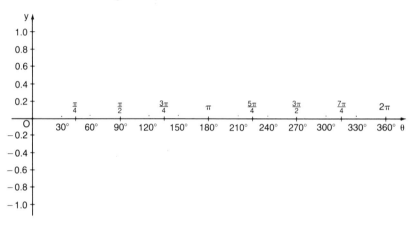

(c) From the graph, find
    (i) the maximum value of $\cos \theta$,
    (ii) the minimum value of $\cos \theta$.
(d) Use your graph to complete the following table.

θ			50°				215°
$\cos \theta$	0.0	0.5		0.41	-0.5	-0.87	

Since every value of θ determines a unique value for cos θ, the graph of the ordered pairs (θ, cos θ) is the graph of a function. This is called the cosine function.

(e) Determine what happens to the curve for values of θ greater than 360° or less than 0°.

4. (a) On the same set of axes, 0° ≤ θ ≤ 360°, draw the graphs of
        (i) y = sin θ   (ii) y = cos θ
   (b) State the values of θ for which
        sin θ = cos θ

5. Draw a graph for y = −sin θ using values of θ from 0° to 360° at 30° intervals.

6. (a) On the same axes, 0° ≤ θ ≤ 360°, draw the graphs of
        (i) y = sin θ   (ii) y = cos θ   (iii) y = sin θ + cos θ
   (b) State the value(s) for which sin θ + cos θ is
   (i) a maximum,   (ii) a minimum,   (iii) zero.

7. The graph of $y = \tan \theta$

(a) Complete the following table using the results of question 1.
Use a dash where the value is undefined.

θ (radians)	0	$\dfrac{\pi}{12}$	$\dfrac{\pi}{6}$	$\dfrac{\pi}{4}$	$\dfrac{\pi}{3}$	$\dfrac{5\pi}{12}$	$\dfrac{\pi}{2}$	$\dfrac{7\pi}{12}$	$\dfrac{2\pi}{3}$	$\dfrac{3\pi}{4}$	$\dfrac{5\pi}{6}$	...	2π
θ (degrees)	0°	15°	30°	45°	60°	75°	90°	105°	120°	135°	150°	...	360°
$\tan \theta$													

(b) Using θ- and y-axes, draw dotted lines parallel to the y-axis at the values of θ for which $\tan \theta$ is undefined. Since $\tan \theta$ is not defined for these values, no point on the graph of $y = \tan \theta$ can lie on these dotted lines. Plot the values of $y = \tan \theta$ from the table above and draw a smooth curve through the points.

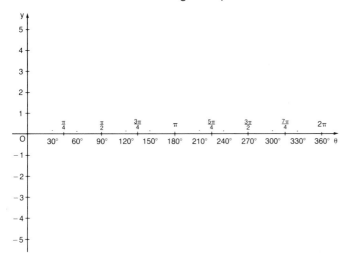

(c) Use your graph to complete the following table.

θ						135°	330°
$\tan \theta$	0	1.0	−1.0	0.7	1.7		

Since every value of θ determines a unique value for $\tan \theta$, the graph of the ordered pairs $(\theta, \tan \theta)$ is the graph of a function. This is called the tangent function.

(d) Determine what happens to the curve for values of θ greater than 360° or less than 0°.

The sine, cosine, and tangent functions are called the primary trigonometric functions.

Spreadsheet activities related to this topic are found in section 15.5.

7.6 AMPLITUDE OF Y = A SIN θ AND Y = A COS θ

We can sketch one cycle of the graph of $y = \sin\theta$ by accurately plotting the five critical points:

$$(0°, 0), (90°, 1), (180°, 0), (270°, -1), \text{ and } (360°, 0).$$

In radian measure these points are

$$(0, 0), \left(\frac{\pi}{2}, 1\right), (\pi, 0), \left(\frac{3\pi}{2}, -1\right), \text{ and } (2\pi, 0).$$

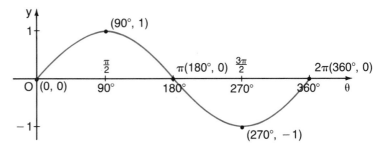

Similarly, we can sketch the graph of $y = \cos\theta$ using the five critical points. If the graph of $y = \cos\theta$ is shifted 90° $\left(\frac{\pi}{2} \text{ rad}\right)$ to the right, it will match the graph of $y = \sin\theta$.

Graphs that look like a graph of $y = \sin\theta$ are called sinusoids.

In this section we will investigate the graph of $y = a \sin\theta$ and discover the five critical points.

Investigation

1. Complete the following table in your notebook.

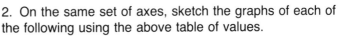

θ	0°	45°	90°	135°	180°	225°	270°	315°	360°
$y = \sin\theta$	0	0.7	1.0	0.7	0	-0.7	-1	-0.7	0
$y = 2\sin\theta$		1.4							
$y = 3\sin\theta$				2.1					
$y = \frac{1}{2}\sin\theta$						-0.35			

2. On the same set of axes, sketch the graphs of each of the following using the above table of values.
(a) $y = \sin\theta$ (b) $y = 2\sin\theta$
(c) $y = 3\sin\theta$ (d) $y = \frac{1}{2}\sin\theta$

These are the graphs defined by

$$y = a \sin \theta, \text{ for a} \in \{\tfrac{1}{2}, 1, 2, 3\}$$

The a in $y = a \sin \theta$ is the amplitude of the function.

3. Complete the following table in your notebook.

Defining Sentence	Maximum Value	Minimum Value	Amplitude
$y = \sin \theta$			
$y = 2 \sin \theta$	2		
$y = 3 \sin \theta$		-3	
$y = \tfrac{1}{2} \sin \theta$			$\tfrac{1}{2}$
$y = a \sin \theta$			

EXERCISE 7.6

A

1. State the amplitude of the following curves.

(a)

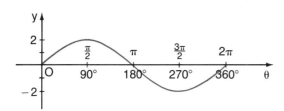

(b)

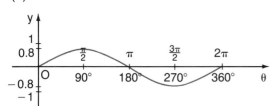

(c)

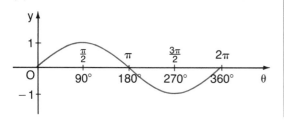

2. State the amplitude of the graph defined by each of the following.
(a) $y = 3 \sin \theta$
(b) $y = 7 \sin \theta$
(c) $y = 24 \sin \theta$
(d) $y = m \sin \theta, m > 0$
(e) $y = -3 \sin \theta$
(f) $y = \tfrac{1}{3} \sin \theta$

B

3. Sketch the graphs defined by each of the following.
(a) $y = 2 \sin \theta$, $0° \leqslant \theta \leqslant 720°$
(b) $y = 3 \sin \theta$, $0° \leqslant \theta \leqslant 540°$
(c) $y = \sin \theta$, $0° \leqslant \theta \leqslant 180°$
(d) $y = 10 \sin \theta$, $0° \leqslant \theta \leqslant 90°$
(e) $y = \sin \theta$, $0° \leqslant \theta \leqslant 720°$

C

4. Sketch the graphs defined by each of the following.
(a) $y = 3 \cos \theta$, $0° \leqslant \theta \leqslant 360°$
(b) $y = 2 \cos \theta$, $0° \leqslant \theta \leqslant 540°$
(c) $y = \tfrac{1}{2} \cos \theta$, $0° \leqslant \theta \leqslant 720°$

5. Use the MICRO MATH on page 189 with $k = 1$ and $c = 0$ to calculate the 5 critical points.

7.7 PERIOD OF Y = SIN Kθ AND Y = COS Kθ

In the previous section we learned how to sketch graphs of y = a sin θ and y = a cos θ using the five critical points method. In this section we will determine the effect that k has on the graphs of the functions y = sin kθ and y = cos kθ.

Example. Sketch the graph of y = sin 2θ for 0° ≤ θ ≤ 360°.

Solution: Prepare a table of values for y = sin θ and y = sin 2θ to find the five critical points. Note that where the pattern is not clear, additional points must be determined.

θ	0°	30°	45°	60°	90°	180°	270°	360°
y = sin θ	0	0.50	0.71	0.87	1.0	0	− 1.0	0
2θ	0°	60°	90°	120°	180°	360°	540°	720°
y = sin 2θ	0	0.87	1.0	0.87	0	0	0	0

Following are the graphs of y = sin θ and y = sin 2θ.

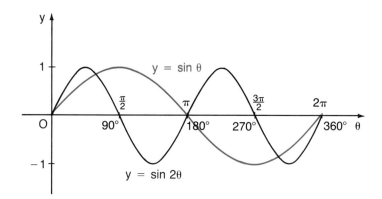

The function y = sin 2θ makes two complete cycles in 360° (2π rad) whereas y = sin θ makes only one complete cycle. Thus the period of y = sin 2θ is 180° (π rad). This suggests that the 2 in y = sin 2θ affects only the period of the function.

Investigation

Complete the following table in your notebook, and sketch the graph of each on the same set of axes.

θ	0°	45°	90°	180°	270°	360°	Additional values if required	Period
y = sin θ	0	0.7	1.0	0	−1.0	0		360°
2θ	0°							
y = sin 2θ			0					
3θ	0°		270°					
y = sin 3θ								
$\frac{1}{2}$θ	0°	$22\frac{1}{2}°$	45°					
y = sin $\frac{1}{2}$θ								

These are the graphs defined by y = sin kθ for k ∈ {$\frac{1}{2}$, 1, 2, 3}.

The k in y = sin kθ determines the period, $\frac{360°}{k}$, of the function. For the defining equation y = 3 sin 4θ, the 3 represents the amplitude. The period is $\frac{2\pi}{4} = \frac{\pi}{2}$.

EXERCISE 7.7

A 1. State the period for each of the following.

(a)

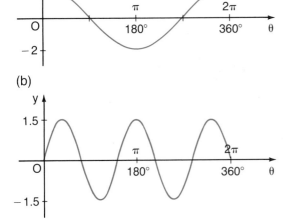

(b)

2. State the period for each of the following.

(a) y = sin θ   (b) y = 2 sin 3θ

(c) y = 3 sin 2θ   (d) y = 5 sin $\frac{1}{2}$θ

(e) y = 3 sin 4θ   (f) y = sin 2θ

B 3. Sketch the graphs defined by each of the following.

(a) y = sin 2θ,   0° ⩽ θ ⩽ 360°

(b) y = sin 4θ,   0° ⩽ θ ⩽ 180°

(c) y = sin $\frac{1}{2}$θ,   0° ⩽ θ ⩽ 720°

4. Sketch the graphs defined by each of the following.

(a) y = 3 sin 2θ,   0° ⩽ θ ⩽ 360°

(b) y = $\frac{1}{2}$ sin 2θ,   0° ⩽ θ ⩽ 360°

5. Sketch the graphs defined by each of the following.

(a) y = 2 cos 2θ,   0° ⩽ θ ⩽ 360°

(b) y = 3 cos $\frac{1}{2}$θ,   0° ⩽ θ ⩽ 720°

7.8 PHASE SHIFT OF Y = SIN (θ + C) AND Y = COS (θ + C)

If the graph of y = cos θ is shifted 90° to the right, then it will match with the graph of y = sin θ. This is called a phase shift.

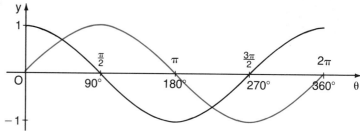

In this section we will investigate the factor that causes the curve to shift to the left or right. In graphing y = sin θ the origin (0, 0) is considered the first critical point in sketching the curve. The values in the following tables provide the five critical points in graphing y = sin(θ + 45°) and y = sin (θ − 45°).

θ	−45°	45°	135°	225°	315°
θ + 45°	0°	90°	180°	270°	360°
sin (θ + 45°)	0	1	0	−1	0

θ	45°	135°	225°	315°	405°
θ − 45°	0°	90°	180°	270°	360°
sin (θ − 45°)	0	1	0	−1	0

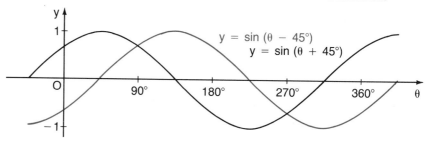

From the graph and tables, we see that the starting point for the cycle has been shifted 45° to the left for y = sin (θ + 45°) and 45° to the right for y = sin (θ − 45°). We call this horizontal displacement the phase shift of the function.

We generalize this result in the following statement.

> The phase angle for y = sin (θ + c) and y = cos (θ + c) is the constant angle c.
> For c > 0, the phase shift is c units to the left.
> For c < 0, the phase shift is c units to the right.

Investigation

1. (a) Complete the following tables in your notebook.
$y = \sin(\theta + 30°)$ and $y = \sin(\theta - 30°)$

θ	0°	30°	60°	90°	120°	150°	180°	210°	270°	300°	360°
$\theta + 30°$											
$\sin(\theta + 30°)$											

θ	0°	30°	60°	90°	120°	150°	180°	210°	270°	300°	360°
$\theta - 30°$											
$\sin(\theta - 30°)$											

(b) Graph the equations on the same set of axes.

2. (a) Sketch the graphs of $y = \sin\theta$ and $y = \cos\theta$ on the same set of axes.
(b) Find a value of c so that the graph of $y = \sin(\theta + c)$ is shifted onto the graph of $y = \cos\theta$.
(c) Find a value of c so that the graph of $y = \cos(\theta + c)$ is shifted onto the graph of $y = \sin\theta$.

EXERCISE 7.8

A 1. State the phase shift of each of the following.
(a) $y = \sin\theta$
(b) $y = \sin(\theta + 30°)$
(c) $y = \sin(\theta - 90°)$
(d) $y = \sin(\theta + 360°)$

2. State the phase shift from the original position of $y = \sin\theta$ in each of the following graphs.
(a)

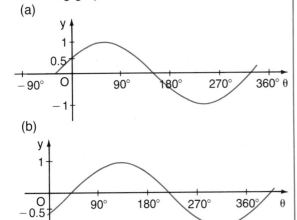

(b)

(c)

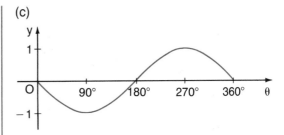

B 3. Sketch the graph of each of the following.
(a) $y = \sin(\theta + 30°)$, $0° \leqslant \theta \leqslant 540°$
(b) $y = \sin(\theta + 45°)$, $0° \leqslant \theta \leqslant 180°$
(c) $y = \sin(\theta - 90°)$, $0° \leqslant \theta \leqslant 270°$
(d) $y = \sin(\theta + 180°)$, $0° \leqslant \theta \leqslant 360°$

4. Sketch the graph defined by the following.
(a) $y = \cos(\theta - 45°)$, $0° \leqslant \theta \leqslant 360°$
(b) $y = \cos(\theta + 45°)$, $0° \leqslant \theta \leqslant 270°$
(c) $y = \cos(\theta - 90°)$, $0° \leqslant \theta \leqslant 540°$
(d) $y = \tan(\theta + 90°)$, $0° \leqslant \theta \leqslant 360°$

5. Use the MICRO MATH on page 189 with $a = 1$ and $k = 1$ to calculate the 5 critical points.

7.9 THE GRAPH OF Y = A SIN K(θ + C)

In the three preceding sections we investigated the amplitude, a, the period, $\dfrac{360°}{k}$, and the phase shift, c, in sinusoids of the type

$$y = a \sin \theta, \quad y = \sin k\theta, \quad \text{and } y = \sin (\theta + c).$$

When we study the amplitude, period, and phase shift of the same curve, the result is a single equation as described below.

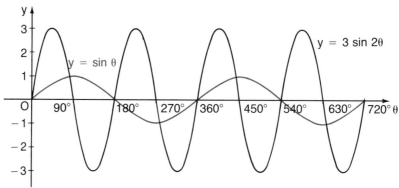

$$y = a \sin k(\theta + c), \quad a, k > 0$$

| amplitude (a) | period $\left(\dfrac{360°}{k}\right)$ | phase shift $c > 0$ (left) $c < 0$ (right) |

Example 1. Sketch the graph of y = 3 sin 2θ, 0° ≤ θ ≤ 720°.

Solution: From the given equation,

amplitude: 3,   period: $\dfrac{360°}{2}$ = 180°,   phase shift: 0°

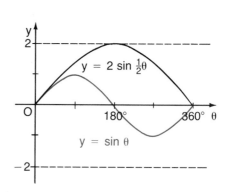

y = 3 sin 2θ

y = sin θ

Example 2. Sketch the graph of y = 2 sin ½θ, 0° ≤ θ ≤ 360°.

Solution:
From the equation, amplitude: 2,

$$\text{period: } \dfrac{360°}{\frac{1}{2}} = 720°,$$

phase shift: 0°

The graph is sketched as follows:
Using a calculator to evaluate
y = 2 sin ½θ for θ = 90°, press

The display is 1.41421356

y = 2 sin ½θ

y = sin θ

Example 3. Sketch the graph of $y = \sin(2\theta + 60°)$, $0° \leqslant \theta \leqslant 360°$.

Solution:
We rewrite the defining sentence

$$y = \sin(2\theta + 60°)$$
$$y = \sin 2(\theta + 30°)$$

The values can now be read from the equation, amplitude:1,

$$\text{period: } \frac{360°}{2} = 180°,$$

phase shift: 30° (left)

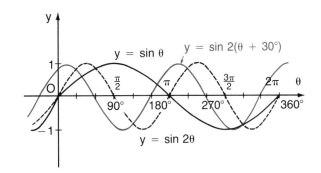

Using a calculator to evaluate $y = \sin 2(\theta + 30°)$ for $\theta = 90°$, press

`9` `0` `+` `3` `0` `=` `×` `2` `=` `sin`

The display is -0.86602541

EXERCISE 7.9

B 1. Complete the following table in your notebook.

Defining Sentence	a	Period	c
$y = 2 \sin \theta$			
$y = 3 \sin 2\theta$			
(sine)	2	360°	0°
$y = 2 \cos(\theta + 45°)$			
(sine)	1	360°	90° left
$y = \sin(2\theta + 90°)$			
(sine)	3	180°	0°
(sine)	2	720°	0°

2. Sketch the graph for the domains indicated in the following.

(a) $y = 3 \sin \theta$, $0° \leqslant \theta \leqslant 720°$
(b) $y = 2 \sin \theta$, $0° \leqslant \theta \leqslant 360°$
(c) $y = 2 \sin(\theta + 45°)$, $0° \leqslant \theta \leqslant 180°$
(d) $y = 2 \sin(\theta - 45°)$, $0° \leqslant \theta \leqslant 180°$
(e) $y = \sin 2\theta$, $0° \leqslant \theta \leqslant 720°$
(f) $y = \sin 3\theta$, $0° \leqslant \theta \leqslant 360°$
(g) $y = 3 \sin \frac{1}{2}\theta$, $0° \leqslant \theta \leqslant 720°$

3. On the same set of axes, sketch the graphs of the following for $-360° \leqslant \theta \leqslant 360°$.
(a) $y = \sin \theta$ (b) $y = 2 \sin \theta$ (c) $y = \sin 2\theta$

C 4. Sketch the graph for each of the following.
(a) $y = 3 \sin 2(\theta - 45°)$, $0° \leqslant \theta \leqslant 180°$
(b) $y = 2 \sin \frac{1}{2}(\theta + 90°)$, $0° \leqslant \theta \leqslant 720°$

MICRO MATH

The following computer program prints the critical points for $y = a \sin k(\theta + c)$

```
NEW
10 PRINT"FIVE CRITICAL POINTS"
20 PRINT"FOR Y = A SIN K(X + C)"
23 INPUT"ENTER VALUE FOR A";A
27 INPUT"ENTER VALUE FOR K";K
30 INPUT"ENTER VALUE FOR C";C
40 PRINT"X","Y"
50 FOR X = 0 TO 4
60 Y=A*SIN(90*X*.0174533)
70 PRINT90*X/K-C,INT(Y*1000)/1000
80 NEXT X
90 END
RUN
```

7.10 APPLICATIONS OF Y = A SIN K(θ + C)

In the previous sections we found that the value of y in y = a sin k(θ + c) repeated itself at regular intervals as θ changed; and that we are able to draw graphs and find the amplitude, period, and phase shift for the given equation. In this section we will combine these concepts in examples that display cyclical patterns to model the real world mathematically.

READ

Example. A bicycle wheel has a radius of 20 cm. A point, P, on the tire travels up and down from the hub as the wheel turns.
(a) Draw a graph to show the height of the point above and below the hub for 1 complete rotation of the wheel.
(b) Write an equation for the graph in (a).

PLAN

Solution: (a) Let the vertical distance above (or below) the hub be y cm.
Let the angle through which the wheel turns be θ°.

SOLVE

Assuming that the wheel is turned counter-clockwise, the graph is as follows:

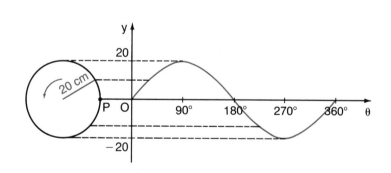

(b) The above graph is related to the general sine function,

$$y = a \sin k(\theta + c)$$

amplitude   period (360°)   phase shift
a = 20   k = 1   c = 0°

ANSWER

∴ an equation of the graph is y = 20 sin θ.

If the wheel in the example had been started from the following position, then the results would be as follows:

$$y = a \sin k(\theta + c)$$

amplitude period phase shift
a = 20   k = 1   c = 45° (left)

An equation for this position would be y = 20 sin (θ + 45°).

EXERCISE 7.10

B

1. A bicycle wheel with a radius of 15 cm turns twice in 1 s.
(a) Draw a graph to show the height above and below the hub during two rotations of a point on the wheel starting at 0°.
(b) State the amplitude, the period, and the phase shift.
(c) Write an equation for the graph.

2. A satellite is launched into orbit from Cape Canaveral, Florida, which has a longitude of approximately 80.5°W. The satellite circles the earth every 90 min, making a sine wave pattern with the Equator as the horizontal axis. The furthest distance the satellite travels from the Equator is approximately 1600 km.

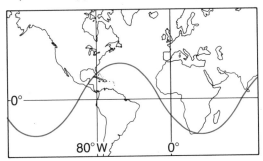

An equation for the path of the satellite is

$$y = 1600 \sin (\theta + 80.5°)$$

(a) What is the distance above or below the Equator at the following longitudes?
   (i) 0°   (ii) 225°   (iii) 300°
(b) How far is Cape Canaveral from the Equator?

3. A carnival ferris wheel has a radius of 10 m. We can assume that the bottom of the wheel almost touches the ground.

(a) Draw a graph to show how a person's height above the ground varies with the angle turned.
(b) Find an equation of the graph using

$$y = a \sin k(\theta + c) + d$$

where d is the height of the hub above the ground.

4. A water-wheel with a radius of 3 m has 0.5 m submerged below the water.

(a) Draw the graph of the height of the point, P, above (or below) the water during two complete cycles.
(b) Write an equation of the sine function that describes the height of the point above (or below) the hub of the wheel.

EXTRA

7.11 BIORHYTHM

Biorhythm is the name given to a theory that describes when a person will experience favourable and non-favourable days. The theory states that starting at birth, a person has the following cycles that simulate a sine wave.

Cycle	Period
Physical	23 d
Emotional	28 d
Intellectual	33 d

Each cycle consists of a high period, a low period, and a critical day when the cycle changes from one period to the other. We can graph these cycles to show when favourable and non-favourable days will occur. Since these functions are cyclical, we can show them on a graph using sine waves. The following graph shows a biorhythm chart for a thirty-one day month. The three graphs representing the physical, emotional, and intellectual cycles have periods of 23 d, 28 d, and 33 d respectively. Since the amplitudes are arbitrary, we give each of the cycles an amplitude of 1. There is no meaning attached to phase shift because the cycles have different periods.

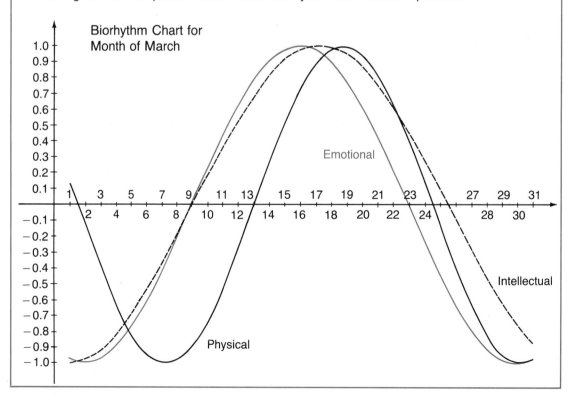

Example. Julius Caesar was born in Rome on July 12, 100 B.C., and died there on March 15, 44 B.C. Calculate Caesar's biorhythm chart for the day he died.

Solution:

Calculate the number of days Caesar lived.

July 12, 100 B.C. to July 12, 45 B.C.:
55 regular years

At 365 d/a plus 13 d for leap years

$$55 \times 365 + 13 = 20\ 088$$

July 13, 45 B.C. to March 15, 44 B.C.:

$$19 + 31 + 30 + 31 + 30$$
$$+ 31 + 31 + 28 + 15 = 246$$

Total number of days Caesar lived: 20 334

Dividing by the periods of the three cycles,

$20\ 334 \div 23 = 884$ cycles with 2 d into the next cycle.

$20\ 334 \div 28 = 726$ cycles with 6 d into the next cycle.

$20\ 334 \div 33 = 616$ cycles with 6 d into the next cycle.

On the day he died, Julius Caesar was into the second day of his physical cycle, the sixth day of his emotional cycle, and the sixth day of his intellectual cycle.
Was this a "good" day?

The following computer program computes a value for the physical, emotional, and intellectual cycles when we enter the number of days the person has been alive. Using the sine function, values from −1 to 1 are produced. By expressing the positions in the cycle as numbers from −1 to 1, we can also define a biorhythm coefficient as the mean value of the three cycles.

NEW

```
10 PRINT"BIORHYTHM CALCULATOR:-1 TO 1"
20 INPUT"NUMBER OF DAYS ALIVE";N
30 P=N/23
40 X = INT(P)
50 E=N/28
60 Y = INT(E)
70 I = N/33
80 Z = INT(I)
90 S=SIN(2*3.14159*(P-X))
110 T=SIN(2*3.14159*(E-Y))
120 U=SIN(2*3.14159*(I-Z))
140 PRINT"PHYSICAL    ";S
150 PRINT"EMOTIONAL   ";T
160 PRINT"INTELLECTUAL";U
170 PRINT"BIORHYTHM COEFFICIENT";(S+T+U)/3
180 PRINT"ANOTHER ENTRY? Y OR N"
190 INPUT Z$
200 IF Z$="Y" THEN 20
210 END
```

RUN

We can use the program to confirm the results of the example.

When the number of days (20 334) is entered, the computer gives the following values:

Physical Cycle:	0.520
Emotional Cycle:	0.975
Intellectual Cycle:	0.910
Biorhythm Coefficient:	0.810

EXERCISE 7.11

1. (a) Graph your own biorhythm cycle for this month.
(b) Calculate the values for the following events.
   (i) the day school started this year
   (ii) the day you entered high school
   (iii) the day you expect to graduate

2. Prepare biorhythm charts and calculate biorhythm values for the following personalities for these historical events.
(a) Napoleon Bonaparte, born on August 15, 1769, was defeated at Waterloo on June 18, 1815.
(b) Madame Marie Curie was born on November 7, 1867 and discovered the radioactive element polonium in July, 1898.

7.12 PROBLEM SOLVING

1. Your first birthday was $\frac{1}{365}$ of your life.

Your second birthday was $\frac{1}{730}$ of your life. What fraction of your life was your sixteenth birthday?

2. Lesa took temperature readings at 9:00 on five consecutive mornings. All five readings were different and the product of the readings was 12.
What were the temperatures?

3. A 6 L solution contains 12% alcohol. How much pure alcohol must be added to make a 25% solution?

4. The product of 15 873 and 7 is 111 111. Use this fact to find the following products mentally.

$$15\ 873 \times 35 = ?$$
$$15\ 873 \times 14 = ?$$
$$15\ 873 \times 49 = ?$$
$$15\ 873 \times 21 = ?$$
$$15\ 873 \times 56 = ?$$
$$15\ 873 \times\ ?\ = 666\ 666$$

5. Joe Lima operates a service station. He bought 100 items consisting of valve caps at 10¢ each, windshield cleaner at $3 per jug, and inner tubes at $8 each. The total cost for these items was $200.
How many of each did he buy?

6. A taxi leaves a downtown hotel and travels at 60 km/h to bring a passenger to the airport, which is 45 km away. The plane will be boarded in 50 min. After driving for 40 min, the taxi has a flat tire that takes 7 min to change.
How fast must the taxi travel to make it in time for the passenger to board the plane?

7. The radius of the earth is about 6400 km. The earth rotates once every 24 h.
How fast is a point on the surface of the earth at the equator moving?

8. The following diagram shows the locations of three pulleys on a truck engine. The crankshaft is turning at 1500 r/min.

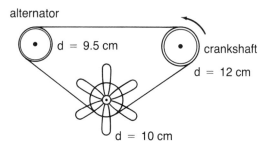

Find the speed of the other two pulleys.

9. A police car with its red beacon rotating pulls up alongside a stadium wall so that the beacon is 9 m from the wall. It takes the beacon 3 s to make one complete rotation.

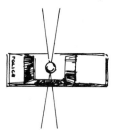

Draw a diagram in your notebook and locate the light spot on the wall 1 s after the beam is perpendicular to the wall.

10. A long-playing record album turns at $33\frac{1}{3}$ r/min while a single turns at 45 r/min.

Locate the information necessary to answer the following question.
How many times faster does a point on the rim of the album turn than a point on the rim of the single?

11. The tread on a new automobile tire is 1.2 cm thick. The outer diameter of the tire when inflated is 71.2 cm. After travelling 50 000 km, the tire has 0.3 cm of tread left. How much does the diameter of the tire decrease with each turn?

12. A police constable uses a wheel device to measure distances in radians when investigating accidents. The diameter of the wheel is 24 cm.
How many times will the wheel turn when the constable measures a distance of 24 m?

13. The shortest minute hand whose motion on a clock can be detected by the human eye is 25 cm.
Find the slowest linear motion in cm/s that the human eye can detect.

14. The following diagram shows two points, A and B, on a wheel.

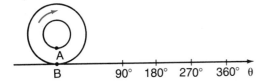

On the same axes, draw the path that each point would make during one complete rotation of the wheel.

15. The distance a javelin is thrown can be calculated using the formula

$$d = \frac{v^2 \sin 2\theta}{g}$$

where v is the velocity with which the javelin is thrown; θ is the angle the javelin makes with the horizontal at the time of release; and g = 9.8 m/s², the acceleration due to gravity.
(a) What measure of angle θ will give the greatest distance?
(b) How far will the javelin travel along the ground with an initial velocity of 16.5 m/s when thrown at this angle?

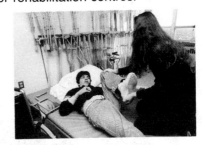

7.13 REVIEW EXERCISE

1. Convert the following radian measures to degree measures.

(a) $\dfrac{\pi}{4}$ (b) $\dfrac{\pi}{6}$ (c) $\dfrac{3\pi}{2}$

(d) 3.5   (e) 2.7   (f) 3.14

2. Convert the following degree measures to radian measure.

(a) 135°   (b) 315°   (c) 180°

(d) 25.7°   (e) 108.6°   (f) 200°

3. A wheel is turning at 15 rad/s. The radius of the wheel is 12.5 cm.
What is the linear velocity of a point on the rim of the wheel in cm/s?

4. Find the angular velocity of a cyclist travelling around a circular track with a radius of 20 m at 12 m/s.

5. What is the linear velocity of a satellite orbiting the earth every 90 min in a circular path with a diameter of 20 000 km?

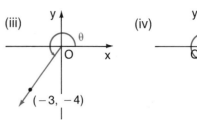

6. For each of the diagrams below,
(a) calculate the value of r,
(b) state the six trigonometric ratios.
(i)   (ii)

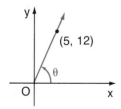
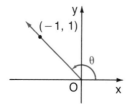

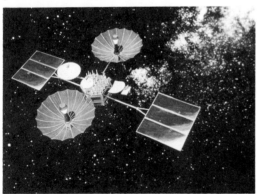

7. If θ is a second quadrant angle and sin θ = 0.5, find the value of tan θ and cos θ.

8. Sketch the graph of each of the following using the five critical points.
(a) y = sin θ,   0° ≤ θ ≤ 360°
(b) y = cos θ,   0° ≤ θ ≤ 720°
(c) y = tan θ,   0° ≤ θ ≤ 540°

9. Sketch the graph defined by each of the following.
(a) y = sin 2θ,   0° ≤ θ ≤ 180°
(b) y = 0.5 sin θ,   0° ≤ θ ≤ 360°
(c) y = sin 0.5θ,   0° ≤ θ ≤ 360°

10. Sketch the graph defined by each of the following.
(a) y = cos 0.5θ,   0° ≤ θ ≤ 360°
(b) y = 3 cos θ,   0° ≤ θ ≤ 180°
(c) y = cos 2θ,   0° ≤ θ ≤ 360°

11. Sketch the graph defined by each of the following.
(a) y = sin (θ + 45°),   0° ≤ θ ≤ 360°
(b) y = sin (θ − 30°),   0° ≤ θ ≤ 360°
(c) y = sin (θ + 180°),   0° ≤ θ ≤ 540°
(d) y = sin (θ + 90°),   0° ≤ θ ≤ 360°

12. (a) On the same set of axes, sketch the graphs of
         y = sin θ,   0° ≤ θ ≤ 360°
and   y = cos θ,   0° ≤ θ ≤ 360°
(b) From your graph, read the values of θ for which sin θ = cos θ. Check your results using a calculator.

θ	sin θ	cos θ

13. Sketch the graph of each of the following.
(a) $y = 2 \sin (\theta + 30)$, $0° \leqslant \theta \leqslant 360°$
(b) $y = 3 \sin 2\theta$, $0° \leqslant \theta \leqslant 360°$
(c) $y = \sin 2(\theta + 45)$, $0° \leqslant \theta \leqslant 360°$

14. Write an equation for each of the following graphs.
(a)

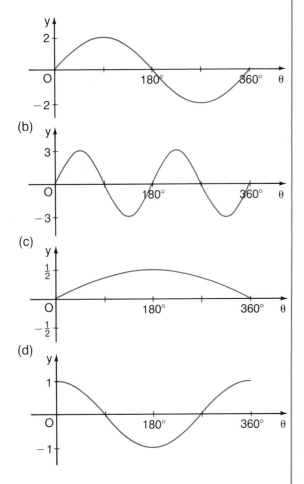

(b)

(c)

(d)

15. A truck wheel has a diameter of 2.4 m. Draw a graph to show the height above and below the hub of a point, P, on the tread during one complete rotation.

Using a computer with a colour graphics card, the following program displays the graphs of

$$y = a \sin \theta$$
$$y = a \cos \theta$$
$$y = a \tan \theta, \quad \text{for } -720° \leqslant \theta \leqslant 1080°.$$

NEW
```
10 CLS
20 PRINT"PROGRAM TO PLOT ANY"
30 PRINT"TRIGONOMETRIC GRAPH"
40 PRINT"OF THE FORM"
50 PRINT
60 PRINT"Y=A*SIN(X), Y=A*COS(X)"
70 PRINT"OR Y=A*TAN(X)"
80 PRINT
90 INPUT"ENTER SIN, COS, OR TAN";B$
100 CLS
110 PRINT"ENTER AN AMPLITUDE VALUE"
120 INPUT"BETWEEN 1 AND 8";A
130 IF A<1 THEN 100
140 IF A>8 THEN 100
150 CLS
160 SCREEN 1
170 PRINT"TRIGONOMETRIC GRAPHER"
180 FOR U=0 TO 360
190 IF B$="SIN" THEN Y=A*SIN(.1*U)
200 IF B$="COS" THEN Y=A*COS(.1*U)
210 IF B$="TAN" THEN Y=A*TAN(.1*U)
220 V=96-10*Y
230 V=INT(V+.5)
240 IF U=0 THEN 260
250 LINE (U,H)-(U+1,V)
260 H=V
270 NEXT U
280 LINE (0,97)-(1000,97)
290 PRINT SPC(17)"Y-AXIS"
300 FOR I=1 TO 12
310 PRINT
320 NEXT I
330 PRINT SPC(1)"X-AXIS"
340 LINE (128,0)-(128,200)
350 FOR P=1 TO 4
360 PRINT
370 NEXT P
380 INPUT"PRESS RETURN TO CONTINUE";R
390 GOTO 10
400 END
```
RUN

EXERCISE

1. Run the program and observe the graphs for A = 1, 2, 3, ..., 8.

7.14 CHAPTER 7 TEST

1. Express $\dfrac{3\pi}{4}$ rad in degree measure.

2. Express 225° in radian measure.

3. A wheel with a radius of 15 cm is turning at 10 rad/s. What is the linear velocity of a point on the rim?

4. Find the six trigonometric ratios for the angle given in each of the diagrams below.

(a)

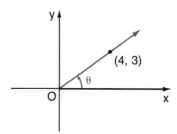

(4, 3)

θ

(b)

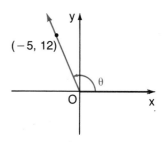

(−5, 12)

θ

5. Write an equation for each of the following graphs.

(a)

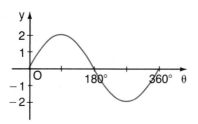

(b)

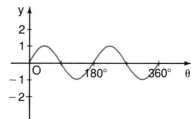

6. Sketch the graph of each of the following.
(a) y = sin θ,   0° ≤ θ ≤ 360°
(b) y = 2 sin θ,   0° ≤ θ ≤ 540°
(c) y = sin 2θ,   0° ≤ θ ≤ 360°
(d) y = sin (θ + 30°), 0° ≤ θ ≤ 360°
(e) y = 3 sin 2θ,   0° ≤ θ ≤ 540°

FORCES AND
VECTORS

8

REVIEW AND PREVIEW TO CHAPTER 8

RIGHT TRIANGLES — PYTHAGORAS

$a^2 + b^2 = c^2$

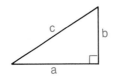

RIGHT TRIANGLES — TRIGONOMETRY

$a = m \cos \theta$

$b = m \sin \theta$

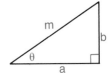

EXERCISE 1

1. Find the length of the indicated side in each of the following to the nearest tenth.

(a)   (b)

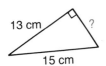

(c)   (d)

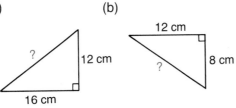

(e)   (f)

(g)   (h)

 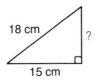

EXERCISE 2

1. Find the value of the variables in each of the following to the nearest tenth.

(a)   (b)

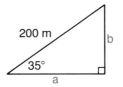

(c)   (d)

 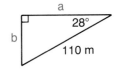

(e)   (f)

 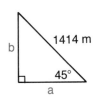

THE RULE OF THREE

Example. A cook at a roadhouse restaurant earns $80.50 for 7 h of work.
How much does the cook earn in 44 h?

Solution:
In 7 h the cook earns $80.50.

In 1 h the cook earns $\dfrac{\$80.50}{7}$.

In 44 h the cook earns $\quad 44 \times \dfrac{\$80.50}{7}$

$\qquad\qquad = \$506.00$

EXERCISE 3

1. If 1.5 L of engine oil costs $3, find the cost of 20 L.

2. It takes 3805 J to vaporize 20 g of dry ice at 56°C.
How much energy is required to vaporize 3 kg of ice at this temperature?

3. It takes 1000 computer chips to manufacture 125 small automobile computers.
How many automobile computers can be manufactured from a shipment of 469 128 chips?

4. It is possible to cut 22 automobile floor mats from 27.5 m of carpet material.
How much material is required to cut 100 floor mats?

5. A diesel engine will run for 3.25 h on 20 L of fuel.
How much fuel is required to run the engine for 24 h?

6. If 150 mL of toothpaste costs $1.49, what is the cost of 250 mL?

DISTANCE, RATE, AND TIME

$$D = RT, \quad R = \frac{D}{T}, \quad \text{and} \quad T = \frac{D}{R}$$

EXERCISE 4

1. How far will a train travel in 3.5 h at 65 km/h?

2. How long will it take to travel 175 km at 70 km/h?

3. What is the average speed of a truck that travels 200 km in 3.5 h?

4. How long will it take to run 10 km at 11 km/h?

5. How far will a train travel at 71.5 km/h in 4.75 h?

6. What is the average speed of a car that travels 210 km in 2.15 h?

7. The diameter of the earth is 12 800 km. A jet aircraft takes off and flies around the earth at the Equator at an average speed of 600 km/h. The aircraft requires 8 h for refuelling stops during the flight.
How many hours does it take to complete this flight around the earth?

8. A police cruiser leaves police headquarters at 09:00 and travels at 60 km/h. Fifteen minutes later, a second cruiser leaves police headquarters and travels at 90 km/h.
(a) How far apart are the cruisers at 10:00 if they travel in opposite directions?
(b) How far apart are the cruisers at 10:00 if they travel in the same direction?

8.1 VECTORS AND UNITS OF FORCE

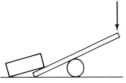

Objects that have magnitude and direction are called vectors. Vectors can be represented by a line segment with an arrow to show direction, or by an ordered pair with square brackets.

$$\overrightarrow{AB} = [4, 3]$$

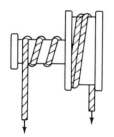

In the above example the vector can be identified geometrically by naming the directed line segment $\overrightarrow{AB}$, or algebraically by the ordered pair [4, 3]. This vector has a direction that causes a movement four units to the right and three units up. The magnitude of the vector can be measured, or calculated using the Pythagorean theorem. The length of the directed line segment shows the magnitude of the vector. The magnitude of $\overrightarrow{AB}$ is 5. In this section we will use vectors in geometric form to represent forces.

Forces are all around us. Our first experience with forces involves muscular exertion such as throwing a ball, lifting a book, or pulling a wagon. Forces are also at work when muscular effort is absent, for example, gravity and magnetism. Other kinds of forces include chemical, mechanical, nuclear, and electrical. In this chapter we will concern ourselves with applications of mechanical forces as shown in the diagrams at the left.

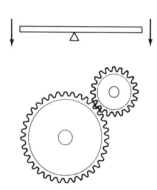

Forces can be represented by vectors. However, we must indicate the point of application in order to fully describe the force.

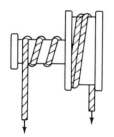

F
O
R
C
E

1. Direction

2. Point of Application

3. Magnitude

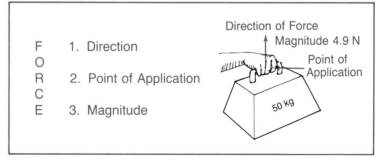

Force is measured in newtons (N). The force that will impart to a mass of 1 kg an acceleration of 1 m/s² has a magnitude of 1 N (newton). The units of force are derived from Newton's Second Law of Motion, $F = ma$, where F is the force, m is the mass of an object, and a is the acceleration. If we substitute $m = 50$ kg and $a = 9.8$ m/s² in the formula $F = ma$ we get

1 N = 1 kg × 1 m/s²

9.8 m/s² is the acceleration due to the earth's gravity.

$$F = (50 \text{ kg}) \times (9.8 \text{ m/s}^2)$$
$$= 490 \text{ N}$$

which is the force required to just lift the object.

Example 1. A force of 100 N is applied to a mass of 20 kg. What acceleration will be imparted to the 20 kg body?

Solution: From Newton's Second Law of Motion,

$$F = ma$$
$$100 \text{ N} = 20 \text{ kg} \times a \text{ m/s}^2$$
$$\frac{100}{20} \text{ m/s}^2 = a$$
$$5 \text{ m/s}^2 = a$$

The force produces an acceleration of 5 m/s².

Example 2. Using a scale of 1 N = 1 cm, draw vectors to represent the following forces.
(a) 3 N left
(b) 2 N down
(c) 1 N 45° upward and to the right

Solution: Scale: 1 N = 1 cm
(a)

3 N
←————————————

(b)

2 N ↓

(c)

1 N ↗ 45°

Note that the scale is always stated when scale drawings are used.

Sir Isaac Newton

Although the units of force have been derived using Newton's second law, this chapter is concerned with problems arising from the first and third laws.

Newton's First Law

When a body is at rest or moving with constant speed in a straight line, the resultant of all the forces exerted on the body is zero.

Newton's Third Law

Whenever one body exerts a force on another, the second always exerts on the first a force that is equal in magnitude but oppositely directed. (This is sometimes stated: For every action there is an equal and opposite reaction.)

EXERCISE 8.1

B

1. Find the force that causes a 25 kg body to accelerate at 15 m/s².

2. Find the mass of a body that is accelerated at 20 m/s² by a force of 3 N.

3. Find the acceleration when a mass of 12 kg is acted upon by a force of 30 N.

4. Find the force of gravity if the earth attracts a mass of 1 kg toward itself, giving it an acceleration of 9.8 m/s².

5. Find the mass of a satellite hurtling through space with an acceleration of 75 m/s², caused by a force of 900 N.

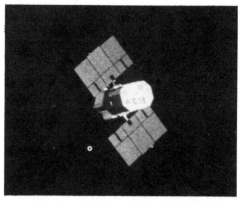

6. Using a scale of 5 N = 1 cm, make vector drawings of the following forces.
(a) 10 N to the right   (b) 20 N to the left
(c) 15 N up   (d) 25 N down
(e) 30 N to the left   (f) 20 N up

7. Using a scale of 10 N = 5 cm, make vector drawings of the following forces.
(a) 30 N, 45° upward and to the left
(b) 40 N, 45° downward and to the right
(c) 35 N, 45° upward and to the right
(d) 20 N, 45° downward and to the left

8.2 ROTATIONAL EFFECT OF FORCES: MOMENTS

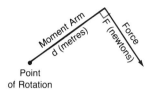

Point
of Rotation

When a force is applied to a box sitting on the floor, any motion applied would be in a straight line. When a force is applied along the rim of a steering wheel, the effect is to turn the wheel. This turning effect of a force about a point is called the moment of the force (measured in newton metres) and is found by multiplying the magnitude of the force by the perpendicular distance from the point of rotation to the line of action of the force.

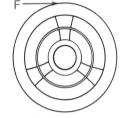

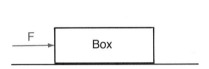

$$M = F \times d \text{ (newton metres)}$$

Example 1. What is the moment produced by a 10 N force applied 2 cm from the point of rotation?

Solution:
2 cm = 0.02 m

$M = F \times d$
$M = 10 \text{ N} \times 0.02 \text{ m}$
$\quad = 0.2 \text{ N·m}$

The moment is 0.2 N·m.

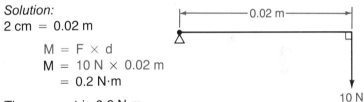

Example 2. What is the sum of the moments produced by forces of 30 N and 50 N applied 0.8 m and 1.2 m respectively from the point of rotation?

Solution:
$M = F \times d$
$M = 30 \text{ N} \times 0.8 \text{ m}$
$\quad = 24 \text{ N·m}$

$M = F \times d$
$M = 50 \text{ N} \times 1.2 \text{ m}$
$\quad = 60 \text{ N·m}$

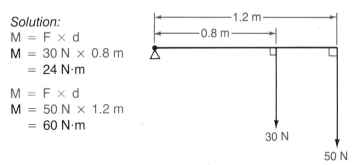

The sum of the moments is 24 N·m + 60 N·m = 84 N·m.

When two children sit on opposite ends of a seesaw, each produces a moment that tends to turn the system either clockwise or counter-clockwise.

How should the children be arranged so they just balance if child A is heavier than child B?

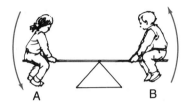

A   B

The mass of a body is the measure of the amount of matter present in the body and remains constant. The force of attraction between a mass and the earth (or any large mass such as the moon) is called the weight.

The weight of the mass on the surface of the earth can be found using the formula $F = ma$.

Weight in newtons $=$ mass in kilograms $\times$ 9.8 m/s^2

Because 9.8 gives awkward values, we sometimes use 10 to simplify calculations so that a mass of 1 kg has an approximate weight of 10 N on Earth.

> Gravity is the force of attraction that exists between any two masses.
>
> The force of gravity between an object and the earth is commonly called the weight of the object on Earth.

INVESTIGATING THE LAW OF MOMENTS

Objective: To compare the clockwise and counter-clockwise moments of a system in equilibrium.

Investigation 1.

1. Suspend a metre stick so that it balances (near the centre) and is free to rotate about the point from which it is suspended.

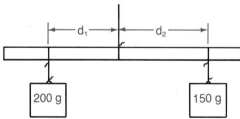

2. Suspend masses of 200 g and 150 g on opposite sides of the point of rotation, adjusting the positions of the masses until equilibrium occurs.

3. Record the distance from each mass to the point of rotation.

> A mass of 100 g has an approximate weight of 1 N.
>
> | Mass | Weight |
> | --- | --- |
> | 100 g | 1 N |
> | 150 g | 1.5 N |
> | 200 g | 2 N |
> | 500 g | 5 N |

4. Repeat the procedure four times, changing the positions of the masses and complete the following table in your notebook.

200 g mass		150 g mass	
d_1	M × Fd_1	d_2	M = F × d_2

5. The 200 g mass produces a counter-clockwise moment, and the 150 g mass produces a clockwise moment. Compare the clockwise moments to the counter-clockwise moments when the system is in equilibrium.

Investigation 2.

1. With the metre stick balanced near the centre, and using masses of 100 g, 50 g, and 200 g, set up five systems in equilibrium as shown in the diagram and complete the following table.

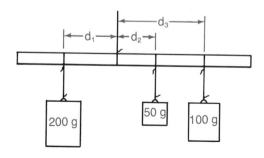

100 g mass		200 g mass		50 g mass		Sum
d_1	M_1 = F × d_1	d_2	M_2 = F × d_2	d_3	M_3 = F × d_3	M_2 + M_3

2. The 200 g mass produces a counter-clockwise moment about the point of rotation, and the 100 g and 50 g masses produce clockwise moments. Compare the clockwise moments and counter-clockwise moments.

Investigation 3.

1. Arrange four or five masses at various positions on a balanced metre stick to form a system in equilibrium.

2. Complete the following table in your notebook.

Counter-clockwise Moments		Clockwise Moments	
Sum		Sum	

3. Compare the sum of the clockwise moments to the sum of the counter-clockwise moments for a system in equilibrium.

Law of Moments

When a system is in equilibrium, the sum of the clockwise moments about any point is equal to the sum of the counter-clockwise moments about the same point.

Example 3. The system in the following diagram is in equilibrium.
Calculate the value of x.

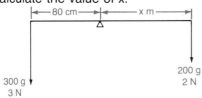

A 300 g mass has an approximate weight of 3 N.

Solution:

Counter-clockwise moment: $3 \text{ N} \times 0.8 \text{ m} = 2.4 \text{ N·m}$

Clockwise moment: $2 \text{ N} \times x \text{ m} = 2x \text{ N·m}$

Since the system is in equilibrium,

$$2x \times \text{N·m} = 2.4 \text{ N·m}$$
$$x = 1.2 \text{ m}$$

Therefore $x = 1.2$ m.

$E=mc^2$

Example 4. The system shown below is in equilibrium.
Calculate the value of x.

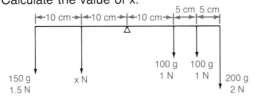

Solution:

Counter-clockwise moments: $1.5\,N \times 0.2\,m = 0.3\,N\cdot m$

$\underline{x\,N \times 0.1\,m = 0.1x\,N\cdot m}$

Total $\quad\quad (0.3 + 0.1x)\,N\cdot m$

Clockwise moments: $1\,N \times 0.10\,m = 0.10\,N\cdot m$

$1\,N \times 0.15\,m = 0.15\,N\cdot m$

$\underline{2\,N \times 0.20\,m = 0.40\,N\cdot m}$

Total $\quad\quad\quad = 0.65\,N\cdot m$

Since the system is in equilibrium,

$$0.30 + 0.10x = 0.65$$
$$0.10x = 0.65 - 0.30$$
$$0.10x = 0.35$$
$$x = 3.5$$

Therefore x is 3.5 N.

When the point of rotation is not at the centre of gravity of the metre stick, we must take into account the weight of the metre stick. The total weight of the metre stick is considered as a single force acting through the centre of gravity of the stick.

Example 5. A uniform 5 m plank has a mass of 20 kg. It is placed over a narrow bar 2 m from one end and two people sit on either end.
If an 80 kg person sits on the short end, what is the mass of the other person if the system is in equilibrium?

Solution:

We consider the 5 m plank to be a uniform rod with its entire mass acting through the centre as shown in the diagram.

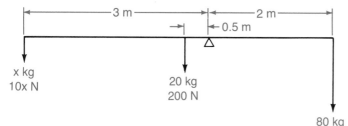

Since the system is in equilibrium, we equate the counter-clockwise and clockwise moments.

$$(10x \times 3) + (200 \times 0.5) = (800 \times 2)$$
$$30x + 100 = 1600$$
$$30x = 1500$$
$$x = 50$$

> A mass of 1 kg has an approximate weight of 10 N.

The other person has a mass of 50 kg.

EXERCISE 8.2

A 1. Calculate the moment of each of the following.

(a)

(b)

(c)

(d)

(e)

(f)

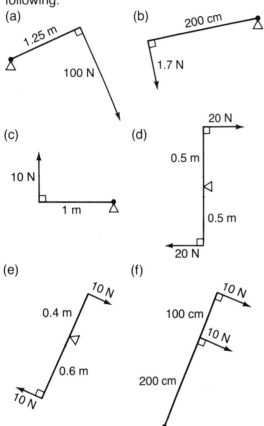

B 2. Assume each system to be in equilibrium and calculate the value of x in each diagram.

(a)

(b)

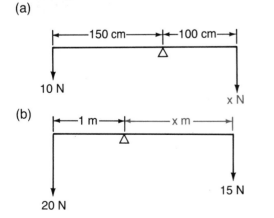

(c)

(d)

(e)

(f)

(g)

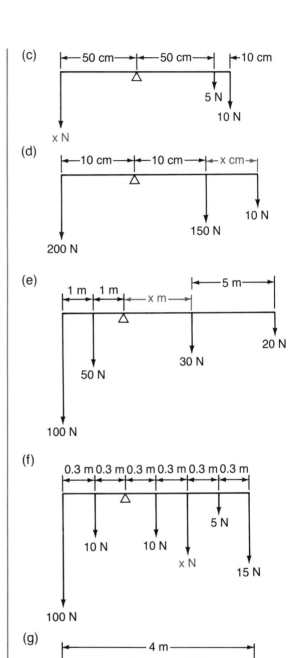

(h)

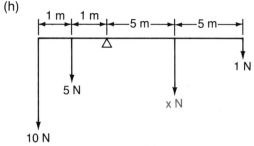

(i)

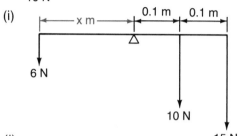

(j)

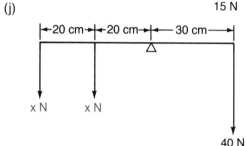

3. (a) Find the force of gravity in newtons exerted by the uniform rod in the following diagram if the system is in equilibrium.

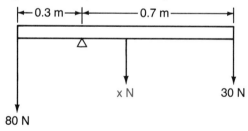

(b) Find the mass of the rod if an object that exerts a force of 10 N has a mass of approximately 1 kg.

4. A uniform rod 6 m long with a mass of 50 kg is placed on a pivot 2 m from one end.
If a 100 kg mass is placed at the short end, what mass must be placed at the long end to keep the system in equilibrium?

5. A 10 m concrete utility pole has its centre of gravity 4 m from the larger end. The pole has a mass of 150 kg and is placed on a trailer so that it pivots about its midpoint.
If a 300 kg mass is placed on the small end, what mass must be placed on the other end to form a system in equilibrium?

6. Find the force in the cable supporting the 10 m boom if the line of action in the cable is 4 m from the point of rotation and a force of 800 N is concentrated through the centre of the boom.

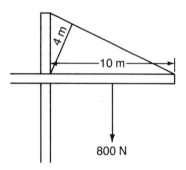

C7. A circular disc 1 m in diameter is pivoted about a horizontal axis through its centre and has a cord wrapped around its rim. A light rod 4 m long is fastened to the disc and an 85 N force is applied as shown in the diagram.

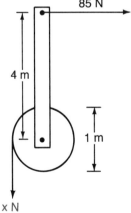

(a) Find the force that must be applied to the cord to form a system in equilibrium.
(b) What mass should be attached to the cord if a 1 kg mass weighs approximately 10 N?

8.3 SIMPLE MACHINES: MECHANICAL ADVANTAGE

A machine is a device that can multiply a force. The purpose of a machine is not to convert one form of energy into another, but to exert a force on an object that is different from (usually greater than) the force that was applied to the machine. Simple machines such as the lever, the inclined plane, the jackscrew, the wheel and axle, and the pulley will be studied in this section.

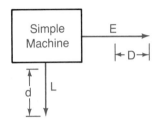

The force multiplication factor of a machine is called the mechanical advantage and is calculated by taking the ratio of the load (resistance to be overcome) to the effort (force applied to the machine to overcome the resistance).

The applied force, E, acts through a distance, D, while the force, L, is exerted through a distance, d.

Mechanical Advantage

$M.A. = \dfrac{L}{E}$	L: load
	E: effort

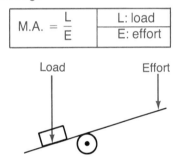

Load   Effort

Example 1. Find the mechanical advantage of the system shown below.

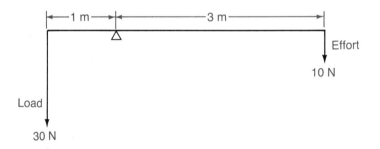

Solution: $M.A. = \dfrac{L}{E}$

$M.A. = \dfrac{30}{10}$

$= 3$

In this case every newton of force applied as effort results in 3 N being delivered to the load.

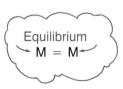

Equilibrium
M = M

THE LEVER

There are three classes of levers, identified by the location of the fulcrum (F), effort (E), and load (L). See the illustration at the right.

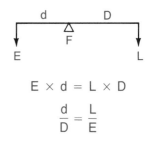

$$E \times d = L \times D$$
$$\frac{d}{D} = \frac{L}{E}$$

The mechanical advantage of the lever in Example 1 could also be calculated as follows:

$$\boxed{\text{M.A.} = \frac{\text{length of effort arm}}{\text{length of load arm}} = \frac{d}{D}}$$

In Example 1, the length of the effort arm is 3 m and the length of the load arm is 1 m.

$$\text{M.A.} = \frac{3}{1}$$
$$= 3$$

This is the same result as was found using $\frac{L}{E}$. Note that this "length method" is used only for a single effort and a single load (assuming the lever has no mass).

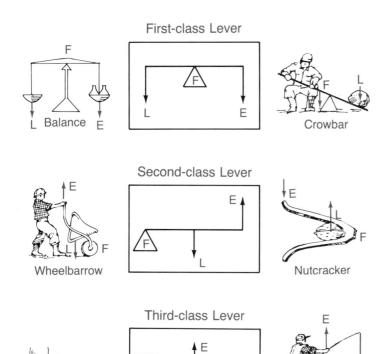

First-class Lever

L Balance E

Crowbar

Second-class Lever

Wheelbarrow

Nutcracker

Third-class Lever

Forearm

Fishing rod

THE INCLINED PLANE

When we wish to raise an object without exerting the required force vertically, we use an inclined plane. An inclined plane is often used to load trucks, and in parking ramps to get from one level to another. If we neglect friction, the mechanical advantage is

$$\text{M.A.} = \frac{\text{length of plane}}{\text{height}} = \frac{\ell}{h}$$

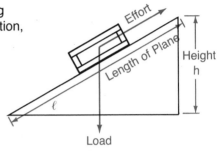

Example 2. An inclined plane is 4 m long and 1 m high. Neglecting friction, find the effort required to slide a load exerting a force of 1000 N up the plane.

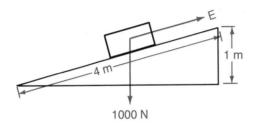

$E=mc^2$

Solution: M.A. $= \dfrac{\ell}{h}$ and M.A. $= \dfrac{L}{E}$

M.A. $= \dfrac{4}{1}$ M.A. $= \dfrac{1000}{E}$

$$\frac{4}{1} = \frac{1000}{E}$$

$4E = 1000$

$E = 250$

∴ an effort of 250 N is required to slide the load up the plane.

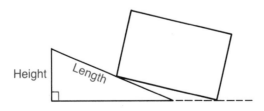

The wedge is considered to be an inclined plane. The applied force must overcome friction as well as raise the load up the slope.

THE JACKSCREW

If we cut a piece of paper in the shape of a right triangle and wrap it around a pencil, we see that a screw is really an inclined plane wound around a cylinder.

When great mechanical advantage is required to raise heavy objects, a jackscrew is used. One complete revolution of the lever arm causes one complete revolution of the screw, which moves the load a distance equal to the pitch of the screw. The mechanical advantage is

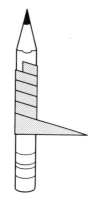

$$M.A. = \frac{2\pi\ell}{P}$$

where ℓ is the length of the lever arm and P is the pitch of the screw.

Example 3. The lever arm of a jackscrew is 1.5 m long.
    (a) If the screw has a pitch of 4 mm, find the mechanical advantage of this machine.
    (b) If friction is neglected, find the force necessary to raise a mass of 5 t.

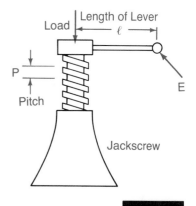

Solution: (a) Pitch: P = 4 mm
                 = 0.004 m

$$M.A. = \frac{2\pi\ell}{P}$$

$$M.A. = \frac{2 \times 3.14 \times 1.5}{0.004}$$

$$= 2355$$

∴ the mechanical advantage of the screw is 2355.

(b) M.A. $= \frac{L}{E}$, and the load L = 5 t

                           = 5000 kg

From part (a), M.A. = 2355

> A mass of 5000 kg has an approximate weight of 50 000 N.

$$2355 = \frac{50\ 000}{E}$$

$$E = \frac{50\ 000}{2355}$$

$$\doteq 21.2$$

∴ an effort of 21.2 N is required to raise a 5 t mass using the given jackscrew.

THE PULLEY

A pulley is either fixed or movable. A pulley can be used to change the direction of a force or to gain mechanical advantage.

The mechanical advantage of a system of pulleys is found by counting the number of ropes pulling in a direction opposite to the load.

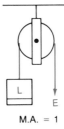

M.A. = 1

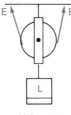

M.A. = 2

Example 4. Find the mechanical advantage and the effort required in each case to lift a mass of 250 kg.

(a)

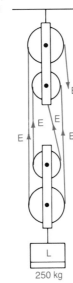

L
250 kg

(b)

L
250 kg

Solution:

(a) M.A. = 4

$$M.A. = \frac{L}{E}$$

$$4 = \frac{2500}{E}$$

$$4E = 2500$$

$$E = 625$$

∴ an effort of 625 N is required.

(b) M.A. = 3

$$M.A. = \frac{L}{E}$$

$$3 = \frac{2500}{E}$$

$$3E = 2500$$

$$E = 833\tfrac{1}{3}$$

∴ an effort of $833\tfrac{1}{3}$ N is required.

THE WHEEL AND AXLE

This machine consists of a wheel that is rigidly attached to an axle so that they turn as a unit. Doorknobs, faucet handles, and the steering wheel of a car are examples of the wheel and axle.

If R is the radius of the wheel, and r is the radius of the axle, then

End view

$L \times r = E \times R$

$$\frac{L}{E} = \frac{R}{r}$$

$$M.A. = \frac{R}{r}$$

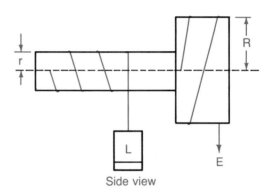

Side view

READ

Example 5. A wheel having a diameter of 0.40 m is attached to an axle with a radius of 2 cm. If a load of 3000 N is applied to the axle, find the effort that must be applied to the wheel to balance the load.

PLAN

Solution: 0.40 m diameter is equivalent to 0.20 m radius.

$2 \text{ cm} = 0.02 \text{ m}$

E=mc²

$$M.A. = \frac{R}{r}$$

$$M.A. = \frac{0.20}{0.02}$$

$$= 10$$

SOLVE

$$M.A. = \frac{L}{E} \quad \text{and} \quad M.A. = 10$$

$$10 = \frac{3000}{E}$$

$$10E = 3000$$

$$E = 300$$

ANSWER

∴ an effort of 300 N must be applied to the wheel.

EXERCISE 8.3

B

1. Identify the class of lever in the following systems and find the unknown quantity.

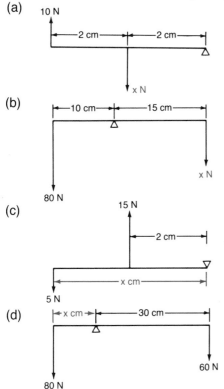

(a)
10 N

—2 cm— —2 cm—

x N

(b)
—10 cm— —15 cm—

x N

80 N

(c)
15 N

—2 cm—

x cm

5 N

(d)
x cm —30 cm—

60 N

80 N

2. What effort must a person apply to lift the wheelbarrow?
What is the mechanical advantage of the system?

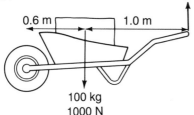

E

0.6 m   1.0 m

100 kg
1000 N

A mass of 100 kg exerts an approximate force of 1000 N.

3. A fishing rod is 1.75 m long.
If a person holds the rod 0.5 m from the end, what effort must be applied to raise a 1 kg fish?

4. A 5.0 m uniform lever having a mass of 50 kg rests on a fulcrum 1 m from one end.
   (a) What is the least distance a 75 kg person can sit from the fulcrum to raise a mass of 300 kg on the short end?
   (b) What is the mechanical advantage of this system?

5. A uniform rod used as a second-class lever is pivoted at one end. The rod is 3 m long and has a mass of 5 kg. Masses of 2 kg and 10 kg are placed 1 m and 2 m from the pivot respectively.
   (a) What effort must be applied to the end of the rod to balance it horizontally?
   (b) What is the mechanical advantage of the system?

6. (a) Calculate the load an effort of 30 N will balance in the given system.

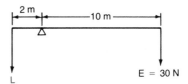

2 m
—10 m—

L

E = 30 N

   (b) What is the mechanical advantage of the system?

7. A uniform rod acting as a third-class lever is 3 m long and has a mass of 5 kg. The force applied is 200 N, 1 m from the fulcrum.
   (a) What is the load that the lever can lift?
   (b) What is the mechanical advantage of the system?

8. A crowbar is used to pry open a window that is stuck. When the crowbar is placed under the window, the fulcrum is 10 cm from the end.
   (a) If the crowbar is 70 cm long and the window offers a resistance of 1 kN, find the force that must be exerted on the end of the bar to open the window.
   (b) What is the mechanical advantage of the system?

9. An inclined plane has a length of 8 m and a height of 2 m.
Neglecting friction, what will be the effort required to move a piano having a mass of 600 kg up the plane?

10. The load on an axle exerts a force of 200 N.
If the radius of the wheel is 40 cm and the radius of the axle is 6 cm, what effort must be applied to the wheel to balance the load?

11. A jackscrew has a lever 1 m long.
If the screw has a pitch of 10 mm, what is the effort required to balance a load of 500 N?

12. (a) What is the mechanical advantage of each system?
(b) What effort is required to balance a load of 800 N for each?

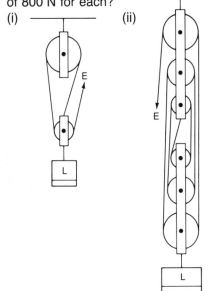

(i)   (ii)

13. The diameters of a wheel and an axle are 24 cm and 8 cm respectively.
If a load of 700 N is attached to the axle, what effort must be applied to the wheel to balance the load?

14. An effort of 500 N is required to slide an object with a mass of 100 kg up an inclined plane.
If the height of the plane is 2 m, what is the length of the plane?

15. The lever of a jackscrew is 1.2 m long and the pitch of the screw is 6 mm.
What is the effort required to balance a load of 8 t?

16. Arrange the cable in each of the following systems to provide the required mechanical advantage.
(a) M.A. = 5   (b) M.A. = 4

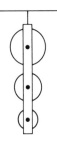   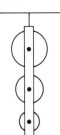

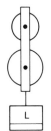   

17. An inclined plane has the dimensions given below.

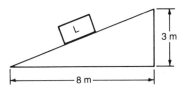

What is the effort required to slide an 800 kg mass up the plane?

18. When an effort of 800 N is applied to a wheel, a load of 2000 N attached to the axle is balanced.
Find the diameter of the wheel if the diameter of the axle is 3 cm.

19. When an effort of 150 N is applied to the lever of a jackscrew, a load exerting a force of 50 000 N is raised.
If the pitch of the screw is 6 mm, what is the length of the lever arm?

8.4 THE RESULTANT

Collinear forces are forces that act in the same straight line. Consider two horizontal forces of 8 N and 6 N acting at a point P and both pulling to the right.

Scale: 2 N = 1 cm

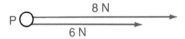

The combined effect of these two forces acting at P is the same as that of a single force of 14 N acting to the right.

Scale: 2 N = 1 cm

This single force that can take the place of the other two forces is called the resultant of the two forces.

The resultant of two non-collinear forces can be found geometrically by adding vectors.

Example. Find the resultant of two forces of 6 N and 8 N acting at an angle of 60° to each other.

Solution:
Scale: 2 N = 1 cm

First, we draw the vectors using a ruler, compass, and protractor.

We then complete the parallelogram ABCD and draw the diagonal AC.

AC represents the resultant of the 6 N and 8 N forces.

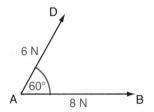

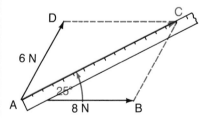

By measurement, the length of AC = 6.1 cm.

∴ the resultant is 6.1 × 2 = 12.2 N.

Using a protractor, we measure ∠CAB and find that the resultant forms an angle of 25° with the 8 N force.

EXERCISE 8.4

A

1. Find the resultant of the following systems of forces.

(a)

10 N   P   16 N

(b)

14 N   Q   10 N   8 N

(c)

10 N   P   20 N   8 N   5 N

(d)

30 N   Q   8 N   20 N   6 N

(e)

15 N   P   4 N   17 N

(f)

2 N   Q   30 N   21 N   18 N

2. Using the scale of 1 N = 1 cm, determine
(a) the resultant in each of the following systems of forces,
(b) the angle the resultant makes with the larger force.

(i)

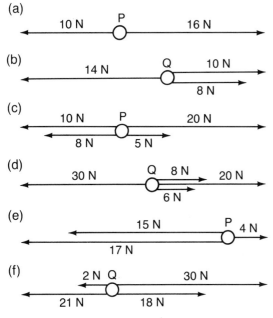

(ii)

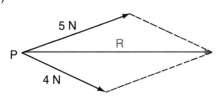

(iii)

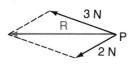

B

3. Using a ruler, compass, and protractor, find the resultant of the following systems of forces.
(a) 10 N and 15 N acting at 30° to each other
(b) 8 N and 12 N acting at 70° to each other
(c) 20 N and 30 N acting at 90° to each other
(d) 6 N and 5 N acting at 80° to each other
(e) 12 N and 16 N acting at 120° to each other
(f) 9 N and 7 N acting at 130° to each other
(g) 10 N and 20 N acting at 90° to each other
(h) 7 N and 8 N acting at 45° to each other
(i) 6 N and 5 N acting at 150° to each other
(j) 11 N and 12 N acting at 80° to each other

4. Two people are pulling a log with forces of 100 N and 125 N respectively.
The towing ropes make an angle of 70°.

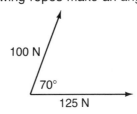

(a) Make a scale drawing.
(b) Find the magnitude of the resultant.
(c) Measure the angle the resultant makes with the 125 N force.

5. Two tugboats are towing a disabled ship. One tugboat exerts a force of 5 kN and the other exerts a force of 7 kN at an angle of 30° to the first tugboat.

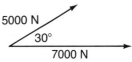

(a) Make a scale drawing.
(b) Find the magnitude of the resultant.
(c) Measure the angle the resultant makes with the 7 kN force.

8.5 FINDING THE RESULTANT WITH TRIGONOMETRY

Trigonometry offers a more accurate way of finding the resultant of two non-collinear forces. Let two forces P and Q act at a point B making an angle θ. We complete the parallelogram of forces as shown in the diagrams below.

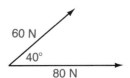

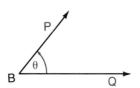

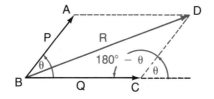

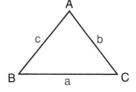

BD is the resultant R of the two forces P and Q.

In △BCD, by the Law of Cosines,

$$R^2 = P^2 + Q^2 - 2PQ \cos(180° - θ)$$

but $\cos(180° - θ) = -\cos θ$

$$R^2 = P^2 + Q^2 + 2PQ \cos θ$$

$$\boxed{R = \sqrt{P^2 + Q^2 + 2PQ \cos θ}}$$

$$\frac{\sin A}{a} = \frac{\sin B}{b} = \frac{\sin C}{c}$$

$$a^2 = b^2 + c^2 - 2bc \cos A$$

$$\cos A = \frac{b^2 + c^2 - a^2}{2bc}$$

$$E=mc^2$$

If θ = 90°, or P and Q act at right angles to each other, then

$$\cos θ = \cos 90° = 0$$
$$2PQ \cos θ = 0$$

$$\boxed{R = \sqrt{P^2 + Q^2}}$$

The angle that R makes with one of the forces can be calculated using the Law of Sines.

Example 1. (a) Calculate the resultant of two forces of 3 N and 4 N acting at 60° to each other.
(b) Calculate the angle that the resultant makes with the 4 N force.

Solution:

(a) $R = \sqrt{P^2 + Q^2 + 2PQ \cos \theta}$

$R = \sqrt{3^2 + 4^2 + 2 \times 3 \times 4 \times \cos 60°}$

$ = \sqrt{9 + 16 + 24 + 0.5}$

$ = \sqrt{37}$

$ \doteq 6.1$

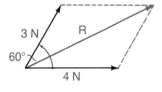

(b) To calculate the angle that R makes with the 4 N force, we draw the parallelogram of forces. Let the angle between R and the 4 N force be α (alpha).

$\angle B = 120°$

In △ABC,

$\dfrac{\sin B}{R} = \dfrac{\sin \alpha}{3}$

$\dfrac{\sin \alpha}{3} = \dfrac{\sin 120°}{6.1}$

$\sin \alpha = \dfrac{3 \times \sin 120°}{6.1}$

$ = \dfrac{3 \times \sin 60°}{6.1}$

$ \doteq \dfrac{3 \times 0.8660}{6.1}$

$ \doteq 0.4259$

$\therefore \alpha \doteq 25°$

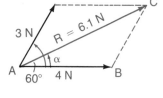

$\sin 120° = \sin (180° - 120°)$
$ = \sin 60°$
$ = 0.8660$

The resultant is a 6.1 N force acting at an angle of 25° with the 4 N force.

Example 2. Calculate the resultant of two forces of 6 N and 8 N acting at an angle of 130° to each other.

Solution:

$R = \sqrt{P^2 + Q^2 + 2PQ \cos \theta}$

$R = \sqrt{8^2 + 6^2 + 2 \times 6 \times 8 \times \cos 130°}$

$ \doteq \sqrt{64 + 36 + 2 \times 6 \times 8(-0.6428)}$

$ \doteq \sqrt{64 + 36 - 61.7}$

$ \doteq \sqrt{38.3}$

$ \doteq 6.2$

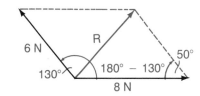

$\cos 130° = -\cos (180° - 130°)$
$ = -\cos 50°$
$ = -0.6428$

The magnitude of the resultant is 6.2 N. The angle the resultant makes with one of the forces can be calculated using the Law of Sines.

EXERCISE 8.5

B

1. Calculate the magnitude and direction (the angle made with the smaller force) of the resultant of the following systems of forces.

(a)   (b)

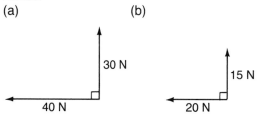

(c)   (d)

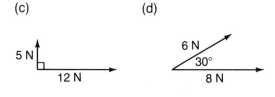

(e)   (f)

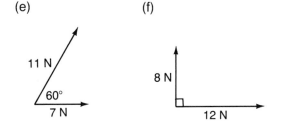

(g)   (h)

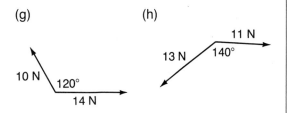

(i)   (j)

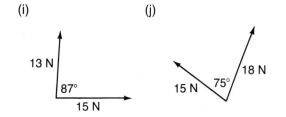

2. Two forces of 10 N each act on a body at 90° to each other.

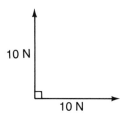

Find the magnitude and direction of the resultant.

3. Two people with ropes at 90° to each other pull a sleigh with equal forces.

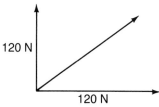

Find the force applied to the sleigh if the tension in each rope is 120 N.

4. Two tow lines at 30° to each other have tensions of 2.5 kN and 4 kN.

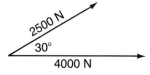

Find the magnitude of the resultant.

5. Two loggers attempt to drag a log with forces of 90 N and 99 N respectively.

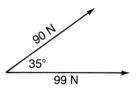

If the angle between the two forces is 35°, what is the magnitude and direction of the force necessary to prevent the motion the loggers tend to produce?

6. Two tow trucks pull a car with forces of 4 kN and 5 kN acting at 15° to each other.

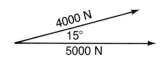

(a) Find the magnitude of the resultant.
(b) In what direction will the car move with respect to the more powerful tow truck?

7. Two tugboats tow a barge with forces of 8 kN and 9.3 kN acting at 65° to each other.

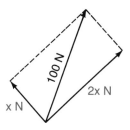

(a) What is the resultant force on the barge?
(b) What angle does the resultant make with the 9.3 kN force?

8. Two machines are driven from the shaft of the same motor by V-belts. The tension in one belt is double that in the other, and the belts are at right angles.

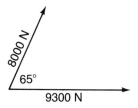

Find the tension in each belt if the force on the motor shaft is 100 N.

9. Two machines are driven by belts from the shaft of the same motor. The tensions in the belts cause forces of 40 N and 60 N acting at right angles to each other on the shaft of the motor as shown in the figure.

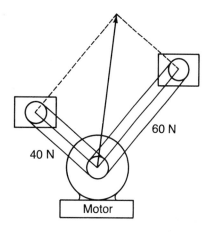

Find the magnitude of the force on the shaft of the motor.

10. Two workers pull on ropes attached to a load with forces of 300 N and 220 N at 90° to each other so that the load just moves.

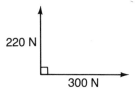

Find the magnitude and direction of the force exerted on the load.

8.6 RESOLUTION OF FORCES

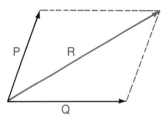

We have seen that the resultant of two forces is represented by the diagonal of the parallelogram of forces from the point of action. Conversely, we can take any force and express it as the diagonal of many parallelograms.

In each of the following parallelograms of forces,

$$\vec{F} = \vec{P} + \vec{Q}$$

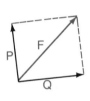 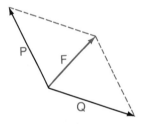 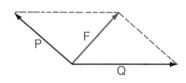

The forces P and Q are called the components of F. We say that the force F has been resolved into its components P and Q. There are many components of the same force F that are perpendicular to each other.

 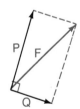 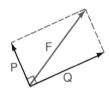

In this section we are interested in the components perpendicular to each other such that one is vertical and one is horizontal.

P is the vertical component of F.
Q is the horizontal component of F.
$P = F \sin \theta$
$Q = F \cos \theta$

Example 1. A player punts a football with a force of 150 N at an angle of 40° to the horizontal.
(a) What is the magnitude of the force that propels the ball forward?
(b) What force raises the ball?

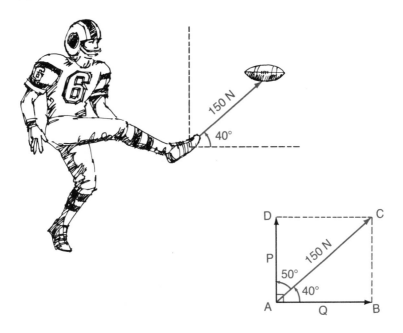

Solution:
(a) The horizontal component Q propels the ball forward.

Since $\dfrac{AB}{AC} = \cos 40°$

$\dfrac{Q}{150} = \cos 40°$

$Q = 150 \times \cos 40°$
$\doteq 150 \times 0.7660$
$\doteq 114.9$

Using a calculator, press

The display is `114.9066665`

Therefore a force of 115 N propels the ball forward.

(b) The vertical component P raises the ball.

Since $\dfrac{AD}{AC} = \cos 50°$

$\dfrac{P}{150} = \cos 50°$

$P = 150 \times \cos 50°$
$\doteq 150 \times 0.6428$
$\doteq 96.4$

Using a calculator, press

The display is `96.41814145`

Recall
sin 40° = cos 50°

Hence a force of 96 N propels the ball upward.

Example 2. When pushing a lawn-mower, a gardener exerts a force of 250 N along the handle.

(a) If the handle is inclined at an angle of 60° to the ground, find the force that pushes the lawn-mower forward.

(b) What is the magnitude of the force that tends to push the lawn-mower into the ground?

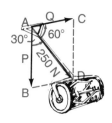

Solution:

(a) Since $\dfrac{AC}{AD} = \cos 60°$

$\dfrac{Q}{250} = \cos 60°$

| |
| Using a calculator, press |

$Q = 250 \times \cos 60°$

$\boxed{2}\boxed{5}\boxed{0}\boxed{\times}\boxed{6}\boxed{0}\boxed{\cos}\boxed{=}$

$= 250 \times 0.5000$

$= 125$

The display is `125.`

A force of 125 N pushes the lawn-mower forward.

(b) Since $\dfrac{AB}{AD} = \cos 30°$

$\dfrac{P}{250} = \cos 30°$

Using a calculator, press

$P = 250 \times \cos 30°$

$\boxed{2}\boxed{5}\boxed{0}\boxed{\times}\boxed{3}\boxed{0}\boxed{\cos}\boxed{=}$

$\doteq 250 \times 0.8660$

$= 216.5$

The display is `216.5063509`

A force of 217 N tends to push the lawn-mower into the ground.

EXERCISE 8.6

B

1. For each of the following forces, make a diagram and then calculate the magnitude of the vertical and horizontal components.
(a) 1000 N at 20° to the horizontal
(b) 300 N at 60° to the vertical
(c) 500 N at 10° to the horizontal
(d) 600 N at 50° to the vertical
(e) 120 N at 140° to the horizontal

2. A person pushes a lawn-mower with a force of 300 N directed down the handle.
(a) If the handle makes an angle of 50° with the ground, what is the magnitude of the force that tends to move the lawn-mower forward?

(b) What is the magnitude of the force that pushes the lawn-mower into the ground?

3. A person pulls a sleigh exerting a force of 200 N along the rope that is at an angle of 35° to the horizontal. Find
(a) the force that moves the sleigh forward,
(b) the force that lifts the sleigh.

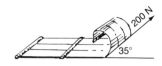

4. A batter hits a ball at an angle of 20° to the horizontal with a force of 400 N.

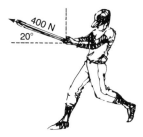

Find the force that moves the ball forward and the force that raises the ball.

5. A quarterback throws a pass with a force of 175 N at an angle of 40° with the horizontal.

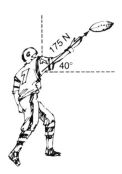

Find the force that moves the ball forward and the force that raises the ball.

6. A person pushes down on the handle of a lawn-mower with a force of 100 N. The handle makes a 30° angle with the ground.

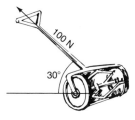

(a) Find the magnitude of the force that acts to push the mower along the ground.
(b) Find the magnitude of the force that acts to push the lawn-mower into the ground.

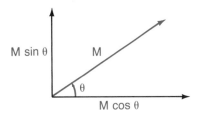

MICRO MATH

The following program prints the magnitude of the horizontal and vertical components of a vector when we enter the magnitude and the angle the vector makes with the horizontal.

NEW
```
10 PRINT"RESOLUTION OF VECTORS"
20 INPUT"VECTOR MAGNITUDE";M
30 INPUT"ANGLE WITH HORIZONTAL";A
40 H = M*COS(A/180*3.14159)
41 V = M*SIN(A/180*3.14159)
50 PRINT"HORIZONTAL COMPONENT:";H
51 PRINT"VERTICAL COMPONENT:";V
60 INPUT"ANOTHER VECTOR? Y OR N";Z$
61 IF Z$ = "Y" THEN 20
70 END
```
RUN

For a vector with a magnitude of 100 making an angle of 30° with the horizontal, the results are as follows:

```
RESOLUTION OF FORCES
VECTOR MAGNITUDE? 100
ANGLE WITH HORIZONTAL? 30
HORIZONTAL COMPONENT: 86.60256
VERTICAL COMPONENT: 49.99997
```

We round these results to give the following magnitudes:

Horizontal component is 87.
Vertical component is 50.

EXERCISE

1. Find the horizontal and vertical components for each vector.
(a)   (b)

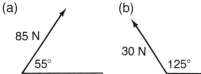

85 N   55°   30 N   125°

8.7 PROBLEM SOLVING

1. The cooling system in a small truck contains 30 L of coolant that is 20% antifreeze.
How much of the original mixture must be removed and 100% antifreeze added to have a 40% mixture?

2. A pup tent has dimensions as shown.

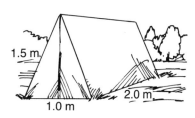

Find the total amount of canvas in the surface area of the tent including the floor.

3. On a blueprint, a square room with walls 8 m long is represented by a square with sides 4 cm long.
How long should a 17 m wall appear on the same blueprint?

4. The outside diameter of a tire is 0.68 m. During a trip, the tire was rotating at 18 000 r/h.
(a) What is the angular velocity of a point on the rim of the tire?
(b) What is the speed of the vehicle?

5. The outside dimensions of a building are 67 m by 130 m. A trench 2 m wide and 2.5 m deep is dug around the building to replace drainage pipes, and then the trench is filled with gravel.
How many truckloads of gravel are required to fill the trench if each load contains 8.5 m?

6. How many squares are in the figure?

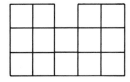

7. A pulley with a diameter of 26 cm is turning at 450 r/min. This pulley drives a larger pulley with a diameter of 50 cm.

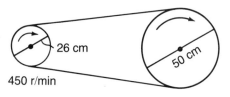

Find the speed of the larger pulley in revolutions per minute.

8. Two pulleys each 19.5 cm in diameter are connected by a belt as shown in the diagram.

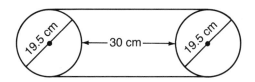

Find the total length of belt required.

9. A piston and rod assembly has the dimensions shown in the diagram below.

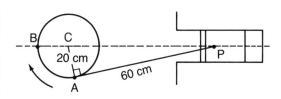

How far will the piston, P, advance as the throw arm moves from position A to position B?

10. A highway sign indicates that the maximum speed allowed is 90 km/h, and the minimum speed allowed is 60 km/h.
(a) What is the range in kilometres that one could travel legally along this highway in 5 h?
(b) What is the range of time required to travel 540 km legally along this highway?

11. (a) A lawn-mower has a mass of 15 kg. Calculate the force of gravity on the lawn-mower using a = 10 m/s^2.

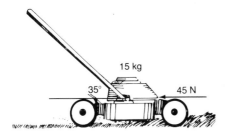

15 kg

35°   45 N

(b) The lawn-mower requires a force of 45 N parallel to the ground in order to move it to cut the grass. The handle of the lawn-mower is inclined at 35° to the ground.
How much force is necessary along the handle to move the lawn-mower through the grass?
(c) How much force is required along the handle to move the lawn-mower through the grass up an incline of 10°?

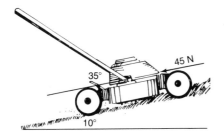

45 N

35°

10°

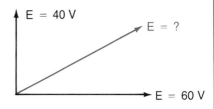

8.8 REVIEW EXERCISE

1. Find the value of x in each of the following.

(a)

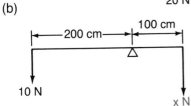

(b)

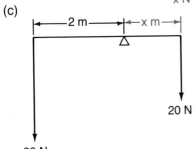

(c)

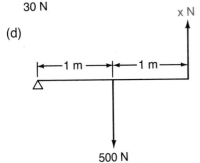

(d)

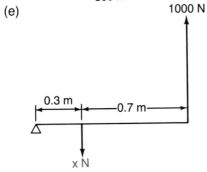

(e)

2. Use a ruler, compass, and protractor to find the resultant of 10 N and 14 N forces acting at 80° to each other.

3. Find the mechanical advantage of each of the following.

(a)

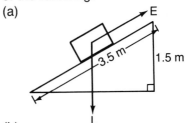

(b)

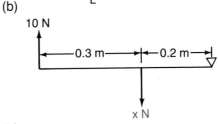

(c)

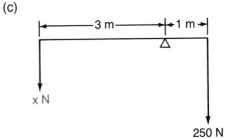

(d)

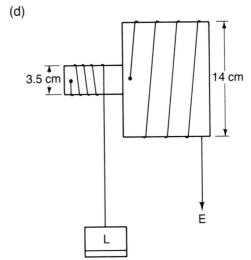

(e)

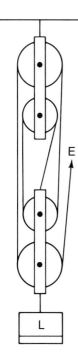

(f)

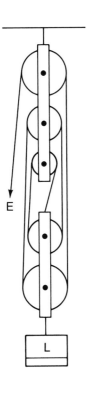

(g)

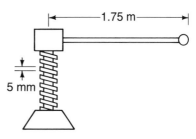

(h) an inclined plane 1.3 m high and 4 m
long
(i) a jackscrew with lever arm 2 m long and
a pitch of 5 mm
(j) a wheel and axle with a wheel diameter
of 0.80 m and an axle diameter of
0.03 m

4. (a) Find the magnitude and direction of
the resultant of two forces of 60 N and 80 N
acting at 50° to each other.
(b) Find the magnitude and direction of the
resultant of two forces of 90 N and 70 N
acting at 140° to each other.

5. A swimmer heads due east at 3 km/h
with the current of the river flowing north at
2 km/h.
Draw a sketch and find the resultant with
respect to a point on the opposite bank of
the river.

6. A force of 60 N is applied down the
handle of a snow scraper. The handle
makes an angle of 40° with the horizontal.
Find the magnitude of the horizontal and
vertical components.

8.9 CHAPTER 8 TEST

1. Find the magnitude of the force required to move a 40 kg body with an acceleration of 20 m/s².

2. Using a scale of 10 N = 1 cm, draw the following vectors.
(a) 30 N to the left
(b) 45 N upward and to the right at 45°

3. Calculate the mechanical advantage (M.A.) of the following system.

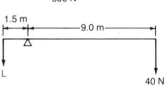

4. (a) Calculate the load necessary to balance the given system.
(b) What is the mechanical advantage (M.A.) of the system?

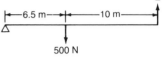

5. (a) (i) Find the mechanical advantage (M.A.) of the given pulley system.
    (ii) What effort is required to balance a load of 1000 N?

(b) Arrange the cable on this pulley system to have the greatest mechanical advantage.

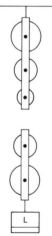

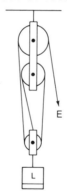

6. Find the magnitude and direction of the resultant of two forces of 50 N and 90 N acting at 60° to each other.

7. Find the magnitude and direction of the resultant of two forces of 12 N and 15 N acting at 120° to each other.

8. Two people are pulling a cart so that one exerts a force of 60 N and the other exerts a force of 80 N at 25° to each other.
(a) Make a scale drawing.
(b) Find the magnitude and direction of the resultant.

STATISTICS

9

REVIEW AND PREVIEW TO CHAPTER 9

READING STATISTICAL GRAPHS

EXERCISE 1

1. Bar Graphs

Bar graphs are used to compare similar things. Bar graphs can be horizontal or vertical.

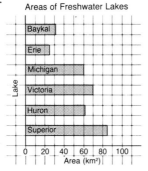

Areas of Freshwater Lakes

(a) Which lake has the largest area?
(b) How much larger is Lake Victoria than Lake Michigan?
(c) What lakes have approximately the same area?

2. Broken Line Graphs

Broken line graphs are used to show how something changes.

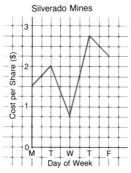

Silverado Mines

(a) What was the highest price reached by the stock in the week?
(b) What was the lowest?

(c) How much would you have paid for 100 shares of Silverado Mines on Tuesday?

3. Circle Graphs

Circle graphs are used to show how something is divided.

Land Use in Canada

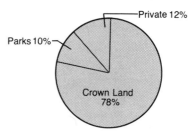

Canada has an area of approximately 10 000 000 km².
(a) How much of Canada is crown land?
(b) How much is privately owned?

4. Pictographs

Pictographs are used to show amounts using pictures.

Provincial Parks by Province	
Nfld.	△ △ △ ◪
P.E.I.	△ △
N.S.	△ △ △ △
N.B.	△ △ ◪
Que.	△ △ △ ◪
Ont.	△ △ △ △ △ ◪
Man.	△ △ △ △ △ △ ◪
Sask.	△ △ △ △ △
Alta.	△ △ ◪
B.C.	△ △ △ △ △ △ △ △ △ △ △ △
Each △ represents 25 parks	

(a) What province has the most parks?
(b) What province has the fewest?
(c) Approximately how many parks are there in Canada?

DRAWING STATISTICAL GRAPHS

EXERCISE 2

1. Draw graphs to display the following data.

(a) the heights of several waterfalls in Canada

Waterfall	Height (m)
Takakkaw Falls, B.C.	380
Horseshoe Falls, Ont.	57
Della Falls, B.C.	440
Churchill Falls, Nfld.	75
Hunlen Falls, B.C.	253
Panther Falls, Alta.	183

(b) the location of buried pirate treasure in North America

Location	Percent
Atlantic Coast	65
Pacific Coast	20
Thousand Islands	15

(c) Babe Ruth's home runs while playing for the New York Yankees

Year	Home Runs	Year	Home Runs
1920	54	1928	54
1921	59	1929	46
1922	35	1930	49
1923	41	1931	46
1924	46	1932	41
1925	25	1933	34
1926	47	1934	22
1927	60		

(d) the way Sandra spends a school day

Activity	Time (h)
Sleeping	8
Homework	3
Eating	2
School	6
Recreation	2
Other	3

(e) where the world's energy comes from

Source	Percent of Total
Oil	48
Coal	25
Natural Gas	19
Water Power	6
Nuclear Power	2

(f) the fastest speeds of several vehicles

Vehicle	Speed (km/h)
Helicopter	500
Rocket Car	1050
Hydroplane	550
Ice Yacht	250
Steam Locomotive	200

9.1 COLLECTING DATA

Statistics is a branch of mathematics that provides techniques for collecting, organizing, analysing, and interpreting numerical information called data.

Statistics helps us make predictions and decisions about a population based on a sample of the population. A sample is a small group of items or individuals selected to represent the larger group called the population.

Population

Sample

To determine the popularity of a new radio station in a city, we could not ask the opinion of everyone in the city. This process would be too time-consuming and expensive, so a sample of the population is surveyed for their opinion.

Collect
Data

The most important requirement of a sample is that it be random. This means that each item in the population has an equally likely chance of being selected.

Analyse
Data

The results of the radio station survey using a sample of the people in the city would be organized and analysed using graphs, tables, and measures like the mean, median, and mode.

Make
Decisions

Based on the analysis of the data, decisions would be made regarding the popularity of the radio station. Is the station getting more, less, or a fair share of the market? Are improvements needed? What's working? What isn't?

The key step in the statistical process is the choosing of the sample. A badly chosen sample will result in poor predictions. A representative sample of a population must contain the relative characteristics of the population in the same proportion. For example, people at a beach might not represent the entire population if the survey was to determine whether or not to build an indoor swimming pool.

The most popular methods of obtaining information about a population are
 (i) questionnaires
 (ii) personal interviews
 (iii) telephone surveys
 (iv) tests
 (v) measurements

EXERCISE 9.1

B

1. List three examples of sampling where taking of the sample destroys the product.

2. Data are classified as "primary" or "secondary." Primary data are collected first-hand by the person interested in the problem. Secondary data are collected by someone else and made available in publications or records.
List four sources of secondary data.

3. List three examples of sampling where the entire population is sampled.

4. Inaccurate or faulty samples can result in misleading predictions.
Give an example of a problem that could result when
(a) the sample is too large,
(b) the sample is too small,
(c) the sample is not random.

5. The table below gives the results of an election survey in Bakersfield, which has 180 000 potential voters. Four hundred people were asked to name their favourite candidate, with the following results.

Candidate	Votes
Carson	78
Clash	89
Dianini	95
Santana	67
Trevelli	71

If the survey is accurate, approximately how many votes should each candidate receive?

6. Some pollsters use the telephone to gather data.
(a) What are the advantages of this type of surveying?
(b) What are the disadvantages?

7. Describe sampling techniques that could be used to estimate the following.
(a) the number of telephone answering machines in homes
(b) the popularity of a new horror movie
(c) the need for a new stoplight in front of a school
(d) the number of fish in a lake
(e) the effectiveness of a seat belt
(f) the gasoline consumption of a car
(g) the chances of a fast food restaurant being profitable at a certain location.

8. A stratified sample resembles a scaled-down version of the population where categories are represented proportionally.
A school has the following numbers of students.

Grade 9	310
Grade 10	285
Grade 11	210
Grade 12	176

If a survey of 100 students is to be stratified, approximately how many students from each grade should be included in the survey?

9. Describe how you would select 50 families at random from a city or town.

10. When would you use a mail survey to collect data as opposed to a telephone survey?

11. One way to estimate the fish population of a lake is to use the "capture-recapture" technique. Suppose that 100 fish were caught, tagged, and then returned to the lake. A few days later, 50 fish were caught, 3 of which wore tags.
What is the approximate fish population of the lake?

9.2 THE MEAN, MEDIAN, AND MODE

We use graphs to get a picture of data. This picture is part of data analysis. Data can also be analysed using the mean, median, and mode — the measures of central tendency.

THE MEAN : the average

The mean, or arithmetic average, of a set of numbers is found by adding the numbers and then dividing the total by the number of numbers added.

Joan received the following marks on an instructor's swimming course.

$$88, \quad 76, \quad 84, \quad 92, \quad 76, \quad 68, \quad 83$$

To find her mean, or average, we proceed as follows:

$$\bar{x} = \frac{88 + 76 + 84 + 92 + 76 + 68 + 83}{7} \quad \longleftarrow \text{ Sum}$$
$$\longleftarrow \text{ Number of Numbers}$$

$$= \frac{567}{7}$$

$$= 81$$

For a set of numbers $x_1, x_2, x_3, ..., x_n$, the mean is

$$\boxed{\bar{x} = \frac{x_1 + x_2 + x_3 + ... + x_n}{n}}$$

THE MEDIAN : the half-way

When a set of numbers is arranged in order from smallest to largest, or largest to smallest, the median is the middle number.

For Joan's marks,

$$88, \quad 76, \quad 84, \quad 92, \quad 76, \quad 68, \quad 83$$

becomes

$$92, \quad 88, \quad 84, \quad \underset{\underset{\text{the median}}{\uparrow}}{83,} \quad 76, \quad 76, \quad 68$$

If there is an even number of numbers, the median is the average of the middle two numbers.

$$21, \quad 23, \quad \underset{\uparrow}{27,} \quad \underset{\uparrow}{28,} \quad 30, \quad 35$$

$$\frac{27 + 28}{2} = 27.5 \longleftarrow \text{the median}$$

THE MODE : the most common

The mode of a set of numbers is the number that occurs most often.

For Joan's marks, 92, 88, 84, 83, 76, 76, 68

the mode is 76

Some sets of numbers do not have a mode.

33, 35, 27, 29, 41, 49, 53, 78

Some sets of numbers have more than one mode.

16, 16, 16, 17, 17, 18, 19, 19, 19, 20

the modes are 16 and 19

If many numbers in a set of data have the same value, we use the weighted mean, or weighted average, to simplify the calculations. If there are four numbers with the value of 11, we multiply 4 by 11 instead of adding 11 + 11 + 11 + 11.

READ

PLAN

SOLVE

Example. Joan gave the students in her class a water safety test. She marked the test out of 15. The following are the results:

7,	8,	14,	12,	11,	10,	7,	9,
8,	11,	12,	15,	13,	13,	12,	7,
11,	11,	9,	10,	8,	8,	7,	9,
10,	13,	11,	9,	8,	10,	11	

Determine
(a) the mean,   (b) the median,   (c) the mode.

Solution: A frequency table simplifies the calculations.

Mark x	Tally	Frequency f	f × x
7	IIII	4	28
8	⊞	5	40
9	IIII	4	36
10	IIII	4	40
11	⊞ I	6	66
12	III	3	36
13	III	3	39
14	I	1	14
15	I	1	15
Total		31	314

(a) $\bar{x} = \dfrac{314}{31}$

$\doteq 10.13$

The mean is 10.1, to the nearest tenth.

(b) There are 31 marks. The median is the sixteenth mark. The median is 10.

(c) The mode is 11.

The moving mean or moving average is also used to interpret data. The table gives the house sales for an eight-month period. A three-month moving mean or average is found by restricting the calculations to a three-month period.

Month	Sales	Three-Month Moving Mean
January	6	
February	9	
March	15	10
April	19	14.3
May	21	18.3
June	22	20.7
July	18	20.3
August	20	20

EXERCISE 9.2

B

1. Calculate the mean of the following sets of numbers to the nearest tenth.
(a) 3, 5, 5, 7, 4, 8, 6, 2, 5, 9
(b) 8, 3, 2, 4, 6, 7, 9, 3, 4, 0
(c) 1, 8, 7, 5, 6, 3, 7, 4, 8, 3
(d) 4, −2, −5, 3, −9, 5, 4, −3, 0, 5
(e) −8, 6, 4, 5, −2, −4, 3, 5, 1, −7
(f) 156, 174, 197, 165, 184
(g) 8.4, 7.5, 9.7, 6.6, 9.2, 8.7
(h) 1075, 8213, 4760, 5120, 3000, 1001

2. Find the median of each set of numbers.
(a) 4, 7, 7, 8, 12
(b) 1, 3, 4, 7, 9, 11
(c) 7, 8, 12, 15, 15, 21, 25
(d) −5, −3, 0, 2, 4, 8, 12, 15
(e) −8, −6, −3, 4, 4, 6, 9, 9, 9
(f) 94, 97, 86, 88, 74, 87, 93, 51, 77

3. Find the mode(s) of each of the following sets of numbers.
(a) 31, 34, 34, 36, 36, 36, 37, 37, 39
(b) 8, 12, 12, 14, 15, 15, 21, 21, 21, 21, 25
(c) 4, 4, 6, 9, 9, 9, 12, 4
(d) 18, 19, 20, 20, 23, 23, 27, 27, 27, 28
(e) −7, −6, −5, −5, 0, 0, 2, 4
(f) 8, 12, 14, 16, 23, 25, 34
(g) 17, 14, 16, 17, 14, 17, 14, 16, 17, 14, 16

4. The Parks Department employs two hundred students every summer. One hundred students earn $20.00/h, fifty students earn $18.00/h, thirty students earn $17.00/h, and twenty students earn $16.00/h.
Find the mean, median, and mode of this data.

5. Calculate the mean, median, and mode for the following data.

Value	Frequency
15	3
16	5
17	9
18	11
19	4
20	2

6. The following are the driving test scores for a senior high school class.

70, 75, 80, 85, 80, 90,
75, 75, 90, 75, 80, 70,
95, 60, 95, 90, 65, 60,
75, 80, 65, 90, 95, 70

Find the mean, median, and mode of the test scores.

7. The table gives the TV sales for Apple TV for a seven-month period.
Calculate the three-month moving mean for this data.

Month	TV Sales
March	67
April	73
May	57
June	45
July	31
August	33
September	46

THE MEAN $\bar{x}$

Calculators with statistical functions can be used to calculate the mean.

To find the mean of 123, 145, 156, and 142,
press `1` `2` `3` `Σ+` `1` `4` `5` `Σ+` `1` `5` `6` `Σ+` `1` `4` `2`

The above procedure enters the data into the statistical registry of the calculator. To find the mean, locate the $\bar{x}$ key. This key is often used with the `INV` key.

Press `INV` $\bar{x}$

The display is `141.5`

The table gives the depths in metres of twelve of the deepest ocean trenches.

Trench	Depth (m)
Mariana (Pacific)	10 915
Puerto Rico (Atlantic)	8605
Bonin (Pacific)	9994
Izu (Pacific)	9695
Java (Indian)	7125
Tonga (Pacific)	10 800
Kermadec (Pacific)	10 047
Cayman (Atlantic)	7535
Philippine (Pacific)	10 057
Romanche (Atlantic)	7726
Palau (Pacific)	8054
Kuril (Pacific)	9750

(a) Find the mean of this data.
(b) Find the mode of this data.

9.3 DISPERSION

The mean, median, and mode of a set of data describe the central tendencies of the data. They do not tell us how the data are spread out. For example, consider the following two sets of data.

	Set A	Set B
	7	1
	8	8
	8	8
	8	11
	9	12
Mean	8	8
Median	8	8
Mode	8	8

The two sets of data above have the same mean, median, and mode, but the second set of data is more spread out than the first.

The amount to which data are spread out is called the dispersion. There are several measures of dispersion. The simplest is called the range.

> The range of a set of data is the difference between the largest number and the smallest number in the set.

For set A above, the range is $9 - 7 = 2$.
For set B above, the range is $12 - 1 = 11$.

The range is simple to calculate because it is determined by two numbers in the set. The range is affected by extreme values in the set and in such cases it is not a good measure of the dispersion.

The most commonly used measure of dispersion is called the standard deviation. For a set of data, the standard deviation is a measure of how the data spreads out from the mean.

To calculate the standard deviation for a set of data, follow these steps:

① Calculate the mean.
② Find the difference between each number in the set and the mean.
③ Square each difference.
④ Find the sum of the squares of the differences.
⑤ Calculate the mean of the squares.
⑥ Find the positive square root of this mean.

Example 1. The heights of several young poplar trees on an experimental farm are 124 cm, 143 cm, 118 cm, 108 cm, 127 cm, 96 cm, 112 cm, and 136 cm. Find the standard deviation.

Solution:

Height	Difference from Mean	Square of Difference
124	3.5	12.25
143	22.5	506.25
118	−2.5	6.25
108	②−12.5	156.25 ③
127	6.5	42.25
96	−24.5	600.25
112	−8.5	72.25
+136	15.5	+240.25
964		1636 ④

① Mean $= \dfrac{964}{8}$

$= 120.5$

⑤ Mean of Squares $= \dfrac{1636}{8}$

$= 204.5$

⑥ Square root of mean $= \sqrt{204.5}$

$= 14.30$

The standard deviation is 14.3, to the nearest tenth.

The symbol for standard deviation is σ and the steps are abbreviated in the formula below.

$$\sigma = \sqrt{\dfrac{(x_1 - \overline{x})^2 + (x_2 - \overline{x})^2 + \ldots + (x_n - \overline{x})^2}{n}}$$

15.6

Spreadsheet activities related to this topic are found in section 15.6.

When studying standard deviation, it is important to look at it with respect to the mean. For example, suppose the standard deviation of the prices for a particular telescope sold by several stores is $50. If the mean price of the telescope is $200, then the standard deviation indicates a wide spread in the selling price. If the mean price of the telescope is $1200, then the standard deviation indicates little variation in the selling price.

In the next section we will see how the standard deviation is used by statisticians to make predictions.

Example 2. Find the standard deviation, to the nearest tenth, for the following selling prices of a Concorde radio: $92, $104, $120, $98, and $106.

Solution:

$$\bar{x} = \frac{92 + 104 + 120 + 98 + 106}{5}$$

$$= 104$$

$$\sigma = \sqrt{\frac{(x_1 - \bar{x})^2 + (x_2 - \bar{x})^2 + (x_3 - \bar{x})^2 + (x_4 - \bar{x})^2 + (x_5 - \bar{x})^2}{n}}$$

$$= \sqrt{\frac{(92 - 104)^2 + (104 - 104)^2 + (120 - 104)^2 + (98 - 104)^2 + (106 - 104)^2}{5}}$$

$$= \sqrt{\frac{(-12)^2 + 0^2 + 16^2 + (-6)^2 + 2^2}{5}}$$

$$= \sqrt{\frac{144 + 0 + 256 + 36 + 4}{5}}$$

$$= \sqrt{\frac{440}{5}}$$

$$\doteq 9.4$$

The standard deviation is 9.4.

EXERCISE 9.3

B

1. Find the range for the following sets of numbers.
(a) 5, 7, 3, 4, 8, 2, 3
(b) 6.4, 5.2, 3.8, 9.7
(c) 6, −4, 1, 0, 5, −1, 2
(d) 3.2, 4.6, 1.3, −2.4
(e) 58.4, 73.2, 61.5, 87.4

2. Find the standard deviation for each set of numbers to the nearest tenth.
(a) 5, 4, 3, 2, 1
(b) 49, 50, 53, 52, 51
(c) 105, 99, 103, 101, 102, 104, 100
(d) 1, 4, 9, 16, 25, 36
(e) 8.7, 9.3, 6.6, 5.8, 7.7

3. A soft drink machine is designed to dispense 250 cm³ for each measure. The actual measures in cubic centimetres for a sample of 10 cups were 246, 252, 251, 248, 249, 250, 246, 253, 250, and 249. Find the standard deviation of the amounts.

C 4. A class of students received the listed marks on a mathematics test.

8,	11,	12,	14,	15,	16,	16,	18,	22,
9,	11,	13,	14,	15,	16,	17,	18,	23,
9,	12,	13,	14,	15,	16,	17,	19,	23,
10,	12,	14,	15,	15,	16,	17,	20,	24

Find the range and standard deviation.

To find the standard deviation of 123, 145, 156, and 142, press

| 1 | 2 | 3 | Σ+ | 1 | 4 | 5 | Σ+ | 1 | 5 | 6 |

| Σ+ | 1 | 4 | 2 | Σ+ | σ |

The display is 11.884864

On some calculators the σ key is used with the INV key.

9.4 FREQUENCY DISTRIBUTIONS AND THE NORMAL CURVE

One way to analyse data is to look at the frequency, or the number of times, each value occurs. The table at the right gives the frequency of certain marks on a driving test. The test was out of 100 and each student received a whole number as a mark.

Mark	Number of Students
30–40	1
40–50	6
50–60	19
60–70	32
70–80	21
80–90	16
90–100	5

The graph shows the frequencies of the marks.

In the 30–40 range, marks from 30–39 are included. A mark of 40 goes in the 40–50 range.

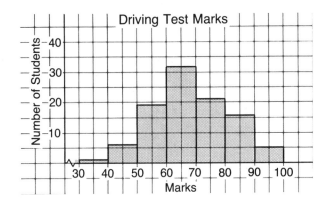

If we join the midpoints of the bars, we get a frequency polygon as shown below.

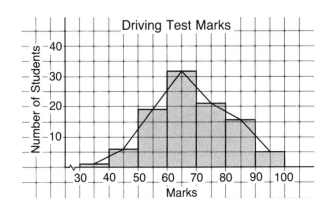

If we had given the driving test to 100 000 students instead of 100, and if we had made the width of each bar 1 instead of 10, we might obtain a frequency polygon or frequency distribution graph like the one shown below.

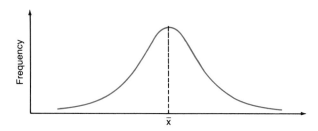

For this model, the mean, median, and mode all have the same value. The graph is in the shape of a bell and is symmetrical. Distributions with such a graph are called normal distributions. The graph is called a normal curve. The normal curve closely matches the distribution for many large sets of numbers.

In a normal distribution, approximately 68% of the numbers fall within 1 standard deviation of the mean, approximately 95% are within 2 standard deviations of the mean, and approximately 99% are within 3 standard deviations of the mean.

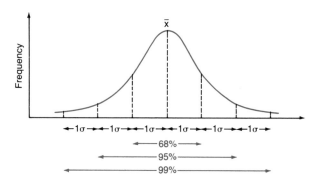

To make the application of the normal distribution easier, the distribution is simplified as follows:

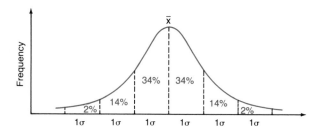

Example. The lifetimes of 10 000 light bulbs are normally distributed with a mean life of 6000 h and a standard deviation of 500 h.
(a) What percentage of the bulbs should last less than 5500 h?
(b) What percentage of the bulbs should last more than 5000 h?
(c) How many bulbs should last less than 6500 h?

Solution:
Draw a normal curve. The mean is 6000 h and the standard deviation is 500 h so we mark the axes accordingly.

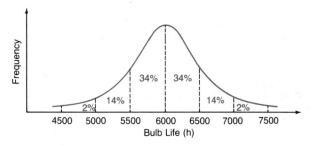

(a) 16% of the bulbs should last less than 5500 h.

(b) 98% of the bulbs should last more than 5000 h.

(c) 84% of the bulbs should last less than 6500 h.

$$0.84 \times 10\,000 = 8400$$

8400 bulbs should last less than 6500 h.

EXERCISE 9.4

B 1. The burning time of a fire log is normally distributed with a mean of 4 h and a standard deviation of 0.5 h. A store ordered 5000 logs to sell.
(a) What percentage of the logs will burn longer than 4.5 h?
(b) What percentage of the logs will burn less than 5 h?
(c) How many logs will burn longer than 3 h?
(d) How many logs will burn between 4 h and 5 h?

2. Eight thousand cars were clocked on the highway. The speeds were normally distributed. The mean speed was 88 km/h with a standard deviation of 9 km/h.
(a) What percentage of the cars travelled under 97 km/h?
(b) How many cars travelled between 79 km/h and 88 km/h?
(c) How many cars travelled faster than 106 km/h?

3. Six thousand jet pilots took a reaction test. The results were normally distributed with a mean of 85 and a standard deviation of 5.
(a) How many scored higher than 90?
(b) What percentage scored lower than 80?
(c) If a pass is 75, how many passed?

4. Park rangers tagged 1000 alligators in the Everglades. The masses of the alligators were normally distributed with a mean of 70 kg and a standard deviation of 4 kg.
(a) What percentage of the alligators have masses less than 74 kg?
(b) What percentage of the alligators have masses between 66 kg and 78 kg?
(c) How many alligators have masses greater than 62 kg?
(d) How many alligators have masses between 66 kg and 74 kg?

9.5 PERCENTILES

We have seen how the mean, median, mode, and standard deviation are used to analyse data. Percentiles allow us to determine the position of a number in a distribution of data.

Carla got 78 on the provincial chemistry exam. There were 2000 students, including Carla, who wrote the exam. Carla learned that 12% of the students scored higher than 78, 4% scored 78, and 84% scored lower than 78.

We can show these results in a table.

Lower than 78	78	Higher than 78
84%	4%	12%

To determine Carla's percentile rank, we add the percentage of students lower than Carla plus one-half of the percentage of students with the same mark as Carla.

$$84 + \tfrac{1}{2}(4) = 86$$

We say that Carla's percentile rank is 86. This means that Carla scored better than approximately 86% of the students and that approximately 14% of the students scored better than Carla.

If X represents a given number, and
    B represents the number of terms below X, and
    E represents the number of terms equal to X, and
    n represents the total number of terms,
then the percentile rank of X is

$$\frac{B + \tfrac{1}{2}E}{n} \times 100$$

READ

Example. Don got 68 on a geography test. The marks of the other students in his class were

    50, 55, 36, 70, 71, 68, 75, 41, 41, 78,
    66, 66, 59, 57, 67, 78, 81, 84, 52

Find Don's percentile rank.

PLAN

Solution: List the marks in order from smallest to largest, including Don's.

    36, 41, 41, 50, 52, 55, 57, 59, 66, 66,
    67, 68, 68, 70, 71, 75, 78, 78, 81, 84

n = 20, since there are 20 students, including Don.
B = 11, the number of marks below 68.
E = 2, the number of marks equal to 68, including Don's.

$E=mc^2$

$$\text{Don's percentile rank} = \frac{B + \frac{1}{2}E}{n} \times 100$$

$$= \frac{11 + \frac{1}{2}(2)}{20} \times 100$$

$$= \frac{11 + 1}{20} \times 100$$

$$= 60$$

ANSWER

Don's grade is in the 60th percentile.

EXERCISE 9.5

A

1. Sam's grade on a history test was in the 45th percentile.
(a) What percentage of the students did Sam score better than?
(b) What percentage of the students scored better than Sam?

B

2. Two hundred eighty students wrote a sailing test. Sonja's mark ranked in the 63rd percentile.
(a) Approximately how many students had a mark lower than Sonja's?
(b) Approximately how many students had a mark higher than Sonja's?

3. Mary scored 83 on a physics test. Of the twenty students who wrote the test, sixteen scored lower than Mary and three got the same mark as Mary.
What was Mary's percentile rank?

4. Roberto got 84 on a biology test. The marks of the other students in his class were as follows:

67, 89, 72, 84, 83, 91,
55, 55, 70, 72, 84, 75,
77, 56, 67, 95, 34, 80,
56, 63, 72, 79, 56, 99

Find Roberto's percentile rank.

5. One hundred students wrote a math test. Lee earned a mark of 76. There were seventeen students that got a mark higher than Lee's and two other students that got 76.
What was Lee's percentile rank?

6. Joe got 76 on an economics exam. The marks of the other students in his class were as follows:

76, 54, 65, 71, 80, 93,
56, 66, 66, 45, 61, 90,
72, 70, 69, 62, 61, 61

Paula got 76 on an economics exam. The marks of the other students in her class were as follows:

84, 86, 90, 92, 91, 66, 67,
55, 90, 77, 81, 85, 51, 64,
79, 90, 52, 87, 66, 86, 73

(a) Calculate Joe's percentile rank in his class.
(b) Calculate Paula's percentile rank in her class.
(c) If the levels of competition are the same in both classes, what might account for the different percentile ranks?

9.6 PROBLEM SOLVING

1. One way to compare the size of a million dollars and a billion dollars is to use time. One million seconds is approximately 11.6 d.
How long is one billion seconds?

2. The rectangle below has been divided into eleven squares of different sizes. The smallest square measures 9 cm by 9 cm. Assume that the next largest square, beside the 9 by 9 square, measures x cm by x cm.

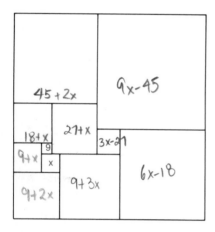

45+2x
9x-45
27+x
18+x
9
3x-27
9+x
x
6x-18
9+2x
9+3x

Find the dimensions of the large rectangle. (The number inside the square represents the length of one side of the square.)

3. Here are four ways to add eight odd numbers to get 20.

$$1 + 1 + 1 + 3 + 3 + 3 + 3 + 5 = 20$$
$$1 + 1 + 1 + 1 + 1 + 1 + 3 + 11 = 20$$
$$1 + 1 + 1 + 1 + 1 + 5 + 5 + 5 = 20$$
$$1 + 1 + 1 + 1 + 3 + 3 + 5 + 5 = 20$$

Find the seven other ways to add eight odd numbers to get 20.
Changing the order of the numbers does not count as a new solution.

4. A train travelling at 60 km/h passes a point in 45 s.

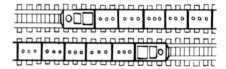

How long is the train?

5. Two trains travelling at 60 km/h but in opposite directions pass each other in 45 s.

(a) If one train is twice as long as the other, how long is each train?
(b) How far is the point where the engines pass from the point where the cabooses pass?

6. When Bill started on a 7650 km trip the odometer on his car read 87 234.9 km. After two days of driving the odometer read 90 003.6 km.
How many more kilometres did he have to drive?

7. A rope ladder hangs over the side of a ship so that the bottom of the ladder is about 5 cm above the water. The rungs of the ladder are 30 cm apart.

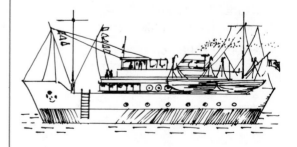

How many rungs will be under water after the tide has risen 100 cm?

8. (a) Approximately how many degrees of latitude separate Ottawa and Houston?
(b) Approximately how many degrees of longitude separate Halifax and Hong Kong?

9. (a) Name four songs whose titles begin with the word *Go*.
(b) Name four songs whose titles begin with the word *Stop*.

10. The area of the sides of three sides of a rectangular solid are 96 m², 128 m², and 192 m².

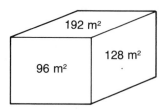

Find the volume of the solid.

11. How many ways can you make change for one dollar?

12. Develop a method of adding both columns of numbers at the same time using your calculator.

23	567
17	323
43	107
66	223
+19	+405

13. What percentage of the first 100 page numbers in a book contains at least one 9?

CAREER

EXERCISE

1. (a) Using graph paper, prepare three floor plans for a typical living-room that includes a chesterfield, two wing chairs, a coffee table, two end tables, two lamps, and a curio cabinet.
(b) What percentage of the floor is open space in each of your plans?

9.7 REVIEW EXERCISE

1. State the method you would use to gather the following data.
(a) the lengths of the seven longest rivers in the world
(b) the popularity of a new TV station
(c) the performance ratings of this year's new cars
(d) the brands of toothpaste used by families
(e) the noise level near an airport
(f) the popularity of a new movie
(g) the list of colleges that offer dental hygiene programs
(h) the level of satisfaction with the current government

2. The table below gives the results of a survey conducted by business advertisers to determine the audience reached by each station.

Station	Frequency
CHAM	56
CHAT	91
CHIN	47
WPTR	26

If there are 35 000 potential listeners, approximately how many listeners does each station have?

3. To determine how many people are making payments on their cars, several pollsters waited at the exits of the baseball stadium. They found that out of the 600 drivers surveyed, 89% of the drivers owned their cars outright.
Is this a good sample of car owners? Explain your answer.

4. Calculate the mean to the nearest tenth.
(a) 45, 56, 78, 34, 52, 67, 58
(b) 101, 107, 111, 108, 102
(c) 8.7, 9.8, 7.4, 6.9

5. Calculate the median.
(a) 56, 67, 44, 34, 87, 11, 12
(b) 102, 203, 304, 222, 212, 252

6. Calculate the mean, median, and mode of the following.

Value	Frequency
30	7
31	9
32	13
33	14
34	3
35	1

7. The table below gives the precipitation in Brownsville for one year.

Month	cm	Month	cm
Jan.	21	July	13
Feb.	27	Aug.	12
March	29	Sept.	10
April	20	Oct.	14
May	18	Nov.	18
June	16	Dec.	20

Calculate the four-month moving mean.

8. The table below gives Joanne's bowling scores for four weeks.

	Game 1	Game 2	Game 3	Average
Week 1	183	210	189	
Week 2	173	191	146	
Week 3	158	229	231	
Week 4	201	204	213	

Determine her average at the end of each week.

9. Find the standard deviation to the nearest tenth and the range for each set of data.
(a) 9, 8, 7, 10, 12, 11, 12, 11
(b) 23, 24, 26, 27, 25

10. The masses of the seven students who wear the animal costumes at the theme park are 69 kg, 72 kg, 74 kg, 70 kg, 68 kg, 70 kg, and 67 kg.
Find the standard deviation of these masses.

11. The masses of basketballs are normally distributed with a mean of 630 g and a standard deviation of 10 g.
(a) What percentage of basketballs have masses greater than 620 g?
(b) What percentage of basketballs have masses between 610 g and 640 g?

12. An automobile manufacturer has determined that the life of the engines in the Coyote car is normally distributed with a mean of 130 000 km and a standard deviation of 12 000 km. There have been 200 000 Coyotes sold.
(a) What percentage of the Coyotes will last longer than 118 000 km?
(b) Approximately how many Coyotes will last between 106 000 km and 142 000 km?
(c) Approximately how many Coyotes will last longer than 154 000 km?

13. Two hundred students wrote the aptitude test for playground supervisor. Frank's mark ranked in the 74th percentile.
(a) Approximately how many students scored higher than Frank?
(b) Approximately how many students scored lower than Frank?

14. Susan got 79 on a history test. The marks of the other students in her class were as follows:

$$66, \quad 78, \quad 81, \quad 94, \quad 79, \quad 55,$$
$$68, \quad 80, \quad 70, \quad 79, \quad 65, \quad 82,$$
$$90, \quad 54, \quad 67, \quad 69, \quad 90, \quad 61$$

Find Susan's percentile rank.

EXTRA

RANDOM SAMPLING

There are several good techniques for determining a random sample.

One way to select fifty students at random is to assign 1000 students a different number from 000 to 999. Then a method can be used to generate 50 three-digit numbers.

To get fifty random numbers, we can use a table of random numbers. A partial table is shown below.

34561	70917	88496	29461
57283	16902	74153	66802
18293	47652	60192	38475

Start at the top and read the numbers horizontally. This gives 345, 617, and 091 as the first three student numbers. Reading vertically, the first three numbers would be 345, 572, and 182.

A computer can also be used. The following program generates random numbers.

```
NEW
10 PRINT"RANDOM NUMBERS"
20 PRINT"HOW MANY NUMBERS?"
30 INPUT N
40 FOR I=1 TO N
50 X=RND(5)
60 PRINT INT(9*X)+1;
70 NEXT I
75 PRINT
80 PRINT"ANOTHER LIST? Y OR N"
90 INPUT Z$
100 IF Z$="Y" THEN 20
110 END
RUN
```

EXERCISE

1. Use each of the methods to select 10 students at random from your class.

9.8 CHAPTER 9 TEST

1. Determine the mean, median, and mode of the following data.

$$55, \quad 46, \quad 48, \quad 59, \quad 47, \quad 55, \quad 54, \quad 52$$

2. Calculate the mean, median, and mode of the following salaries.

Title	Number	Salary
President	1	$400 000
Vice-President	1	$200 000
Treasurer	1	$150 000
Accountant	5	$80 000
Salesperson	10	$50 000
Secretary	3	$40 000
Receptionist	1	$25 000

3. Calculate the range and standard deviation to the nearest tenth.

$$37, \quad 49, \quad 56, \quad 70, \quad 38$$

4. The lifetime of the Acme coffee maker is normally distributed with a mean of nine years and a standard deviation of one year.
The Acme company has sold 60 000 coffee makers.
(a) What percentage of the coffee makers will last between seven years and ten years?
(b) Approximately how many of the coffee makers will last longer than eight years?
(c) Approximately how many of the coffee makers will last between nine years and ten years?

5. Justine got 83 on a math test. The marks of the other students in her class were as follows:

$$79, \quad 90, \quad 88, \quad 84, \quad 66, \quad 67, \quad 83, \quad 83, \quad 65, \quad 50,$$
$$79, \quad 91, \quad 64, \quad 83, \quad 62, \quad 62, \quad 60, \quad 52, \quad 51, \quad 98$$

Determine Justine's percentile rank.

SAVINGS ACCOUNTS, CERTIFICATES, AND SAVINGS BONDS

10

REVIEW AND PREVIEW TO CHAPTER 10

PERCENT

EXERCISE 1

1. Calculate.
(a) 3% of $23
(b) 3% of $168
(c) 8% of $489
(d) 4% of $1898
(e) 1% of $287
(f) 7% of $782
(g) 9% of $67
(h) 7% of $1299
(i) 123% of $782
(j) 8% of $437
(k) 9% of $623
(l) 4.5% of $78
(m) 12% of $879
(n) 10.25% of $789
(o) $3\frac{1}{2}$% of $645
(p) 5% of $809
(q) 15.5% of $1932
(r) 12.5% of $567
(s) 100% of $342
(t) 0.87% of $1238
(u) $4\frac{1}{3}$% of $389
(v) 125% of $2345
(w) 12.5% of $2345
(x) 1.25% of $2345

2. What percent is
(a) 15 of 30?
(b) 16 of 64?
(c) 2 of 16?
(d) 4 of 16?
(e) 8 of 16?
(f) 20 of 16?
(g) 20 of 50?

FRACTION OF A YEAR

EXERCISE 2

Since interest is usually given in per annum (per year) rates, time must be expressed as a fraction of a year.

When months are given, assume 30 d/month, and remember there are 365 d in a year.

1. Express each as a fraction of a year.
(a) 34 d
(b) 64 d
(c) 97 d
(d) 8 months
(e) 2 months
(f) 7 months
(g) 12 weeks
(h) 27 weeks
(i) 60 d
(j) 90 d
(k) 120 d
(l) 3 weeks, 2 d
(m) 7 weeks, 2 d
(n) 11 weeks
(o) 10 months
(p) 30 months
(q) 5 weeks, 2 d
(r) 6 weeks, 5 d
(s) 48 h
(t) 72 h
(u) 84 h
(v) 5 d, 12 h
(w) 10 d
(x) 12 d

DAYS OF A YEAR

EXERCISE 3

The table Days Expressed in Decimal Equivalents of a Year — 365 d Basis in the Appendix is used to find the number of days for each date and the equivalent decimal fraction.

The dates in this exercise are expressed month–day.

1. Find the number of days between the following dates and the equivalent fraction of the year.

(a) 01–07, 03–17
(b) 03–14, 08–30
(c) 03–28, 07–19
(d) 11–02, 01–01
(e) 04–25, 11–01
(f) 10–03, 11–17
(g) 11–17, 05–06
(h) 05–12, 09–07
(i) 12–20, 07–09
(j) 01–02, 01–01

> All dates are in the same or successive years.

2. Find the following dates.

(a) 90 d after 03–07
(b) 75 d after 03–04
(c) 30 d after 07–23
(d) 120 d after 08–11
(e) 24 d after 06–09
(f) 95 d after 04–01
(g) 80 d after 11–08
(h) 210 d after 12–25
(i) 45 d after 09–23
(j) 57 d after 08–25

>
> Using a computer and spreadsheet software, prepare a table of decimal equivalents of a year on a 365 d/a basis by developing and entering a formula.

EQUATIONS

EXERCISE 4

1. Solve each formula for the indicated variable.

(a) $I = prt$ for t
(b) $I = prt$ for r
(c) $I = prt$ for p
(d) $a = 3b + 4c$ for c
(e) $a = \dfrac{4rf}{a + b}$ for f
(f) $a = \dfrac{4rf}{a + b}$ for b
(g) $c^2 = a^2 + b^2$ for c, $c > 0$
(h) $c^2 = a^2 + b^2$ for b^2
(i) $c^2 = a^2 + b^2$ for b, $b > 0$

FORMULAS

EXERCISE 5

1. Find the value of the missing term for the formula $a = bcd$ to the nearest hundredth.

(a) $b = 0.7$, $c = 1.23$, $d = 123$
(b) $a = 45$, $b = 29$, $d = 12.3$
(c) $a = 23.8$, $b = 1.8$, $c = 3.5$
(d) $a = 12.8$, $c = 23.5$, $d = 45$

2. Find the value of the missing term for the formula $a = \dfrac{bc}{d}$ to the nearest hundredth.

(a) $b = 0.2$, $c = 1.2$, $d = 23.4$
(b) $a = 4.5$, $b = 2.9$, $d = 123$
(c) $a = 12$, $b = 7$, $c = 23$
(d) $a = 1.23$, $c = 235$, $d = 4.5$

10.1 INVESTMENT INSTRUMENTS

Whether you have money in excess of your immediate financial needs or you are saving for future needs, your money should be invested so that it is working for you by earning interest or dividends. Financial institutions such as chartered banks, credit unions, and trust companies offer many methods for you to invest your money through savings plans that earn interest in a predetermined way.

Different savings plans offer different rates of interest. The interest rates vary according to how accessible you want your money to be after you have invested it. The more readily available the funds are for withdrawal, the lower the rate of interest.

Type of Account	Interest Rate	Deposit	Withdrawal
Savings/ Chequing	low (flexible)	passbook bank machine	• anytime • cheque • bank machine
Savings	moderate (flexible)	passbook bank machine	• anytime • passbook • bank machine
Systematic Savings Plan	moderate (flexible)	direct deposit pay deduction	• anytime • passbook
Deposit Certificates	moderately high (fixed)	$5000+ for a fixed term, 30 d to 5 a	• only at end of term • transferable
Savings Certificates (Financial Institution)	relatively high (fixed)	$100+ for an agreed time to maturity, up to 5 a	• at maturity • non-transferable
Savings Bonds (Government)	relatively high (fixed)	$100+ for an agreed time to maturity, up to 5 a	• at maturity • non-transferable
Bearer Deposit Notes	high (fixed)	$30 000+ for a fixed term, 30 d to 1 a	• only at end of term • transferable

The following are some of the terms used with investment instruments.

Principal (P). The amount deposited.

Interest (I). The amount earned from the deposit of the principal.

Interest Rate per Annum (r). The percentage of the principal earned in interest in one year.

Time (t) or Term. The length of time on which the interest is earned.

Amount (A). The amount of the principal plus the interest earned.

Flexible Rate of Interest. A rate of interest that changes without notice due to changes in economic conditions.

Fixed Rate of Interest. A predetermined rate of interest at time of deposit that does not change over the term of the deposit.

Transferable. The ability to transfer an amount from one form of saving to another usually with the payment of an amount called a penalty.

Maturity. The predetermined date at which a savings bond or certificate gains its full amount, interest earned at fixed rate plus principal.

EXERCISE 10.1

A 1. (a) If you want to save $50/month on a regular basis, which savings plan would you choose?
(b) What is your total principal after one year?

2. You are a student with an $1800 student loan, which you need to pay your tuition in three instalments.
Which savings plan would you choose? Why?

3. You are the president of a large corporation with a refund for materials of $120 000.
If this amount is needed in 3 months, which savings plan would you choose? Why?

4. You are newly married with plans to purchase a home within five years.
Which savings plan would you choose to save for the down payment? Why?

B 5. Contact several local financial institutions to determine the current rates of interest being charged on each savings plan listed in the table.

6. For each savings plan in the table, list the circumstances under which a person would choose each plan.

7. Savings plans have three variables: interest rate, deposit, and withdrawal method. How do these three variables relate to each other?

10.2 SIMPLE INTEREST

Interest is the amount of money earned on the principal deposited. Interest is calculated as a percentage of the principal over a specific period of time, which is usually one year.

$$\text{Interest} = \text{Principal} \times \text{Rate} \times \text{Time}$$
$$I = Prt$$

$$\text{Amount} = \text{Principal} + \text{Interest}$$
$$A = P + I$$

By substitution,
$$A = P + Prt$$
$$A = P(1 + rt)$$

$$\text{Principal} = \frac{\text{Amount}}{1 + \text{rate} \times \text{time}}$$

$$P = \frac{A}{1 + rt}$$

Example 1. Find the interest and the amount in a savings account at the end of six months if $586 is deposited at 7% per annum.

Solution: P = $586   r = 7%   t = 6 months
                              = 0.07   = 0.5 a

I = Prt	A = P + I
I = 586 × 0.07 × 0.5	A = 586 + 20.51
= 20.51	= 606.51

The interest earned is $20.51, and the amount in the account is $606.51.

READ

PLAN

$E=mc^2$

SOLVE

Example 2. Find the original amount invested and the interest earned if $4530 is in a savings account after 78 d. The interest rate is 8.5% per annum.

Solution: A = $4530   r = 8.5%   t = 78 d
                              = 0.085   = 0.2137 a

$$P = \frac{A}{1 + rt}$$

$$P = \frac{4530}{1 + 0.085 \times 0.2137}$$

$$= \frac{4530}{1 + 0.018\ 164\ 5}$$

$$= \frac{4530}{1.018\ 164\ 5}$$

$$= 4449.18 \quad \text{(rounded to the nearest cent)}$$

I = A − P
I = 4530 − 4449.18
= 80.82

ANSWER

The original investment was $4449.18, and $80.82 in interest was earned.

EXERCISE 10.2

B

1. Find the missing quantities.

	Interest	Principal	Rate	Time	Amount
(a)	*41.02*	$1893.00	6.5%	4 months	*1934.02*
(b)	*84.12*	$712.89	11.8%	1 a	*797.01*
(c)	$78.50	*1670.21*	9.4%	6 months	*1748.71*
(d)	$90.00	*4211.54*	13%	60 d	*4301.54*
(e)	$550.00	$7425.00	*9.88%*	9 months	*7975*
(f)	$389.00	$19 450.00	*8 %*	3 months	*19839*
(g)	$2.25	$90.00	6%	*5/12 ÷ 22/52 ÷ 153/366*	*92.25*
(h)	$3750.00	$50 000.00	7½%	*1 year*	*53750*
(i)	*913.92*	*44836.08*	12%	62 d	$45 750.00
(j)	*243.82*	*956.18*	8.5%	3 a	$1200.00

2. Solve the formula I = Prt for P, t, and r.

3. Calculate the simple interest paid on each of the following investments and the current amount in the account.
(a) $4897 at 6% for 4 a
(b) $186 at 7.5% for 6 months
(c) $1127.89 at 9% for 121 d
(d) $789 at 12½% for 8 months
(e) $723.89 at 7¾% for 9 weeks
(f) $24 890 at 11% for 60 d

4. If you invested an amount at 7% simple interest and at the end of 170 d had $10 326.03 in the account, how much had you originally deposited? *0000*

5. The credit union pays an interest rate of 7½% per annum on deposits in its savings accounts. At the end of 6 months, the interest is calculated and added to the account. The interest for the next period is calculated on the new balance.
If you deposit $567.89 in an account and leave it for 2 a, what will be your balance in the account at the end of the term?
657.98

6. If you invest $500 on January 1 in an account that calculates and pays interest monthly at a flexible rate, and if each month the interest paid is added to the principal and you made no withdrawals, find the amount in the account at the end of 6 months if the rates of interest were as follows:

January interest rate	7%,
February interest rate	7%,
March interest rate	7.25%,
April interest rate	7.5%,
May interest rate	8%,
June interest rate	8.25%

519.04

C

7. Using the information in question 6, construct a graph to represent the cumulative interest by month over the six-month period.

8. Using the information in question 6, construct a graph to represent the amount in the account each month over the six-month period.

10.3 THE GEOMETRIC SEQUENCE

The terms of a sequence form a set of numbers that are written in a definite order.

In the sequence 3, 6, 12, 24, ... , notice that

$$6 \div 3 = 2$$
$$12 \div 6 = 2$$
$$24 \div 12 = 2$$
$$\vdots$$

that is, the ratio of each succeeding pair of terms is a constant. Sequences of this form are called geometric sequences. This particular sequence could be written

$$3, \quad 3 \times 2, \quad 3 \times 2^2, \quad 3 \times 2^3, \quad ...$$

The general geometric sequence is a, ar, ar^2, ar^3, ... where a is the first term and r is the common ratio.

t_1 means the first term. ⟶ $t_1 = a$
$t_2 = ar$
$t_3 = ar^2$
$$\vdots$$
$t_n = ar^{n-1}$

Example 1. Find t_5 and t_n for the geometric sequence 3, 6, 12, ...

Solution: a = 3 and r = $\frac{6}{3}$ = 2.

$$t_5 = ar^4 \qquad\qquad t_n = ar^{n-1}$$
$$t_5 = 3 \times 2^4 \qquad\quad t_n = 3(2)^{n-1}$$
$$= 48$$

$t_5 = 48$ and $t_n = 3(2)^{n-1}$.

Example 2. How many terms are in the sequence 2, 6, 18, ... , 486?

Solution: The sequence is geometric: a = 2, r = 3.

$E=mc^2$

$$t_n = ar^{n-1}$$
$$486 = 2(3)^{n-1} \longleftarrow \text{Divide by 2.}$$
$$243 = 3^{n-1}$$
$$3^5 = 3^{n-1}$$
$$n - 1 = 5$$
$$n = 6$$
$$486 = t_6$$

The exponents are equal. ⟶

∴ the sequence has 6 terms.

EXERCISE 10.3

A

1. Which of the following are successive terms of a geometric sequence?
For those that are geometric sequences, state the value of r.

(a) 1, 2, 4, 8, ...
(b) 4, 12, 36, 108, ...
(c) 6, 24, 48, 144, ...
(d) 16, 8, 4, 2, ...
(e) 1, 3, 9, 18, ...
(f) 4, -8, 24, -48, ...
(g) 27, -9, 3, -1, ...

B

2. Find the terms indicated for each of the following geometric sequences.

(a) t_6 and t_n for 1, 2, 4, ...
(b) t_5 and t_n for 5, 15, 45, ...
(c) t_7 and t_k for 3, 6, 12, ...
(d) t_8 and t_k for 64, 32, 16, ...
(e) t_5 and t_n for 4, -8, 16, ...
(f) t_7 and t_n for 81, -27, 9, ...

3. How many terms are in the following geometric sequences?

(a) 3, 6, 12, ... , 384
(b) 4, 8, 16, ... , 256
(c) 4, 12, 36, ... , 972
(d) 625, 125, 25, ... , $\frac{1}{25}$
(e) 2, -4, 8, ... , -256
(f) 1458, 486, 162, ... , 2

C

5. Find a, r, and t_n for the following geometric sequences.

(a) $t_3 = 36$, $t_4 = 108$
(b) $t_5 = 48$, $t_8 = 384$
(c) $t_2 = 28$, $t_4 = 448$
(d) $t_3 = 64$, $t_8 = 2$
(e) $t_4 = -9$, $t_5 = -3$
(f) $t_2 = 12$, $t_4 = 192$

6. A virus reproduces by dividing into two, and after a period of growth by dividing again.
How many viral organisms will be in a system after division has taken place ten times?

MIND BENDER

Place the numbers from 1 to 8 in the circles so that the sum of each side is the same.

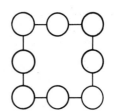

4. (a) When money is lent and compound interest is charged, the amount required to repay the loan at the end of each year forms a geometric sequence.

Year	Now	1	2	3	4	...	n
Amount	P	P(1 + i)	P(1 + i)²	P(1 + i)³	P(1 + i)⁴	...	P(1 + i)ⁿ

where P represents the principal and i the annual rate of interest.

If $100 is lent at 5% per annum compounded annually, show the amount at the end of 1, 2, 3, 4, and n years.
Show a and r for the sequence.
(b) Repeat part (a) for $500 invested at 8% per annum compounded annually.

10.4 COMPOUND INTEREST

Compound interest is interest that is paid at regular intervals during the time the principal is invested. The interval of time over which interest is calculated is called the conversion period. At the end of each conversion period, interest is paid into the account and added to the principal. At the second conversion period, interest is paid on the principal and the interest from the first conversion period. This process continues over the term that the money and accumulating interest remain in the account. This method of calculating interest is called compound interest.

Example 1. If $100 is invested at 9% per annum compounded annually, show how the amount grows over a term of n years.

Solution:

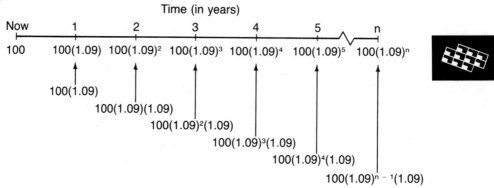

Notice that the amounts at the end of each year form a pattern.

Term 1, $t_1 = 100(1.09)$
Term 2, $t_2 = 100(1.09)(1.09)^1$
Term 3, $t_3 = 100(1.09)(1.09)^2$
Term 4, $t_4 = 100(1.09)(1.09)^3$
Term 5, $t_5 = 100(1.09)(1.09)^4$
. . .
Term n, $t_n = 100(1.09)(1.09)^{n-1}$

The pattern or sequence is a geometric sequence.

> Each term, t_n, of a geometric sequence can be expressed as $t_n = ar^{n-1}$, where a is a real coefficient, r is the base, and $n - 1$ is the exponent.

In the example, $a = \$100(1.09)$,
               $r = 1.09$, and
               t_n is the nth term of the sequence.

The amount after n years,

$t_n = ar^{n-1}$
$t_n = 100(1.09)(1.09)^{n-1}$
    $= 100(1.09)^n$

Example 2. If $100 is invested at 9% per annum compounded semi-annually, show how the amount grows over a term of 10 a.

Solution:
9% compounded semi-annually gives an interest rate of 4.5% per conversion period.
10 a gives 20 semi-annual conversion periods.

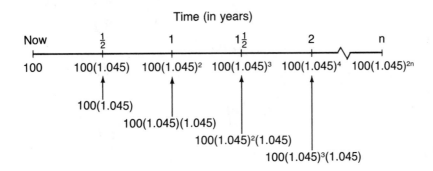

The amount at the end of each half year forms the terms of a geometric sequence, where a = $100(1.045) and r = 1.045. The amount after 10 a is the 20th term of the sequence, $t_n = 100(1.045)^n$.

We may generalize from the above example to the relationship

$$A = P(1 + i)^n$$

where A is the amount,
P is the principal invested,
i is the rate of interest per conversion period, and
n is the total number of conversion periods.

To simplify calculations, use the table of values for $(1 + i)^n$ in the Appendix or a calculator.

Example 3. Find the amount of $5000 invested at 9% per annum compounded semi- annually for 15 a.

Solution:
At 9% compounded semi-annually, i = (0.5)(9%)
 = 4.5%
For 15 a compounded semi-annually, n = 15 × 2
 = 30

Using tables,

$A = P(1 + i)^n$
$A = 5000(1 + 0.045)^{30}$
$\doteq 5000(3.745\ 32)$
$\doteq 18\ 726.60$

Using a calculator, press

$\boxed{5}\boxed{0}\boxed{0}\boxed{0}\boxed{\times}\boxed{1}\boxed{.}\boxed{0}\boxed{4}\boxed{5}\boxed{y^x}\boxed{3}\boxed{0}\boxed{=}$

The display is 18726.591

The amount is $18 726.60.

EXERCISE 10.4

A

1. Complete the following.

	Per annum Rate	Term (a)	Conversion Period	n	i
(a)	10%	20	semi-annually	40	5% .05
(b)	12%	10	quarterly	40	3%
(c)	8%	5	semi-ann	10	4%
(d)	8%	15	semi-annually	30	4%
(e)	18%	6	monthly	72	1.5%
(f)	9%	2	monthly	24	0.75%
(g)	6%	4	annually	4	6%
(h)	8%	1.5	quarterly	6	2%

B

2. Find the amount of each of the following investments.

	Principal	Per annum Rate	Conversion Period	Term (a)
(a)	$4500	12%	semi-annually	6
(b)	$750	6%	quarterly	1
(c)	$15 000	8%	annually	20
(d)	$3250	6%	quarterly	$8\frac{1}{2}$
(e)	$730	12%	monthly	$2\frac{1}{3}$

$A = 4500(1.06)^{12} = 9054.8$
$= 750(1.015)^4 = 796.02$
$= 15000(1.08)^{20} = 69914.$
$= 3250(1.015)^{34} = 5391.$
$= 730(1.01)^{28} = 964.5$

3. (a) What amount is required to pay off a loan of $4000 after 2 a if it has earned interest at the rate of 12% per annum compounded semi-annually?
(b) How much of this amount is interest?

4. Find the amounts that $1000 invested at 12% for 3 a will grow to if the interest is compounded
(a) semi-annually,
(b) quarterly,
(c) monthly.

5. How long must money be invested at 8% compounded semi-annually to double? (To the nearest 0.5 a.)

6. Two loans of $5000 each are taken out on Feb. 1 and Aug. 1 for vacation expenses. They are repaid the following Aug. 1.
If interest is charged at 11% compounded semi-annually, what total amount must be repaid?

7. (a) A savings account pays 1% per month on the minimum monthly balance with interest added every 3 months. Find the interest paid for the period June 1 to Sept. 1 given the following:

Balance: June 1 $465
Deposits: June 12 $250
          July 17 $175
          Aug. 20 $315

No withdrawals were made.
(b) If the only entry for September in the account from part (a) was a deposit of $85, on what amount would the interest for September be calculated?

8. Mr. Collins noted that he could use collateral to borrow at 9% compounded semi-annually and invest in second mortgages at 16% compounded quarterly.
(a) If he borrowed and reinvested $80 000 under these terms for 5 a, what profit did he make?
(b) What had Mr. Collins done to "earn" this money?

C
9. If money is borrowed at 8% compounded quarterly and reinvested at 12% compounded monthly, what annual rate of return is being made? (Consider a principal of $1 invested at each rate for 1 a.)

10. Four years ago, $10 000 was invested at 8% compounded semi-annually. If the principal and interest are now invested at 11% compounded semi-annually for 5 a, what will the investment be worth?

Using a computer and spreadsheet software, develop compound interest tables for fixed values of P and variable values of i and n, as described in section 15.7.

MICRO MATH

COMPOUND AMOUNT

The following program calculates the amount, A, of a principal, P, invested at i% for n conversion periods.

```
NEW
 10 PRINT"COMPOUND AMOUNT"
 20 PRINT"ENTER P"
 30 INPUT P
 40 PRINT"ENTER I AS A DECIMAL"
 50 INPUT I
 60 PRINT"ENTER N"
 70 INPUT N
 80 A=P*(1+I)^N
 90 PRINT"THE AMOUNT IS"
100 PRINT"$";A
RUN
```

EXERCISE

1. Use the program to calculate A under the following conditions.
(a) $2000 invested for one year at 10% per annum compounded quarterly
(b) $100 000 invested for six years at 8% per annum compounded semi-annually
(c) $50 000 invested for three years at 6% per annum compounded monthly
(d) $250 000 invested for ten years at 12% per annum compounded quarterly
(e) $1 000 000 invested for two years at 4% compounded semi-annually

10.5 EFFECTIVE AND NOMINAL RATES OF INTEREST

When interest rates are compounded more than once per year, the stated annual rate is not the actual interest rate. The actual interest rate is higher than the stated, or advertised, rate. The stated annual rate is called the nominal rate. The actual interest rate is called the effective rate.

> The effective interest rate is the rate that gives the same amount, A, with one conversion period per year as a nominal rate with m conversion periods per year.

Example 1. If you deposit $1 in a savings account that pays 12% per annum compounded quarterly, what is the effective rate of interest?

Solution: The stated interest rate of 12% compounded quarterly is the nominal rate of interest.
m is the number of conversion periods per year, which is equal to 4.
i is the rate of interest per conversion period.

$$i = \frac{0.12}{m}$$
$$= \frac{0.12}{4}$$
$$= 0.03$$

P is the principal, which is equal to $1.

Let A be the amount based on the nominal rate of interest for n conversion periods.

$$A = P(1 + i)^n$$
$$A = 1(1 + 0.03)^4$$

Using a calculator, press `1` `.` `0` `3` `yˣ` `4` `=`
The display is `1.12550881`

The effective interest rate is the rate that gives the same amount, 1.125 51, with one conversion period per year as the nominal rate with m conversion periods per year.

If the rate was compounded annually for one year, i would be the equivalent effective rate of interest.

Let A_e be the amount based on the effective rate of interest.

$$A_e = P(1 + i)^1$$
$$A_e = P(1 + i)$$
$$A_e = 1(1 + i)$$
$$1.125\ 51 = 1 + i$$
$$i = 0.125\ 51$$

The effective rate of interest is 12.551%.

12.551% is the effective rate of interest when the nominal rate of interest is 12% compounded quarterly because both result in the same amount.

Using the method in Example 1, we can develop a formula.

With principal P, nominal annual rate of interest j, and m conversion periods per year, find the effective annual rate of interest, i.

$$A_e = A$$

$$P(1 + i) = P\left(1 + \frac{j}{m}\right)^m$$

Divide by P.

$$(1 + i) = \left(1 + \frac{j}{m}\right)^m$$

Solve for i.

$$i = \left(1 + \frac{j}{m}\right)^m - 1$$

We can find the effective rate of interest from the nominal rate using the formula

$$i = \left(1 + \frac{j}{m}\right)^m - 1$$

where i is the effective rate of interest as a decimal,
      m is the number of conversion periods per year, and
      j is the nominal rate of interest as a decimal.

Example 2. What is the effective rate of interest for an investment at 9% compounded semi-annually?

Solution: j = 9 and m = 2.

$$i = \left(1 + \frac{j}{m}\right)^m - 1$$

$$i = \left(1 + \frac{0.09}{2}\right)^2 - 1$$

$$= (1 + 0.045)^2 - 1$$

Using the tables,

$i = 1.092\ 03 - 1$

$i = 0.092\ 03$

Using a calculator, press

`1` `.` `0` `4` `5` `x²` `−` `1` `=`

The display is `0.092025`

The effective rate of interest is approximately 9.2%.

The more times the nominal interest rate is compounded per year, or the more conversion periods per year, the higher the effective rate of interest.

The graph below illustrates this principle for a 12% nominal rate of interest.

From the formula, when

$m = 1,$ j and i are 12%

$m = 2,$ $j = (1 + 0.06)^2 - 1,$ and $i = 12.36\%$

$m = 3,$ $j = (1 + 0.04)^3 - 1,$ and $i = 12.486\%$

Using a calculator, press

`1` `.` `0` `4` `yˣ` `3` `−` `1` `=`

The display is `0.124864`

$m = 4,$ $j = (1 + 0.03)^4 - 1,$ and $i = 12.551\%$

$m = 6,$ $j = (1 + 0.02)^6 - 1,$ and $i = 12.616\%$

$m = 8,$ $j = (1 + 0.015)^8 - 1,$ and $i = 12.649\%$

$m = 12,$ $j = (1 + 0.01)^{12} - 1,$ and $i = 12.683\%$

$m = 24,$ $j = (1 + 0.005)^{24} - 1,$ and $i = 12.716\%$

Effective Rate of Interest as k Increases

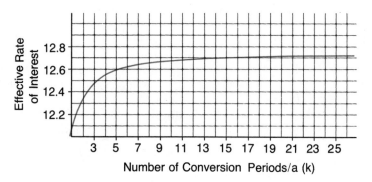

EXERCISE 10.5

B

1. Complete the table.

	Nominal Rate	Conversion Periods per year	Effective Rate
(a)	12%	semi-annually	12.36%
(b)	16%	semi-annually	16.64%
(c)	16%	quarterly	16.99%
(d)	6%	6 times per year	6.15%
(e)	18%	annually	18%
(f)	24%	12 times per year	26.82%

2. You deposit $4897 in a savings account that pays 9% per annum compounded semi-annually.   450.65
What is the interest per year and the effective rate of interest?   9.2%

3. Your savings account earns a nominal rate of 8%.
What is the effective rate if the nominal rate is compounded
(a) annually,
(b) semi-annually,
(c) quarterly,
(d) 8 times per year,
(e) 16 times per year.

4. From the information in question 3, graph the effective rate of interest as the number of conversion periods increases.

5. From the graph in question 4, predict the approximate rate if there were
(a) 20 conversion periods,
(b) 30 conversion periods.

6. Graph the results of question 5.
What do you observe about the effective rate of interest as m becomes larger and larger?
Is there a limit to the effective rate of interest?

Using a computer and spreadsheet software, enter the formula for effective rate of interest, as described in section 15.7.

For a nominal rate of 10%, calculate the effective rate of interest for m = 1 to 20.

Repeat this program, using a nominal rate of 20%.

M I C R O   M A T H

EFFECTIVE RATE OF INTEREST

The following program calculates the effective rate of interest given the nominal rate of interest and the number of conversion periods per year.

```
NEW
10 PRINT"EFFECTIVE RATE OF INTEREST"
20 PRINT"ENTER J, THE NOMINAL RATE"
30 PRINT"OF INTEREST AS A DECIMAL"
40 INPUT J
50 PRINT"ENTER M, THE NUMBER OF"
60 PRINT"CONVERSION PERIODS PER YEAR"
70 INPUT M
80 E=(1+J/M)^M-1
90 PRINT"THE EFFECTIVE RATE IS";E"%"
RUN
```

EXERCISE

1. Calculate the effective rate of interest under the following conditions.
(a) a nominal rate of 12% compounded semi-annually
(b) a nominal rate of 8% compounded quarterly
(c) a nominal rate of 6% compounded bimonthly
(d) a nominal rate of 10% compounded every four months

10.6 PRESENT VALUE

Present value refers to the amount of money that must be invested now, at a current rate of interest, to produce a desired amount at a later date. The present value depends on how long the money will be invested, the return that is expected on the investment, and the amount of money that is received at the end of the term.

For example, when you purchase a government treasury bill that has a value of $10 000 at maturity, the amount you pay for this investment today is called the present value.

The rate of interest at which a bond or investment is made that causes the bond to grow to the future amount at maturity is called the effective interest rate. This rate is also known as the current going market rate.

Governments and financial institutions set a rate for savings bonds and savings certificates that will not only be attractive to customers but will also be profitable for the organization offering the bonds or certificates.

Example 1. What must you pay today for a savings bond with a value of $100 in n years at 9% compounded annually?

Solution: The principal to be invested is called the present value. It is represented by PV.

Time (in years)

Now	1	2	3	n − 1	n
PV	PV(1.09)	PV(1.09)^2	PV(1.09)^3	PV(1.09)$^{n-1}$	PV(1.09)^n

The last term of the sequence PV(1.09)^n represents the value of the investment after n years, which we know must be equal to $100 by the conditions of the question.

$$PV(1.09)^n = \$100$$
$$PV = 100\,\frac{1}{(1.09)^n}$$
$$= \frac{100}{(1.09)^n}$$

$E=mc^2$

Example 2. What principal invested now at 9% compounded semi-annually will amount to $100 in n years?

Solution: Since the interest is compounded semi-annually, the number of conversion periods is 2n, and the interest rate per conversion period is $\frac{9\%}{2}$ or 4.5% or 0.045.

$$\therefore PV = \frac{100}{(1.045)^{2n}}$$

From the above example we can generalize the relationship to

$$PV = \frac{A}{(1 + i)^n}$$

where PV is the present value,
A is the amount to be achieved,
i is the rate of interest per conversion period, and
n is the total number of conversion periods.

A table of values for $\frac{1}{(1 + i)^n}$ is given in the Appendix.

Example 3. Rosalyn wants to buy a boat ten years from now. She estimates that the boat will cost $200 000.
How much should she invest today at 10% per annum compounded semi-annually to have $200 000 in ten years?

Solution:

$A = \$200\ 000$, $i = \frac{10}{2} = 5\%$, and $n = 2 \times 10 = 20$.

$$PV = \frac{A}{(1 + i)^n}$$
$$PV = \frac{200\ 000}{(1 + 0.045)^{20}}$$
$$= \frac{200\ 000}{(1.045)^{20}}$$
$$= 200\ 000 \times \frac{1}{(1.045)^{20}}$$
$$= 200\ 000 \times 0.414\ 64$$
$$= 82\ 928$$

Using a calculator, press

The display is `82928.572`

She should invest $82 928.

EXERCISE 10.6

B

1. Find the present value of a savings bond with each of the following amounts at maturity.

	Amount	Per annum Rate	Conversion Period	Term (a)
(a)	$1500	10%	semi-annually	10
(b)	$350	12%	quarterly	4
(c)	$750	6%	annually	2
(d)	$1250	8%	semi-annually	$5\frac{1}{2}$
(e)	$20 000	10%	quarterly	$8\frac{3}{4}$

(a) *565.33*

(e) *8421.42*

2. How much money must be invested now at 7% per annum compounded semi-annually to replace a $300 000 machine that is expected to wear out in 5 a?

3. Mr. Jones has a paid-up endowment policy that will pay him $200 000 on his 65th birthday.
What is the present value of this policy on his 60th birthday if money is worth 9% compounded semi-annually?

4. Compare the present values of $1000 due in 3 a at 12% if the interest is compounded
(a) semi-annually,
(b) quarterly,
(c) monthly.

5. You have signed a promissory note that requires you to pay $500 on Dec. 15.
What is the value of the note on the 15th of June before the due date if money is worth 9% compounded semi-annually?

6. Two debts of $500 come due in six months and one year respectively.
If money is worth 11% per annum compounded semi-annually, what amount paid now will discharge both debts?

7. What amount must you invest now at 12% compounded annually in order to be a millionaire in 25 a?

8. What amount must you invest now at 12% compounded semi-annually in order to be a millionaire in 25 a?

9. What amount must you invest now at 12% compounded quarterly in order to be a millionaire in 25 a?

C

10. What principal invested for the next 5 a at 9% compounded semi-annually, and for the following 3 a at 7% compounded semi-annually will amount to $10 000?

11. Six years ago a sum of money was invested at 7% per annum compounded semi-annually.
If the principal and interest are now invested at 12% compounded semi-annually and in two years will amount to $1430.77, what was the principal originally invested.

$x(1.035$

$PV. = 1430$

$(1.06$

$x(1.035)^{12} = \dfrac{1430.77}{(1.06)^4}$

MIND BENDER

If it is 10:00 now, what time will it be 121 036 842 h from now?

Using a computer and spreadsheet software, prepare a table that will calculate the present value of guaranteed investment certificates (GICs) in the following amounts, interest rates, conversion periods, and terms, holding the single value constant and varying the value in the multiples given.

Amount	Per annum Rate	Conversion Period	Term (a)
100, 150, 200, 250	10%	quarterly	5
1000	10%, 11%, 12%, 13%	semi-annually	5
10 000	8.5%	quarterly, semi-annually, annually	10
5000	12%	quarterly	2, 3, 4, 5

$$x(1.045)^{10}(1.035)^{6} = 10000$$

PRESENT VALUE

The following program calculates the present value, PV, of an amount A invested at i% for n periods.

```
NEW
 10 PRINT"PRESENT VALUE"
 20 PRINT"ENTER A"
 30 INPUT A
 40 PRINT"ENTER I AS A DECIMAL"
 50 INPUT I
 60 PRINT"ENTER N"
 70 INPUT N
 80 PV=A/(1+I)^N
 90 PRINT"THE PRESENT VALUE IS"
100 PRINT"$";PV
RUN
```

EXERCISE

1. Use the program to solve the following.
(a) How much must be invested now at 8% per annum compounded semi-annually to give $10 000 in five years?
(b) How much must be invested now at 12% per annum compounded quarterly to give $500 000 in six years?

10.7 DETERMINING INTEREST RATE

The interest rate set for savings bonds and savings
certificates by financial institutions and governments depends
on many economic factors. If you are looking for the best
possible investment in a bond or certificate, you can
calculate the approximate annual nominal rate of interest if
you know
(i)   the current cost of the bond, PV;
(ii) the amount at maturity, A; and
(iii) the number of conversion periods, n.

Example. You can purchase a $100 savings bond that
matures in 5 a for $50.
What is the approximate rate of interest
compounded annually?

Solution: Solve the PV formula for i.

$$PV = \frac{A}{(1 + i)^n}$$

$$PV(1 + i)^n = A$$

$$(1 + i)^n = \frac{A}{PV}$$

$$1 + i = \sqrt[n]{\frac{A}{PV}}$$

$$i = \sqrt[n]{\frac{A}{PV}} - 1$$

Substitute A = 100, PV = 50, and n = 5.

$$i = \sqrt[5]{\frac{100}{50}} - 1$$

$$i = \sqrt[5]{2} - 1$$

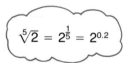

$$\sqrt[5]{2} = 2^{\frac{1}{5}} = 2^{0.2}$$

Using a calculator, press

| 2 | yˣ | 0 | . | 2 | − | 1 | = |

The display is `0.1486984`

The rate of interest is 14.9% to the nearest tenth.

EXERCISE 10.7

A

1. Considering current trends, what factors effect the rate of interest that the government and financial institutions give on savings bonds and certificates.

2. Under what set of economic circumstances would the government and financial institutions lose on bonds that mature in 5 a?

B

3. Evaluate to the nearest hundredth.
(a) 1.09^{10}
(b) 1.022^{11}
(c) 1.11^9
(d) 1.06^5

4. Evaluate to the nearest hundredth.
(a) $\sqrt[5]{1.5}$
(b) $\sqrt[11]{1.9}$
(c) $\sqrt[9]{3.3}$
(d) $\sqrt[7]{2.5}$

5. Complete the following table.

	Principal	Amount at Maturity	Per annum Rate	Conversion Period	Term (a)
(a)	$150	$300	36.2 %/a	quarterly	2
(b)	$10 000	$25 000	19.19 %/a	semi-annually	5
(c)	$10	$100	84.61 %/a	quarterly	3
(d)	$5000	$15 000	19.17 %/a	semi-annually	6

6. You have your choice of two savings bonds. Both have a present value of $500. The first matures in 5 a at a value of $750. The second matures in 10 a at a value of $1750. Interest on both is compounded annually.
Which bond has the best rate of interest?

7. If you invest $1 and at the end of 12 a you have $3.23, what is the approximate interest earned compounded annually?

(10.26 %/o)

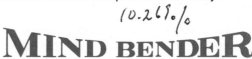
MIND BENDER

Put the numbers from 1 to 9 in the squares to make the statements true.

$$\blacksquare \times \blacksquare - \blacksquare = 5$$
$$\blacksquare \div \blacksquare + \blacksquare = 5$$
$$\blacksquare + \blacksquare - \blacksquare = 5$$

Using a computer and spreadsheet software, prepare a table similar to the table of exponential values of n in the Appendix.

10.8 PROBLEM SOLVING

1. What is the last digit of each of the following?

(a) 5^{63} (b) 6^{109} (c) 11^{48}

2. Five people ran a 100 m race. Allison came in first. Barb came in last. Don was ahead of Chris, and Ed was behind him. Who came in second?

3. Myles opened a book where the product of the two page numbers was 76 452. What were the page numbers?

4. In one season major league baseball games will require about 51 000 baseballs. How far would they reach if the balls were lined up in a row?

5. Name the wheels that are turning counter-clockwise.

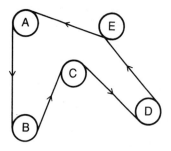

6. How many different ways can four keys be arranged on a key ring?

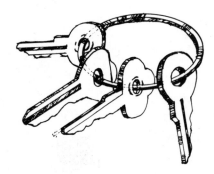

7. The value of 30 coins is $2.35. The coins are dimes and nickels. How many dimes are there?

8. Thirty-seven pipes are strapped together in the shape of a hexagon as shown. The outside diameter of each pipe is 10 cm. The inside diameter of each pipe is 8 cm.

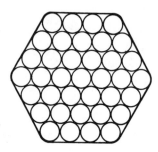

(a) Is the hexagon formed by the pipes a regular hexagon?
(b) Calculate the length of strapping needed, to the nearest centimetre, to hold the pipes together.
(c) The pipes are 5 m long.
   What is the volume of fluid these pipes can hold?
(d) A truck can carry 15 bundles of pipes. How many pipes is that?
(e) Each bundle of pipes must be strapped in three places.
   What is the total length of strapping needed?

9. Eleven toothpicks are placed in a row.

To play the game, two players each pick up 1, 2, or 3 toothpicks in turn. The player picking up the last toothpick loses the game.
Find a rule so that the player who picks first always wins.

10. Place the numbers from 1 to 12 in the circles so that the sum along each row is 26. (Four of the numbers have been placed for you.)

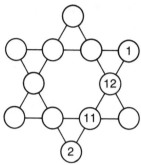

11. Evaluate.

$$\cfrac{1}{1 + \cfrac{1}{1 + \cfrac{1}{1 + \frac{1}{2}}}}$$

12. Identical boxes are stacked in the corner of a room as shown in the diagram.

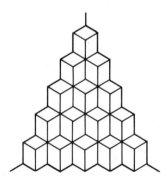

How many boxes are not visible?

13. On a digital watch, what times form mirror images with the colon being the axis of symmetry?

14. Draw the figure that comes next.

CAREER

EXERCISE

1. The average hourly wage including benefits for 412 employees is $17.37. A one-year contract is negotiated providing an increase of 4.2%.
(a) What is the new hourly wage for these employees?
(b) What is the total hourly cost increase to the company?

2. A person-year is about 2000 h. What is the dollar value of 65 person-years in a contract that is worth $16.65/h including benefits over a two-year period?

10.9 REVIEW EXERCISE

1. For each savings method listed in section 10.1, state one circumstance under which it would be an advantageous savings method and one circumstance under which it would be disadvantageous.

2. Why do you get a higher interest rate for money invested for longer periods of time than for money invested for shorter periods of time?

3. Your savings account earns a nominal rate of 12%.
What is the effective rate if the nominal rate is compounded
(a) semi-annually,
(b) quarterly,
(c) 12 times per year,
(d) 24 times per year?

4. A rubber ball is dropped from a height of 16 m. On each bounce it rebounds to $\frac{3}{4}$ of its previous height.
How high does it bounce after hitting the ground
(a) for the third time?   (b) for the fifth time?

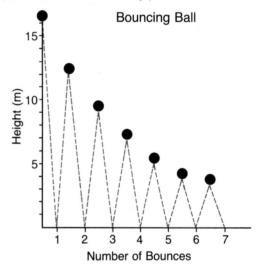

Bouncing Ball

5. Complete the table.

	Principal	Per annum Rate	Conversion Period	Term (a)	Amount
(a)	$2500	6%	semi-annually	6	
(b)	$475	8%	quarterly	2	
(c)	$5000	10%	annually	6	
(d)	$8000	7%	semi-annually	5	
(e)	$6000	12%	monthly	4	

6. Complete the table.

	Present Value	Per annum Rate	Conversion Period	Term (a)	Amount
(a)		9%	semi-annually	16	$15 000
(b)		12%	quarterly	10	$20 000
(c)		7%	quarterly	6	$30 000
(d)		8%	every 4 months	8	$25 000
(e)		6%	monthly	10	$40 000

7. Complete the simple interest table.

	Interest	Principal	Rate	Time	Amount
(a)		$1345.78	12.5%	64 d	
(b)	$90.50		9.4%	6 months	
(c)	$340.00	$8980.00		1 a	
(d)	$12.00	$90.00	8%		
(e)			12%	90 d	$55 150.00
(f)			8.5%	3 a	$3500.00

8. How much money must you invest now at 9% per annum compounded semi-annually to replace a $1 000 000 press in 20 a?

9. If you invest $1 and at the end of 25 a you have $4.81, what is the approximate interest earned compounded annually?

10. Five years from now, Mary will need $7000 for school. Eight years from now, Tom will need $9000. Ten years from now, Ellen will need $11 000.
How much should their parents invest now at 8% per annum compounded semi-annually to meet these requirements?

11. How much money must be invested now to replace a $750 000 moonraker in ten years and an $800 000 orbital arm in twelve years?
The interest rate is 10% per annum compounded quarterly.

12. At the beginning of each month, an investor puts $100 into an account that pays 1% per month interest. At the end of one year, the last deposit is worth $100(1.01), the second last is worth $100(1.01)^2, the third last is worth $100(1.01)^3, and so on.
Write an expression for the total value of his 12 deposits.

MIND BENDER

The name of the game is "Petals Around A Rose."

The game is played with five dice.

The answer for the following roll is 6.

For this roll, it is 10.

For this roll, it is 4.

Find the answer for these rolls.
(a)

(b)

10.10 CHAPTER 10 TEST

1. Find the interest and the amount in a savings account at the end of one year if $950 is deposited at 8% simple interest.

2. Find the original amount invested and the simple interest earned if $3600 is in a savings account after 10 a.
The interest rate is 8% per annum.

3. Find t_8 and t_n for the geometric sequence

$$5, 10, 20, 40, ...$$

4. Find the amount of $20 000 invested at 8% per annum compounded semi-annually for 12 a.

5. Find the amount of $50 000 invested at 10% per annum compounded quarterly for 6 a.

6. What is the effective rate of interest for an investment at 8% compounded quarterly?

7. How much should be invested today at 12% per annum compounded semi-annually in order to have $100 000 in 20 a?

8. How much should be invested today at 6% per annum compounded quarterly in order to have $80 000 in 10 a?

9. Carl can purchase a $1000 bond for $600. The bond matures in 6 a.
What is the approximate rate of interest compounded annually?

ANNUITIES, MORTGAGES, AND LIFE INSURANCE

REVIEW AND PREVIEW TO CHAPTER

PERCENTAGES

EXERCISE 1

1. Complete the following calculations.
(a) 6% of $45.65
(b) 12% of $274.98
(c) 43% of $154.70
(d) 150% of $400
(e) 95% of $214.75
(f) 18% of $348.71
(g) $5\frac{1}{2}$% of $5700
(h) $2\frac{1}{2}$% of $974.63
(i) $1\frac{1}{4}$% of $870
(j) $24\frac{1}{2}$% of $700
(k) $\frac{3}{4}$% of $58.93
(l) $\frac{4}{5}$% of $8000

2. Express the first quantity as a percentage of the second.
(a) $4.50, $4500
(b) $85, $1700
(c) $3.75, $7500
(d) $43, $34 400
(e) $74, $370
(f) $6840, $57 000
(g) $300, $12 000
(h) $3.45, $460
(i) $928, $5800
(j) $0.81, $54
(k) $4500, $3000
(l) $387, $180
(m) $43.34, $788
(n) $5.12, $640
(o) $2.24, $256
(p) $6.30, $480
(q) $1001, $910
(r) $801, $900
(s) $0.90, $24

GEOMETRIC SEQUENCES AND SERIES

Sequences such as 2, 5, 8, 11, ... and 5, 1, -3, -7, ... are called arithmetic sequences.

Sequences such as 2, 6, 18, 54, ... and 5, -20, 80, -320, ... are called geometric sequences.

The general term of a geometric sequence is
$$t_n = ar^{n-1}$$

The formula for the sum of a geometric series is
$$S_n = \frac{a(r^n - 1)}{(r - 1)}$$

The following table of powers of 2 and 3 will be helpful in the exercise.

n	2^n	3^n
1	2	3
2	4	9
3	8	27
4	16	81
5	32	243
6	64	729
7	128	2 187
8	256	6 561
9	512	19 683
10	1024	59 049

EXERCISE 2

1. Write the first five terms of the following geometric sequences.
$$t_n = ar^{n-1}$$

(a) $a = 1, r = 2$ (b) $a = 32, r = \frac{1}{2}$

(c) $a = 27, r = \frac{2}{3}$ (d) $a = 4, r = -3$

(e) $\frac{1}{2}, 1, —, —, —$ (f) $\frac{5}{8}, \frac{5}{2}, —, —, —$

(g) $\frac{1}{9}, \frac{1}{3}, —, —, —$ (h) $1, -2, —, —, —$

2. Find the required term for each of the following geometric sequences.

(a) $a = 2, r = 2; t_7$

(b) $a = -5, r = 3; t_8$

(c) $a = \frac{1}{4}, r = -2; t_9$

(d) $a = 9, r = \frac{2}{3}; t_6$

(e) $\frac{1}{8}, -\frac{1}{2}, 2, ...; t_5$

3. Find the required sum for the following geometric series.

$$S_n = \frac{a(r^n - 1)}{r - 1}$$

(a) $a = 1, r = 2; S_{10}$

(b) $a = 2, r = 3; S_8$

(c) $a = 5, r = -2; S_7$

(d) $a = -9, r = \frac{1}{3}; S_4$

USING THE **EXP** KEY

The **EXP** key can be used to enter powers of 10.

1. Complete the following table.

Press	Display
1 EXP 3 =	
1 EXP 5 =	
2 EXP 4 =	
2 EXP 6 =	

SIMPLE INTEREST

EXERCISE 3

1. Find the missing quantities.

	Interest	Principal	Rate	Time(a)	Amount
(a)		$4500	12%	0.500	
(b)		$760	9.5%	0.750	
(c)	$24.50		8%	0.250	
(d)	$4.80		16%	0.125	
(e)		$560		0.500	$610.40
(f)		$1250		0.126	$1287.80
(g)	$1179.50	$50 000	7%		
(h)		$250	11%		$266.50
(i)		$975	7%	0.663	
(j)	$3.92			0.967	$54.62
(k)	$2.87	$350	10%		
(l)	$21.36		5.5%	0.411	
(m)			12%	0.126	$24.97
(n)			9%	0.751	$2028.42

Cover the one you want to find.

11.1 AMOUNT AND PRESENT VALUE

AMOUNT OF A LOAN

When a person or company borrows money, the amount of the loan is the total of the principal (the money borrowed) and the interest (the cost of borrowing the money). Interest on a loan can be calculated on the basis of simple interest or compound interest. The following formulas are used to determine the amount, A, of a loan, based on both simple and compound interest.

Simple Interest

$$A = P(1 + rt)$$

where P is the principal,
r is the interest rate, and
t is the time in years.

Compound Interest

$$A = P(1 + i)^n$$

where P is the principal,
i is the interest rate per conversion period, and
n is the number of conversion periods.

Example 1. One trust company offers a $100 000 loan at 8% simple interest over a five-year period, and a second trust company offers a $100 000 loan at 8% compound interest, compounded annually, over the same period.
How much greater is the amount of the loan that is calculated on compound interest?

Solution:
Simple Interest

P = $100 000, r = 0.08, and t = 5 a.

$$A = P(1 + rt)$$
$$A = 100\,000(1 + 0.08 \times 5)$$
$$= 100\,000(1.4)$$
$$= 140\,000$$

The amount is $140 000.

Compound Interest

P = $100 000, i = 0.08, and n = 5.
$$A = P(1 + i)^n$$
$$A = 100\,000(1 + 0.08)^5$$

Using the tables in the Appendix,

$A = 100\ 000(1.469\ 33)$
$= 146\ 933$

The amount is $146 933.

The difference between the two methods of calculating interest is

$$146\ 933\ -\ 140\ 000\ =\ 6933$$

∴ the loan at compound interest costs the borrower $6933 more over five years than the loan at simple interest.

Example 2. Joslin borrowed $200 000 for five years at 10% per annum compounded quarterly in order to renovate his ski resort.
What was the amount of the loan?

Solution:

The loan was for five years compounded quarterly so there were $5 \times 4 = 20$ conversion periods.

The interest rate per conversion period is $\frac{10}{4} = 2.5\%$.

We can show how the amount of the loan increases using a time diagram.

$i = 0.025$
$n = 20$

Now	1	2	19	20
200 000	200 000(1.025)	200 000(1.025)²	200 000(1.025)¹⁹	200 000(1.025)²⁰

$A = P(1\ +\ i)^n$
$A = 200\ 000(1\ +\ 0.025)^{20}$

Using the tables,

$A = 200\ 000(1.638\ 62)$
$= 327\ 724$

The amount of the loan is $327 724.

PRESENT VALUE OF A LOAN

When you borrow money, you have the use of the money immediately but pay for the use of the money in the future. The rate of interest charged for the use of the money now is established by considering how much the money will be worth in the future. The present value of a loan is the amount paid now that will discharge, or pay off, an amount due in the future.

Example 3. You have signed a promissory note with a financial institution that requires you to pay $1000 in three years.
If money is worth 11% per annum compounded semi-annually, what amount paid now will discharge the debt?

Solution:
Let PV be the present value of the note. n, the total number of conversion periods, is 6, and i, the interest rate per conversion period, is 5.5% or 0.055.

$$A = P(1 + i)^n$$

Draw a time diagram to represent the debt for each conversion period.

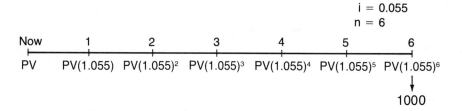

$i = 0.055$
$n = 6$

Now   1   2   3   4   5   6
PV   PV(1.055) PV(1.055)² PV(1.055)³ PV(1.055)⁴ PV(1.055)⁵ PV(1.055)⁶

1000

$$PV(1.055)^6 = 1000$$
$$PV = \frac{1000}{(1.055)^6}$$
$$= \frac{1000}{(1 + 0.055)^6}$$

Using the table in the Appendix,

$PV = 1000(0.725\ 25)$
$= 725.25$

Using a calculator, press

The display is `725.24583`

You may pay $725.25 to discharge the debt now or pay $1000 in three years if money is worth 11% compounded semi-annually.

Similar to present value for an investment, the formula for present value of a loan can be generalized to

$$PV = \frac{A}{(1 + i)^n}$$

where PV is the present value,
i is interest per conversion period, and
n is the total number of conversion periods.

EXERCISE 11.1

A

1. Explain why a loan at compound interest costs more than a loan at simple interest, as shown in Example 1.

B

2. Find the amount of a loan of $100 000 at the following rates.
(a) 10% simple interest for 10 a
(b) 10% compound interest for 10 a compounded annually
(c) 10% compound interest for 10 a compounded semi-annually
(d) 10% compound interest for 10 a compounded quarterly

3. Construct a bar graph to show the difference in the amounts for the four rates of interest in question 2.

4. What is the amount of a loan of $100 at 8% simple interest for
(a) 1 d?
(b) 90 d?
(c) 278 d?

5. Calculate the present value of each loan.
(a) $1000 due in 3 a at 6% per annum compounded annually
(b) $20 000 due in 2 a at 8% per annum compounded quarterly
(c) $100 000 due in 5 a at 10% per annum compounded semi-annually
(d) $50 000 due in 1 a at 12% per annum compounded monthly.

6. Complete the time diagram for the present value of a loan with an amount of $80 000 due in six years at 8% per annum compounded annually.

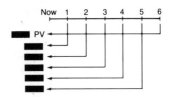

(a) What is the present value?
(b) What amount will discharge the debt one year from now?
(c) What amount will discharge the debt two years from now?
(d) What amount will discharge the debt three years from now?
(e) What amount will discharge the debt four years from now?
(f) What amount will discharge the debt five years from now?

7. Jean borrowed $1000 at 10% simple interest per year. At the end of each year, she pays $200 on the amount due. Calculate the amount of the loan at the end of the first year, deduct $200, and calculate the amount of the loan based on the new principal. Continue to perform these calculations until the last payment is made. (The last payment will be less than $200.)
(a) How many years did it take Jean to pay for her loan?
(b) How much was her last payment?
(c) How much total interest did she pay for the loan?

Using a computer, spreadsheet software, and the present value formula, repeat question 5 over ten years, finding the amount that would discharge the loan now and at the end of each year over the ten-year period.

11.2 ORDINARY ANNUITIES

An ordinary annuity is a series of payments of a specific amount at equal intervals over a period of time called the term. Payments are made at the end of the agreed time interval. At the end of the annuity's term, when it matures, the principal plus accrued interest is payable either in one lump sum or in a series of additional payments.

A person purchases an annuity as an investment or to insure a level of income at a future date. An annuity is like a savings account, savings bond, or savings certificate but is usually purchased over a long period of time.

Example. What will be the accumulated amount of an annuity that requires payments of $1000 at the end of each six-month interval for two years at 9% per annum compounded semi-annually?

Solution: We are asked to find the amount of an annuity of 4 semi-annual payments of $1000 each at 9% per annum compounded semi-annually so that $i = 0.045$.

The fourth or last payment receives no interest. The third payment is in for one conversion period. The second payment is in for two conversion periods. The first payment is in for three conversion periods.

A time diagram illustrates the interest earned for each deposit.

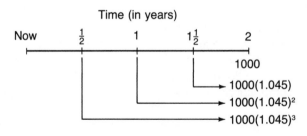

To calculate the amount for each conversion period,

$$A = P(1 + i)^n$$

where $P = \$1000$ and $i = 0.045$.

The amounts are

First Payment $A_1 = 1000(1.045)^3$
                        $= 1000(1.141\ 17)$
                        $= 1141.17$

Second Payment $A_2 = 1000(1.045)^2$
                        $= 1000(1.092\ 03)$
                        $= 1092.03$

Third Payment $A_3 = 1000(1.045)$
                        $= 1045.00$

Fourth Payment $A_4 = 1000.00$

The amount of the annuity is

$A = A_1 + A_2 + A_3 + A_4$
$A = \$1141.17 + \$1092.03 + \$1045.00 + \$1000.00$
$\quad = \$4278.20$

The accumulated amount of the annuity is $4278.20.

In general, for an annuity with n terms, the accumulated value would be

$A = P + P(1 + i)^1 + P(1 + i)^2 + P(1 + i)^3 + ... + P(1 + i)^{(n-1)}$

where n is the number of conversion periods in the term.
The terms of the equation form a geometric sequence.

When the terms of a geometric sequence are added, we get a geometric series.
In the next section we will develop a formula to simplify calculations with geometric series.

Using a calculator, press

The display is 1141.17

$S_n = \dfrac{1000(1.045^4 - 1)}{.045}$

$\quad = 4278.20$

EXERCISE 11.2

A 1. Under what circumstances would a person wish to purchase an annuity?

2. State the positive and negative aspects of annuities.

B 3. What will be the accumulated amount of an annuity that requires payments of $2000 at the end of each six-month interval for two years at 10% per annum compounded semi-annually?
Draw a time diagram to illustrate your solution.

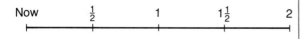

4. Nancy buys into an annuity to save for a vacation.

The terms of the annuity require payments of $1000 at the end of each three-month interval for two years. The interest rate is 8% per annum compounded quarterly.
(a) What will the annuity be worth at the end of the term?
(b) Draw a time diagram to illustrate your solution.

11.3 THE SUM OF A GEOMETRIC SERIES

In Chapter 10 we investigated the geometric sequence 3, 6, 12, 24, ..., which can be written

$$3, \qquad 3 \times 2, \qquad 3 \times 2^2, \qquad 3 \times 2^3, \qquad ...$$

The general representation of a geometric sequence is

$$a, \qquad ar, \qquad ar^2, \qquad ar^3, \qquad ...$$

where a is the first term and r is the common ratio.

$$t_1 = a$$
$$t_2 = ar$$
$$t_3 = ar^2$$
$$.$$
$$.$$
$$.$$
$$t_n = ar^{n-1}$$

When the terms of a sequence are added, the indicated sum is called a series.

Thus the sequence 3, 6, 12, 24, ... written as a series is 3 + 6 + 12 + 24 + ...

Example 1. Find the sum of the series 3 + 6 + 12 + 24 + 48 + 96 + 192.

Solution:
We can find the sum of this series by addition or by the following procedure.
There are seven terms in the series.
a = 3 and r = 2.

Subtract
the top
row from
the bottom
row.

$$S_7 = \quad 3 + 6 + 12 + 24 + 48 + 96 + 192$$
$$2 \times S_7 = \qquad 6 + 12 + 24 + 48 + 96 + 192 + 384$$
$$\longrightarrow S_7 = -3 \qquad\qquad\qquad\qquad\qquad\qquad + 384$$
$$S_7 = 381$$

The sum of the series is 381.

We now use the method of Example 1 to develop a formula for the sum of the general geometric series,

$$S_n = a + ar + ar^2 + ar^3 + ... + ar^{n-1}$$

Multiply
by r.
Subtract
the bottom
row from
the top
row.

$$S_n = a + ar + ar^2 + ... + ar^{n-1}$$
$$\longrightarrow rS_n = \quad ar + ar^2 + ... + ar^{n-1} + ar^n$$
$$\longrightarrow S_n - rS_n = a \qquad\qquad\qquad\qquad\qquad - ar^n$$
$$(1 - r)S_n = a - ar^n$$
$$S_n = \frac{a(1 - r^n)}{(1 - r)}$$

If we factor (-1) from both the numerator and denominator, we get the second form of the formula

$$S_n = \frac{a(r^n - 1)}{(r - 1)}$$

To keep the denominator positive,

when $r > 1$, we use $S_n = \dfrac{a(r^n - 1)}{(r - 1)}$.

when $r < 1$, we use $S_n = \dfrac{a(1 - r^n)}{(1 - r)}$.

Example 2. Find S_{10} for the series $1 + 2 + 4 + ...$

Solution: $a = 1$, $r = 2$, and $n = 10$.

$$S_n = \frac{a(r^n - 1)}{(r - 1)}$$
$$S_{10} = \frac{1(2^{10} - 1)}{2 - 1}$$
$$= \frac{1024 - 1}{1}$$
$$= 1023$$

$E=mc^2$

Example 3. Find S_{12} for $3 - 6 + 12 - 24 + ...$

Solution: $a = 3$ and $r = -2$.

$$S_n = \frac{a(1 - r^n)}{(1 - r)}$$
$$S_{12} = \frac{3(1 - (-2)^{12})}{(1 - (-2))}$$
$$= \frac{3(1 - 4096)}{3}$$
$$= -4095$$

$E=mc^2$

EXERCISE 11.3

B

1. Find the sum of each series.

(a) S_8 of $10 + 20 + 40 + ...$
(b) S_{10} of $2 + 6 + 18 + ...$
(c) S_5 of $3 + 15 + 75 + ...$
(d) S_{12} of $4 + 8 + 16 + 32 + ...$
(e) S_7 of $5 + 20 + 80 + ...$
(f) S_{100} of $1 + 1 + 1 + 1 + 1 + ...$

2. Find the sum of each series.

(a) S_8 of $2 - 6 + 18 - ...$
(b) S_6 of $256 + 128 + 64 + ...$
(c) S_5 of $486 + 162 + 54 + ...$
(d) S_{10} of $1 - 2 + 4 - 8 + ...$
(e) S_{100} of $1 - 1 + 1 - 1 + ...$

11.4 AMOUNT OF AN ANNUITY

In our earlier work, we saw that if a sum of money is paid as a series of regular equal payments, it is called an annuity. The name comes from the word *annual* or yearly. However, payments may be made monthly, quarterly, semi-annually, or at any other agreed-on interval. Unless otherwise stated, the payment is made at the end of the payment interval.

The amount of an annuity is the sum of the amounts of the individual payments invested at the stated interest rate from the time of payment until the end of the annuity when the last payment is made plus the interest earned.

To find the amount:

Example 1. Mr. Howard deposits $500 in the bank every Dec. 1 and June 1 for ten years.
If interest is earned at 8% compounded semi-annually, how much will he have in the bank at the time of the last payment?

Solution:
You are asked to find the amount of an annuity of 20 semi-annual payments of $500 at 8% compounded semi-annually so that $i = \dfrac{8\%}{2} = 4\%$.

The time diagram below illustrates the problem.

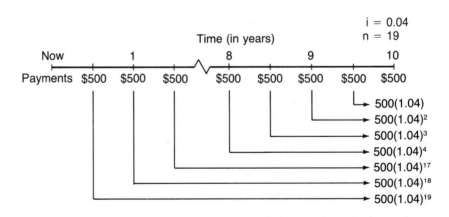

The amount of the annuity is given by the sum of the 20 compound amounts:

A = $500 + $500(1.04) + $500(1.04)² + ... + $500(1.04)¹⁹

which is a geometric series with a = 500, r = 1.04, and n = 20.

Since r > 1, we use the following formula and substitute:

$$S_n = \frac{a(r^n - 1)}{(r - 1)}$$

$$S_{20} = \frac{500(1.04^{20} - 1)}{1.04 - 1}$$

Using the tables,

$$S_{20} = \frac{500(2.191\ 12 - 1)}{0.04}$$

$$= \frac{500(1.191\ 12)}{0.04}$$

$$= 14\ 889$$

Using a calculator, press

The display is `14889.039`

The amount of the annuity is $14 889.

The regular annuity payment is called the periodic rent. In Example 1 we determined the amount of an annuity after a certain rent was deposited for a certain length of time. In the next example we will determine what the periodic rent, or deposits, should be in order to end up with a required amount at the end of the payments.

To find the rent:

Example 2. How much money must you invest every six months at 9% compounded semi-annually in order for it to amount to $25 000 after the 25th payment?

Solution:

There are 25 semi-annual payments so $i = \frac{9\%}{2} = 4.5\%$ and $n = 25$.

The amount of the annuity is

$$R + R(1.045) + R(1.045)^2 + \ldots + R(1.045)^{23} + R(1.045)^{24} = 25\ 000$$

Now ────┼────┼────┼──╲╱──┼────┼────┼────┼──── n = 25
       R   R   R   R   R   R   R

Since r > 1, we use the formula

$$S_n = \frac{a(r^n - 1)}{(r - 1)}$$

$$25\ 000 = \frac{R(1.045^{25} - 1)}{(1.045 - 1)}$$

$$25\ 000 = \frac{R(3.005\ 43 - 1)}{0.045}$$

$$25\ 000 = \frac{R(2.005\ 43)}{0.045}$$

$$\frac{25\ 000 \times 0.045}{2.005\ 43} = R$$

$$R \doteq 560.98$$

Estimate.
$$20\ 000 \times 0.05 \div 2$$
$$= 750$$

You must invest $560.98 every six months.

We will now develop a formula to simplify the calculations in the previous examples.

To find a general expression for the amount of an annuity, we consider n payments of $1 each at a rate i per payment interval.

Now   1   2   3   n

          1     $1(1 + i)$ $1(1 + i)^2$ $1(1 + i)^{n-1}$

The amount of this annuity is given by the series

$$1 + 1(1 + i) + 1(1 + i)^2 + 1(1 + i)^3 + ... \text{ to n terms}$$

This quantity is represented by the symbol $S_{\overline{n}|i}$ and is evaluated in an annuity table in the Appendix for various values of i and n.

$$S_n = \frac{a(r^n - 1)}{(r - 1)}$$

$$S_{\overline{n}|i} = \frac{1[(1 + i)^n - 1]}{(1 + i) - 1}$$

$$= \frac{(1 + i)^n - 1}{i}$$

$$S_{\overline{n}|i} = \frac{(1 + i)^n - 1}{i} \qquad \begin{array}{l}\text{The amount of an annuity of n}\\ \text{payments of \$1 at i\% per interval.}\end{array}$$

If the payments are $R instead of $1, then the formula becomes

$$RS_{\overline{n}|i} = \frac{R[(1 + i)^n - 1]}{i} \qquad \begin{array}{l}\text{The amount of an annuity of}\\ \text{n payments of \$R at i\% per}\\ \text{payment interval.}\end{array}$$

Example 3. Find the amount of an annuity if $1000 is deposited every six months for eight years at 6% per annum compounded semi-annually.

Solution:

Now

      1000   1000   1000   1000   1000

$n = 16$, $i = \dfrac{6\%}{2} = 3\%$, and $R = 1000$.

$S_{\overline{n}|i} = S_{\overline{16}|3} = 20.156\ 881$ (from the tables)

$RS_{\overline{n}|i} = 1000(20.156\ 881)$

$= 20\ 156.88$

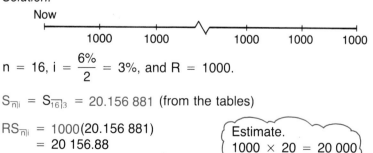
Estimate.
$1000 \times 20 = 20\ 000$

The amount is $20 156.88.

Amount of an Annuity of 1
$S_{\overline{n}|i}$

n	3%
1	1.000 000
2	2.030 000
3	3.090 900
4	4.183 627
5	5.309 136
6	6.468 410
7	7.662 462
8	8.892 336
9	10.159 106
10	11.463 879
11	12.807 796
12	14.192 030
13	15.617 790
14	17.086 324
15	18.598 914
16	20.156 881
17	21.761 588
18	23.414 435
19	25.116 868
20	26.870 374
⋮	⋮

Example 4. How much must be invested every three months for two years at 8% per annum compounded quarterly if the required amount is $20 000?

Solution:

$n = 8$

Now	1	2	3	4	5	6	7	8
	R	R	R	R	R	R	R	R

$n = 8$ and $i = \dfrac{8\%}{4} = 2\%.$

$RS_{\overline{n}|i} = A$

$RS_{\overline{8}|2} = 20\ 000$

$R = \dfrac{20\ 000}{S_{\overline{8}|2}}$

$= \dfrac{20\ 000}{8.582\ 969}$

$= 2330.196$

Using a calculator, press

$\boxed{2}\ \boxed{\text{EXP}}\ \boxed{4}\ \boxed{\div}\ \boxed{8}\ \boxed{\cdot}\ \boxed{5}\ \boxed{8}\ \boxed{2}\ \boxed{9}\ \boxed{6}\ \boxed{9}\ \boxed{=}$

The display is 2330.195996

$2330.20 must be invested every three months.

EXERCISE 11.4

A 1. Using the table in the Appendix, find the value for each of the following.

(a) $S_{\overline{30}|2}$ (b) $S_{\overline{46}|3.5}$

(c) $S_{\overline{26}|1.5}$ (d) $S_{\overline{16}|5.5}$

(e) $S_{\overline{50}|5}$ (f) $S_{\overline{36}|6}$

(g) $S_{\overline{30}|2}$ (h) $S_{\overline{6}|4.5}$

B 2. Using the table in the Appendix, find the value for each of the following.

(a) $RS_{\overline{3}|2.5}$, R = $123.89

(b) $RS_{\overline{41}|4.5}$, R = $438.83

(c) $RS_{\overline{16}|4.5}$, R = $1895

(d) $RS_{\overline{16}|5.5}$, R = $3400

3. Find the missing quantities in the following using the $S_{\overline{n}|i}$ table.

	Amount	Periodic Rent	Number of Payments	Payment Interval Conversion Period	Interest Rate per annum
(a)		$300	20	semi-annually	8%
(b)		$500	24	quarterly	12%
(c)		$100	36	monthly	12%
(d)		$4000	10	annually	6%
(e)	$20 000		40	semi-annually	8%
(f)	$6000		24	quarterly	12%
(g)	$2500		18	monthly	12%
(h)	$12 000		15	annually	6%

4. Mr. Wilson bought a new taxi on June 30. He expects the car to last 2 a as a taxi, and then he will trade it in on a replacement. He estimates that he will require $10 000 plus his old car for the new taxi.
Starting July 30, how much must he invest monthly in an account paying 12% compounded monthly to meet this expense in two years?

This type of investment plan to meet a future expense is called a sinking fund.

5. Mrs. Brewer is self-employed and must make provision for her own pension. If she invests $1000 every 6 months, starting 6 months before her 35th birthday, in a fund that pays 8% compounded semi-annually, how much will she have after the last payment on her 55th birthday?

6. Acme Manufacturing Co. has a $650 000 custom-designed press that has a useful life expectancy of 15 a.
How much should they invest semi-annually in a sinking fund at 9% per annum compounded semi-annually to meet this expense in 15 a?

7. An investor deposited $200/month for 6 months in an account and then allowed the amount to remain for an additional 6 months.
If interest was paid at the rate of 1.5% per month, what was the final amount?

8. Mr. Shapiro has just purchased a used car for $18 000. In planning for future transportation he makes the following assumptions:
• He will keep the present car for 4 a.
• In that time it will depreciate 66%.
• The cost of cars will increase by 36%.
• There will be a 7% sales tax on the difference between the trade-in and the new car.
• He can invest money at 12% compounded quarterly.

Starting 3 months after the purchase date, how much should he invest every 3 months in a sinking fund to purchase his new car 4 a from now?

9. Ten semi-annual payments of $750 are paid into an annuity earning 9% compounded semi-annually. The amount is then invested for 4 a at 12% compounded quarterly.
Construct a time diagram and find the final amount.

Using a computer and spreadsheet software, enter the formulas for $S_{\overline{n}|i}$ and R in terms of $S_{\overline{n}|i}$.

Using the formulas, calculate the following.
(a) the amount of an annuity of $1000/a for 1 a, 2 a, 3 a, 4 a, 5 a, and 6 a at 8% compounded annually
(b) the amount of an annuity of $100, $200, $300, $400, and $500 for 6 a at 8% compounded semi-annually
(c) Construct a bar graph to show the results of parts (a) and (b).

11.5 PRESENT VALUE OF AN ANNUITY

The present value of an annuity is the principal that must be invested now at a given rate of interest to provide the given periodic rent. It is equal to the sum of the present values of each of the payments.

Example 1. How much money must be invested now at 8% per annum compounded annually to provide an annuity of 5 annual payments of $600, the first payment being made in one year?

Solution:
The problem can be illustrated by a time diagram as follows:

$$PV = \frac{A}{(1 + i)^n}$$

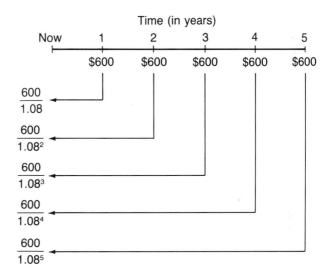

The present value of the annuity is given by the sum of the five present values:

$$PV = \frac{\$600}{1.08} + \frac{\$600}{(1.08)^2} + \frac{\$600}{(1.08)^3} + \frac{\$600}{(1.08)^4} + \frac{\$600}{(1.08)^5}$$

which is a geometric series where

$$a = \frac{\$600}{1.08}, r = \frac{1}{1.08}, \text{ and } n = 5.$$

Since $r < 1$, we use the formula,

$$S_n = \frac{a(1 - r^n)}{(1 - r)}$$

$$PV = \frac{600}{1.08}\left(\frac{1 - \dfrac{1}{1.08^5}}{1 - \dfrac{1}{1.08}}\right)$$

$$= \frac{600(1 - 0.680\ 58)}{1.08(1 - 0.925\ 93)}$$

$$= \frac{600(0.319\ 42)}{1.08(0.074\ 07)}$$

$$\doteq 2395.78$$

Estimate.
$$\frac{600 \times 0.3}{1 \times 0.1} = 1800$$

ANSWER

$2395.78 must be invested now to provide the annuity.

An expression for the present value of an annuity of $1 for n payment intervals at rate i per payment interval, one payment interval before the first payment, is given by the series

$$\frac{1}{1 + i} + \frac{1}{(1 + i)^2} + \frac{1}{(1 + i)^3} + \dots \text{ to n terms}$$

This quantity is represented by the symbol $a_{\overline{n}|i}$ and is evaluated in a table in the Appendix for various values of i and n.

$Ra_{\overline{n}|i}$ represents the present value of an annuity of n payments of $R at i% per interval.

Example 2. Find the price of an annuity of ten semi-annual payments of $750, the first payment to be made in 6 months, if money is worth 7% per annum compounded semi-annually.

Solution:

Time (in years)

Now $\frac{1}{2}$ 1 $1\frac{1}{2}$

$$\frac{750}{(1.035)}$$

$$\frac{750}{(1.035)^2}$$

$$\frac{750}{(1.035)^3}$$

$R = \$750$, $n = 10$, and $i = (0.5)(7\%) = 3.5\%$.

From the table for $a_{\overline{n}|i}$ in the 3.5% column, n = 10 row,

$$a_{\overline{10}|3.5} = 8.316\ 605$$

$$Ra_{\overline{10}|3.5} = 750(8.316\ 605)$$

$$= 6237.453$$

Estimate.
$$1000 \times 8 = 8000$$

The price of the annuity is $6237.45.

Example 3. Mrs. Rainey has an endowment insurance policy that pays her $50 000 at age 60, or she may leave the money invested with the insurance company at 6% per annum compounded semi-annually and withdraw it in 30 equal semi-annual payments. The first payment is made 6 months after her 60th birthday.
How large is each payment?

Solution:

PLAN

Let each payment in dollars be R.

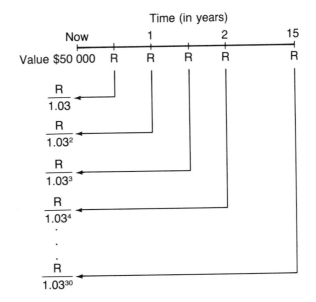

SOLVE

$$Ra_{\overline{n}|i} = 50\ 000$$

$$Ra_{\overline{30}|3} = 50\ 000$$

$$R = \frac{50\ 000}{a_{\overline{30}|3}}$$

$$= \frac{50\ 000}{19.600\ 441}$$

$$\doteq 2250.96$$

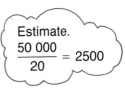

Estimate.
$$\frac{50\ 000}{20} = 2500$$

ANSWER

Each payment will be $2250.96.

EXERCISE 11.5

A

1. Using the table in the Appendix, find the value for each of the following.

(a) $a_{\overline{34}|2.5}$

(b) $a_{\overline{40}|5.5}$

(c) $a_{\overline{6}|1.5}$

(d) $a_{\overline{26}|3.5}$

(e) $a_{\overline{50}|5}$

(f) $a_{\overline{16}|4}$

(g) $a_{\overline{30}|0.5}$

(h) $a_{\overline{8}|1.5}$

B

2. Using the table in the Appendix, find the value for each of the following.

(a) $Ra_{\overline{3}|2.5}$, R = \$123.89

(b) $Ra_{\overline{50}|4.5}$, R = \$148

(c) $Ra_{\overline{46}|4.5}$, R = \$1895

(d) $Ra_{\overline{16}|5.5}$, R = \$3400

(e) $Ra_{\overline{39}|5}$, R = \$120

(f) $Ra_{\overline{36}|6}$, R = \$1

(g) $Ra_{\overline{11}|2}$, R = \$100 000

(h) $Ra_{\overline{6}|4.5}$, R = \$178.98

3. Find the missing quantities in the following using the $a_{\overline{n}|i}$ table.

	Present Value	Periodic Rent	Number of Payments	Payment Interval Conversion Period	Interest Rate per annum
(a)		$300	20	semi-annually	8%
(b)		$500	24	quarterly	12%
(c)		$100	36	monthly	12%
(d)		$4000	10	annually	6%
(e)	$20 000		40	semi-annually	8%
(f)	$6000		24	quarterly	12%
(g)	$2500		18	monthly	12%
(h)	$12 000		15	annually	6%

(i) Construct a time diagram for all problems.

4. Find the present value of an annuity of $100/month for 3 a beginning 1 month hence if interest is earned at 1.5% per month.

5. John Fairchild has won $12 000 to go to a community college for a three-year technician course.
If he invests the money at 12% per annum compounded monthly on Aug. 1, how much may he draw monthly for the next 3 a starting Sept. 1?

6. Draw a time-payment diagram and use the formula $S_n = \dfrac{a(1 - r^n)}{(1 - r)}$ with tables for $(1 + i)^{-n}$ to find the present value of the following annuities, first payment to be made after one period.

(a) 20 annual payments of $1000 at 8% compounded annually

(b) 15 annual payments of $650 at 7% compounded annually

(c) 36 monthly payments of $200 at 1.5% per month

(d) 4 quarterly payments of $500 at 18% compounded quarterly

7. An insurance policy pays $150 000 cash at age 60, or it may be taken in 30 equal half-yearly payments with the endowment earning interest at 8% per annum compounded semi-annually.
If the first payment is made 6 months after the 60th birthday, how large is each payment?

8. Mrs. Comtois sold her condominium for $250 000. She invested the money in an annuity to receive payments over the next 10 a.
(a) How much will she receive every 3 months if the money is invested at 12% per annum compounded quarterly?
(b) Consider your answer to part (a), the amount of a three-month annuity, and approximate how much she could receive if she took payments monthly and the interest was paid at 1% per month.
(c) When would she receive her first payment?

9. Mr. MacDonald owns an annuity that pays $20 000 semi-annually for 8 a. What is the present value of the annuity if money is worth 11% compounded semi-annually and

Now

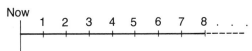

(a) the first payment is due in 6 months;
(b) the first payment is due now.

C

10. Use the formula $S_n = \dfrac{a(1 - r^n)}{(1 - r)}$ and a time diagram to find the annual payment for a five-year annuity with a present value of $10 000. Money is worth 8% compounded annually.

11. Use the formula and a time diagram to find the present value of an annuity of 10 annual payments of $2000 if money is worth 9% compounded semi-annually. First payment is due in one year.

MIND BENDER

A group of grade twelve students started an antique automobile club. The club needed several committees to operate effectively. The committees were organized as follows:
(i) Each member of the club had to belong to two different committees.
(ii) Every two different committees had one, but only one, member in common.
(iii) There were four different committees with the same number of members in each.
(iv) Each committee must have more than one member; otherwise two committees with one member in common would not be different.
What was the minimum number of students in the club?

Using a computer and spreadsheet software, enter the formulas for $a_{\overline{n}|i}$ and R in terms of $a_{\overline{n}|i}$.

Investigate the relationship by varying i, n, and R.

11.6 PAYMENT OF LOANS

When a loan is repaid in regular instalments, the result is called an annuity. Loans from financial institutions usually require repayment in equal amounts, which are due at regular time intervals. A loan repayment is amortized over the term.

Example 1. A loan is repaid in equal instalments of $500 at the end of every six months for a two-year period.
What is the amount of the original loan if the interest rate is 7% per annum?

Solution: Let P be the amount of the loan, R be the payment, n be the number of payments to be made, and r be the rate of interest per conversion or payment period.

P is the amount of the loan that is given to the borrower now. The first payment of $500 is borrowed for only one conversion period, the second payment for two, the third payment for three, and the fourth payment for four. The result is equivalent to the present value of an annuity. Each time a payment is made, the interest is compounded. The number of payments per year is equivalent to the number of conversion periods per year.

$$R = \$500$$
$$i = 0.035$$
$$n = 4$$

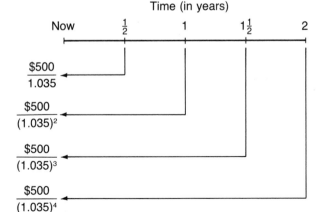

We obtain a geometric series as in present value.

$$P = \frac{\$500}{1.035} + \frac{\$500}{(1.035)^2} + \frac{\$500}{(1.035)^3} + \frac{\$500}{(1.035)^4}$$

Therefore we can use the "Present Value of an Annuity of 1" table in the Appendix, $a_{\overline{n}|i}$.

$$\therefore P = Ra_{\overline{n}|i}$$
$$P = 500a_{\overline{4}|3.5}$$
$$= 500(3.673\ 079)$$
$$= 1836.54 \quad \text{(nearest cent)}$$

Estimate.
$500 \times 4 = 2000$

The amount of the original loan is $1836.54.

Example 2. Diane borrowed $5000 for a computer system. She agreed to pay off the loan in monthly payments in one year. The interest rate was 18% per annum.
How much was each monthly payment?

For monthly payments, interest is compounded monthly.

Solution:

$18\% = 0.18$
$n = 12$

Time (in months)

Now 1 2 3 4 5 6 7 8 9 10 11 12

R R R R R R R R R R R R

$$n = 12,\ i = \frac{0.18}{12} = 0.015,\ \text{and}\ P = 5000.$$

$$P = Ra_{\overline{n}|i}$$
$$5000 = Ra_{\overline{12}|1.5}$$
$$5000 = R(10.907\ 505)$$
$$R = \frac{5000}{10.907\ 505}$$
$$= 458.40 \quad \text{(nearest cent)}$$

Estimate.
$5000 \div 12 \doteq 416$

Each monthly payment was $458.40.

EXERCISE 11.6

B

1. Find the missing quantities in the following.

	Loan	Payment	Payment Interval	Term of Loan	Rate per annum
(a)		$500	quarterly	5 a	16%
(b)		$129	monthly	2.5 a	24%
(c)		$1000	semi-annually	20 a	12%
(d)		$789.87	monthly	3 a	18%
(e)	$12 000		monthly	3.5 a	24%
(f)	$100 000		semi-annually	25 a	12%
(g)	$3487		quarterly	3 a	20%
(h)	$25 892		monthly	3 a	6%

2. For each problem, state i, n, and the value of $a_{\overline{n}|i}$.

(a) a loan at 24% per annum paid in monthly payments for 4 a

(b) a loan at 12% paid in semi-annual payments for 10 a

(c) a loan at 14% paid in quarterly payments for 5 a

(d) a loan at 18% paid in monthly payments for 3 a

(e) a loan at 6% paid in monthly payments for 6 months

(f) a loan at 18% paid in one monthly payment

3. The Cedar-Wood Siding Company borrowed working capital at 9% per annum to keep the plant producing over the slack months. They paid back the money in 3 payments, one every six months, with each payment being $10 326.45.
How much had they borrowed?

4. The Western Computer Company borrowed $500 000 and repaid the amount in quarterly payments for 4 a.
If the company negotiated the loan at 8% per annum, what quarterly payment was necessary to discharge the loan as required?

5. Terry wants to buy a new sports car that costs $42 892.

What is the monthly payment if the auto dealership will finance the car at 12% per annum over 4 a?

6. What principal must be loaned at 9% to give a return that totals $5000 over 12 semi-annual payments?

7. The North-Western Trust Co. offers loans at a rate of 12% per annum, requiring montly payments.
Find the following.

(a) the monthly payment if $1000 is borrowed with a term of one year

(b) the monthly payment if $1000 is borrowed with a term of two years

(c) the monthly payment if $1000 is borrowed with a term of three years
(d) the monthly payment if $1000 is borrowed with a term of four years
(e) What is the difference in the monthly payment as the term increases?
(f) Are the differences equivalent?
(g) Construct a bar graph to illustrate the increase in monthly payments.

8. The North-Western Trust Co. offers loans at a rate of 12% per annum, requiring monthly payments.
Find the following.
(a) the monthly payment if $1000 is borrowed with a term of two years
(b) the monthly payment if $1500 is borrowed with a term of two years
(c) the monthly payment if $2000 is borrowed with a term of two years
(d) the monthly payment if $2500 is borrowed with a term of two years
(e) the monthly payment if $3000 is borrowed with a term of two years
(f) What is the difference in the monthly payments as the amount increases?
(g) Are the differences equivalent?
(h) Construct a bar graph to illustrate the increase in monthly payments.

9. The North-Western Trust Co. offers corporate loans at a flexible rate, depending on the credit rating of the company. The loans are repaid in four quarterly payments.
Find the following.
(a) the quarterly payment if $100 000 is borrowed at 8% per annum
(b) the quarterly payment if $100 000 is borrowed at 10% per annum
(c) the quarterly payment if $100 000 is borrowed at 12% per annum
(d) the quarterly payment if $100 000 is borrowed at 14% per annum
(e) the quarterly payment if $100 000 is borrowed at 16% per annum
(f) What is the difference in the quarterly payments?
(g) Are the differences equivalent?
(h) Construct a bar graph to illustrate the increase in monthly payments.

MIND BENDER

What relation is Ted's father's sister's husband's daughter to Ted?

Using a computer and spreadsheet software, enter the formula that will calculate the payment and the amount of a loan.
As in questions 4, 7, and 8, investigate the change in
(a) the monthly payment as the interest rate increases, the term and amount are fixed;
(b) the monthly payment as the amount of the loan increases, the term and interest rate are fixed;
(c) the monthly payment as the term increases, the amount of the loan and the rate of interest are fixed.

11.7 THE COST OF BORROWING MONEY

Another form of a loan is called an instalment plan. If you purchase an item from a store by making a down payment and agreeing to discharge the debt by making regular payments, then, in effect, you are borrowing money from the store, and a finance or instalment charge will apply.

Example 1. You purchase a ring for $1200, including sales tax. You make a down payment of $200 and agree to pay the remainder, including a 10% per annum finance charge, in 2 equal semi-annual payments.
(a) Calculate the amount of each semi-annual payment.
(b) Analyse the costs involved in this plan.

Solution:
(a) Outstanding principal = purchase price – down payment
$$= \$1200 - \$200$$
$$= \$1000$$

To find the interest or finance charge, $P = \$1000$, $r = 0.10$, and $t = 1$ a.

$$I = Prt$$
$$I = 1000 \,(0.10)(1)$$
$$= \$100$$

$$\text{Semi-annual instalment payment} = \frac{\text{principal} + \text{finance charge}}{\text{number of payments}}$$
$$= \frac{1000 + 100}{2}$$
$$= \$550$$

The amount of each semi-annual payment is $550.

(b) We calculate the interest owed based on the outstanding principal and compare it with the amount actually paid. For the first semi-annual payment, $P = \$1000$, $r = 0.10$, and $t = \frac{1}{2}$ a.

$$I = Prt$$
$$I = 1000 \,(0.10)\tfrac{1}{2}$$
$$= \$50$$

The first payment of $550 is made up of $50 interest and $550 − $50 = $500 principal.

Amount owing for the second six months = $1000 − $500
$$= \$500$$

$E=mc^2$

To find the interest for the second six months, P = $500,
r = 0.10, and t = $\frac{1}{2}$ a.

$$I = Prt$$

$$I = 500 \, (0.10)\tfrac{1}{2}$$

$$= \$25$$

Amount owing = $500 + $25

$$= \$525$$

Actual payment = $550

From these calculations, we see that, based on the outstanding principal, an overpayment of $25 has been made.

To determine the rate of interest actually charged, we may reason as follows:

For the first 6 months, the outstanding principal was $1000. For the second 6 months, the outstanding principal was $500.

The average outstanding principal for the year was

$$\frac{\$1000 + \$500}{2} = \$750$$

The amount of interest paid based on the average outstanding principal is $\dfrac{\$100}{\$750} \doteq 0.133$ or 13.3%.

The amount of interest paid is, effectively, 13.3%.

The following formula gives the effective annual rate of interest.

$$r = \frac{2NI}{P(n + 1)}$$

where r is the effective annual rate,
N is the number of payment periods in 1 a,
I is the interest charged,
P is the principal, and
n is the total number of payments.

In Example 1,

$$r = \frac{2NI}{P(n + 1)}$$

$$r = \frac{2(2)(100)}{1000(3)}$$

$$\doteq 0.133$$

The effective annual rate is 13.3%

Example 2. Find the effective rate of interest on a loan of $10 000 with quarterly payments of $1400 for two years.

PLAN

Solution:

In the formula $r = \dfrac{2NI}{P(n+1)}$, we have P = $10 000, N = 4, n = 8, and I may be determined from the data as follows:

The amount paid is A = 8 × $1400
= $11 200

$$A = P + I$$
$$11\ 200 = 10\ 000 + I$$
$$I = 11\ 200 - 10\ 000$$
$$= \$1200$$

SOLVE

$\therefore r = \dfrac{2(4)(1200)}{10\ 000(9)}$

$\doteq 0.107$

Using a calculator, press

2 × 4 × 1 2 0 0 ÷
1 0 0 0 0 ÷ 9 =

The display is 0.106666666

ANSWER

The effective annual rate is 10.7% to the nearest tenth.

EXERCISE 11.7

B

1. Find the finance charges and the effective annual rate of interest, to the nearest tenth, for each of the following.

	Loan	Payment	Payment Interval	Term of Loan
(a)	$7500	$500	quarterly	5 a
(b)	$5987	$220	monthly	2.5 a
(c)	$12 000	$1000	semi-annually	20 a
(d)	$20 000	$789.87	monthly	3 a

2. A debt of $12 000 is to be paid off by 10 equal annual instalments, each to be paid at the end of the year. Each instalment is $1600.
What is the effective rate of interest per annum?

3. The City Centre Corporation wants to improve its property and takes a corporate loan of $500 000.
What is the effective rate of interest if
(a) it is repaid in 5 annual payments of $120 000 each?

(b) it is repaid in 5 a through semi-annual payments of $70 000?

(c) it is repaid in 5 a through payments of $40 000 quarterly?

4. Using the information in question 3,

(a) what amount of interest is paid in each case?

(b) what is the difference in the amounts as the number of conversion periods increases?

(c) what is the percentage increase in interest charged as the repayment schedule changes from annual to semi-annual to quarterly?

5. You want to purchase new furniture for $4789. The sales manager says that you can own the furniture for no-money-down and $178/month for 3 a.

(a) What amount of interest are you paying?

(b) What is the effective rate of interest per annum?

6. The sales manager gives you the option of making a monthly payment of $253 for 2 a for the same furniture as in question 5.

(a) What amount of interest are you paying?

(b) What is the effective rate of interest per annum?

(c) Under which payment plan do you pay the least interest, the two-year or the three-year term?
By how much?

(d) Which payment plan offers the smaller effective rate of interest?
By how much?

7. A car is advertised at $36 000 with $4000 down. If the effective annual rate is 10% and there are 60 monthly payments, use the formula $r = \dfrac{2NI}{P(n + 1)}$ to calculate the total interest charged.
Add the interest to the principal borrowed and divide by 60 to find the monthly payment.

MONTHLY PAYMENTS

The interest paid, I, can be expressed in terms of the principal, P, the monthly payment, p, and the total number of payments, n.

$$I = np - P$$

Substituting for I in the effective interest rate formula, we have

$$r = \frac{2NI}{P(n + 1)}$$

$$r = \frac{2N(np - P)}{P(n + 1)}$$

Solving for p, the result is

$$p = \frac{P[2N + (n + 1)r]}{2Nn}$$

For monthly payments, N = 12, and

$$p = \frac{P[24 + (n + 1)r]}{24n}$$

This formula is incorporated into the following BASIC program to calculate monthly payments when the principal, P, the total number of payments, n, and the annual interest rate, r, are known.

NEW
```
10 PRINT"EQUAL MONTHLY PAYMENTS"
20 INPUT"PRINCIPAL";P
30 INPUT"TOTAL NUMBER OF PAYMENTS";M
40 INPUT"ANNUAL RATE OF INTEREST (%)";R
50 MP = P*(24+(M+1)*.01*R)/24/M
60 PRINT"THE MONTHLY PAYMENT IS $";MP
70 INPUT"ANOTHER QUESTION? Y OR N";Z$
71 IF Z$ = "Y" THEN 20
80 END
```
RUN

EXERCISE

1. Calculate the monthly payments for each of the following.

(a) P = $16 500, n = 24, r = 15%

(b) P = $170 000, n = 48, r = 9%

(c) P = $37 000, n = 72, r = 8%

(d) P = $210 000, n = 108, r = 10%

11.8 AMORTIZATION SCHEDULES FOR MORTGAGES

When purchasing a home or other major property, the agreement between the money lender and the borrower is called a mortgage. This is a loan for the purchase of real property and as such is secured based on the value of the property.

The debt represented by a mortgage, like other consumer loans, is repaid in equal periodic payments that include both the principal and the interest.

We use the same formula for mortgages as for other loans.

$$P = Ra_{\overline{n}|i}$$

where P is the amount of the mortgage,
$a_{\overline{n}|i}$ is the general expression (values in table in the Appendix),
R is the payment in dollars,
i is the interest rate per conversion period, and
n is the number of payments.

Because mortgages are usually long-term debts, an amortization schedule is prepared that shows the interest and the principal that is applied against the loan.

Example. Prepare an amortization schedule for the first six months of a mortgage of $10 000 over 4 a at 12% interest. Payments are made monthly.

Solution: We first must find the monthly payment, R.

$$P = \$10\,000$$
$$i = \frac{0.12}{12} = 0.01$$
$$= 1\%$$
$$n = 48$$

$$P = Ra_{\overline{n}|i}$$
$$10\,000 = Ra_{\overline{48}|1}$$
$$10\,000 = R(37.973\,959)$$
$$R = \frac{10\,000}{37.973\,959}$$
$$\doteq 263.34 \quad \text{(to the nearest cent)}$$

The monthly payment is $263.34.

The interest each month is the interest for the month on the principal.

For the first month, P = $10 000, r = 0.12, and t = $\frac{1}{12}$.

I = Prt
I = 10 000 × 0.12 × $\frac{1}{12}$
   = 10 000 × 0.01
   = 100

The interest is $100.

Each subsequent month the interest is calculated on the new principal.

	Amortization Schedule First 6 months Loan of $10 000 at 12% per annum			
Month	Principal Balance	Interest/ month	Monthly Payment	Payment of Principal
1	$10 000	$100	$263.34	$163.34
2	$9836.66	$98.37	$263.34	$164.97
3	$9671.69	$96.72	$263.34	$166.62
4	$9505.07	$95.05	$263.34	$168.29
5	$9336.78	$93.37	$263.34	$169.97
6	$9166.81	$91.67	$263.34	$171.67

Notice from the example that with each subsequent payment the amount of the payment that applies to the principal increases. A graph illustrates this relationship.

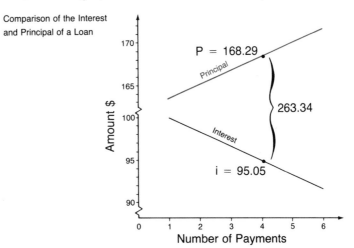

Comparison of the Interest and Principal of a Loan

When you purchase a home, the amortization for a mortgage is usually over 15 a, 20 a, 25 a, or 30 a. As a result, your monthly payment in the first years of the mortgage is almost entirely interest. Over a long term, the amount of interest paid exceeds the principal originally owed.

The table below illustrates the relationship between the principal and the interest over a long term.

	Total Interest Outlay and Monthly Payment for Principal and Interest on a $30 000 Loan			
Interest Rate	Total Interest 25 a	Monthly Payment 25 a	Total Interest 30 a	Monthly Payment 30 a
8.5%	$41 582.72	$238.61	$51 922.24	$227.58
9%	$44 517.97	$248.39	$55 625.92	$237.85
9.5%	$47 492.49	$258.31	$59 375.84	$248.27
10%	$50 503.85	$268.35	$63 168.14	$269.44
10.5%	$53 549.67	$278.50	$66 999.14	$269.44
11%	$56 627.63	$288.76	$70 865.29	$280.18
11.5%	$59 735.45	$299.12	$74 763.25	$291.01
12%	$62 870.96	$309.57	$78 689.84	$301.92
12.5%	$66 032.04	$320.11	$82 642.07	$312.89
13%	$69 216.67	$330.72	$86 617.14	$323.94

EXERCISE 11.8

A

1. From the table of "Total Interest Outlay and Monthly Payment" above, answer the following questions.

(a) What is the total interest paid for a $30 000 loan at 11.5% for 30 a?

(b) What is the total interest paid for a $30 000 loan at 11.5% for 25 a?

(c) The total interest paid for a $30 000 loan at 11.5% for 30 a is what percentage of the original principal of the loan?

(d) The total interest paid for a $30 000 loan at 11.5% for 25 a is what percentage of the original principal of the loan?

B

2. Complete the following amortization table for a loan of $10 000 at 16% interest paid quarterly with a quarterly payment of $735.82 for five years.

Amortization Schedule First 6 quarters Loan of $10 000 at 16% per annum				
Quarter	Principal Balance	Interest per quarter	Quarterly Payment	Payment of Principal
1	$10 000		$735.82	
2				
3				
4				
5				
6				
Total				

3. Using the information in question 2, construct a frequency polygon to compare the amount of interest and principal that make up the monthly payment over the 6 quarters.

4. From the information in question 2, the total interest is what percentage of the total principal?

5. A mortgage of $1500 at 8% per annum over 10 a is paid in equal semi-annual payments.
(a) Find the amount of the semi-annual instalment.
(b) Construct an amortization schedule. Using a computer and spreadsheet software, construct the schedule over 20 semi-annual payments.

A computer and spreadsheet software could be effectively used to produce simple amortization tables. This is the type of calculation, based on a formula, that the computer can do quickly and accurately. It also shows the change over time or changes to variables.

Complete the amortization schedule in question 2 over the total term of 20 quarters.

Continue the frequency polygon constructed in question 3 over the 20 quarters.

Amortization schedules on a spreadsheet can be found in section 15.10.

11.9 LIFE INSURANCE

The main reason people buy life insurance is to provide money for dependants in the event of the policyholder's death. Life insurance policies are also purchased, however, as an investment that will provide extra income in the future. The policy chosen depends on the cost, the family budget, the policyholder's age when the insurance is purchased, and the family's financial plans for the future.

TERM LIFE INSURANCE

Term insurance is the least expensive. It only provides death benefits for a specific term. Many employers offer term insurance as an employee benefit. The term of the insurance is only as long as the person is employed with the company.

Term insurance does not have a cash value. When the term ends, the policyholder receives nothing from the insurance company and the insurance terminates.

If the policyholder dies during the term, the total value of the policy is paid to the beneficiary, or the person designated by the policyholder to receive the benefits.

When you purchase trip insurance from an airline or mortgage insurance, which pays off the mortgage on the death of the mortgage holder, you are buying a type of term insurance. In the case of the airline, the term is the length of the trip. Mortgage insurance has a decreasing term; as you pay off your mortgage, the policy decreases according to the balance on the principal.

WHOLE LIFE INSURANCE

This insurance continues as long as the premium is paid by the policyholder. Upon the death of the insured, the beneficiary receives the entire face value, or the amount, of the insurance. This type of insurance does have a cash value.

A typical life insurance policy is a type of whole life insurance that is inexpensive but has a perpetual term. As long as the policyholder lives, payments must be made.

A limited payment life insurance policy is a type of whole life insurance that is more expensive but has a fixed term. The policyholder makes payments only for a specific term, but the policy continues until the death of the policyholder.

ENDOWMENT LIFE INSURANCE

If the policyholder of an endowment life insurance plan dies before a certain age or before the end of the policy's term, then the face value of the policy is paid to the dependants. If the policyholder lives beyond the term or to a specific age, usually 65, then the cash value of the policy is paid to him or her. An endowment life insurance policy is a form of annuity with the additional feature of providing death benefits.

LIFE INSURANCE PREMIUMS

Although life insurance rates vary from company to company, the table below illustrates the method of calculating the premium based on the face value of the insurance policy purchased.

Annual Premium per $1000 of Insurance					
Age at purchase	Type of Policy				
	Term	Whole Life		Endowment	
		Ordinary	Limited Pay	Term–20 a	Age 65
15 to 19	$5.03	$15.98	$24.89	$68.45	$19.75
20 to 24	$5.70	$18.02	$27.98	$69.14	$21.56
25 to 29	$6.79	$22.23	$32.07	$69.99	$25.89
30 to 34	$8.20	$26.98	$36.01	$70.64	$32.74
35 to 39	$9.98	$30.03	$40.87	$71.32	$40.01
40 to 44	$12.03	$35.12	$46.76	$72.43	$48.83
45 to 49	$18.30	$42.10	$52.18	$75.18	$69.11
50 to 54	$26.67	$47.80	$60.16	$81.89	$97.45
55 to 59	$37.80	$60.13	$73.67	$115.89	$136.76

Example 1. From the table of "Annual Premiums," what is the premium payable per year on $175 000 in term insurance if the policyholder is 43 a old?

Solution: From the table, at age 43, the price per $1000 is $12.03.

$$\text{Total premium per annum} = \frac{175\ 000}{1000} \times 12.03$$
$$= 175 \times 12.03$$
$$= 2105.25$$

Estimate.
200 000 ÷ 1000 × 10
= 2000

The annual premium is $2105.25.

Example 2. An employer pays 85% of the $2105.25 annual premium on a term insurance policy. The employee pays the remainder in equal payments per month.
How much is deducted from the pay of the policyholder each month?

Solution: Employee share = 2105.25 × 0.15
= 315.79

$$\text{Deduction each pay} = \frac{315.79}{12}$$
= 26.32

The employee pays $26.32 per month.

Example 3. If a person at age 24 wants to purchase $50 000 worth of insurance, compare the premium and the value at age 44 of
(a) an ordinary whole life policy,
(b) a 20-pay limited payment life policy,
(c) a 20 a endowment policy.

Solution:

Premium in each case is calculated on $\frac{50\ 000}{1000}$,

50 units at $1000 per unit.

(a) Whole life = 50 × 18.02
= 901

The premium is $901/a.

If the policyholder is alive at age 44, then the policy is not in force. The policy has no value and the policyholder is not insured further.

(b) 20-pay life = 50 × 27.98
= 1399

The premium is $1399/a.

If the policyholder is alive at age 44, then the policy is worth $50 000 at his or her death.

(c) 20 a endowment = 50 × 69.14
= 3457

The premium is $3457/a.

If the policyholder is alive at age 44, then he or she may receive a cash payment of $50 000 or receive payments in the form of an annuity.

As can be seen from the increase in premiums, if you want a more permanent life insurance policy or if you want a cash value at the end of the term, you will pay more.

EXERCISE 11.9

B

1. Complete the table by giving the premium.
Use the table of "Annual Premiums" on page 319.

	Age	Type of Life Insurance	Amount	Premium
(a)	18	Ordinary	150 000	
(b)	55	Term	200 000	
(c)	37	Endowment, 20 a term	55 000	
(d)	41	Limited Pay	175 000	
(e)	53	Endowment, at age 65	20 000	

2. Compare the cost and describe the value if a twenty-one-year-old wants to purchase $43 000 worth of the following types of insurance.

(a) an endowment, 20 a term
(b) term insurance
(c) whole life, 20 a term

3. If the policyholder is still alive at age 41, what is the status of each policy in question 2?

4. If the policyholder dies at age 40, what will the dependants receive under each policy in question 2?

5. If the policyholder dies at age 47, what will the dependants receive under each policy in question 2?

6. If your employer pays 75% of the premium on the first $50 000 in term insurance and 50% of the premium on each $1000 above $50 000, how much would the employee, aged 33, pay for $128 000 of term insurance?

7. As part of her financial plan, a twenty-seven-year-old purchases $100 000 in term insurance, her employer paying 60% of the premium; $40 000 in limited pay life; and an endowment policy maturing at age 65 for $30 000.
What is the total annual premium paid by this person?

8. A surviving spouse who is the beneficiary of an endowment insurance policy has the option of taking either $500 from the endowment at the end of each semi-annual period for 20 a or a cash settlement now to the value of the policy. If the interest rate is 8% compounded semi-annually, what is the value of the cash settlement now?

11.10 PROBLEM SOLVING

1. A triangular field measures 30 m by 30 m by 20 m. Fence posts are located at each vertex and 2 m apart along each side. How many fence posts are there?

2. How many times larger in area is the province of Ontario than the province of New Brunswick?

3. Stan asked Harry, "How many children do you have?"
Harry replied, "Three daughters."
Stan asked, "What are their ages?"
Harry replied, "I'll tell you in a riddle. The product of their ages is 36. The sum of their ages is your house number."
Stan said, "But that's not enough information."
Harry said, "I'll give you another clue. The oldest plays the guitar."
What are the ages of the three daughters?

4. Caroline goes jogging every day. She jogs from Aston to Bower and back. There are four jogging routes between Aston and Bower.

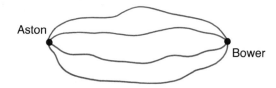

Caroline would like to vary her routes as much as possible and always return by a different route.
How many different ways can she make the trip?

5. How many different licence plates can be made if each must start with three letters and end with three numbers?

6. Can you walk through all the rooms by going through each door only once?

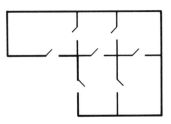

7. The figure shows two views of a cube without a top.

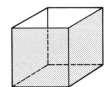

Use solid lines, dotted lines, and shading to show six other views of the same cube.

8. How many months contained a Friday the thirteenth in 1970?

9. Place the numbers from 1 to 13 in the circles so that the sum of each row is the same.

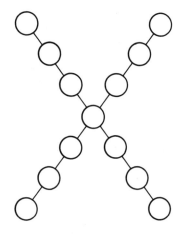

10. The formula for the height of an object after t seconds is
$$h = 5t(20 - t)$$
At what time is the greatest height reached?

11. The midpoints of the sides of a square are joined to form a second square. This process is repeated as shown in the diagram. The first square has sides 16 m long.

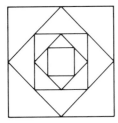

What is the sum of the areas of the five squares?

12. Erika drove 6 km to the library in 12 min. She returned in 18 min.
What was her average speed for the round trip in kilometres per hour?

13. How many litres of water must be added to 20 L of a 40% salt solution to obtain a 25% salt solution?

14. Two concentric circles are shown in the diagram. A chord of the larger circle is 36 cm long and is trisected by the smaller circle. The sum of the radii of the small circle and the large circle is 36 cm.

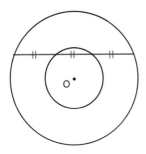

Find the length of the radius of the small circle.

11.11 REVIEW EXERCISE

1. Pat borrowed $70 000 for four years to buy a specialized delivery truck for her computer company. The interest was 8% per annum compounded quarterly.

What was the amount of the loan? *Compound Interest*

2. Larry borrowed $200 000 for five years to build a camp for disabled children. The interest was 10% per annum compounded semi-annually.
What was the amount of the loan?

3. Jennifer signed a note with a trust company that required her to pay $10 000 in five years. The interest was 7% per annum compounded semi-annually. *PV*
What was the present value of the loan?

4. Klaus signed a promissory note with a bank that required him to pay $21 000 in four years. The interest rate was 6% per annum compounded quarterly. *PV*
What was the present value of the loan?

5. Find the sum of each series.
(a) S_6 of $4 + 12 + 36 + ...$
(b) S_9 of $1 + 2 + 4 + 8 + ...$
(c) S_7 of $2 - 4 + 8 - 16 + ...$

6. Find the missing values.

	Principal	Per annum rate	Conversion Period	Term (a)	Amount
(a)	$2500	6%	semi-annually	6	
(b)	$475	8%	quarterly	2	

$A = P(1+i)^n$

7. Find the missing values.

	Present Value	Per annum rate	Conversion Period	Term (a)	Amount
(a)		9%	semi-annually	16	$15 000
(b)		12%	quarterly	10	$20 000

$PV = \dfrac{A}{(1+i)^n}$

8. Find the missing values.

	Amount	Periodic Rent	Number of Payments	Payment Interval/ Conversion Period	Per annum rate
(a)		$150	30	monthly	18%
(b)		$250	20	semi-annually	12%

$S_n = \dfrac{a(r^n - 1)}{r - 1}$

9. Find the missing values.

	Present Value	Periodic Rent	Number of Payments	Payment Interval/ Conversion Period	Per annum rate
(a)	$15 000		30	semi-annually	7%
(b)	$520		24	monthly	12%
(c)		$29	36	monthly	18%
(d)		$125	30	quarterly	10%

$P.V. \ d$

$S_n = a \left(\dfrac{r^n - 1}{r - 1} \right)$

10. Bob Beaman deposits $500 in the bank every six months for ten years. The interest earned is 10% per annum compounded quarterly.
How much will he have in the bank at the time of the last payment?

11. To save for the college education of their triplets, the Cavendish family deposited $2000 in a trust company every six months for sixteen years. The interest rate was 10% compounded semi-annually. How much did they have in the account at the time of the last payment?

12. How much money must you invest every six months at 7% per annum compounded semi-annually in order to have $20 000 at the end of the fourteenth payment?

13. How much money must you invest every three months at 8% per annum compounded quarterly in order to have $15 000 at the end of the thirty-second payment?

14. How much money must you invest now at 7% per annum compounded annually in order to provide 20 annual payments of $1000, the first payment being made in one year?

15. Julie has $100 000. She invests the money with a credit union at 9% per annum compounded semi-annually. She will withdraw the money in eighteen semi-annual payments, the first payment being made six months from now.
How much will each payment be?

16. Mr. Morgan invested $500 every six months for twenty years in a retirement fund.
If the fund earned 7% per annum compounded semi-annually, how much did he have when he retired?
The last payment was deducted from the final pay cheque.

17. Goman Delivery Service finds it economical to trade in their trucks every three years.
If a new truck costs $84 000 plus trade-in, how much money must be invested monthly in a sinking fund at 12% compounded monthly to replace a truck after 36 payments?
The first payment is made one month after purchase.

18. You bought a car for $46 000 with $5000 down and monthly payments of $1141.91 for 4 a.
What is the effective rate?

19. Starting on his daughter's first birthday, Mr. Pitman invested $250 each year in an account bearing annual interest at 8%. He did this up to and including her 18th birthday. The money was left in the account until she was 25.
Use a series of calculations and compound interest tables to calculate the amount of the investment.

20. A loan is repaid in equal instalments of $1900 at the end of every year for eight years.
What was the amount of the original loan if the interest rate was 7% per annum?

11.12 CHAPTER 11 TEST

1. Claire borrowed $100 000 for six years to add an addition to her house for her mother. The interest was 8% per annum compounded quarterly.
What was the amount of the loan?

2. Fred signed a promissory note with a bank that required him to pay $5000 in three years. The interest rate was 10% per annum compounded semi-annually.
What was the present value of the loan?

3. Find the sum of each series.
(a) S_8 of 5 + 10 + 20 + 40 + ...
(b) S_{10} of 3 − 6 + 12 − 24 + ...

4. Scott deposits $1000 in the bank every six months for eight years. The interest earned is 12% per annum compounded semi-annually.
How much will he have in the bank at the time of the last payment?

5. How much money must you invest every year at 6% per annum compounded annually in order to have $15 000 at the end of the tenth payment?

6. How much money must you invest now at 6% per annum compounded semi-annually to provide 10 annual payments of $500, the first payment being made in one year?

7. Ralph has $80 000. He invests the money with an insurance company at 12% per annum compounded quarterly. He will withdraw the money in twenty-four quarterly payments, the first payment being made three months from now.
How much will each payment be?

8. A loan is repaid in equal instalments of $700 at the end of every six months for a three-year period.
What was the amount of the original loan if the interest rate was 8% per annum?

9. You bought a sound system for $2995 with $200 down and monthly payments of $138.90 for 2 a.
What is the effective rate?

10. List an advantage and a disadvantage of
(a) term insurance,
(b) ordinary whole life insurance,
(c) an endowment, 20 a term.

BONDS AND STOCKS

12

REVIEW AND PREVIEW TO CHAPTER 12

PERCENT

EXERCISE 1

1. Evaluate.
(a) 10% of $350
(b) 33% of $156
(c) 6% of $560
(d) 1% of $23
(e) 200% of $198
(f) 125% of $610
(g) $1\frac{1}{4}$% of $185 212.80
(h) $12\frac{1}{2}$% of $3709.40
(i) $16\frac{2}{3}$% of $7253.49
(j) $5\frac{1}{4}$% of $93 900
(k) $4\frac{1}{2}$% of $64 949.95
(l) $5\frac{1}{2}$% of $74 900
(m) $10\frac{3}{4}$% of $45 925.50
(n) $2\frac{1}{2}$% of $202 493.18

2. (a) What percentage of $200 is $40?
(b) What percentage of $80 is $5?
(c) What percentage of $350 is $50?
(d) What percentage of $4 is $0.25?
(e) What percentage of $7.50 is $1.50?
(f) What percentage of $1000 is $156?

3. A coat costs $456. The sales tax is 7%.
What is the total cost of the coat?

4. A TV set is listed at $980. The sales tax is 6%.
What is the total cost of the TV set?

5. A price tag on a new bicycle reads $350. The owner of the store offers a 15% discount.
What is the cost of the bike before sales tax?

SIMPLE INTEREST

EXERCISE 2

1. Bryan invested $5000 for 3 a at 8% simple interest.
(a) How much interest did he earn?
(b) What was the amount of his investment after 3 a?

2. Lesa invested $2500 for 5 a at $6\frac{1}{2}$% simple interest.
(a) How much interest did she earn?
(b) What was the total amount of her investment after 5 a?

3. Floren invested $6000 for 6 months at 9% simple interest.
(a) How much interest did she earn?
(b) What was the total amount of her investment after 6 months?

4. Clive invested $8500 for 2 months at $8\frac{1}{4}$% simple interest.
(a) How much interest did he earn?
(b) What was the total amount of his investment after 2 months?

5. The Argand Corporation invested $100 000 for 51 d at 7% simple interest.
(a) What was the interest earned?
(b) What was the total amount of the investment after 51 d?

6. How much money must you invest at 8% simple interest for 2 a to earn $1120 in interest?

7. For how long must you invest $9000 at 6% simple interest to earn $1620 in interest?

8. At what rate of simple interest must you invest $20 000 to earn $700 in interest after 6 months?

COMPOUND INTEREST

EXERCISE 3

1. Find the amount if $7000 is invested at 8% per annum compounded annually for 7 a.

2. Find the amount if $950 is invested at 10% per annum compounded semi-annually for 3 a.

3. Find the amount if $12 000 is invested at 6% per annum compounded quarterly for 2 a.

4. Find the amount if $8000 is invested at 12% per annum compounded monthly for 5 a.

5. Find the amount if $11 500 is invested at 6% per annum compounded quarterly for 6 a.

6. How much money must be invested today at 6% per annum compounded annually in order to have $5000 in 6 a?

7. How much money must be invested today at 7% per annum compounded semi-annually in order to have $8000 in 3 a?

8. How much money must be invested today at 8% per annum compounded quarterly in order to have $4000 in 5 a?

9. How much money must be invested today at 6% per annum compounded quarterly in order to have $1 000 000 in 8 a?

10. How much money must be invested today at 12% per annum compounded monthly in order to have $4500 in 4 a?

11. How much money must you invest today at 10% per annum compounded semi-annually in order to have $1 000 000 when you are 50 a old?

ANNUITIES

EXERCISE 4

1. Find the amount of an annuity if $500 is deposited every six months for ten years at 8% per annum compounded semi-annually.

2. Find the amount of an annuity if $1000 is deposited every year for twelve years at 7% per annum compounded annually.

3. Find the amount of an annuity if $2000 is deposited every three months for six years at 6% per annum compounded quarterly.

4. How much money must be invested every six months for three years at 8% per annum compounded semi-annually if the required amount is $10 000?

5. How much money must be deposited every three months for five years at 12% per annum compounded quarterly if the required amount is $30 000?

6. How much money must be invested now at 6% per annum compounded annually to provide an annuity of five annual payments of $1000, the first payment being made in one year?

7. Find the price of an annuity of eight semi-annual payments of $500, the first payment to be made in six months, if money is worth 5% per annum compounded semi-annually.

8. Find the present value of an annuity of ten quarterly payments of $1000, the first payment to be made in three months, if money is worth 12% per annum compounded quarterly.

12.1 TYPES OF INVESTMENTS

"What am I bid for the use of my $10 000?"

The Government of Canada might pay you $400 every 6 months (8% per annum compounded semi-annually). In return for your money, you would receive $10 000 in bonds.

Gagetown needs money to build a new pollution control centre. The town council, with the approval of the municipal board of the provincial government, has issued debentures at $8\frac{1}{2}\%$ per annum and would use your money in return for one of these debentures.

King Corn Cannery Co. Ltd. is expanding its factory and must borrow $1 500 000. They have issued mortgage bonds and will pay $9\frac{3}{4}\%$ per annum for the use of your money.

South-Western Trust can lend mortgage money at $11\frac{1}{2}\%$ per annum. They will pay you 10% on a term savings certificate so that they may reinvest the money.

Perhaps you would like to buy part ownership in the Bamboo Cycle Company and share their profits. In that case you might buy stock in that company.

Any investment you make that yields additional monies or income adds to your financial position and is treated as income for tax purposes. The government, however, encourages investment and gives incentives through the tax system.

INVESTING IN SECURITIES

When you lend money to the government or to a company, you are investing in a debt security. You can do this by buying bonds or debentures. These are usually classified according to the security behind them.

Government bonds are secured by the ability of the government to raise money by taxation.

Mortgage bonds are secured by the property of the company. If the company defaults, holders of these bonds will have first claim to the revenue from the sale of assets.

Collateral trust bonds are secured by the money invested by the borrowing company in the bonds or securities of other companies.

Income bonds are bonds on which interest is paid only if the company makes a profit.

Debentures are secured by the general assets and earning power of the company or corporation.

INVESTING IN THE STOCK MARKET

When you buy part ownership of a company, you are purchasing equity securities. In this case you are buying stock that is sold as shares in the company.

Common stock   A dividend will usually be declared at a rate per share if the company makes money. Also, holders of common stock have a voice in setting company policy at the annual stockholders' meeting (one vote per share). These shares usually have no initial or par value; their price is set by what people are willing to pay on the open market.

Preferred stock   These shares have a par value and a fixed return set in dollars per share or as a percentage of the par value of the stock. The market value of the stock may vary considerably from the par value.

It is also possible to invest money in other ways such as putting it in bank savings, buying mutual funds, buying life insurance, or buying real estate.

RATE OF RETURN ON AN INVESTMENT

What determines the rate of return on an investment?

One of the major factors is supply and demand. If money is readily available and many investors are looking for places to invest, then the rates will be lowered. If money is not readily available to lend and there are many potential borrowers, the rates will go up.

Another important factor is risk. The most obvious risk is that you may lose your investment. If you invest in a high-risk venture such as the search for a mine or an oil well, you will expect a high return on your investment if the search is successful. If you are investing in a company with a long record of success in the business world, then it appears there will be little risk and the rates will therefore be lower.

A second risk that an investor takes is not so obvious. What will the value of your money be when it is returned? If you invest $1000 in a 20-year bond, what will your $1000 buy when you get it back? If the cost of living doubles approximately every ten years, what will your $1000 be worth in twenty years?

Before a company can issue stocks it must receive a charter from the provincial government. The government requires that the company file a copy of its constitution and the names of the members of its board of directors, that it issue an audited annual financial statement and report to the stockholders, and that it hold an annual stockholders' meeting for the election of the board of directors.

Since a company that is not fulfilling these obligations can lose its charter, there is a measure of protection for the investor.

To illustrate the relative risks in the securities named so far, it is worth noting the order of priority of the financial obligations a company incurs.

First, bond and debenture interest must be paid.
Second, if the company has made a profit, preferred shareholders will receive dividends.
Third, dividends will be paid to common shareholders from remaining profits as declared by the board of directors.

If the company finds that it is unable to meet its financial obligations and declares bankruptcy, the revenue from the sale of assets will be distributed in the same order, with bond holders being paid off first, preferred shareholders next, and the residue, if any, being distributed among the common shareholders on the basis of the formula:

$$\frac{\text{Residual assets}}{\text{Total outstanding shares}} \times \text{Number of shares held}$$

Since banks operate under strict government control, funds deposited with them are as secure as government bonds, which are generally considered the safest of all investments.

EXERCISE 12.1

A

1. Rank the following investments in order of relative security from most to least.

Common stock, Company mortgage bonds, Debentures, Government bonds, and Preferred stock

Remember that any form of investment is only as secure as the organization standing behind it.

2. (a) Which securities involve purchasing part ownership of a company?
   (b) Which securities involve lending money to a company?

B

3. If a company has a net worth of $5 000 000 and you own 100 shares out of a total of 100 000 shares, what is the value of your shares if the company is dissolved?

4. In winding up the affairs of a company that has gone out of business, there is $1 462 700 left after settling all debts. If there are 500 000 shares of common stock outstanding, how much will the owner of 1500 shares receive?

5. A company wishes to raise capital by selling a bond issue of $1 500 000 in $8\frac{1}{2}\%$ mortgage bonds.
If the interest is paid semi-annually, how much money will the company pay in interest each half year?

6. A company has 800 000 shares in the hands of shareholders. The company declares a dividend of $1.35 per share.
   (a) How much money will the company pay out in dividends?
   (b) How much money will a shareholder with 2000 shares receive?
   (c) If this is an annual dividend and the shares have a market value of $60, what rate of return is this on the investment?

7. A company declares $617 500 in dividends. There are 950 000 shares in the hands of shareholders.
   (a) What is the dividend per share?
   (b) What dividend will a shareholder with 500 shares receive?

12.2 BOND PRICES

Bonds are a debt security. They represent a loan by the purchaser to the government or to the company who issues the bond. Recall the five types of debt security mentioned in section 12.1 and the security that each represents.

Every bond displays four pieces of information: the amount or "face" of the bond, the interest rate or "bond rate," the maturity date, and the name of the issuing organization.

Bonds may be fully registered, in which case the name of the holder is recorded and interest payments are mailed out when due. On this type of bond certificate, nothing is lost if it is stolen. Alternatively, the bond may be registered as to principal only, in which case the certificate will contain dated interest coupons to be clipped and redeemed at a bank. Since the name of the bond holder is recorded, the principal is safe if the certificate is stolen, but the interest will probably be lost unless the theft is traced through the serial number on the bond. Bearer bonds, as the name implies, are valuable to whoever is holding them. If stolen, they are easily sold. For this reason, they should be kept in a safety deposit box or some other safe place.

When a company wishes to raise money through a bond issue, it must file particulars and obtain permission from the government. The bonds will then be offered for sale to securities companies who will bid on large blocks of bonds and then sell them to individual investors at a profit. In many cases the announcement appears after all the bonds have been purchased by large investors and is a matter of record only.

Example 1. A $5000, $8\frac{1}{2}$% bond bears quarterly coupons.

What is the value of each coupon when due?
How much will the owner of the bond receive on the date of the last coupon?

Solution: $I = Prt$
$I = \$5000 \times 0.085 \times 0.25$
$= \$106.25$

Therefore each coupon is worth $106.25 when due, and on the date of the last coupon the owner will receive $5000 + \$106.25 = \$5106.25$.

The face value and bond rate are printed on the bond, so these quantities cannot change. The value of free investment capital, however, changes as supply and demand vary. This change is reflected in the market value of the bond. These values are listed in the newspaper and brokerage offices under a "bid" price (what people are offering to pay) and an "ask" price (what people want for their bonds). The amounts quoted are for $100 of face or par value. If current interest rates were 10%, and a bond carried $7\frac{1}{2}$%, would investors pay more or less than par?

Example 2. What is the price of a $1000 bond sold at $89\frac{1}{2}$?

Solution: $\text{Price} = \dfrac{1000}{100} \times 89.5$
$= \$895.00$

The price of the bond is $895.

No matter what the purchase price, a bond is worth its face value at the time of maturity.

Bonds are bought and sold through investment brokers and banks. They will arrange for the sale or purchase of bonds on the bond market. The price arrived at will be a trading price somewhere between the "bid" and the "ask." For handling a sale, the broker will usually charge a commission of 0.5% of the purchase price, with a minimum of $0.50 per $100 face value. Banks will handle Canada Savings Bonds without charging commission.

The seller of the bond will also receive from the purchaser the interest that has accrued from the date of the last coupon up to the time of purchase.

Example 3. Find the price of a $2000, 9% Government of Canada bond bought through a bank at the ask price of $84\frac{1}{2}$ on September 15. The last coupon date was June 15.

Solution: Price $= \dfrac{2000}{100} \times 84.5$

$= \$1690.00$

Add interest for 92 d.

Accrued interest $= \$2000 \times 0.09 \times \dfrac{92}{365}$

$= \$45.37$

> Estimate.
> $2000 \times 0.1 \times 100 \div 400$
> $= 50$

Total cost $= \$1690.00 + \$45.37$

$= \$1735.37$

The price of the bond is $1735.37.

Example 4. Find the proceeds from the sale of a $5000, $8\frac{1}{4}$% bond at $101\frac{1}{2}$ through a broker charging $\frac{1}{2}$% commission on the price of the bond (but not less than $0.50 per $100). The bond was sold July 10. The last coupon date was June 15.

Solution: Price $= \dfrac{5000}{100} \times 101.5$

$= \$5075$

Add interest for 25 d.

Accrued interest $= \$5000 \times 0.0825 \times \dfrac{25}{365}$

$= \$28.25$

Total cost $= \$5075.00 + \$28.25$

$\doteq \$25.38$

Commission $= 0.005 \times 5075$

$= \$25.38$

Proceeds $=$ Total cost $-$ Commission

Proceeds $= \$5103.25 - \$25.38$

$= \$5077.87$

The proceeds from the sale are $5077.87.

EXERCISE 12.2

A

1. What are the advantages of a registered bond?
Of a bearer bond?

2. Would you expect a bond to bring a higher or lower return than preferred shares?
Why?

3. Besides theft, what other sources of physical loss are securities liable to?
How can they be guarded against?

B

4. Calculate the coupon value for each of the following bonds bearing half-yearly coupons.

(a) $2000, Government of Canada, $9\frac{1}{4}$%

(b) $1000, Traders Group, $7\frac{3}{4}$%

5. A bank buys a $10 000 bond at a bid price of 85 and sells it at an ask price of 87.
What profit is made in dollars and as a percentage of the bid price?
No other commission is charged.

6. Find the cost of the following bonds.
The minimum commission, if any, is $0.50 per $100 face value.

	Face	Bond Rate (%)	Price	Commission	Last Coupon Date	Sale Date
(a)	$1000	8.75	81.00	—	July 15	Oct. 15
(b)	$3000	9.75	89.00	$\frac{1}{2}$%	March 1	May 1
(c)	$500	10.00	94.00	$\frac{1}{2}$%	Dec. 15	Jan. 30
(d)	$2000	7.75	74.00	$\frac{1}{2}$%	Oct. 1	Oct. 25
(e)	$5000	8.00	79.00	$\frac{1}{2}$%	Feb. 1	April 15
(f)	$12 000	9.75	88.50	$\frac{1}{2}$%	Dec. 15	Jan. 3

7. Find the proceeds from the sale of the following bonds.
The minimum commission, if any, is $0.50 per $100 face value.

	Face	Bond Rate (%)	Price	Commission	Last Coupon Date	Sale Date
(a)	$500	10.75	101.00	$\frac{1}{2}$%	Sept. 15	Sept. 30
(b)	$3000	9.00	91.50	$\frac{1}{2}$%	Feb. 15	Feb. 20
(c)	$1500	6.75	69.00	$\frac{1}{2}$%	June 1	June 28
(d)	$2000	8.75	80.00	$\frac{1}{2}$%	July 15	Aug. 12

12.3 YIELD RATE OF BONDS

Bonds are usually offered for sale at a premium or a discount.

Premium bonds are bonds selling for more than their face value. Discounted bonds are bonds selling for less than their face value.

To compare the relative value of bonds offered for sale, the yield of each bond should be calculated.

Before considering the yield rate of bonds, we will consider the yield rate of any investment.

If you invest $1000 in a company, and you receive a dividend of $200 after one year, then the yield rate is found as follows:

$$\text{Yield rate} = \frac{\text{dividend}}{\text{investment}} \times 100\%$$

$$\text{Yield rate} = \frac{200}{1000} \times 100\%$$

$$= 20\%$$

To calculate the yield rate of a bond, we use the formula

$$\text{Yield rate} = \frac{\text{average income}}{\text{average principal}} \times 100\%$$

To determine the average income and the average principal, we use the fact that with bonds, barring default, the value of the bond at maturity will be the face value of the bond.

AVERAGE INCOME

If a $1000 bond selling at 90 matures in five years, then in addition to the interest over the five years, you will make $100 on the principal, since you buy it for $900 and redeem it for $1000. We could approximate this amount as $20 in income per year. In general, for a bond maturing in n years:

Discounted bonds

$$\text{Average income} = \text{interest} + \frac{\text{face value} - \text{market value}}{n}$$

Premium bonds

$$\text{Average income} = \text{interest} - \frac{\text{market value} - \text{face value}}{n}$$

When we say "selling at 90," we mean 90% of the face value.

AVERAGE PRINCIPAL

$$\text{Average principal} = \frac{\text{face value} + \text{market value}}{2}$$

Example 1. Find the approximate yield rate of a $9\frac{1}{2}$% bond selling at 90, maturing in 5 a.
(Note that yield is a percentage and may be worked from 100 for any face value.)

Solution:
The bond is offered at a discount.

$$\text{Average income} = 9.50 + \frac{100 - 90}{5}$$
$$= 9.50 + 2$$
$$= \$11.50 \quad (\text{per year})$$

$$\text{Average principal} = \frac{100 + 90}{2} = \$95$$

$$\text{Yield rate} = \frac{11.50}{95} \times 100\%$$
$$\doteq 12.1\%$$

The approximate yield rate is 12.1%.

Example 2. Find the approximate yield rate of a 12% bond selling at 101.5, maturing in $8\frac{1}{2}$ a.

Solution:
The bond is offered at a premium.

$$\text{Average income} = 12.00 - \frac{101.5 - 100}{8.5}$$
$$= 12.00 - 0.18$$
$$= \$11.82 \quad (\text{per year})$$

$$\text{Average principal} = \frac{100 + 101.5}{2} = \$100.75$$

$$\text{Yield rate} = \frac{11.82}{100.75} \times 100$$
$$\doteq 11.7\%$$

The approximate yield rate is 11.7%.

EXERCISE 12.3

B 1. Find the yield rate for each of the following bonds.

(a) $8\frac{1}{2}$% selling at 78, maturing in 10 a

(b) $7\frac{3}{4}$% selling at 88.5, maturing in $3\frac{1}{2}$ a

(c) 9% selling at 80, maturing in 9 a

(d) 8% selling at 76, maturing in 17 a

(e) $5\frac{1}{4}$% selling at 74.5, maturing in $8\frac{1}{2}$ a

2. Find the yield rate for each of the following bonds.

(a) 11% selling at 101.5, maturing in 12 a

(b) $10\frac{3}{4}$% selling at 101, maturing in 8 a

(c) $9\frac{1}{4}$% selling at 100.25, maturing in 2 a

(d) 12% selling at 103, maturing in 6 a

3. (a) Calculate the yield rate for each bond and decide which gives the better return on the investment.
(i) 6% selling at 86, maturing in 3 a
(ii) $9\frac{1}{4}$% selling at 87, maturing in 16 a

(b) What other factor would you consider when deciding which bond to invest in?

4. (a) Calculate the yield rate on each bond.
(i) 9% selling at 95, maturing in 5 a
(ii) 9% selling at 95, maturing in 15 a
(iii) 12% selling at 102, maturing in 5 a
(iv) 12% selling at 102, maturing in 15 a

(b) For premium and discounted bonds, what is the effect of the length of time to maturity on the yield?

12.4 PRESENT VALUE OF A BOND

Before you purchase a bond, you should determine what you should pay for the bond, based on the desired or expected rate of return. For example, if interest rates were 10% per annum, how much should you pay for a $1000, 7% bond? Although the price would depend on the bond's maturity date, the price would be less than $1000.

When determining the price to pay for a bond there are two quantities to consider:

(i) the face value of the bond, and
(ii) the interest payments.

The following is the formula used to calculate the price:

$$\text{Price} = \left(\begin{array}{l}\text{present value of the} \\ \text{face value of the} \\ \text{bond}\end{array}\right) + \left(\begin{array}{l}\text{present value of the} \\ \text{annuity formed by the} \\ \text{bond's interest payments}\end{array}\right)$$

The present value of the face value is really the present value of an amount, which we found in section 10.6.

$$\text{PV(face value)} = \frac{A}{(1 + i)^n}$$

where A is the face value of the bond.

We found the present value of an annuity in section 11.5.

$$\text{PV(annuity)} = Ra_{\overline{n}|i}$$

where there are n payments of $R at i% per interval.

Example 1. Find the price of a $100, 7% bond bearing semi-annual coupons and maturing in 15 a, if it is to yield 10% compounded semi-annually.

Solution:

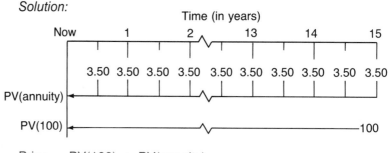

Price = PV(100) + PV(annuity)

$$\text{PV(100)} = \frac{A}{(1 + i)^n}, \text{ where A} = \$100, i = 0.05, \text{ and n} = 30.$$

$E=mc^2$

PV(annuity) = Ra$_{\overline{n}|i}$, where R = \$3.50, i = 0.05, and n = 30.

Price = $\dfrac{\$100}{(1 + 0.05)^{30}}$ + \$3.50(a$_{\overline{30}|0.05}$)

(100)(.035) *From the table,*
= 3.50   a$_{\overline{30}|0.05}$ = 15.372 451
interest
6 mths.

= \$100(0.231 38) + \$3.50(15.372 451)

≐ \$23.138 + \$53.804

= \$76.942

The price is \$76.94.

To find the price of a bond between coupon dates,
(i) find the price at the last previous coupon date, and
(ii) find the amount of the price invested at the desired yield
rate from the previous coupon date to the date of sale.

Example 2. Find the price of a \$4000, 8% bond bearing
semi-annual coupons on February 1 and
August 1 and maturing on February 1, 2000.
The bond is purchased on December 15, 1995
to yield 10% compounded semi-annually.

Solution:

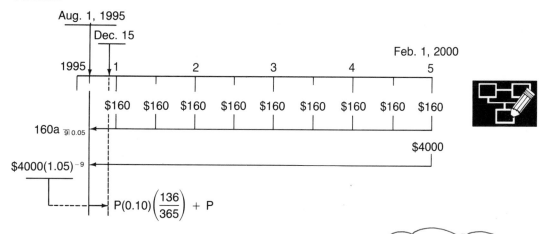

Price (Aug. 1, 1995) = $\dfrac{\$4000}{(1.05)^9}$ + \$160(a$_{\overline{9}|0.05}$)

From the table,
a$_{\overline{9}|0.05}$ = 7.107 822

= \$4000(0.644 61) + \$160(7.107 822)

≐ \$2578.44 + \$1137.25

= \$3715.69

There are 136 d from August 1 to December 15.

Price (Dec. 15, 1995) = \$3715.69(0.10)$\left(\dfrac{136}{365}\right)$ + \$3715.69

≐ \$138.45 + \$3715.69

= \$3854.14

The price on December 15, 1995 is \$3854.14.

EXERCISE 12.4

If the face value of a bond is not stated, use $100 as the face value.

A

1. Why is it not practical to adjust the yield of a bond by changing the coupon rate?

2. (a) If you buy a 7% bond when money is worth 10% on the market, would you pay more or less than face value?
   (b) If you buy a 10% bond when money is worth 8% on the market, would you pay more or less than face value?

B

3. Find the price of the following bonds.
   (a) a 6% bond bearing semi-annual coupons, maturing in 9 a to yield 9% per annum compounded semi-annually
   (b) a 9% bond bearing semi-annual coupons, maturing in 12 a to yield 11% per annum compounded semi-annually
   (c) a $7\frac{1}{2}$% bond bearing semi-annual coupons, maturing in 8 a to yield 10% per annum compounded semi-annually
   (d) an 8% bond bearing quarterly coupons, maturing in 6 a to yield 12% compounded quarterly
   (e) a $5\frac{1}{2}$% bond bearing semi-annual coupons, maturing in 10 a to yield 11% per annum compounded semi-annually

4. Find the price of the following bonds.
   (a) a 12% bond bearing semi-annual coupons, maturing in 5 a to yield 9% per annum compounded semi-annually
   (b) an 11% bond bearing semi-annual coupons, maturing in 8 a to yield 8% per annum compounded semi-annually

(c) a 12% bond bearing quarterly coupons, maturing in 4 a to yield 10% per annum compounded quarterly
(d) a 9% bond bearing semi-annual coupons, maturing in 12.5 a to yield 8% per annum compounded semi-annually
(e) a 10% bond bearing semi-annual coupons, maturing in 6 a to yield 9% per annum compounded semi-annually

5. Find the cost of a $500, $7\frac{1}{2}$% bond bearing semi-annual coupons and maturing in 10.5 a.
It is to yield 11% compounded semi-annually. Include $\frac{1}{2}$% commission.

6. Find the cost of a $5000, 10% bond bearing semi-annual coupons.
There are 25 coupons remaining, and the bond is purchased 90 d after the last previous coupon date to yield 8% per annum compounded semi-annually.

7. Find the cost of a $10 000, $7\frac{1}{2}$% bond bearing semi-annual coupons.
There are 31 coupons remaining, and the bond is purchased 46 d after the last previous coupon date to yield 11% per annum compounded semi-annually.

8. Find the price of a 12% bond bearing semi-annual coupons on January 15 and October 15 and maturing on January 15, 1997. The bond is purchased on February 15, 1991 to yield 9% per annum compounded semi-annually.

Additional work on present value, using a spreadsheet, can be found in section 15.7.

12.5 BUYING AND SELLING STOCKS

Financial advisors suggest that you do not keep all of your resources in one type of investment such as term deposits. In many cases it is best to diversify your investments.

Ben Dalton decided to invest money in the stock market by buying shares. When you buy shares in a company, you are speculating that the price of the shares will increase, and then you can sell the shares for a profit. However, there is always the possibility that the price of the shares will decrease and if you sell them, you will lose money.

Ben consulted a stockbroker and decided to invest in Gulf Resources, an oil company. The stockbroker obtained a quote on Gulf Resources from the teletype linking her office computer to the stock exchange.

Ben purchased 400 shares of Gulf Resources at $16 a share.

The stock exchange has ruled that most trading is to be done in board lots. The transaction is called trading because when you buy stocks, you are trading someone for the stocks they own for money that you have. Trading units of board lots are based on the price of one share of the stock being traded.

Selling under $0.10	1000 shares
Selling at $0.10 and under $1	500 shares
Selling at $1 and under $100	100 shares
Selling at $100 and over	10 shares

After the stockbroker had purchased the 400 shares of Gulf Resources for Ben, the transaction was displayed on the electronic ticker tape as shown below.

CDN TIRE	GLF	TRIDONT	McDONALD
32	4.16	$10.9\frac{5}{8}$	$56\frac{7}{8}$ B/$57\frac{1}{4}$

The information on this portion of the tape is

100 shares of Canadian Tire were sold at $32

400 shares of Gulf Resources were sold at $16

1000 shares of Tridont were sold at $9\frac{5}{8}$

a bid to buy 100 shares of McDonald's at $56\frac{7}{8}$, and an offer to sell 100 shares of the same stock at $57\frac{1}{4}$

Soon after seeing the transaction on the electronic ticker tape, the stockbroker would receive confirmation of Ben Dalton's purchase.

The next step is to calculate the broker's commission for completing the transaction. The following formulas are used to do this for transactions under $20 000. This includes selling as well as buying shares.

In the table, C represents the commission in dollars;
x represents the value of the order, up to $20 000; and
n represents the number of shares.

Selling Price per share	Commission	Formula
Under $14	2.5% of the order	$C = 0.025x$
$14 to $30	0.875% of the order plus 22.575¢ per share	$C = 0.008\ 75x + 0.225\ 75n$
Over $30	1.64% of the order	$C = 0.0164x$

Purchasers are also permitted to negotiate a lesser rate of commission with the broker.

Example 1. Find the total cost to purchase 300 shares of Crownx at $12.50 per share.

Solution: Cost of shares $= 300 \times \$12.50$
$= \$3750$

Commission $= 0.025 \times \$3750$
$= \$93.75$

Cost to purchaser $= \$3750 + \$93.75$
$= \$3843.75$

The total cost is $3843.75.

1·2·3

Commission is added to purchases.

Example 2. Find the total cost to purchase 400 shares of Gulf Resources at $16 per share.

Solution: Cost of shares $= 400 \times \$16$
$= \$6400$

Commission $= 0.008\ 75 \times \$6400 + \$0.225\ 75 \times 400$
$= \$56 + \$90.30$
$= \$146.30$

Cost to purchaser $= \$6400 + \$146.30$
$= \$6546.30$

The total cost is $6546.30.

Example 3. Find the net proceeds to the seller of 200 shares of IBM at $120\frac{3}{4}$ per share.

Solution: Proceeds = 200 × $120.75
= $24 150

Commission = 0.0164 × $24 150
= $396.06

> Commission is deducted from proceeds.

Net proceeds = $24 150 − $396.06
= $23 753.94

The net proceeds are $23 753.94.

Example 4. An investor bought 600 shares of CHUM at $17\frac{3}{8}$ and sold it at $18\frac{1}{4}$.
Calculate the net profit or loss after these transactions.

Solution:

Buying

Cost of shares = 600 × $17.375
= $10 425

Commission = 0.008 75 × $10 425 + $0.225 75 × 600
$\doteq$ $91.22 + $135.45
= $226.67

Cost to purchaser = $10 425 + $226.74
= $10 651.67

1·2·3

Selling

Proceeds = 600 × $18.25
= $10 950

Commission = 0.008 75 × $10 950 + $0.225 75 × 600
= $95.81 + $135.45
= $231.26

Net proceeds = $10 950 − $231.26
= $10 718.74

Profit or loss = net proceeds − total cost
Profit or loss = $10 718.74 − $10 651.67
= $67.07

There was a profit of $67.07.

EXERCISE 12.5

B

1. Find the cost of the following purchases, excluding the commission.
(a) 200 shares of Chrysler at $29
(b) 500 shares of Abitbi at $49\frac{1}{2}$
(c) 600 shares of Coleco at $6\frac{3}{4}$
(d) 100 shares of Exador at $12\frac{1}{8}$
(e) 700 shares of Ivaco at $7\frac{3}{8}$
(f) 300 shares of Tesco at $3.65
(g) 5000 shares of Exo at $0.09

2. Calculate the commission on each of the following purchases.
(a) 500 shares of Cognos at $7
(b) 2000 shares of Franco at $6\frac{1}{2}$
(c) 100 shares of Cominco at $13\frac{1}{4}$
(d) 200 shares of Newtel at $17
(e) 100 shares of Suncor at $23\frac{5}{8}$
(f) 600 shares of Laidlaw G at $22\frac{7}{8}$
(g) 500 shares of IBM at $156
(h) 100 shares of Sterling at $49\frac{3}{4}$
(i) 800 shares of Imp Oil at $55\frac{1}{2}$

3. Calculate the total cost of the following purchases, including the commission.
(a) 100 shares of Dover Industrial at $13
(b) 500 shares of Bralor at $6\frac{1}{2}$
(c) 200 shares of Pacific at $40\frac{5}{8}$
(d) 300 shares of Placer at $15
(e) 1000 shares of Great West Life at $25\frac{3}{4}$
(f) 200 shares of Weston at $32\frac{1}{4}$

4. Calculate the net proceeds of each of the following sales, including commission.
(a) 100 shares of Pine Point at $11
(b) 600 shares of Prairie Oil at $7\frac{1}{2}$
(c) 1000 shares of Loblaws at $43\frac{1}{4}$

(d) 2000 shares of Greyhound at $19\frac{5}{8}$
(e) 700 shares of Consumers Gas at $27\frac{1}{8}$
(f) 500 shares of Stuart at $36\frac{3}{4}$

5. Calculate the cost of each of the following purchases as shown on the electronic ticker tape.

(a)

MOFFAT
$12\frac{1}{4}$

(b)

MOORE
3.26

(c)

ROYEX
$6.9\frac{3}{4}$

(d)

UGAS
$5.32\frac{1}{8}$

(e)

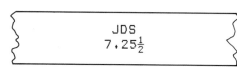

JDS
$7.25\frac{1}{2}$

6. Calculate the profit or loss from each of the following transactions.
(a) 100 shares of Barik were purchased at $10 and sold at $11
(b) 300 shares of Fleet Arrow were purchased at $5 and sold at 4\frac{1}{2}$
(c) 1000 shares of Nova were purchased at 26\frac{3}{4}$ and sold at 29\frac{1}{8}$
(d) 400 shares of Teck were purchased at 36\frac{5}{8}$ and sold at 32\frac{1}{4}$
(e) 2000 shares of Canfor were purchased at 26\frac{3}{8}$ and sold at $31

MIND BENDER

You are riding a horse around a track. You have a ball in your left hand. You drop the ball.
Where will the ball land?
(a) in front of you
(b) beside you
(c) behind you
Explain your answer.

12.6 DIVIDENDS

Individuals and organizations invest money in stocks in the hope of increasing their wealth. With stocks the increase may come in the form of a dividend or as a capital gain.

A capital gain (or loss) is the profit (or loss) from buying stocks at one price and selling at another, hopefully higher. This was discussed in the previous section.

In this section we will discuss dividends, which represent the return or yield on investments. Before examining dividends, however, we must distinguish between the types of stocks.

When you purchase stocks, you are buying part ownership of the company in the form of shares. The two basic types of shares are common shares and preferred shares.

When you own common stock, you are a stockholder and represent the ownership of the company. The amount of ownership that an individual has is determined by the amount of common stock owned. For example, if a company has 1 000 000 shares outstanding, and you own 250 000 of them, then you own 25% of the company.

Preferred stock has a par value, usually $100 per share, and a fixed rate of return, shown as a percentage of the par value.

When a company makes a profit, the owners are entitled to share in the surplus income. The board of directors will decide how much of the profit should be used to expand or improve the company, often called "ploughing money back in," and how much should be distributed to the shareholders as dividends.

If a company has 500 000 shares of stock distributed among its stockholders and the directors wish to distribute $100 000 in earnings, they will declare a dividend of 20¢ per share. ($100 000 ÷ 500 000 shares)

At the right is a dividend report as it might appear in the newspaper.

Note that the top line states that corporate dividends are quarterly unless otherwise noted.

Unless the letters pfd. are used, the dividends are for common shares.

Livingfield Industries has declared a dividend on common stocks of $8\frac{1}{2}$ cents per share, payable on October 31 to shareholders on record as of October 15. If a shareholder sold the shares of Livingfield on October 17, they would still receive the dividend on October 31.

DIVIDENDS

Corporation dividends quarterly unless otherwise noted.

Canfor International Power C Ltd., 43 cents, Sept. 30, record Sept. 24.

Cookfield Smith and Co. Ltd., 16 cents, Sept. 30, record Sept. 18.

Dallex Co. Ltd., $2.75, Sept. 30, record Sept. 20.

Highland Brown Canada Ltd., 18 cents, Oct. 14, record Sept. 25; 6 percent pfd., $1.50, Oct. 3, record Sept. 21.

payday

Livingfield Industries Ltd., $8\frac{1}{2}$ cents, Oct. 31, record Oct. 15. *on record*

Example 1. Stephanie Edwards owned 500 shares of Dallex Co. on September 21. Use the dividend report from the previous page to calculate the dividend she received.

Solution: Dividend declared $2.75
Dividend receivable   500 × $2.75 = $1375.00

The total dividend receivable is $1375.00.

Example 2. Use the dividend report from the previous page to determine the dividend receivable if you owned 300 shares of Highland Brown common and 700 shares of Highland Brown at 6% preferred on September 25.

Solution: Common share dividend $0.18
Dividend receivable   300 × $0.18 = $54.00

6% preferred shares $1.50 per share
Dividend receivable   700 × $1.50 = $1050.00

Total dividend receivable = $54.00 + $1050.00
                          = $1104.00

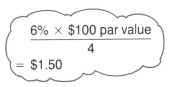

$$\frac{6\% \times \$100 \text{ par value}}{4}$$
$$= \$1.50$$

The total dividend receivable is $1104.00.

EXERCISE 12.6

B Use the dividend report below to answer the following questions.

DIVIDENDS

Corporation dividends quarterly unless otherwise noted.

Alcorn International Co., 23 cents, June 30, record June 20.

Bytown Power Corporation, $1.75, March 31, record March 24.

Celeste Radio Co., 25 cents, Sept. 30, record Sept. 21; 5% pfd., $1.25, Oct. 1, record Sept. 24.

Dalberg Branton Co., 17 cents, March 30, record March 25; 8% pfd., $2.00, April 1, record March 25.

Estivan Industrials, $2.50, Sept. 30, record Sept. 25.

Freelton Marine Co., 36 cents, June 29, record June 23; 7% pfd., $1.75, June 30, record June 25.

---

1. Grace owned 5000 shares of Alcorn on June 21.
Calculate the dividend.

2. Gary owned 300 shares of Bytown on March 26.
Determine the dividend receivable.

3. Lenore owned 300 shares of Dalberg at 8% preferred on March 27.
Determine the dividend receivable.

4. Jamie sold his 1600 shares of Freelton Marine common on June 23.
What dividend did he receive?

5. Daniel sold his 700 shares of Estivan Industrials on September 24.
What dividend can he expect?

6. On June 25, Monika owned 1000 shares of Freelton Marine common and 2000 shares of Freelton Marine at 7% preferred.
What was her total dividend?

12.7 YIELD RATE FOR STOCKS

If you want to compare two investments to determine which is the most profitable at current prices and dividend rates, you must calculate the yield rate for each investment and compare the rates.

The current value of a stock investment depends upon two things:

(i) the price per share of the stock, and
(ii) the dividend rate.

In section 12.3, the following formula was used to calculate the yield rate for bonds:

$$\text{Yield rate} = \frac{\text{dividend}}{\text{investment}} \times 100\%$$

To calculate the yield rate for a stock, we use a similar formula:

$$\text{Yield rate} = \frac{\text{dividend per share}}{\text{current price per share}} \times 100\%$$

Example 1. Find the yield rate for shares of the Copperhill Company if it pays a dividend of $15 per share per year.
The current price of a share of Copperhill is $240.

Solution: Yield rate $= \dfrac{15}{240} \times 100\%$

$= 6.25\%$

$E=mc^2$

The yield rate is 6.25%.

Example 2. The Boston Celtics declared a quarterly dividend of $0.20.
If the stock is currently trading at $12.50 per share, find the yield rate.

Solution: Annual dividend per share $= 4 \times \$0.20$

$= \$0.80$

Yield rate $= \dfrac{0.80}{12.50} \times 100\%$

$= 6.4\%$

The yield rate is 6.4%.

PRICE/EARNINGS RATIO

If you are considering buying a stock, or if you own stock, you are naturally interested in whether your company is making money. The price/earnings ratio compares the price of the stock to the earnings per share of the company.

Example 3. Computer Space Inc. with 1 000 000 shares outstanding earned $800 000 last year. The current price is $22 per share.
Find the price/earnings ratio.

Solution: Earnings per share $= \dfrac{\$800\ 000}{\$1\ 000\ 000}$

$ = \$0.80$

If the current market price of the shares is $22, then

$$\text{price/earnings ratio} = \dfrac{\$22}{\$0.80}$$

$$\phantom{\text{price/earnings ratio}} = 27.5$$

The price/earnings ratio is 27.5 : 1.

EXERCISE 12.7

B

1. The Boeing Company paid a dividend of $1.40 per share per year. The current price of a share is $40.
Calculate the yield rate.

2. The Heinz Company paid a dividend of $1.24 per share per year. The current price of a share is $43\frac{1}{2}$.
Calculate the yield rate to the nearest hundredth.

3. Find the yield rate from shares of Loews if a quarterly dividend of $0.25 was paid and the current price of one share is $71\frac{1}{8}$.

4. Constar has a current price of $80 per share. The company paid a dividend of $1.75 per year. Tricorp has a current price of $40 per share, and it paid a dividend of $0.88 per year.
Which company has the better yield rate?

5. The Everlast Company has 2 000 000 shares outstanding. The company earned $1 500 000 last year. The current price per share is $15.
Calculate the price/earnings ratio.

6. For each of the following stocks, calculate the price/earnings ratio to the nearest tenth.

	Stock	Price per share	Earnings per share
(a)	Harley	$13	$0.60
(b)	MMM	$66\frac{1}{2}$	$1.60
(c)	Dravo	$11\frac{3}{4}$	$0.45
(d)	RTE	$19\frac{5}{8}$	$2.10

7. Hammer Aerodynamics has 5 000 000 shares outstanding that have a current price of $20\frac{1}{2}$. The company earned $6 000 000 last year.
Calculate the price/earnings ratio.

12.8 ANNUAL REPORTS

When you own stock in a company, you receive an invitation to the annual general meeting and a copy of the company's annual report. The annual report is the means by which the company communicates its status. It is used to sell the company to the shareholders as a wise investment.

The contents of a typical annual report for a company, which we will call the National Transport and Communication Company, are given below.

CONTENTS
Directors and Officers
Directors' Report
Summary of Significant Accounting Policies
Statement of Consolidated Income
Statement of Consolidated Retained Income
Statement of Consolidated Source and Application of Funds
Consolidated Balance Sheet and Auditors' Report
Other Financial Information
Notes to Consolidated Financial Statements
Five-Year Summary

The National Transport and Communication Company has a net income for the year of almost $84 million. The Statement of Income shown below is a summary of the company's income. The current price per share is $32.00, up $3.00 from 1992.

Summarized Statement of Income			
(All figures in millions except amounts per share)	1993	1992	Increase or (Decrease)
Net income from:			
National Trucks	$23.6	$24.5	$(0.9)
National Ships	3.1	3.3	(0.2)
National Telecommunications	12.8	10.7	2.1
National Investments	33.1	30.9	2.2
Miscellaneous	5.2	4.8	0.4
Income before extraordinary items	77.8	74.2	3.6
Extraordinary items	6.1	3.1	3.0
Net Income	83.9	77.6	6.3
Dividend per Common share	0.55	0.50	0.05

The directors' report will explain in general, easily understood terms the activities of the company. An example of a directors' statement is given below.

"Two problems, inflation and energy, are on everyone's mind. They will have a profound effect on business decisions and activities. Vacillations and changes in the policies of governments on these two issues add to the difficulty of developing sound business policies.

The extraordinary income for the year came from the sale of your rail operations. With the liquidation of this non-profitable division of the company, our financial base is secure.

Growth is predicted for the Canadian economy in 1994. This expectation can be transferred to the predictions of National Transport and Communication.

The directors express appreciation for the skills and energy displayed by officers and employees and for their work and contributions to the company."

National Ships and National Investments are two of the subsections of the National Transport and Communication Company.

The annual report gives general information about the revenue and expenses of the company.

Statement of Consolidated Income		
(All figures in thousands)	1993	1992
National Trucks 　Revenue 　Expenses including taxes	$772 928 749 315	$711 208 686 685
Net Income	23 613	24 523
National Ships 　Revenue 　Expenses including taxes	64 128 61 004	52 893 49 566
Net Income	3 124	3 327
National Telecommunications 　Revenue 　Expenses including taxes	49 378 36 544	45 819 35 109
Net Income	12 834	10 710
National Investments 　Revenue 　Expenses including taxes	878 876 845 748	499 765 468 820
Net Income	33 128	30 945
Miscellaneous		
Net Income	5 233	4 858
Income from Extraordinary Items	117 834	74 237
Extraordinary items after income taxes	6 141	3 121
Net Income	83 926	77 611
Dividend per Common share	0.55	0.50

As can be seen from the revenue and expenses, we do not get the total picture of the activities of a company from the net income alone.

It is from the annual report that the shareholders learn of the health of the company, but they should read the report with care because it is used to sell the company.

If a person wishes to purchase stock in a company, they would be wise to obtain the last annual report and study it carefully.

EXERCISE 12.8

B

1. Obtain the annual reports of local companies for analysis.

2. What did the director of the National Transport and Communication Company cite as concerns for the future?
What is believed to aggravate these concerns?

3. Why is income before extraordinary income reported?
Why is the differentiation between ordinary and extraordinary incomes of importance to stockholders?

4. From the 1993 Annual Report of the National Transport and Communication Company, answer the following.
(a) What is the total revenue?
(b) What is the total expenditure including taxes?
(c) If a shareholder owns 1200 shares, what is the value of the shares in 1993?
(d) If a shareholder owns 1200 shares, what is the total dividend received in 1993?
(e) What is the yield of the stock in 1992?
(f) What is the yield of the stock in 1993?
(g) If the company has 20 000 000 outstanding shares, what is the price/earnings ratio in 1992?
(h) If the company has 20 000 000 outstanding shares, what is the price/earnings ratio in 1993?

(i) What is the most active subsection of the company with respect to generating revenue?
(j) What is the most profitable subsection of the company with respect to generating revenue?

5. From the 1993 Annual Report of the National Transport and Communication Company, answer the following.
(a) What percent of revenue are expenses for
  (i) National Trucks,
  (ii) National Ships,
  (iii) National Telecommunications,
  (iv) National Investments?
(b) What percent of revenue is net income for
  (i) National Trucks,
  (ii) National Ships,
  (iii) National Telecommunications,
  (iv) National Investments?

MIND BENDER

You have a 7 min sand timer and a 4 min sand timer.
How can you time exactly 9 min?

Using a computer and spreadsheet software, enter the values from the annual report for the Summarized Statement of Income and the Statement of Consolidated Income.

Link the values with formulas.

Speculate on changes to expenses, income, etc. to see the effect on the overall performance of the company.

12.9 INFLATION

"Money just doesn't go as far as it used to!"

This lament comes from an inflationary trend. During times of inflation, incomes and prices increase. A person has more money to spend, but everything costs more.

> Inflation is a rise in the general level of prices of consumer goods and a decline in the value of money.

As mentioned by the directors of the National Transport and Communication Company in section 12.8, inflation causes instability in the market-place and makes realistic planning difficult.

Example 1. Assume an annual inflation rate of 6%.
If you invest $100 at 9% per annum, what is the real return on your investment after one year?

Solution: After one year, the amount of money you have is $A = P(1 + rt)$, where $P = \$100$, $r = 0.09$, and $t = 1$ a.

$$A = P(1 + rt)$$
$$A = 100(1.09)$$
$$= \$109$$

$E=mc^2$

But during the year, money has decreased in buying power by 6%, or for each dollar the purchasing power has decreased $\$1 \times 0.06 = \$0.06$ or 6¢.

The $1 you had at the beginning of the year is now worth $\$1 - \$0.06 = \$0.94$ or 94¢.

Current Purchasing Power $= 109 \times 0.94$
$= 102.46$ (in previous year's dollars)

The real return on the investment is $2.46.

Example 2. A reforestation project has a harvest cycle of 76 a.
Assuming an annual inflation rate of 5%, what would be the value of the lumber when the new trees are ready for harvest?

Solution: For every $1 in current price, we have

Year 1	Year 2	Year 3	...	Year 76
$\$1(1 + 0.05)$	$\$1(1 + 0.05)^2$	$\$1(1 + 0.05)^3$		$\$1(1 + 0.05)^{76}$

or after 76 a, $1 would be worth $(1.05)^{76} = \$40.77$.

EXERCISE 12.9

B

1. Complete the following consumer price index table, assuming a 1988 dollar as the base.

	Year	Inflation Rate per year	Current Value of Goods	Value in 1988 Dollars
	1988	base	$1.00	$1.00
	1989	4.8%	$1.048	$0.952
(a)	1990	5%		
(b)	1991	4%		
(c)	1992	6%		
(d)	1993	4%		
(e)	1994	3.5%		
(f)	1995	6%		
(g)	1996	7%		
(h)	1997	4%		

2. What is the effect of inflation on people who are currently in the work force?

3. What is the effect of inflation on people who are on fixed incomes such as retired people earning a fixed pension?

4. A person received a pension of $500/month, indexed for inflation at 4%. What was the effect on the purchasing power of a dollar if actual inflation for the year was 7%?

5. A company has a fund that provides for the replacement of machinery.
If a particular piece of equipment costs $500 000, how much money will be necessary to replace the equipment in 25 a if we assume 8% inflation per year?

6. A union negotiated an annual increase in salary of 7%.
If a person earns $30 000/a, what is the real effect on the dollar value of the income if inflation in the same year is 10%?

7. The annual inflation rate is 5%.
If you invest $5000 at 8% per annum, what is the real return on your investment after 1 a?

MIND BENDER

After a baseball game, a group of friends ate at a restaurant. The total bill was $156. They agreed to split the bill equally. However, two of the friends had no money so the others paid an extra $2.60 each to cover the bill. How many people were in the group?

12.10 PROBLEM SOLVING

1. Twenty teams are entered in a basketball tournament. The teams are divided into four divisions, A, B, C, and D, with five teams in each division. Each team plays all of the teams in its division once to determine a division winner. Then the four division winners play each other until they are eliminated.
If there are no ties, how many games are necessary to declare a tournament winner?

2. What do the numbers 20/20 mean on a vision test?

3. The year is not a leap year. There are 100 more days left in the year than have gone by.
What is the date?

4. Place the numbers from 1 to 7 in the circles so that each row adds to the same number.

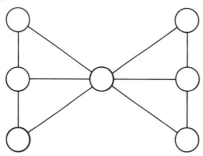

5. Black Monday occurred on October 19, 1987. On that day the stock market crashed for the second time. In the United States, the "on paper" loss was $600 billion during one trading day.
(a) On the average, what was the loss in dollars per minute that the market was open for trading?
(b) If 4% of the population of the United States invests in the stock market, what was the average loss per investor?
(c) How many points did the Dow Jones drop on October 19, 1987?
(d) How many points did the Toronto Stock Exchange drop?

6. The number 76 is called an automorphic number because 76 appears at the end of the square of 76.

$$76^2 = 5776$$

What is the first automorphic number greater than 10?

7. If it is 13:30 in Vancouver, what time is it in Paris, France?

8. A room measures 5.6 m by 4.2 m. Square floor tiles measure 10 cm by 10 cm. How many tiles will be needed to cover the floor?

9. Which is heaviest, a million dollars in gold, a million dollars in $1 dollar bills, or a million dollars in silver?

10. How many ways can you make change for a fifty-cent piece without using any pennies?

11. The numbers in the large squares are found by adding the numbers in the small squares.

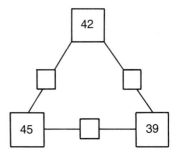

Find the numbers in the small squares.

12. When the train arrived at Walker Station, 16 people got on and 12 people got off. At Ulster Station, 20 people got on and 26 got off. At Trammel Station, 34 people got on and 14 people got off. When the train left Trammel Station there were 163 people on it.
How many people were on the train when it arrived at Walker Station?

13. Cut a penny-sized hole in a piece of paper.
Fold the paper so that you can get a quarter through the hole without tearing the paper.

14. The diagram below shows a large square, ABCD, with lines drawn from each vertex to the midpoint of one of the sides.

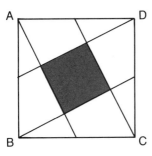

What fraction of the large square is the small square?

15. How many ways can you arrange 25 students into three groups so that there is an odd number of students in each group?

16. If you multiply a number by 52, and then add 12 you get 1104.
What is the number?

17. What is the next year that you will be able to use this year's calendar?

18. How many different ways can four books be arranged on a shelf?

19. How many ways can you write the number 57 as the sum of consecutive whole numbers?

CAREER

SECURITIES COUNSELLOR

As a securities counsellor, Michele Wong provides financial counselling services to bank, trust, and brokerage company officials and their customers regarding the purchase and sale of securities. She analyses the financial backgrounds and the future trends of stocks and bonds to make recommendations regarding investments. Other tasks include transmitting "buy" and "sell" orders to the trading desks and calculating accounts and commissions for billing. Michele also provides direction for a team of clerks who process security transactions and prepare periodic reports and returns on security transactions.

EXERCISE

1. Calculate the cost of 200 units of Roy Industrial, a mutual fund selling at $19.17 per unit, including commission.

2. Calculate the cost to the customer of 250 units of American Growth Real Estate, a mutual fund selling at $24.65. Commission is 9%.

12.11 REVIEW EXERCISE

1. You own 1000 shares of a company that has issued a total of 3 000 000 shares. The company has a net worth of $500 000 when it is dissolved.
What is the value of your shares?

2. The Northstar Company declares a dividend of $2.75 per share. There are 2 000 000 shares in the hands of shareholders.
(a) How much money will the company pay out in dividends?
(b) How much money will a shareholder with 4500 shares receive?
(c) If this is an annual dividend and the shares have a market value of $40, what is the rate of return on this investment?

3. The South Side Company declares $3 600 000 in dividends. There are 2 000 000 shares in the hands of shareholders.
(a) What is the dividend per share?
(b) What dividend will a shareholder with 2000 shares receive?
(c) The dividend is a semi-annual one. Each share has a market value of $50. What annual rate of return does this dividend represent?

4. A $10 000, 10% bond bears quarterly coupons.
(a) What is the value of each coupon when due?
(b) How much will the owner of the bond receive on the date of the last coupon?

5. What is the price of a $1000 bond sold at 92?

6. Find the price of a $5000, 8% Government of Canada bond bought through a bank at the ask price of $86\frac{1}{2}$ on November 15.
The last coupon date was May 1.

7. What is the price of a $1000 bond sold at $94\frac{1}{2}$?

8. Find the approximate yield of an 8% bond selling at 91 and maturing in ten years.

9. Find the yield rate of an 11% bond selling at 102.5 and maturing in twelve years.

10. Find the yield rate of a $5\frac{1}{4}$% bond selling at 77.5 and maturing in nine years.

11. Find the yield rate of a $10\frac{1}{2}$% bond selling at 103 and maturing in seven years.

12. Find the price of a $100, 6% bond bearing semi-annual coupons and maturing in twelve years, if it is to yield 10% compounded semi-annually.

13. Find the price of a 7% bond bearing semi-annual coupons if it matures in eleven years to yield 9% per annum compounded semi-annually.

14. Find the price of a 10% bond bearing semi-annual coupons if it matures in eight years to yield 9% per annum compounded semi-annually.

15. Find the cost to purchase 500 shares of Devon Inc. at $11.33 per share.

16. Find the cost to purchase 800 shares of The Freeboard Company at $22.35 per share.

17. Find the cost to purchase 5000 shares of Acron-Brown at $43.75 per share.

18. Find the net proceeds to the seller of 700 shares of Romflex at $21.80 per share.

19. Find the net proceeds to the seller of 5000 shares of The Greenton Company at $56.77 per share.

20. An investor bought 900 shares of Hayes at $9\frac{1}{8}$ and sold it at $8\frac{5}{8}$.
Calculate the net profit or loss after these transactions.

21. An investor bought 1500 shares of Dofasco at $26\frac{1}{2}$ and sold it at $26\frac{7}{8}$. Calculate the net profit or loss after these transactions.

22. Use the dividend chart to answer the questions.

DIVIDENDS

Corporation dividends quarterly unless otherwise noted.

Natisco Company, 42 cents, March 30, record March 20.

Franklin Power Corp., 56 cents, June 30, record June 19; 9% pfd., $2.25, April 2, record March 25.

Northways Resources, 78 cents, Sept. 30, record Sept. 21; 8% pfd., $2.00, Oct. 1, record Sept. 25.

(a) Frank owned 5000 shares of Natisco on March 25.
Calculate his dividend.
(b) On September 26, Colleen owned 700 shares of Northways common and 1000 shares of Northways 8% pfd.
Calculate her dividend.
(c) On March 15, Robert bought 1000 shares of Natisco and 300 shares of Franklin Power 9% pfd.
What were his total dividends for the year?
(d) On August 15, Jan bought 2000 shares of Northways common at $3\frac{1}{2}$ per share.
She sold them on October 25 at $3\frac{7}{8}$ per share.
Include the net proceeds, commissions, and dividend to determine what her profit or loss was.

(e) On February 14, Carl bought 900 shares of Natisco common at $21\frac{1}{4}$ per share. On June 11, he bought 1000 shares of Franklin Power common at $10\frac{3}{8}$ per share. Carl sold his Natisco shares and Franklin Power shares on September 30. He got $22\frac{1}{2}$ per share for his Natisco shares and $9\frac{7}{8}$ per share for his Franklin Power shares.
Include the dividends and calculate his total profit or loss on these transactions.

23. Find the yield rate from shares of the Goodran Company if it pays a dividend of $5.60 per share and the current price of a share is $80\frac{1}{2}$.

24. The Dakota Mining Company has 20 000 000 shares outstanding. The company earned $400 000 000 last year.
The current price is $20\frac{1}{2}$ per share.

Calculate the price/earnings ratio.

25. A college trust fund has been established to provide maintenance for the school buildings. The fund pays $100 000/a and is indexed for inflation at 5%.
What is the effect on the purchasing power of the fund if the inflation rate for the year is 7%?

12.12 CHAPTER 12 TEST

1. The Brunswick Company declared a dividend of $5.75 per share. There are 1 000 000 shares in the hands of shareholders.
(a) How much money will the company pay out in dividends?
(b) If this is an annual dividend and the shares have a market value of $56, what is the rate of return on this investment?

2. What is the price of a $1000 bond sold at 95?

3. Find the approximate yield of a 7% bond selling at 94 and maturing in nine years.

4. Find the yield rate of a 12% bond selling at 104 and maturing in twelve years.

5. Find the price of a 10% bond bearing semi-annual coupons if it matures in nine years to yield 8% compounded semi-annually.

6. Find the cost to purchase 400 shares of Hillcrest Mines at $35 per share.

7. Find the cost to purchase 800 shares of Southwind Electronics at $18 per share.

8. Find the yield rate from shares of the Foxcroft Company if it pays a yearly dividend of $2.50 per share and the current price of a share is $47.

9. Actutron Industrials has 5 000 000 shares outstanding. Last year the company earned $20 000 000. The current price of a share of Actutron is $55.
Calculate the price/earnings ratio.

PERSONAL FINANCE

13

REVIEW AND PREVIEW TO CHAPTER

CALCULATING

EXERCISE 1

1. Add.

(a)　　$1123.67
　　　　23.89
　　　456.78
　+　　78.90

(b)　　$129.89
　　　345.89
　　　　67.89
　+　457.90

(c)　　$845.70
　　　259.78
　　　456.21
　+　567.89

(d)　　$3456.89
　　　1029.48
　　　878.50
　+　5898.45

2. Subtract.

(a)　　$123.89
　−　107.45

(b)　　$728.12
　−　457.89

(c)　　$995.13
　−　789.45

(d)　　$5123.75
　−　3489.98

3. Multiply.
(Answer to the nearest cent.)

(a)　　$567.23
　×　10.78

(b)　　$57.98
　×　12.48

(c)　　$678.13
　×　0.07

(d)　　$1246.89
　×　0.0987

4. Divide.
(Answer to the nearest cent.)

(a) $\dfrac{\$1247.90}{0.078}$

(b) $\dfrac{\$57.98}{0.89}$

(c) $\dfrac{\$678.13}{1.12}$

(d) $\dfrac{\$1246.89}{0.075}$

5. State each as a percent.
(Answer to the nearest tenth.)

(a) $\dfrac{\$787.12}{\$1234.89}$

(b) $\dfrac{\$17.98}{\$459.98}$

(c) $\dfrac{\$171.83}{\$183.23}$

(d) $\dfrac{\$1246.89}{\$567.89}$

6. Calculate.
(a) $45.89 + $34.89 − $123.45
(b) $12.89 − $45.83 + $123.84
(c) $123.48 + $234.89 − $322.89
(d) $1238.90 − $457.89 − $234.85

7. Calculate.
(Answer to the nearest cent.)
(a) 6% of $123.45
(b) 9% of $34.20
(c) $8\frac{3}{4}$% of $98.45
(d) 12% of $1238.78
(e) 103% of $328.93
(f) 27.3% of $234.89
(g) 223% of $18 893.45
(h) 0.8% of $2346.87

CALCULATOR REVIEW

EXERCISE 2

1. Perform the following calculations.
(a) $9200(1.0935)^{10}$
(b) $1600(1.1275)^{12}$
(c) $44\ 900(1.1125)^{7}$
(d) $55\ 700(1.135)^{6}$
(e) $66\ 900(1.0635)^{8}$
(f) $7300 \times \dfrac{1}{(1.125)^{4}}$
(g) $1575 \times \dfrac{1}{(1.0675)^{6}}$
(h) $7760 \times \dfrac{1}{(1.095)^{8}}$
(i) $8150 \times \dfrac{1}{(1.1275)^{6}}$
(j) $2136 \times \dfrac{1}{(1.085)^{7}}$
(k) $5650 \times \dfrac{1}{(1.1175)^{10}}$

SIMPLE INTEREST FORMULAS

Interest = Principal × Rate × Time

   I = Prt

Amount = Principal + Interest

   A = P + I
   A = P + Prt
   A = P(1 + rt)

Cover the one you want to find.

EXERCISE 3

1. What is the interest and the amount for the following?
(a) principal of $55 000 at 12% per annum for 6 months
(b) principal of $789 at $9\frac{1}{2}$% per annum for 18 months
(c) principal of $1238 at 7% per annum for 48 months
(d) principal of $234.89 at 10% per annum for 36 months

2. What is the principal and the amount for the following?
(a) interest of $24.50 at 8% per annum for 0.25 of a year
(b) interest of $4.80 at 16% per annum for 0.125 of a year

3. What is the interest and the principal for the following?
(a) rate of 12% per annum for 0.126 of a year gives an amount of $24.97
(b) rate of 9% per annum for 0.751 of a year gives an amount of $2028.42

4. What is the time and the amount for the following?
(a) interest of $1179.50, principal $50 000 at 7% per annum
(b) interest of $2.87, principal $350 at 10% per annum

5. What is the interest and the amount for the following?
(a) a principal of $30 000 is invested for 6 months at 10.5% per annum, and then the amount is invested at 12% per annum for an additional 6 months
(b) a principal of $120 000 is invested at 12% per annum for 30 d; this amount is then invested at 18% per annum for the next 60 d; the new amount is then invested at 24% per annum for the next 90 d
(c) a principal of $10 000 is invested for 3 a at 8.5% per annum, simple interest, and the amount is invested for an additional two years at 10% per annum
(d) a principal of $25 000 is invested at 9.25% per annum, simple interest; after 6 months, the rate increases to 12% and the amount is reinvested for the next 18 months

6. (a) A principal of $10 000 is invested for 122 d at 15% per annum simple interest.
What is the amount?
(b) An amount of $10 000 results from an investment for 122 d at 15% per annum, simple interest.
What is the principal?

13.1 CALCULATING INCOME

An individual who earns an average of $40 000/a will earn $1 000 000 over 25 a. Managing such a sum of money should be done with care and with financial planning. This money will be used for the necessities of life and some luxuries and for savings and investment. It is important to receive the greatest benefit from this income. The way to ensure the greatest benefit is through smart money management.

GROSS INCOME

Gross income is the amount of money that is paid before deductions. Income tax, unemployment insurance, medical insurance, and pension plans are examples of deductions, and they are subtracted from gross pay. After the deductions are made, the take-home portion is called the net earnings, or take-home pay. Income can be earned in several ways. The following are some of the methods of calculating earned income.

Calculating Gross Income
Income based on yearly salary, which may be paid weekly, bi-weekly, monthly, or quarterly.
Income based on hourly rate, which is calculated as follows: (Number of hours worked) × (Hourly rate of pay)
Income based on straight commission, which is calculated as follows: (Value of sales/service) × (Rate of commission)
Income based on salary plus commission, which is calculated as follows: (Salary) + (Value of sales/service) × (Rate of commission)
Income based on graduated commission, which is calculated as follows: (Initial value of sales/service) × (Initial rate of commission) + (Second value of sales/service) × (Second rate of commission) + ... + (nth value of sales/service) × (nth rate of commission)
Income based on piecework, which is calculated as follows: (Number of pieces completed) × (Rate per piece)

Example 1. Claudette has the option of taking a job at an annual salary of $28 000 or working a 40 h week, 52 weeks per year for $13.75/h.

    (a) Calculate the weekly pay for each option.

    (b) Which option gives Claudette the greater gross income?

Solution: (a) At the annual salary,

$$\text{Weekly pay} = \$28\,000 \div 52$$
$$\doteq \$538.46$$

At the annual salary, the weekly pay is $538.46.

At the hourly rate,
$$\text{Weekly pay} = 40 \times \$13.75$$
$$= \$550.00$$

At the hourly rate, the weekly pay is $550.00.

    (b) The hourly rate of pay gives Claudette the greater gross income.

Example 2. Three salespeople work part-time for a company. The first is paid a straight commission of 25% of total sales per week. The second is paid a weekly salary of $200 plus a commission of 15% of total sales. The third is paid a graduated commission of 20% on sales up to $1000, 25% on the next $500 or part, and 30% on sales over $1500.
Calculate the gross weekly income for each salesperson if they all had sales of $1750.

Solution:

First salesperson's weekly income $= \$1750 \times 0.25$
$$= \$437.50$$

Second salesperson's weekly income $= \$200 + (\$1750 \times 0.15)$
$$= \$200 + \$262.50$$
$$= \$462.50$$

Third salesperson's weekly income
$$= \$1000 \times 0.2 + \$500 \times 0.25 + \$250 \times 0.3$$
$$= \$200 + \$125 + \$75$$
$$= \$400$$

The gross weekly incomes are $437.50, $462.50, and $400.

Example 3. What is the gross weekly income for an automobile cleaner who earns $22 per car if the person cleans six cars each day for a five-day week?

Solution: Weekly pay = $22 × 6 × 5
= $660

The weekly pay is $660.

EXERCISE 13.1

B

1. Henry Fong works for a computer company earning $12.80/h.
What is his bi-weekly (once every two weeks) pay for a 37 h week?

2. Mabel Carson earns a straight commission of 5% of sales as an automobile salesperson.
What is her gross pay for the week if she sold two cars, one for $11 892 and the other for $27 109?

3. Hania earns $2289 every two weeks.

What are her

(a) gross yearly earnings?
(b) gross weekly earnings?
(c) gross daily earnings, based on a five-day week?
(d) gross hourly earnings, based on a 40 h week?

4. Complete the table below given that the employer pays time and a half for overtime hours.

Gross Earnings			
Hourly Rate	Number of Regular Hours	Number of Overtime Hours	Gross Weekly Pay
$16.75	30	11	
$9.88	35	15	
$12.90	37.5	12	
$17.12	37.5	10.5	

5. Complete the table below for straight commission.

Gross Earnings		
Rate of Commission	Total Monthly Sales	Gross Monthly Earnings
17%	$1789	
2.5%	$122 893	
34%	$2765	
6%	$35 892	

6. Aziz has the option of taking a job at a weekly salary of $575 or working a 40 h week, 52 weeks a year at $13.90/h as a computer operator.

(a) Calculate his gross pay for one week for each option.
(b) Which option gives Aziz the greater gross income?

(c) What is the yearly gross pay at the greater rate in (b)?

7. The Surefire Advertising Company has three plans for paying its salespeople. Plan A pays $750/month plus 15% commission on total sales for the month. Plan B pays a graduated commission of 20% on the first $5000 of sales, 25% on the next $5000 of sales or part, and 30% on sales over $10 000. Plan C pays a straight commission of 25% of total sales per month.
(a) Calculate the gross monthly income on sales of $12 500 using each of the three plans.
(b) Construct a line graph for sales up to $15 000 for one month, using each of the following on the same axes.
  (i) payment under Plan A
  (ii) payment under Plan B
  (iii) payment under Plan C
(c) At what value in sales does Plan B begin to pay the highest gross income?

8. A salesperson in a video store earns a graduated commission of 12% on the first $3000 of sales, 15% on the next $2000 of sales, and 19% on all other sales. In December, the person sells $9850 worth of products and services.

What is the gross monthly income if in addition to the regular commission, the manager includes a 2% bonus on total sales?

9. Helen works on the basis of salary plus commission. She earns $8.85/h selling cameras in a photography store plus 15% commission on total sales. Her time-card is shown below, and she is paid for each hour worked, to a 15 min interval. Helen's total sales for the week were $2118.

NAME _____ #_____			
WEEK ENDING May 2 _____			
DAY	IN	OUT	HOURS
MON			
TUE	12:27	18:33	
WED	12:25	17:32	
THU	12:20	16:33	
FRI	12:25	19:30	
SAT	12:23	19:45	
SUN			
TOTAL HOUR WAGE		TOTAL RATE	8.85
TOTAL COMMISSION			
TOTAL GROSS WAGE			

Calculate her gross earnings for the week.

10. A job offer to key legal documents at a law firm is made at a rate of $2.15 per page. Over a few weeks, the average is 123 pages per week for several different lawyers. One lawyer offers a job at $345 per week.
(a) What is the difference in the gross income that is earned now and what would be paid?
(b) What are the advantages and disadvantages of each method of earning income?

13.2 NET EARNINGS

When a person earns income, certain deductions are made at the source — where the person works. The amount of pay that remains after these deductions are made is called the net earnings.

> Net earnings = gross income − deductions

Some examples of deductions made by the employer at the source include income tax, pension plan, unemployment insurance premiums, medical insurance premiums, and union dues.

INCOME TAX DEDUCTIONS

The largest deduction from gross pay is usually income tax. Each person who works and earns above a minimum income level is obliged to pay income tax.

The amount of income tax deducted depends primarily on the level of income and the number of dependants that a person has. The relationship among income, number of dependants, and amount of tax to be deducted is presented elsewhere in this book. As a general rule, the amount of income tax deducted can be estimated according to the following table of income levels with the assumption that the person is single with no dependants.

Total Yearly Income	Tax Deducted (%)
$0 to $5000	0%
$5000 to $10 000	12%
$10 000 to $15 000	16%
$15 000 to $20 000	18%
$20 000 to $25 000	20%
$25 000 to $30 000	23%
$30 000 to $40 000	28%
$40 000 and over	35%

Note: These estimates are for use in this section. The actual rates are subject to change from year to year.

GOVERNMENT DEDUCTIONS

Deductions that are required by the government to be taken from your gross income by your employer include:
• Canada Pension Plan contributions
• Unemployment Insurance premiums
• medical insurance premiums

The Canada Pension Plan contribution (C.P.P.) is determined by level of income and is like a savings plan with a guaranteed pay when the person retires. The appropriate amount of the contribution is deducted by the employer and paid to the federal government on the employee's behalf.

The Unemployment Insurance premium (U.I.) is deducted so that the employee will have a guaranteed income if the job is lost. As with the C.P.P. contribution, the U.I. premium is deducted by the employer and paid to the federal government on behalf of the employee.

Medical insurance is mandatory in most provinces. In a family with two or more income earners, only one income earner is usually required to pay the medical insurance premiums on behalf of all family members who qualify.

In this chapter we will use the following rates to calculate the deductions.

C.P.P.   2% of gross income
to a maximum of $25/week

U.I.   0.8% of gross income
to a maximum of $10/week

Example. Julius works as a licensed auto mechanic, making $27/h based on a 40 h week, 52 weeks per year. If C.P.P. is deducted at a rate of 2% of gross income, and U.I. is deducted at a rate of 0.8%, what is his estimated weekly net income?

Solution:
Weekly income = 40 × $27 = $1080 gross pay per week
Yearly income = $1080 × 52 = $56 160
From the tables in this section, income tax for this individual is deducted at approximately 35% of gross income.

Income tax deducted = $1080 × 0.35
= $378.00

C.P.P. deducted = $1080 × 0.02
= $21.60

U.I. deducted = $1080 × 0.008
= $8.64

Total deductions = $378.00 + $21.60 + $8.64
= $408.24

Net income = $1080.00 − $408.24
= $671.76

His estimated weekly income is $671.76.

EMPLOYER DEDUCTIONS

The following deductions may be required as a condition of employment:
• Company Pension Plan (private)
• Life Insurance
• Union Dues

In many cases the employer will pay all or part of a premium as an employee benefit — a reward for working for that particular company. The private pension plan premiums that are paid by the employee are tax deductible up to the maximum allowed by the government. The rates for an insurance plan that is a condition of employment may be lower than conventional rates because the insurance company is guaranteed a fixed number of people to enrol in each plan.

Union or professional dues are often required to be paid before a person can work at a particular trade or profession.

EMPLOYEE DEDUCTIONS

The following types of deductions are usually optional and at the discretion of the employee and may be paid by direct payroll deduction:
• Long Term Disability Insurance
• Supplementary Life Insurance
• Extended Medical Insurance
• Dental Insurance
• Savings Plans and Savings Bonds
• Charitable Donations

Because insurance plans may be purchased by a group of employees, rates are usually lower. A portion of the premium for insurance plans may be paid for by the employer.

Savings plans and charitable donations are controlled by the employee. The employer provides a convenient method for making the donation or deposit to a savings plan.

EXERCISE 13.2

B

1. Complete the table below by stating the estimated level of tax to be deducted, the amount of tax deducted from gross pay, and the income after taxes are deducted. Round calculations to the nearest cent.

Gross Income	Tax Deducted (%)	Amount Deducted	Pay After Taxes
$4786.00			
$9895.56			
$23 407.00			
$54 893.00			

2. A person works for an annual income of $27 897. C.P.P. contributions are 2% of gross income and U.I. premiums are 0.8% of gross income.
What is the net income after these deductions and the income tax deduction?

3. A salaried employee at the botanical gardens receives a weekly gross income of $735.
What is the weekly income after a tax deduction of 28%?

4. A salesperson in a computer store works on a straight commission of 12% of total sales per month. The sales for the month are $18 892.
What is the estimated take-home pay after taxes are deducted if these monthly earnings are taken as an average over the year?

5. A public relations consultant works at a rate of $320/d. The consultant works a total of 212 d in the year.
(a) What is the gross yearly wage?
(b) What is the net yearly wage after income tax, Canada Pension Plan contributions at a rate of 2%, and Unemployment Insurance premiums at a rate of 0.8% are deducted?

6. If the Unemployment Insurance premium has a maximum contribution in any one tax year of $512.03, what is the maximum U.I. premium as a percent of the gross incomes given below to the nearest tenth of a percent?
(a) $28 876
(b) $56 789
(c) $33 129
(d) $12 678

7. If the Canada Pension Plan has a maximum contribution in any one tax year of $1350, what is the maximum C.P.P. contribution as a percent of the gross incomes given below to the nearest tenth of a percent?
(a) $45 893
(b) $33 897
(c) $78 890
(d) $29 289

8. Joy McLean works at Eastern Plumbing and Heating. Joy's gross income is $62 250.
(a) Calculate the following government deductions of income tax at the rate in the table, $15.20 per month as the employee portion of the medical plan premiums, C.P.P. at 2% to a maximum of $1350, and U.I. at 0.8% to a maximum of $512.03.
(b) Calculate the following employer deductions of a company pension plan at 4% to a maximum of $2000, life insurance at $1.50 per thousand dollars of salary, and union dues of $42 per month.
(c) Calculate the total of the following employee deductions: supplementary life insurance at $0.50 per thousand dollars of gross income, and extended medical coverage of $2.75 per month.
(d) Calculate the net earnings after the above deductions have been made.

13.3 DISPOSABLE INCOME

When you receive a pay cheque, you are receiving your net income. The net income that is available for spending is also called disposable income. This income is to be spent on necessities as well as for those things that improve the quality of life. Money should also be saved for future security or for major purchases.

NON-DISCRETIONARY SPENDING

Money that is spent for the necessities of life is called non-discretionary spending. The following is a list of non-discretionary expenses:

Housing
   Rent or Mortgage payment
   Utilities (heat, light, water)
   Insurance
   Property Taxes
Food
   Cost
   Preparation
Transportation
   Car Payment
   Insurance
   Gasoline/Oil
   Maintenance
Clothing
   Cost
   Laundry and Cleaning
Medical
   Insurance
   Medicine (supplies)

Although these are considered to be necessities, the lifestyle that a person chooses and the income level determine the type of housing, transportation, clothing, and food purchased.

Example 1. A family of four with an annual gross income of $58 500 makes mortgage payments of $900/month and pays property taxes of $1800/a. Heating costs $78/month over 10 months, electricity costs $86 paid bi-monthly (every two months), and water costs $76 paid tri-monthly (every three months). The home-owners' insurance premiums are $179 every 6 months. What percentage of its gross income does the family spend on housing?

Solution:
Calculate all expenses on a yearly basis.

Yearly mortgage payments = $900 × 12
                                           = $10 800

Yearly property taxes = $1800

Heat for the year = $78 × 10
                                = $780

Electricity for the year = $86 × 6
                                    = $516

Water for the year = $67 × 4
                            = $268

Insurance for the year = $179 × 2
                                  = $358

Housing costs = $10 800 + $1800 + $780 + $516 + $268 + $358
                      = $14 522

As a percentage of gross income $= \dfrac{14\ 522}{58\ 500}$
$\doteq 0.248$

The family spends approximately 25% of its gross income for housing.

DISCRETIONARY SPENDING

The money that you earn should cover more than the necessities. There are other expenses that enhance the quality of life. The amount that is available to spend on these items depends on the level of income. Some of these expenses are to help provide for a better future; others are to make the present more enjoyable.

Future Planning
    Savings
    Education
Present
    Recreation
    Entertainment

Example 2. A family has decided that it will save at the same level as it spends for entertainment. The gross income is $67 380, and the total deductions per month are $2122.47. The family plans to spend $230/month on entertainment. What percentage of
(a) the gross income, and
(b) the net income
is the total expenditure for savings per year?

Solution:

The gross family income = $67 380

$$\begin{aligned} \text{The net family income} &= \$67\ 380 - 12 \times \$2122.47 \\ &= \$67\ 380 - \$25\ 469.64 \\ &= \$41\ 910.36 \end{aligned}$$

$$\begin{aligned} \text{Amount per year for entertainment} &= 12 \times \$230 \\ &= \$2760 \end{aligned}$$

Amount per year for savings = $2760

(a) Percent of yearly savings to gross income = $\dfrac{2760}{67\ 380}$

$$\doteq 0.041$$
$$= 4.1\%$$

The family should save 4.1% of its gross income.

(b) Percent of yearly savings to net income = $\dfrac{2760}{41\ 910.36}$

$$\doteq 0.066$$
$$= 6.6\%$$

The family should save 6.6% of its net income.

Example 3. A two-income family has gross incomes of $39 000/a and $33 000/a. It spends 25% of its income on housing, 10% on food, 10% on transportation, 12% on clothing, and 7% on medical.
What percentage of its gross income is non-discretionary, and what percentage is discretionary?

Solution:

Food, clothing, transportation, medical, and housing are all non-discretionary.

$$\begin{aligned} \text{Percent non-discretionary} &= 25\% + 10\% + 10\% + 12\% + 7\% \\ &= 64\% \end{aligned}$$

$$\begin{aligned} \text{Percent discretionary} &= 100\% - 64\% \\ &= 36\% \end{aligned}$$

∴ 64% of its gross income is non-discretionary and 36% is discretionary.

The following list provides some estimates for spending disposable income.

Non-discretionary		Discretionary	
Housing	20%–30%	Recreation and	
Food	15%–25%	Entertainment	5%–7%
Transportation	10%–20%	Savings and	
Clothing	8%–12%	Education	5%–7%
Medical	7%–10%		

EXERCISE 13.3

A 1. What is discretionary about non-discretionary spending?

2. Explain how choice of lifestyle is tied to income level.

B 3. In the table below, determine what percentage of the gross income the housing costs are.

Gross Yearly Income	Monthly Housing Costs	Percentage of Gross Income
$42 789	$1050	
$44 892	$1200	
$54 183	$1500	
$65 129	$1400	

4. It is recommended by many home economists that housing should cost in the range of 20% to 30% of gross income. Which of the housing costs and incomes in question 3 fall within this range?

5. If you want to move into an apartment with rent of $1054/month including utilities, what range of gross income should you have to support this level of housing?

6. A family has two incomes consisting of $475/week and $689/week. It is recommended that no more than 20% of its gross is spent on food.

(a) If the family spends $150/week on food, is it within the recommendation?

(b) What percentage of its gross income does the family spend on food?

7. A person has a gross income of $34 840/a. It is recommended that no more than 20% of gross income be spent on transportation. The person's car payments are $310/month, gasoline costs $100/month, maintenance costs $897/a, and liability insurance costs $986/a. Is this person within the 20% recommendation?

8. Two households have gross incomes of $42 094/a and $63 923/a respectively. They both have identical apartments in the same building and pay $1497/month for rent, including utilities.

(a) What percentage of gross income does each spend on housing?

(b) What conclusions can be drawn about the householders' choices of housing?

9. Two households have gross incomes of $36 897/a and $56 789/a respectively. The rent, including utilities, for each is $1200/month.

(a) What percentage of gross income does each spend on housing?

(b) What conclusions can be drawn about the householders' choices of housing?

13.4 BUDGETING

The level of spending, discretionary and non-discretionary, is determined by several factors. Although housing, food, and transportation are necessities, the amount of money you decide to spend on these items depends on your income and the importance you place on each. One person may see transportation as just a means to get from one place to another and will find the least costly means, usually public transportation. Another may prefer convenience and will purchase a very modest car. Still another may want luxury and will purchase a more expensive automobile.

Each person must make decisions based not only on income level but also on lifestyle preferred. In this way, a person's spending habits are determined by income level, tastes, and preferences.

It is important that each person determine his/her spending priorities and understand what he/she can and cannot afford. This is accomplished by making a spending plan called a budget.

CASH FLOW

The first step in building a budget is to understand the current cash flow, or how much money is coming in in the form of income and going out in the form of expenditures. When the expenditures exceed the income, we say that the person is in a position of negative cash flow. In order to have a clear picture of the cash flow, it is necessary to keep track of expenditures over a period of several months.

> Cash flow = net income − expenditures

A Cash Flow table is shown on the next page. The table gives information about three months of actual income and expenditures. This is the first stage in preparing a financial plan — in order to plan what you want to do, you must first examine what you have done. In the expenditures section, the table also shows the percentage that each expenditure is of the net income.

Cash Flow	Month 1		Month 2		Month 3	
Income	January		February		March	
Take-home Pay (Net Income)	$1823.48		$1823.48		$1912.23	
Interest and Dividends	$55.50		$50.89		$102.30	
Miscellaneous Income	$0.00		$275.00		$0.00	
Total Income	$1878.98		$2149.37		$2014.53	
Expenditures	January	%	February	%	March	%
Rent/Mortgage Payment	$645.50	34.4	$645.50	30.0	$645.50	32.0
Utilities	$75.75	4.0	$23.40	1.1	$80.89	4.0
Food	$378.54	20.1	$445.23	20.7	$402.40	20.0
Transportation	$302.40	16.1	$328.12	15.3	$298.45	14.8
Insurance — Home	$235.00	12.5	$0.00	0.0	$0.00	0.0
Insurance — Life	$65.00	3.5	$67.00	3.1	$67.00	3.3
Insurance — Car	$0.00	0.0	$215.00	10.0	$0.00	0.0
Clothing	$75.00	4.0	$112.00	5.2	$32.00	1.6
Credit Card Payments	$55.00	2.9	$55.00	2.6	$60.00	3.0
Loan Payments	$120.00	6.4	$120.00	5.6	$120.00	6.0
Medical/Dental	$0.00	0.0	$35.00	1.6	$0.00	0.0
Miscellaneous and Unexpected	$76.00	4.0	$120.56	5.6	$98.75	4.9
Total Expenditures	$2028.19	107.9	$2166.87	100.8	$1804.99	89.6

From the three-month Cash Flow table shown, we can calculate the amount of income over expenses as a positive or negative value for each month as in the following summary:

Income greater (+)					$209.54	10.4
Spending greater (−)	$149.21	7.9	$17.50	0.8		

From this information, we see that the person was in a position of negative cash flow for two of the three months, where the expenditures were greater than the income. This pattern indicates that it was necessary for the person to use savings to make up the short-fall. It also indicates that discretionary spending should be reconsidered, as well as the level of non-discretionary spending.

The percentage of each expenditure to income is also important information when preparing a budget. The budget should reflect the same or adjusted percentages as indicated by the monthly cash flow.

BUDGET

Once the cash flow is understood, the discretionary and non-discretionary spending can be adjusted, and a realistic monthly budget, or plan, can be prepared.

A form for a Monthly Money Plan/Budget is given below.

Monthly Money Plan/Budget			
Income	Planned	Actual	+ or (−)
Take-home Pay (Net Income)			
Other Income			
Total Income			
Expenditures	Planned	Actual	+ or (−)
Non-discretionary, fixed amount			
Non-discretionary, varying amounts			
Discretionary, varying amounts			
Contingency (Unexpected Expenditure)			
	Planned	Actual	Savings (+/−)
Totals			

To complete the Monthly Money Plan/Budget, follow these steps:

Step 1. Estimate your expenses based on the financial realities as indicated by the cash flow. Remember to include all of your discretionary and non-discretionary amounts. The percentages calculated in the cash flow of each actual expense to total income can be a guide to your plan. As a general rule, the following percentages are recommended:

Housing	20%–30% of net income
Food	15%–25% of net income
Transportation	10%–20% of net income
Clothing	8%–12% of net income
Personal and Medical	7%–10% of net income

Step 2. Estimate a contingency. A contingency is an amount of money that you estimate you may need each month for unexpected expenses. It can be thought of as savings and should be deposited each month in a savings account. If the money is not needed, that is, if income exceeds expenses, then the money remains as savings. If the amount is required, it can be withdrawn from the account.

Step 3. At the end of each month, calculate the actual amounts and the difference, + or −. Make sure you account for every amount. This is not easy because many expenses are small. Small amounts can be combined under miscellaneous.

Step 4. Based on actual expenditures, adjust your budget for the next month. If you spend your contingency each month, then it may indicate that you cannot easily afford your level of discretionary and non-discretionary spending.

You can set up a budget on a spreadsheet.

EXERCISE 13.4

B

1. Complete the cash flow table given below by stating the percentages and totals.

Cash Flow	Month 1		Month 2		Month 3	
Income	September		October		November	
Take-home Pay (Net Income)	$1478.90		$1478.90		$1502.23	
Interest and Dividends	$212.00		$220.00		$202.50	
Miscellaneous Income	$0.00		$0.00		$110.00	
Total Income	$1690.90		$1698.90		1814.73	
Expenditures	September	%	October	%	November	%
Rent/Mortgage Payment	$489.20	28.9	$489.20	28.9	$489.20	27
Utilities	$67.55	4	$45.40	2.7	$70.19	3.9
Food	$299.22	17.7	$321.00	18.9	$309.89	17.1
Transportation	$34.00	2	$40.00	2.4	$38.00	2.1
Insurance — Home	$72.00	4.3	$72.00	4.2	$72.00	4
Insurance — Life	$49.00	2.9	$49.00	2.9	$53.00	2.9
Insurance — Car	$0.00	0	$0.00	0	$345.00	19
Clothing	$120.00	7.1	$175.00	10.3	$89.00	4.9
Credit Card Payments	$78.00	4.6	$89.00	5.2	$110.00	6.1
Loan Payments	$200.00	11.8	$200.00	11.8	$200.00	11
Medical/Dental	$70.00	4.1	$35.00	2.1	$0.00	0
Miscellaneous and Unexpected	$123.48	7.3	$345.89	20.4	$298.75	16.5
Total Expenditures	1602.45	94.8	1861.49	109.6	2075.03	114.3
Income greater (+)	88.45	5.2				
Spending greater (−)			162.59	9.6	260.30	14.3

2. (a) How would you assess the spending as compared to income of the person in question 1?
(b) How do the levels of expenditure compare to those recommended on the previous page?

3. Using the information given in the cash flow table in question 1, prepare a budget using the Monthly Money Plan.
Use the last month's income as the income given.

4. List and calculate the total amount of discretionary spending in the cash flow table given in question 1.

5. List and calculate the total amount of non-discretionary spending in the cash flow table given in question 1.

Questions 6, 7, 8, and 9 relate to the cash flow table on page 377.

6. List and calculate the total amount of discretionary spending in the cash flow table.

7. List and calculate the total amount of non-discretionary spending in the cash flow table.

8. State the areas where the person could reduce expenditures so that the cash flow would be positive, that is, at the end of each month, income would be left over for savings.

9. Using the information given in the cash flow table, prepare a budget using the Monthly Money Plan.
Use the last month's income as the income given.

10. Prepare a cash flow table and a Monthly Money Plan for the family with income and expenses described below. Estimate any expenditure not listed and the amount of the contingency.
(a) A couple both work outside the home. They have two children.
(b) One has a yearly income of $27 892 gross, net is 71% of income; and the other has a yearly income of $32 892 gross, net is 65% of income.
(c) They live in a duplex with a mortgage payment, including taxes, of $678/month.
(d) They pay for child care and house cleaning at a rate of $175/week.
(e) Their food bill averages $495/month.
(f) They have a car and make a car payment of $289/month. They drive an average of 1200 km/month at an estimated cost of $0.25/km.
(g) They pay a life insurance premium of $107 monthly.
(h) They pay a home-owners' insurance premium of $376/a, payable monthly.
(i) They pay a car insurance premium of $598/a, payable bi-monthly.
(j) They have a home-improvement loan with payments of $211/month.
(k) Their heating is paid in ten equal payments and costs a total of $765/a.
(l) They pay hydro bi-monthly at an average of $120 per payment.

(m) They pay water tri-monthly at an average of $43 per payment.
(n) One child has braces at a cost of $110/month with dental insurance paying for 12% of the payment.
(o) They owe $789 on one credit card and $590 on another. Each credit card requires a monthly payment of 20% of the balance.

11. Using the amounts you listed in the cash flow table, complete the budget by giving actual expenditures and the positive or negative values.
Estimate any actual expenditure not listed and the contingency actually needed.

These questions may be done using a computer and spreadsheet software.

MIND BENDER

A 3 cm by 3 cm by 3 cm cube is painted red on all of its faces. It is then cut into 1 cm by 1 cm by 1 cm cubes.

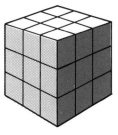

How many of these cubes will be red on
(a) 3 faces?
(b) 2 faces?
(c) 1 face?

13.5 THE COST OF CREDIT BUYING

When planning for a major purchase, it may become necessary to borrow money. A house, car, major appliance, and furniture are some examples of purchases that may require a person to secure a loan. There are many forms of credit buying, credit cards, and time-payment plans.

FEATURES OF METHODS OF PURCHASE

Cash   There is no additional cost to the purchaser, although it may be necessary to secure the cash by withdrawing it from a savings account. This would result in the loss of interest.

Lay-away   The store will hold the item for the customer and when the last payment is made, the customer receives the goods. Lay-away plans cost the customer nothing in addition to the cost of the goods.

Time-Payment Plans and Personal Loans   Money may be borrowed from a bank, trust company, credit union, or other financial institution to make a major purchase. The customer receives the goods immediately and makes regular payments at a fixed amount and given rate of interest. The goods will cost the original cost of the item (principal, P) plus the interest charged (I).

READ

Example 1. You borrow money to purchase a major appliance that costs $879 and agree to make payments of $46/month for 24 months. Calculate the total amount you will pay for the appliance and the effective rate of interest.

PLAN

$E=mc^2$

Solution:
Recall the simple interest formulas.

Simple Interest

Interest = Principal $\times$ Rate $\times$ Time

$\qquad$ I = Prt

Amount = Principal + Interest

$\qquad$ A = P + I

$\qquad$ A = P + Prt

$\qquad$ A = P(1 + rt)

Cover the one you want to find.

Where regular payments are made over a period of time, the formula for effective rate of interest is

$$r = \frac{2NI}{P(n + 1)}$$

where N is the number of payment periods per year,
          I is the interest charged,
          P is the principal, and
          n is the total number of payments.

In this example, N = 12, P = \$879, and n = 24.

$$I = A - P$$
$$I = \$46 \times 24 - \$879$$
$$= \$1104 - \$879$$
$$= \$225$$

Substitute into the formula.

$$r = \frac{2NI}{P(n + 1)}$$
$$r = \frac{2(12)(225)}{879(24 + 1)}$$
$$= \frac{5400}{21\ 975}$$
$$\doteq 0.246 \quad \text{(rounded to the nearest thousandth)}$$

You will pay \$1104 for the appliance, and the effective rate of interest is 24.6%.

Even though the monthly payment may be attractive and within your budget, you should look closely at the effective rate of interest. If it is necessary to make a credit purchase, you should shop around for the best effective rate.

Credit Cards   Credit cards are becoming popular as a method of purchasing consumer goods. The credit card is simple to use and gives you an accurate record of your purchases. If the total amount of the purchases for the month is paid in full by the payment date, there is usually no interest charged, although a fee per use may be charged. If the amount is not paid in full by the payment date, interest is charged. The effective rate of interest charged on a credit card purchase is difficult to calculate because additional purchases are being made and payments are being deducted at irregular intervals. The effective rate of interest is often twice the interest rate you could obtain through a personal loan, from 18% to 26%. Credit cards are convenient, but it is important to use them wisely.

You should be aware of the method used to calculate interest on your credit card purchases, and you should verify that the company has credited and debited your account correctly.

Example 2. Calculate the amount of interest charged over the statement period, the total debits, the new balance, and the minimum payment due for the following credit statement.

Interest is charged at 1.5% per month on the average daily balance, and the minimum payment required is 15% of the new balance, to the next dollar.

YOU-CAN-CHARGE-IT CREDIT CARD COMPANY OF THE KING BANK OF CANADA			
Date Posted	Transactions	Purchases (Debits)	Payments (Credits)
05Sep	Cross-Roads Dress Shop	$ 75.89	
12Sep	Ye Olde Book Shop	$ 34.12	
15Sep	Payment — Thank You		$ 125.00
03Oct	Interest	$	

Account No.	Previous Balance	Total Credits	Total Debits	New Balance
4429599	$ 655.98	$	$	

Statement Date	Date Payment Due	Past Due	Minimum Payment	Credit Limit
Oct 3	Nov 4	.00		$1 500.00

Solution:

The daily balance changes each time the account is credited or debited between the statement dates of September 3 and October 3. The statement period has 30 d. The average daily balance is calculated by finding the balance at each period over the month.

For two days the balance was $655.98, for seven days the balance was $655.98 + $75.89 = $731.87, for three days the balance was $731.87 + $34.12 = $765.99, and for eighteen days the balance was $765.99 − $125.00 = $640.99.

$$\text{Average daily balance} = \frac{(\$655.98 \times 2) + (\$731.87 \times 7) + (\$765.99 \times 3) + (\$640.99 \times 18)}{30}$$

$$= \frac{\$1311.96 + \$5123.09 + \$2297.97 + \$11\,537.82}{30}$$

$$= \$675.69$$

Interest charges = $675.69 × 0.015
= $10.14

Total debits = $75.89 + $34.12 + $10.14
= $120.15

Total credits = $125.00

New balance = Previous balance − Total credits + Total debits
= $655.98 − $125.00 + $120.15
= $651.13

Minimum payment = $651.13 × 0.15
≐ $98.00

The interest charged is $10.14, the total debits are $120.15, the new balance is $651.13, and the minimum payment due is $98.00.

EXERCISE 13.5

B1. Find the interest charged and the effective rate of interest to the nearest tenth of a percent for each of the following.

	Principal	Monthly Payment
(a)	$200	12 of $17.98
(b)	$12 000	36 of $410
(c)	$20 000	120 of $250
(d)	$3234	24 of $144

2. You are going to buy a $1000 sofa and want to know how much less it will cost to pay cash than to make time payments. If you pay cash, you must withdraw $1000 from a savings account that would pay interest of 8.5% compounded semi-annually. If you make time payments, you can purchase the sofa from your monthly income, earn interest on the $1000 in the bank, and pay $100/month for 12 months.

(a) What is the real amount in dollars of the two methods?
(b) What is the effective rate of interest on the time-payment offer?

3. A grandmother bought a bike for her grandchild. She paid $25 cash and $25/month for six months.
If the cash price was $110, what was the effective rate of interest?

4. A motorcycle may be purchased for $78 down and $22/month for 18 months.
If the finance charges are $46, what is the cash price?

5. Obtain a copy of a credit card contract from your local bank.
What are your obligations as a user of the credit privileges?
What will you receive from the company as a benefit of using the credit card?

6. Obtain a copy of a loan contract from your local bank or credit union.
Compare your obligations and rate of interest with those for the use of a credit card.

7. For the credit card bill given below, the interest rate is 1.75% per month on the average daily balance, and the minimum payment required is 20% of the new balance.

YOU-CAN-CHARGE-IT CREDIT CARD COMPANY OF THE KING BANK OF CANADA			
Date Posted	Transactions	Purchases (Debits)	Payments (Credits)
09Dec	The Crest Shop	$ 115.11	
20Dec	Goody Restaurant	$ 44.50	
27Dec	Payment — Thank You		$ 200.00
03Jan	Interest	$	
Account No.	Previous Balance	Total Credits	Total Debits	New Balance
4429599	$ 489.03	$	$	
Statement Date	Date Payment Due	Past Due	Minimum Payment	Credit Limit
Jan 3	Feb 4	.00		$1 500.00

Find.
(a) the Average Daily Balance
(b) the Interest Due
(c) the Total Credits
(d) the Total Debits
(e) the Minimum Payment Due
(f) the New Balance

13.6 COMPARING ACCOMMODATION COSTS

In larger cities and urban areas, people have a larger selection of alternatives when selecting a home. Apartments are available as rental units or for purchase as condominiums. Houses and town houses may also be rented or purchased.

The choice between purchasing or renting an accommodation is often determined by the amount of money one has available and the lifestyle one wants to pursue. Factors affecting the size of payments include: the size of the down payment, the interest rate, and the length of the term over which the mortgage is amortized. For the purchase of a given property, a larger down payment will reduce the size of the mortgage payments. It is also clear that a higher interest rate will result in higher payments. Another way to reduce the size of the payment is to extend the time required to repay the mortgage loan. All three of these factors need to be considered when comparing accommodation costs.

It is suggested by family financial counsellors that no more than 27% of the borrower's income go towards mortgage payments of principal, interest, and taxes. When making this "27% calculation" for a two-income family, it is customary to include all of the higher income and one-half of the lower income to arrive at the total income that is used in making the calculation as in Example 1.

Example 1. Bill Sampson has an annual income of $48 130, and his wife Marion earns $32 750/a.
What is the highest monthly mortgage payment that they should consider according to these guidelines?

Solution:

Highest income = $48 130

One-half lower income = 0.5 × $32 750
= $16 375

Total available income = $48 130 + $16 375
= $64 505

Maximum annual payment = 27% of $64 505
= 0.27 × $64 505
= $17 416.35

Maximum monthly payment = $17 416.35 ÷ 12
≐ $1451.36

> The calculation can also be used as a guide to the amount of rent a family can afford to pay.

The guide recommends that Bill and Marion Sampson can meet monthly mortgage payments of up to $1451.36.

The following terms are used in acquiring accommodations:

Purchasing

> Vendor: The person, persons, or company selling the property.

> Purchaser: The person or persons buying the property.

Renting

> Lessor: The person, persons, or company who owns the rental property.

> Lessee: The person or persons renting the property, the tenant.

When entering into a contract to purchase or rent, it is wise to have the advice of a lawyer. To ensure that the vendor really owns the property that is being sold, and that it is free from liens or other encumbrances, the lawyer will search the title. When renting an apartment or town house, the landlord and tenant are protected by a signed agreement called a lease. The lessor (the owner) agrees to rent to the lessee (the tenant) the accommodation for a stated rent over a fixed number of months. A lawyer will be able to advise the prospective tenant of any hidden obligations that might be assumed.

When choosing an accommodation, the following criteria should be ranked in order of importance so that the various properties can be compared in a systematic and organized manner.

Community: Is the dwelling situated in a community in which you would enjoy living?

Location: Is the dwelling close to the location of your leisure activities?

Work: Is the dwelling close to your place of work?

External: Do you like the external design of the building and is it well maintained?

Outside: Is there an outside area for living and recreation?

Children: Is there an outside area for children to play unsupervised?

Privacy: Will there be privacy from the neighbours?

Street: Are there street lights and sidewalks?

Room: Is there enough room for the furniture and appliances?

Areas: Are the working areas, kitchen, and laundry room well-arranged?

Cupboards: Is there adequate cupboard space?

Ventilation: Is there adequate ventilation (windows or air conditioning)?

RENTING ACCOMMODATION

The answers to the above questions, the family income level, and lifestyle are factors to consider when deciding on a rental accommodation. When renting over a long term, the lessee must sign a lease, which places an obligation on the lessee to make regular rental payments over a fixed length of time. Sample copies of a lease and apartment rules and regulations are given on the following pages.

This Indenture

made in duplicate the   14th   day of   June

one thousand and nine hundred and   ninety-two (1992)

IN PURSUANCE OF THE SHORT FORMS OF LEASES ACT.

BETWEEN   Ashton Apartments Limited
hereinafter called the LANDLORD of the FIRST PART

AND   John Smith and Mary Smith
hereinafter called the TENANT of the SECOND PART

WITNESSETH that in consideration of the rents, covenants, and agreements hereinafter reserved and contained on the part of the TENANT the LANDLORD DOTH demise and leave unto the TENANT, his executors, administrators, and assigns. ALL that certain parcel or tract of land and premises situate, lying, and being

In the County of   Sussex   In the City of   Maple
          Known as   Suite 405

TO HAVE AND TO HOLD the said demised premises for and during the term of
ONE YEAR   to be computed from the   1st   day of   July
one thousand nine hundred and   ninety-two (1992)   and thenceforth next ensuing and fully to be completed and ended   June 30, 1993

YIELDING AND PAYING therefore yearly and every year during the said term unto the LANDLORD, his heirs, executors, administrators, or assigns, the sum of $7200.00

SEVEN THOUSAND TWO HUNDRED DOLLARS

of lawful money of Canada; to be payable on the following days and times, that is to say, on the   1st   day of each and every month, the sum of $600.00   until the expiration of this lease. THE FIRST of such payments to become due and be made on the   1st   day of   July   next, and the last payment to become due and to be paid in advance on the   1st   day of   July 1992

IT IS AGREED AND UNDERSTOOD THAT THE TENANT WILL PAY FIRST AND LAST MONTHS RENT UPON SIGNING OF THIS LEASE.

IN WITNESS WHEREOF, the said parties hereto have hereunto set their hands and seals.

DATED AT   Maple   this   14th   day of   June   19 92.

SIGNED, SEALED, AND DELIVERED   TENANT _____
in the presence of   TENANT _____

WITNESS _____   LANDLORD _____

RULES AND REGULATIONS
OF THE RENTED PREMISES AND ITS ENVIRONS

1. The water closets and other apparatus shall not be used for any purpose other than those for which they are constructed and no sweepings, garbage, rubbish, rags, ashes, or other substance shall be thrown therein. The Tenant will be responsible for any damage therefrom.

2. Tenants must observe strict care not to allow windows and doors to remain open as to admit rain or snow or so as to risk the freezing of plumbing, heating, or other facilities. The Tenant will be responsible for the cost of repairing or replacing such damaged radiators and pipes together with any other damage to the premises or property of others resulting therefrom.

3. Tenants shall be responsible for keeping locks and trimmings whole in or upon the doors and windows of the rented premises; wherever any part thereof shall become lost or broken the same shall be immediately replaced or repaired under the direction and to the satifaction of the Landlord and shall be paid for by the Tenant responsible. No additional locks shall be placed upon or on any door without the prior written consent of the Landlord.

4. All garbage to be securely wrapped and placed or deposited, as directed from time to time by the Landlord.

5. No goods, chattels, fixtures, or other items that might overload the floors of the rented premises shall be brought into the said premises nor shall items be moved on, in, or over floors, sidewalks, steps, stairways, lawns, or other property of the Landlord so as to damage same; Tenants will be held responsible for any damage caused by movements of their items in, out of, or about the rented premises.

6. Nothing shall be thrown by Tenants, their families, guests, visitors, or servants out of the windows or doors or down stairwells or other areas of the premises.

7. The Tenant shall not place or allow to be placed bicycles, baby carriages, or other personal property in public areas or on sidewalks, neither shall articles be permitted to remain outside in such areas overnight or when not in use. Personal property left in public areas may be removed and disposed of by the Landlord.

8. No telegraphic or telephone connections shall be made without the prior written consent of the Landlord except to facilities provided by the Landlord within the rented premises and no electric wiring shall be installed and no electric fixtures shall be installed except where provision therefor has been made by the Landlord without the prior written consent of the Landlord.

9. No sale or auction of any kind shall be held in or about the rented premises without the prior written consent of the Landlord.

10. The water shall not be left running unless in actual use in the rented premises.

11. Garage doors must be closed when the Tenant has entered or left the garage and must be kept closed when not in use.

12. No cooking shall be done in or about any demised premises except in kitchen areas provided therefor.

13. Entrance doors of residential suites shall remain closed except during ingress or egress.

EXERCISE 13.6

B

1. What is the highest monthly cost for housing that each of the following should consider?
(a) Paul James earns $48 500/a.
(b) Mary Stewart earns $894.30/week.
(c) Edna and Yuri Yakuchev have two incomes. Edna earns $53 000, and Yuri earns $47 500.
(d) Abe Samuel has a gross income of $73 780/a, and his wife Stella has an income of $1580/month.
(e) Jennifer and Norm Lee work at similar jobs and both earn $54 325.

2. What is the minimum annual income required in order to be within the 27% recommendation to assume the following monthly mortgage payments?
(a) $15 550   (b) $985
(c) $750   (d) $2500

3. As though you were choosing an apartment, rank the following in order of importance:

Entrance: Is there a private entrance?
Parking: Is there any?
Garage?
Open-Air?
Visitors: Is there visitor parking?
Halls: Are halls and stairways well-lighted?
Exits: Are there adequate fire exits?
Garbage: Are there garbage facilities?
Television: Is cable or antenna included or available?
Appliances: Are kitchen appliances included and in good condition?
Air: Is there air conditioning?
Interior: Is the interior pleasingly decorated and well-kept?
Pool: Is there a swimming pool for tenants' use?
Lease: What are the terms of the lease?

4. Esther and Mark Green meet the minimum recommended requirement to assume a monthly mortgage payment of $2015.82. Mark has an annual income of $68 752.
What is Esther's annual income?

5. As though you were considering buying a house, rank the following in order of importance:

Water: Is there an adequate water supply?
Sewers: Is the property serviced by public sewers?
Deliveries: Can fuel deliveries and meter readings be made from the outside?
Electrical: Is there adequate safe electrical wiring, including well-placed outlets?
Heating: What is the method of heating? Are fuel costs reasonable?
Basement: Is the basement area usable, that is, dry, clean, high, or finished?
Windows: Are there storm windows and screens?
Plumbing: Are plumbing and heating units in good condition?
Payments: Are the down payment and monthly payment within the guide?
Mortgage: What are the terms of the mortgage?

6. A bachelor apartment is advertised for $910/month with a 12 month lease.
What weekly income should a prospective tenant have if a guide of 27% for accommodation is used?

7. A condominium is for sale at $208 000. After the down payment, the mortgage payment will be $1686/month with taxes of $107/month and maintenance fees of $90/month.

(a) What minimum annual income should a prospective purchaser have?

(b) If the lower income in a two-income family is $39 500/a, what annual income would the principal earner need to have?

(c) If the lawyer charges a fee of 1.25% of the total purchase price, what will the lawyer's fee be?

8. The monthly mortgage payments on a house are $1765.30, including principal, interest, and taxes. Utilities, electricity, heating, and water are estimated to cost $325/month.

(a) What is the minimum annual income required for this housing if there is one income?

(b) What is the minimum annual principal income if there are two incomes in the household and the lower income is $35 000?

9. A house is for sale at $245 000. A down payment of $65 000 leaves a mortgage with monthly payments of $2080. The annual tax bill is $2045, and gas company records show that annual heating costs are $789.20. Electricity and telephone charges will average $96.80/month. The house is insured for 80% of its estimated value, which is $165 000, at an annual premium of $3.75/$1000.
Find the average monthly cost of running this house.

10. A house is purchased for $96 000 with a down payment of $20 000.
Use the formula for present value to calculate the half-yearly payment on a 20 a mortgage if interest is charged at 10% compounded semi-annually.

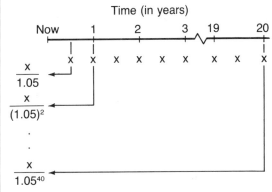

11. Use the classified section of your local newspaper or information obtained from a local real estate agent to complete the tables.

Typical Cost			
Buying	2 Bedrooms	3 Bedrooms	4 Bedrooms
Detached House			
Semi-detached House			
Town House			
Apartment			

Typical Monthly Rental		
Rental	Apartment	Town House
1 Bedroom		
2 Bedrooms		
3 Bedrooms		

13.7 BUYING A HOUSE OR CONDOMINIUM

When buying a house or condominium, purchasers must decide on the amount they can afford to pay monthly for principal, interest, and taxes. They must also decide on the location and the size of house desired. After these decisions have been made, it is advisable to contact a reputable real estate agent and describe the type of house desired. The agent will show prospective buyers a number of houses listed by the agent's company. A listing means that the real estate firm has signed an agreement with a home-owner stating that if the firm can sell the house for a predetermined sum, the seller of the house will pay the real estate firm a fee, usually 5% to 8% of the sale price. For the higher fee, the house will be put on a multiple listing service (M.L.S.), which allows any member real estate company to arrange a sale. This means that the real estate agent is paid by the seller, or vendor, not the buyer.

Why do developers put multiple units, such as the one shown, on corner lots?
How many similar models can you find in the picture below? Use driveways as a clue.

When the desired house is located, the buyer or buyers sign an offer to purchase in which the buyer(s) agrees to purchase the house for a stated sum of money and provides a deposit to show that they are serious about the offer to purchase. If the vendor accepts the offer before a specified time, called the expiry date, then the vendor signs the offer to purchase. The offer to purchase also includes a closing date, at which time the final transaction is completed. A copy of an offer to purchase follows on the next page.

REAL ESTATE ASSOCIATION
AGREEMENT OF PURCHASE AND SALE

PURCHASER John Smith and Mary Smith   offers to buy from

VENDOR   William Brown   through Vendor's

AGENT   Sunshine Realty Company Limited   the following

PROPERTY: fronting on the   South   side of   Alberta Avenue
known municipally as   Municipal No. 23
in the   City   of   Maple
and having a frontage of   15 m   more or less by a depth of   45 m   more or less and
described as   part of Lot No. 46 and 47 according to Plan No. 563B
at the PURCHASE PRICE OF
Two Hundred Seven Thousand Five Hundred   CanadianDollars ($Can   207 500.00)
on the following terms:

1. Purchaser submits with this offer
    Five Thousand Five Hundred   Dollars ($ 5500.00)
    cash/cheque payable to the Listing Broker as a deposit to be held by him in trust pending completion
    or other termination of this Agreement and to be credited towards the Purchase Price on completion.

2. Purchaser agrees to pay the sum of One Hundred Two Thousand Dollars in cash on
    closing, subject to adjustments, and to give back to the vendor a ten-year
    mortgage on said property in the amount of One Hundred Thousand Dollars,
    repayable at $1445.50 per month, which includes interest at 12% per annum,
    said payments to commence September 1, 1990 and thereafter due of the 1st
    day of each succeeding month for a period of ten years from the date of
    issuance.

DATED at   Maple   this   15th   day of   July   19 90

SIGNED, SEALED, AND DELIVERED   IN WITNESS whereof I have hereunto set my
in the presence of: hand and seal
_____   _____ Date _____

_____   _____ Date _____

The undersigned accepts the above Offer and agrees with the Listing Broker above named in
consideration for his services in procuring the said Offer , to pay him on the date above fixed for
completion, a commission of   5   % of an amount equal to the above mentioned sale price,
which commission may be deducted from the deposit. I hereby irrevocably instruct my Solicitor
to pay direct to the said Listing Broker any unpaid balance of commission from the proceeds of
the sale.

DATED at   Maple   this   16th   day of   July   19 90

SIGNED, SEALED, AND DELIVERED   IN WITNESS whereof I have hereunto set my
in the presence of: hand and seal
_____   _____ Date _____

MORTGAGES

Since few people are able to pay cash for a house, it is often necessary to arrange a mortgage. This may be done through the seller, another individual, a credit union, or a commercial institution. The mortgage represents an agreement between the mortgagee (person buying the house) and the mortgagor (person lending the money). The mortgagee promises to pay the mortgagor a certain amount of money at regular intervals, usually every month, until the total mortgage is amortized or paid off.

Since a mortgage is usually paid by means of equal monthly payments, it is basically an annuity, and payments can be calculated using the methods and formulas for annuities. Since mortgage calculations are very common, tables have been prepared giving the monthly payment per $1000 for various terms and interest rates. A sample table is given.

Partial Basic Monthly Payment Table For a Loan of $1000							
Years	Months	Periods	8%	$8\frac{1}{2}$%	9%	$9\frac{1}{2}$%	10%
10	0	120	12.0641	12.3202	12.5789	12.8399	13.1034
15	0	180	9.4815	9.7616	10.0452	10.3323	10.6227
20	0	240	8.2836	8.5856	8.8919	9.2023	9.5166
25	0	300	7.6321	7.9536	8.2798	8.6103	8.9449
30	0	360	7.2471	7.5854	7.9283	8.2755	8.6267
35	0	420	7.0083	7.3606	7.7174	8.0781	8.4423
40	0	480	6.8556	7.2195	7.5874	7.9587	8.3330

Years	Months	Periods	$10\frac{1}{2}$%	11%	$11\frac{1}{2}$%	12%	$12\frac{1}{2}$%
10	0	120	13.3629	13.6373	13.9077	14.1803	14.4550
15	0	180	10.9164	11.2133	11.5132	11.8161	12.1987
20	0	240	9.8347	10.1564	10.4815	10.8097	11.1411
25	0	300	9.2833	9.6253	9.9706	10.3190	10.6702
30	0	360	8.9814	9.3394	9.7003	10.0639	10.4298
35	0	420	8.8097	9.1797	9.5522	9.9268	10.3032
40	0	480	8.7098	9.0888	9.4696	9.8519	10.2355

Example 1. Find the equal monthly payment required to amortize a mortgage of $78 500 at $9\frac{1}{2}$% over 25 a.

Solution:

Payment per $1000	8.6103	From the table, $9\frac{1}{2}$% column for 25 a.
Amount of loan in $1000	× 78.5	Means
	675.91	1000 × 78.5 = 78 500.

The monthly payment is $675.91.

Example 2. Use 27% as a guide to find the largest mortgage a person should assume with an annual income of $48 500.

The mortgage is for 20 a at $9\frac{1}{2}$%.

Solution:

$$\text{Monthly income} = \frac{\$48\ 500}{12}$$
$$\doteq \$4041.67$$

27% of $4041.67 \doteq $1091.25

Monthly payment per $1000 at $9\frac{1}{2}$% for 20 a is $9.2023.

$$\therefore \text{maximum mortgage} = \frac{1091.25}{9.2023} \times 1000$$
$$\doteq 118\ 584.48$$

The maximum mortgage would be $119 000.

Some mortgages are paid by making a regular monthly payment against the principal and a separate semi-annual interest payment. In these cases a schedule of payments must be prepared.

Example 3. A mortgage of $36 000 assumed on March 1, 1990 is repaid by payments of $150/month on the principal plus semi-annual interest payments. Interest is charged at 10% on the unpaid balance.
Draw up a schedule of payments for the first 6 months.

Interest Calculation

$$\$36\ 000 \times 0.10 \times \frac{31}{365}$$

$$\$35\ 850 \times 0.10 \times \frac{30}{365}$$

$$\$35\ 700 \times 0.10 \times \frac{31}{365}$$

Solution:

Date	Principal (before payment)	Monthly Interest	Payment Principal	Payment Interest	Payment Total	Principal (after payment)
March 1	$36 000					
April 1	$36 000	$305.75	$150.00		$150.00	$35 850
May 1	$35 850	$294.66	$150.00		$150.00	$35 700
June 1	$35 700	$303.21	$150.00		$150.00	$35 550
July 1	$35 550	$292.19	$150.00		$150.00	$35 400
August 1	$35 400	$300.66	$150.00		$150.00	$35 250
	$35 250	$299.38	$150.00	$1795.85	$1945.85	$35 100
		$1795.85				

With a principal of $36 000 and monthly payments of $150, in how many months will the mortgage be paid off?
What equal monthly payment would amortize the mortgage at 10% over 240 months? (See table on previous page.)

SOURCES AND TYPES OF MORTGAGES

A first mortgage is a mortgage on the balance of your home after the down payment. Financial institutions who loan mortgage money define a level of down payment they find acceptable given the value of the house. If a person does not have a down payment to the level that is required by the mortgagor (the lending institution from whom you receive the money), a second mortgage, or money to make up the required down payment, may be secured. The interest rate for a second mortgage is higher than for a first mortgage, and second mortgages usually have a shorter term. As a rule, conventional first mortgage loans are no greater than $\frac{2}{3}$ of the appraised value of the house.

Example 4. A family wishes to purchase a home with a value of $120 000. The bank offers a first mortgage of $\frac{2}{3}$ of the value.

If the family has only $12 000 cash for a down payment, how much must it obtain in a second mortgage?

Solution:

First mortgage $= \$120\ 000 \times \frac{2}{3}$

$\qquad\qquad\qquad = \$80\ 000$

The required down payment $= \$120\ 000 - \$80\ 000$

$\qquad\qquad\qquad\qquad\qquad = \$40\ 000$

The amount of second mortgage $= \$40\ 000 - \$12\ 000$

$\qquad\qquad\qquad\qquad\qquad\qquad = \$28\ 000$

The family must obtain $28 000 in a second mortgage.

Most people obtain a first mortgage from a bank, credit union, or trust company. There are other sources such as insurance companies and the Central Mortgage and Housing Corporation, a federal government agency. A second mortgage may be obtained from a credit union, from loans as an employee benefit, or from a private mortgage company.

The most popular method of payment of a conventional mortgage is the equalized monthly payment. The amount due each month includes interest on the unpaid balance and principal to a fixed amount. As the principal is reduced, the interest portion of each payment decreases.

You may also obtain a decreasing payment mortgage. This method of payment includes a fixed amount of principal and interest on the unpaid balance. As the principal is reduced, the interest decreases, and the total payment per month is reduced.

A mortgage is a long-term commitment. The interest rate is high, and the term is long. Any payment of principal reduces significantly the total amount of interest charged over the years the mortgage is in force. The rate of interest of the mortgage is fixed for a period of 1 a to 5 a. At the end of each period, you renegotiate the rate of interest. Most mortgages on this date allow you to pay off an amount of the principal. Open end mortgages allow for partial payback of principal before the end of the interest period. The more open a mortgage is to paying principal outside the amortization payment schedule, the more flexible the mortgagee can be to pay off the mortgage quickly and thus pay less interest.

EXERCISE 13.7

A

1. Why must a deposit accompany an offer to purchase for the protection of the vendor?

2. Why must an expiry date be shown on the offer to purchase for the protection of the purchaser?

3. When a vendor asks for terms of "Cash to mortgage", what is being requested?

B

4. Use the table on page 394 to calculate the monthly payment for each of the following mortgages.

	Full Price	Down Payment	Interest Rate	Time
(a)	$156 000	$60 000	$10\frac{1}{2}$%	20 a
(b)	$105 000	$45 000	9%	15 a
(c)	$132 500	$40 000	10%	30 a
(d)	$175 000	$60 000	$9\frac{1}{2}$%	25 a
(e)	$249 000	$100 000	12%	35 a
(f)	$212 000	$100 000	10%	25 a

5. Using 27% of salary as a guide for payments and assuming a 25 a mortgage at 10%, determine to the nearest $1000 the largest mortgage a person with each of the following incomes should undertake.
(a) $1550/month   (b) $1200/month
(c) $40 500/a   (d) $63 000/a

6. A mortgage for $135 000 is repaid by monthly payments of $500 against the principal with semi-annual interest payments. Interest is charged at $9\frac{1}{2}$% on the unpaid balance.
If the mortgage is assumed on June 15, 1990, draw up a schedule of payments for the first 6 months.

7. A mortgage for $40 500 is repaid by monthly payments of $175 against the principal with semi-annual interest payments. Interest is charged at $10\frac{1}{2}$% on the unpaid balance.
If the mortgage is assumed on April 15, 1990 with payments on the 15th of each month, draw up a schedule of payments for the first half year.

8. On the purchase of a $75 000 house, it was found necessary to take a second mortgage of $6500 from a trust company at 14% interest compounded quarterly. The terms of the mortgage were $450 quarterly for principal and interest for a three-year term.
(a) Prepare a schedule of payments as shown in the table.
(b) How much principal is still owing at the end of the 3 a?

Day of Month	Jan.	Feb.	March
1	1	32	60
2	2	33	61
3	3	34	62
4	4	35	63
5	5	36	64
6	6	37	65
7	7	38	66
8	8	39	67
9	9	40	68
10	10	41	69
11	11	42	70
12	12	43	71
13	13	44	72
14	14	45	73
15	15	46	74
16	16	47	75
17	17	48	76
18	18	49	77
19	19	50	78
20	20	51	79
21	21	52	80
22	22	53	81
23	23	54	82
24	24	55	83
25	25	56	84
26	26	57	85
27	27	58	86
28	28	59	87
29	29		88
30	30		89
31	31		90

Day of Month	Apr.	May	June
1	91	121	152
2	92	122	153
3	93	123	154
4	94	124	155
5	95	125	156
6	96	126	157
7	97	127	158
8	98	128	159
9	99	129	160
10	100	130	161
11	101	131	162
12	102	132	163
13	103	133	164
14	104	134	165
15	105	135	166
16	106	136	167
17	107	137	168
18	108	138	169
19	109	139	170
20	110	140	171
21	111	141	172
22	112	142	173
23	113	143	174
24	114	144	175
25	115	145	176
26	116	146	177
27	117	147	178
28	118	148	179
29	119	149	180
30	120	150	181
31		151	

13.8 ADJUSTMENTS TO THE PURCHASE PRICE

When a house or condominium is sold, the purchaser takes over all obligations relating to the property as of the date the sale is closed. The vendor is responsible for all obligations up to that point. It is highly unlikely that taxes and insurance will be paid up to exactly the date of sale. If some services are unpaid, the purchaser must be given credit; if some services are prepaid, the purchaser will be charged.

It is the responsibility of the lawyer for the vendor to prepare a "Statement of Adjustments." This document will set out the amounts that are allowed the purchaser and the amounts that are charged to the purchaser. It is arranged in the form of a balance sheet and will give the amount due to the vendor on closing.

Example 1. The closing date on a sale is October 15, 1990. Calculate the amount allowed in each of the following cases and to whom it is allowed.
  (a) A $95 insurance premium for 1 a, expiry date March 30, 1991.
  (b) Annual taxes of $790, $300 paid to date.

Solution:

(a) The purchaser is responsible for insurance from the date of purchase.

$$
\begin{aligned}
&\text{(March 30 is day 89)} &89& \\
&\text{(New year)} &+365& \\
\hline
& &454& \\
&\text{(Oct. 15 is day 288)} &-288& \\
\hline
& &166 \text{ d}&
\end{aligned}
$$

The vendor is allowed $\dfrac{166}{365}$ of the premium.

$$\frac{166}{365} \times \$95 = \$43.21$$

Allow the vendor $43.21.

(b) The vendor is responsible for taxes up to October 15. October 15 is day 288.

The vendor must pay $\dfrac{288}{365}$ of the year's taxes.

$$\frac{288}{365} \times \$790 = \$623.34$$

The vendor has paid $300.

$$623.34 - 300 = 323.34$$

Allow the purchaser $323.34.

All companies and public utilities supplying services to the dwelling, such as electricity, gas, water, or phone, should be informed of the closing date. The vendor will ask to have meters read so that he is not responsible for charges due to the new tenants. The purchaser will make arrangements for the services to be continued. If he is moving into a community where he is not known, deposits may be required and should be allowed for when planning finances.

Example 2. Mr. R. Williams is selling his house, located at 15 Orange Cres., to Mr. and Mrs. B. Jones.

> Particulars:
> Closing date — May 3, 1990
> Sale price — $156 000
> Deposit — $1600
> 1990 taxes — $1850
> First instalment paid on taxes — $350
> Fire insurance — one-year premium — $130, expires October 15, 1990
>
> Mr. Williams will be paying off an open mortgage with some of the proceeds from the sale. Mr. and Mrs. Jones have arranged for a mortgage of $80 000 to finance their purchase.
> Draw up a statement of adjustments and calculate the balance due on closing.

Solution:

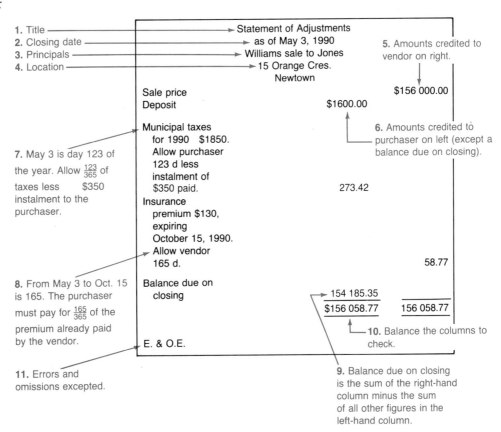

1. Title ———— Statement of Adjustments
2. Closing date ———— as of May 3, 1990
3. Principals ———— Williams sale to Jones
4. Location ———— 15 Orange Cres.
   Newtown

5. Amounts credited to vendor on right.

Sale price		$156 000.00
Deposit	$1600.00	

6. Amounts credited to purchaser on left (except a balance due on closing).

7. May 3 is day 123 of the year. Allow $\frac{123}{365}$ of taxes less $350 instalment to the purchaser.

Municipal taxes for 1990 $1850. Allow purchaser 123 d less instalment of $350 paid.   273.42

Insurance premium $130, expiring October 15, 1990. Allow vendor 165 d.   58.77

8. From May 3 to Oct. 15 is 165. The purchaser must pay for $\frac{165}{365}$ of the premium already paid by the vendor.

Balance due on closing   154 185.35

$156 058.77   156 058.77

10. Balance the columns to check.

E. & O.E.

11. Errors and omissions excepted.

9. Balance due on closing is the sum of the right-hand column minus the sum of all other figures in the left-hand column.

Day of Month	July	Aug.	Sept.
1	182	213	244
2	183	214	245
3	184	215	246
4	185	216	247
5	186	217	248
6	187	218	249
7	188	219	250
8	189	220	251
9	190	221	252
10	191	222	253
11	192	223	254
12	193	224	255
13	194	225	256
14	195	226	257
15	196	227	258
16	197	228	259
17	198	229	260
18	199	230	261
19	200	231	262
20	201	232	263
21	202	233	264
22	203	234	265
23	204	235	266
24	205	236	267
25	206	237	268
26	207	238	269
27	208	239	270
28	209	240	271
29	210	241	272
30	211	242	273
31	212	243	

Day of Month	Oct.	Nov.	Dec.
1	274	305	335
2	275	306	336
3	276	307	337
4	277	308	338
5	278	309	339
6	279	310	340
7	280	311	341
8	281	312	342
9	282	313	343
10	283	314	344
11	284	315	345
12	285	316	346
13	286	317	347
14	287	318	348
15	288	319	349
16	289	320	350
17	290	321	351
18	291	322	352
19	292	323	353
20	293	324	354
21	294	325	355
22	295	326	356
23	296	327	357
24	297	328	358
25	298	329	359
26	299	330	360
27	300	331	361
28	301	332	362
29	302	333	363
30	303	334	364
31	304		365

When the vendor and the purchaser have made their mortgage arrangements independently of each other, there is no mention of them in the statement of adjustments.

Example 3. Mr. and Mrs. G. Stanley are selling their condominium, Unit 4, 16 Pleasant View Ave., to Mr. and Mrs. F. McDonald.

Particulars:
Closing date — July 31, 1990
Sale price — $127 000
Deposit — $1000
Mortgage — McDonalds assume an existing mortgage. Last payment date — June 30, 1990
Principal after last payment — $74 500

Interest rate — $9\frac{1}{2}$% per annum

1990 taxes — $875, not paid to date
Fire insurance — one-year premium — $195, expires August 25, 1990

Draw up a statement of adjustments and calculate the balance due on closing.

Solution:

Statement of Adjustments
as of July 31, 1990
Stanley sale to McDonald
Unit 4, 16 Pleasant View Ave.
Easton

Sale price		$127 000.00
Deposit	$ 1 000.00	
Mortgage		
Principal	$ 74 500.00	
Interest		
$9\frac{1}{2}$ June 30 – July 31		
Allow to purchaser 31 d.	$ 601.10	
1990 taxes $875		
Allow purchaser 212 d.	$ 508.22	
Insurance premium $95.		
Expires Aug. 25, 1990.		
Allow vendor 25 d.		$6.51
Balance due on closing	$ 50 397.19	
	$127 006.51	$127 006.51

E. & O.E.

EXERCISE 13.8

A

1. State whether each of the following items would be credited to the vendor or to the purchaser when a statement of adjustments is drawn up.
   (a) the sale price
   (b) the deposit
   (c) the portion of a fire insurance policy premium covering future time
   (d) the unpaid municipal taxes
   (e) the value of furnace oil in the storage tank
   (f) the taxes prepaid by the vendor
   (g) the interest accrued since the last payment on a mortgage assumed by the purchaser

B

2. Calculate the amount allowed in each of the following cases, and state to whom it is allowed.
   (a) an insurance premium for 1 a in the amount of $170; closing date September 24; expiry date December 30
   (b) an insurance premium for 3 a in the amount of $240; closing date January 31, 1991; expiry date April 4, 1992
   (c) municipal taxes of $643; instalment of $250 paid; closing date September 30
   (d) municipal taxes of $759.30; instalment of $500 paid; closing date May 31
   (e) mortgage assumed by the purchaser; principal at date of last payment, $96 250 as of January 15; closing date January 30; interest at $10\frac{1}{2}$% per annum
   (f) mortgage assumed by the purchaser; principal at date of last payment, $84 500 as of May 5; closing date May 31; interest accrued at 9% per annum
   (g) an insurance premium for 2 a in the amount of $560; closing date February 15, 1990; expiry date June 30, 1991

3. Ms. J. Payne is selling her property to Mrs. W. Hanson.

Closing date — April 30, 1992
Location — 240 Sandford St.
　　　　　　　Norton
Sale price — $88 500
Deposit — $2000
Municipal taxes — $738, none paid this year
Fire insurance — premium for 1 a — $176, expires July 10

Draw up a statement of adjustments and calculate the balance due on closing.

4. Ms. W. Morton is selling her cottage to Mr. I. Sorenson.

Closing date — February 28, 1990
Location — Lot 45 Lakeside Rd.
　　　　　　　Cowan Township
Sale price — $126 900
Deposit — $600
First mortage — Mr. Sorenson is to assume the existing mortgage. The principal at the time of the last payment was $58 450.
Interest is accrued at $10\frac{1}{2}$% per annum from January 31.
Municipal taxes — $300 in arrears from previous year to be assumed by the purchaser.
Taxes for this year $450.
Fire insurance — premium for 1 a, $96.50, expires July 30.

Draw up a statement of adjustments and calculate the balance due on closing.

13.9 UTILITY COSTS

Home-owners are responsible for utilities, as well as house and property taxes and the mortgage.

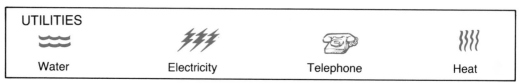

UTILITIES			
Water	Electricity	Telephone	Heat

Most homes are hooked up to water, electricity, the telephone, and some form of heating.

WATER

The amount of water used is measured by a water meter in cubic metres. Each home connected to a municipal water supply has a water meter.

Once each billing period, a municipal employee reads the water meter. If customers are not home, they are asked to read the meter and phone in the information.

WATER METER

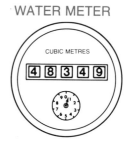

CUBIC METRES

4 8 3 4 9

Example 1. The reading of the water meter for the previous three-month billing period was 48 169.

The new reading is 48 349.
(a) How many cubic metres of water were used?
(b) If water is charged at the following rates:

First 5 m³	$1.20/m³
Next 40 m³	$0.58/m³
Next 200 m³	$0.25/m³
Next 1000 m³	$0.12/m³
Additional m³	$0.09/m³

plus a surcharge for new equipment of 1%, how much is owed for water over the three-month billing period?

Solution:

(a) Water used = 48 349 − 48 169
        = 180
∴ 180 m³ of water were used.

(b) Charges for Water = 5 × $1.20 + 40 × $0.58 + 135 × $0.25
        = $6.00 + $23.20 + $33.75
        = $62.95

Surcharge = $62.95 × 0.01
        ≐ $0.63

Total amount owed = $62.95 + $0.63
        = $63.58

The total amount owed is $63.58.

ELECTRICITY

Like water, electricity is measured by a meter located in each home. The unit of measure is the kilowatt hour (kW·h). The electricity meter is similar to the water meter, except that it has a large wheel that indicates the rate at which electricity is being used. A kilowatt hour is the number of kilowatts used multiplied by the number of hours of use.

Once each billing period the meter is read by an employee of the electricity or hydro company. The former reading is subtracted from the present reading to determine the number of kilowatt hours used.

ELECTRICITY METER

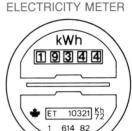

Example 2. The current reading of the electricity meter is 19 344. The reading at the end of the last two-month billing period was 17 720.
(a) How many kilowatt hours were used between billing periods?
(b) If electricity is charged at the following rates:

Customer charge per month $9.89
First 800 kW·h $0.0631 kW·h
Over 800 kW·h $0.037 128 kW·h

how much is owed for electricity over the current two-month period?

Solution:
(a) Electricity used = 19 344 − 17 720
           = 1624
∴ 1624 kW·h were used.

(b) Charges for electricity = 800 × $0.0631 + 824 × $0.037 128
                      = $50.48 + $30.59
                      = $81.07

Total amount owed = $9.89 + $81.07
                  = $90.96

The total amount owed is $90.96.

Like water, the charges are scaled. The more used, the lower the cost per unit.

Example 3. How many kilowatt hours of electricity are used by twenty 100 W bulbs in 8 h?

Solution:
Use the following formula to find the amount of electricity.

$$\text{Amount of electricity (kW·h)} = \frac{\left(\begin{array}{c}\text{Number}\\\text{of Bulbs}\end{array} \times \begin{array}{c}\text{Wattage}\\\text{(W)}\end{array}\right) \times \left(\begin{array}{c}\text{Time}\\\text{(h)}\end{array}\right)}{1000}$$

$$= \frac{20 \times 100 \times 8}{1000}$$

$$= 16$$

In 8 h, the twenty bulbs used 16 kW·h of electricity.

TELEPHONE

Most people see the telephone as a necessity. As a public utility, the charges for its use are controlled by the government. The monthly bill looks simple, but it is really very complex.

Features of a monthly telephone bill:
• A service charge, which is the same for all users.
• An equipment rental charge, which varies according to the number of telephones and telephone connections in the home.
• Tax is charged on basic service and equipment rental.
• Chargeable long distance calls plus tax.
• Discounts are applied to long distance calls within a stated area, usually local province.

All these charges add up to the monthly charge for using your telephone.

THE TELEPHONE COMPANY

Telephone Number 613 555 1111   Date   09 10   Amount Due $34.38

M. A. Smith
7 Rockcliffe Road
Kanata

Account Summary

Basic Service	$12.70
Equipment Rental	8.65
Tax	1.49
Total Current Charges	$22.84

Chargeable Calls

No. Date	Number Called			Start	Min	Charge	Discount	Amount
1 08 10	Berwyn	MD	301 555 0747	1858	6			$3.15
	from An Arb MI							
2 08 15	Toronto	ON	416 555 1091	0919	5	3.16		3.16
3 08 17	Ottawa	ON	613 555 7423	2115	7	4.96	.90	4.06
4 08 18	Dir. Assistance		555 7186					.60
						Total Chargeable Calls		$10.97
							Tax	.57
								$11.54

HEATING

The most common methods of heating a home are electricity, oil, and natural gas. At times, oil has been less expensive than electricity and natural gas. At other times, natural gas and electricity have been the most economical choice.

Home-owners should compare the advantages and disadvantages of one form of heating over the others. Current fuel costs and the cost of converting from one heating method to another should be checked.

ELECTRICITY

Electricity for home heating is charged at a lower rate than electricity for appliances. As stated earlier, the more electricity consumed, the lower the price is per unit.

OIL

Furnace oil is delivered to a home in large tanker trucks. The average oil tank holds about 1000 L of oil. The tank has a meter so that the home-owner can tell how much oil is left in the tank. In Canada, most home-owners pay for their fuel in ten equal instalments. The amount of the monthly payment is estimated from the history of oil consumption. The customer then pays one-tenth of the estimated amount per month from September to June. This is a reasonable method of payment because during the extremely cold months the fuel bill would be doubled or tripled.

Fuel is charged a given amount per litre. There is no graduated scale as with electricity or water. You pay the same price per litre no matter how many litres are used.

The meter of the tank truck records the amount being delivered and a notice of the amount of fuel delivered is given to the customer.

An example of a notice is given at the right.

1355305	100	100	1	1
ACCOUNT NUMBER	DRIVER	TRUCK	DEL'Y.	ZONE

12 20	624048	107
INVOICE DATE	INVOICE NUMBER	BILLING CODE

00433, 4	00000, 0	00433, 4
END VOLUME	START VOLUME	LITRES DELIVERED

	PER LITRE	
PRODUCT PRICE	037, 4	0162, 09
PROVINCIAL TAX	00, 0	0000, 00
FEDERAL TAX	00, 0	0000, 00
PLEASE PAY THIS AMOUNT.		0162, 09

NATURAL GAS

Natural gas is not available in all communities. Where it is available, it is piped into a central reservoir and then sent under pressure through underground pipes to homes. A meter is in each home with natural gas service.

GAS METER

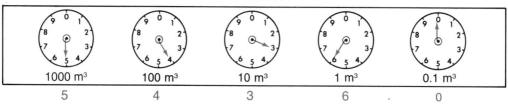

| 1000 m³ | 100 m³ | 10 m³ | 1 m³ | 0.1 m³ |
| 5 | 4 | 3 | 6 | . | 0 |

Gas is measured in cubic metres. To find the number of cubic metres of gas used, you must read each dial separately. The first dial on the meter measures tenths of cubic metres, the next units, the next tens, and the next hundreds. The digits are then recorded to give the total number of cubic metres. The gas meter is usually read and billed once a month, particularly during the winter months.

Example 4. The current reading on the gas meter is 5436.0 m³. The previous month's reading was 5414.0 m³.

(a) How many cubic metres of natural gas were used?

(b) Gas is charged according to the following rates:

From 0 m³ to 0.1 m³   flat charge of $17.89
From 0.1 m³ to 2 m³ $5.12/m³ plus a service charge of 2%
From 2 m³ to 7 m³ $3.79/m³ plus a service charge of 1.5%
From 7 m³ to 100 m³ $2.11/m³ plus a service charge of 1%
Over 100 m³ $1.45/m³ plus a service charge of 0.5%

How much is owed for gas over the monthly billing period?

Solution:

(a) Gas used $= 5436 - 5414$
$ = 22$
∴ 22 m³ of natural gas were used.

(b) This calculation can be organized in a table.

Range	Calculation	Total
0 to 0.1	Flat Charge	$17.89
0.1 to 2.0	2 × $5.12 = $10.24 2% of $10.24 = $0.20	$10.44
2.0 to 7.0	5 × $3.79 = $18.95 1.5% of $18.95 = $0.28	$19.23
7.0 to 100	15 × $2.11 = $31.65 1% of $31.65 = $0.32	$31.97
Total Amount		$79.53

The amount owed is $79.53.

B

1. Using the water rates stated in Example 1, calculate the bill for the following consecutive meter readings.
(a) 45 789   45 998   (b) 99 823   00 123
(c) 87 634   89 123   (d) 12 811   13 009

2. Using the electricity rates stated in Example 2, calculate the bill for the following consecutive meter readings.
(a) 19 388   21 899   (b) 98 344   02 321
(c) 81 000   99 901   (d) 45 711   98 345

3. Using the gas rates stated in Example 4, calculate the bill for the following consecutive meter readings.

(a)   501.1

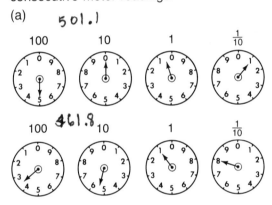

461.8

(b)   202.5

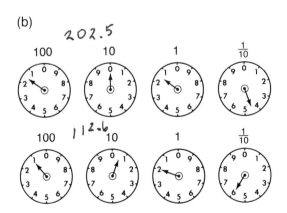

112.6

4. Decide which method of heating you prefer and defend your position as if you were a typical home-owner.

5. A family uses 4907 L/a of oil.
(a) What is the cost of heating their home for a year if oil cost $0.42/L?
(b) What is their estimated monthly payment on the ten-month equalized payment plan?

6. What is the phone bill for a family who has the following charges?
(a) basic service charge of $12.98 taxed at 7%
(b) three phones with a rental charge of $3.89 each taxed at 7%
(c) one call costing $9.89 with a discount of 1.5% taxed at 4.2%
(d) one call costing $7.89 taxed at 4.2%
(e) one call costing $11.98 taxed at 4.2%
(f) nine directory assistance calls at 0.60 each, not taxed

7. Contact your local hydro company, home heating oil company, and natural gas company to compare the following.
(a) average cost of heating a home in January
(b) the advantages of one method of heating over the others
(c) the rate per unit
(d) the method of calculating the monthly bill

MIND BENDER

Place the numbers from 1 to 9 in the squares to make the statements true.

(a) ■ × ■ + ■ = 7
    ■ ÷ ■ + ■ = 7
    ■ + ■ − ■ = 7

(b) ■ × ■ + ■ = 9
    ■ × ■ − ■ = 9
    ■ ÷ ■ + ■ = 9

13.10 CASE STUDIES FOR PERSONAL INCOME TAX

Income tax forms and their method of completion are undergoing constant revision. Because tax rates, deductions, and credits change from year to year, worked examples are not provided in this section.

Current tax forms are available at the District Taxation Office or at the post office.

The exercises that follow provide data so that tax forms can be completed. Since Canada Pension Plan (C.P.P.) contributions and Unemployment Insurance premiums (U.I.) change every year, values for these contributions are not provided. The word "maximum" is used to mean the greatest amount that can be deducted from one job without overpayment.

EXERCISE 13.10

B

1. Dan Levy was born on May 14, 1966 and lives at 234 Acorn Ave. in Dalton. Dan is single and works as a reporter for The Daily News. In addition to his newspaper salary, Dan earned $3500 writing articles for a mystery magazine. The magazine publisher did not make any deductions on Dan's behalf. Dan donated $300 to charity and paid tuition fees of $1200 for a creative writing course.
The interest for the year on his bank savings account as shown on his T5 slip was $234.90.
The following is the financial data for Dan as supplied by the newspaper.

Total Earnings Before	
Deductions	$34 567.45
Deductions	
Income Tax	$8224.90
Registered Pension Plan	$666.66
C.P.P.	Maximum
U.I.	Maximum
Professional Dues	$789.90

Complete Dan's income tax return.

2. Sandra Houston was born on July 15, 1964. Her address is 1567 Stanford St., Apt. 1009 in Ajax. She is single and is employed as a forensic science technician for the government. Sandra is also a part-time student, and her tuition fees were $1500 this year. Sandra also donated $250 to charity.
The following is the financial data for Sandra.

Total Earnings Before	
Deductions	$37 123.98
Deductions	
Income Tax	$9123.56
Registered Pension Plan	$766.90
C.P.P.	Maximum
U.I.	Maximum
Professional Dues	$456.78

Complete an income tax return for Sandra.

3. Shirley Lee was born on July 10, 1960. She is married and lives with her husband, Terry, at 234 Drew St. in Carlisle. Terry is employed as a teacher by the Carlisle Board of Education. Shirley works as a mechanic for Air Canada.

During the year Shirley donated $200 to charity, and her T5 slips show that she earned $560.56 in interest from her account at the Bank of Montreal and $789.32 from her account at Canada Trust.

The Lees have one child, Donna, who is six years old. The Lees receive Family Allowance payments for her each month. Shirley claims Donna on her income tax return.

The following is the financial data for Shirley as supplied by her employer.

Total Earnings Before Deductions	$57 890.89
Deductions	
Income Tax	$13 087.56
Registered Pension Plan	$579.36
C.P.P.	Maximum
U.I.	Maximum
Union Dues	$845.98

Complete Shirley's income tax return.

4. Wanda Stabler is a self-employed interior decorator. She lives at 234 Hillcrest Ave. in Dundurn. Wanda's brother Derek lives with her. Because of an illness, Derek does not work and relies totally on Wanda for his support.

Last year Wanda's business earned $78 890 before business expenses. Her business expenses amounted to $29 945. Wanda paid the government $9875 during the year for income tax. She made the maximum contributions for C.P.P. and U.I. She has a self-directed pension plan to which she contributed $500.

Wanda donated $100 to charity.

To supplement her income, Wanda taught a college course on interior design. She was paid $5000 for teaching the course. The college did not make any deductions from the $5000.

Complete Wanda's income tax return.

5. David Vanderpool was born on December 14, 1962. He lives with his wife Julie at 1254 Webb St. in Exeter. David is employed as a fire fighter for the Exeter Fire Department. Julie works part-time teaching computer science. Last year she earned $5500.

The Vanderpools have three children, Robert, 12; Paula, 10; and Susan, 7. They receive Family Allowance payments for the children each month.

Last year David contributed $300 to charity. His T5 slip from the Toronto Dominion Bank showed $1298.98 as interest earned on a savings account.

The following is the financial data for David as supplied by his employer.

Total Earnings Before Deductions	$56 706.20
Deductions	
Income Tax	$12 456.99
Registered Pension Plan	$806.30
C.P.P.	Maximum
U.I.	Maximum
Union Dues	$708.67

Complete David's income tax return.

6. Bob Winter was born on May 1, 1960 and lives at 345 Otto St. in Fairfield. Bob is a single parent with two children, Janet, 4, and Colleen, 3. Bob received Family Allowance payments for both children. He paid the Happy Days Nursery $150 a week for 48 weeks to take care of his children while he was at work. Bob is a teacher. His T5 slip shows $346.89 in interest from the Teachers' Credit Union. Bob donated $200 to charity.

The following is the financial data for Bob.

Total Earnings Before Deductions	$55 783.12
Deductions	
Income Tax	$10 003.20
Registered Pension Plan	$3724.90
C.P.P.	Maximum
U.I.	Maximum
Professional Dues	$987.90

Complete Bob's income tax return.

13.11 PROBLEM SOLVING

1. Figure ABCD–EFGH is a cube.
Find the measure of each angle in △ACH.

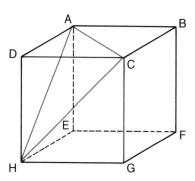

2. Anne Weber, a disc jockey, wants to play both sides of 5 records in order.
In how many different orders can the 10 sides be played?

3. Two houses are next to each other on the same side of the street. The product of the house numbers is 27 224.
Find the house numbers.

4. Two houses are next to each other on the same side of the street. The product of the house numbers is 27 555.
Find the house numbers.

5. When 2^4 is written $2^4 = 16$, the units digit is 6.
Find the units digit when each of the following is written in standard form.
(a) 2^8 (b) 2^{20} (c) 2^{100}
(d) 3^9 (e) 3^{21} (f) 3^{100}
(g) 7^{125} (h) 5^{150} (i) 23^{82}

6. Insert $+$, $-$, $\times$, $\div$, or ( ) to make the following equations true.
(a) 3   3   3   3 = 1
(b) 3   3   3   3 = 2
(c) 3   3   3   3 = 3
(d) 3   3   3   3 = 4
(e) 3   3   3   3 = 5
(f) 3   3   3   3 = 6

7. In economics, we are concerned with business cycles. With two dice we can manufacture something that looks a little like a business cycle. The following are the results of ten successive rolls:

10, 7, 3, 4, 11, 2, 4, 9, 3, 12

We then find the five-period moving averages.

$(10 + 7 + 3 + 4 + 11) \div 5 = 7$
$(7 + 3 + 4 + 11 + 2) \div 5 = 5.1$
$(3 + 4 + 11 + 2 + 4) \div 5 = 4.8$
...

(a) Find the remaining five-period moving averages in the above experiment.
(b) Roll a pair of dice ten times and record the values for each roll in order. Calculate the five-period moving averages for this set of rolls.
(c) Compare the two sets of moving averages.

8. Propane is a combination of carbon and hydrogen in the ratio of 9 : 2 by mass.

How much hydrogen is there in a barbecue tank that contains 8.2 kg of propane?

9. When water freezes to make ice, it expands. The volume of the ice formed is 9% more than the water.
How much water must you freeze to make 655 m³ of ice?

10. An astronaut whose "earth weight" is 90 kg has a "moon weight" of 15 kg.

(a) What is the moon weight of an astronaut whose earth weight is 75 kg?

(b) What is the earth weight of some moon rocks that weighed 200 kg on the moon?

11. In the major diatonic musical scale, the frequencies of the notes are in the ratios of simple whole numbers. In a major triad within the scale, the frequencies of the notes are in the ratio of 4 : 5 : 6.

(a) Find the frequencies of the notes in the major triad C, E, and G, if you begin with E having a frequency of 330.

(b) Play the notes of the major triad C, E, and G and describe the sound.

(c) Starting at middle C on a piano, and playing only white keys towards the right, find within only nine notes two other major triads besides C, E, and G.

12. Three circles with radii of 10 cm are inscribed in a circle as shown.

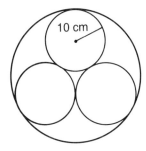

What is the radius of the larger circle to the nearest tenth?

PERSONNEL OFFICER

Anita Gonzalez and Adam Perini are personnel officers with a large Canadian company. They provide administrative services for the company. These services include conferring with management representatives and department supervisors to determine personnel needs and to put together detailed information about job descriptions. They advertise the jobs, hold interviews, and select the most suitable applicants to recommend to management. It is also part of their job to inform employees about pay, hours of work, attendance, and promotional opportunities. As personnel officers, they are also called upon to act as resource persons for both supervisors and employees about policies on performance, classification, welfare, and health. Anita and Adam are also called upon to set up company courses for retraining.

EXERCISE

1. An across-the-board increase in pay of $0.85/h is granted to 745 employees at a factory. Each employee works 40 h/week and is paid for 52 weeks.

(a) What increase in pay does this amount to for an employee in one year?

(b) What is the additional cost in wages to the company for one year?

2. What is the cost to the company to set up a computer retraining course for its employees if 12 people attend at $175/d for 3 d?

13.12 REVIEW EXERCISE

1. A salesperson makes 7% commission on the first $1000 in sales, 10% commission on the next $2000 in sales, 15% commission on the next $2000 in sales, and 25% commission on the next $10 000 in sales.
What is the monthly salary of a person who sells $12 000 worth of goods in the month?

2. A person earns $27 895/a. The net salary is 71% of the gross salary.
What is the value of the pay cheque if the employee is paid monthly, weekly, bi-weekly, quarterly, and bi-monthly?

3. A licensed auto mechanic makes $19.17/h, based on a forty-hour week, 52 weeks/a.
If C.P.P. is deducted at a rate of 2.2% of gross income and U.I. is deducted at a rate of 0.7% of gross income, and the mechanic makes a charitable donation of $12/week, what is the weeky net income?

4. List the deductions required by federal law.

5. List the deductions that may be deducted as a condition of employment.

6. List deductions that are discretionary for the employee.

7. Using the recommended spending levels below, find the recommended upper and lower limit for each expenditure for a family with a total net income of $31 000/a.

Housing	20% to 30% of net income
Food	15% to 25% of net income
Transportation	10% to 20% of net income
Clothing	8% to 12% of net income
Personal and Medical	7% to 10% of net income

8. Find the interest charged and the effective rate of interest to the nearest tenth of a percent for each of the following.

	Principal	Monthly Payment
(a)	$700	12 of $71.08
(b)	$2000	24 of $110
(c)	$27 000	36 of $1050
(d)	$8120	24 of $374

9. (a) Give three advantages of living in a house.
(b) Give three advantages of apartment living.

10. Why is it wise to have a lawyer to protect your interests when purchasing a house?

11. What items are usually considered in calculating the fair rented value of a property?

12. What items are usually considered in the adjustment to the sale price of a dwelling?

13. Mr. Collins is considering the purchase of a house. The purchase price is $142 000, requiring a down payment of $35 000. A first mortgage amortized over 25 a at $9\frac{1}{2}$% is available. Taxes are estimated at $1900/a and heating at $500/a. Electric power, water, and phone average $125/a. Mr. Collins has saved $20 000 and can get a second mortgage for $15 000 at 11%, requiring payments of $175/month.
(a) Calculate the total average monthly cost for accommodation.
(b) If 27% of his income is the maximum that Mr. Collins will allocate to accommodation, what should the family income be if they are to purchase this home?

14. (a) A mortgage for $190 000 is amortized over 30 a at 11%.
What is the monthly payment?

(b) A second mortgage is taken out for $30 000 to meet the down payment. This mortgage is amortized over 10 a at $12\frac{1}{2}\%$.
What is the total monthly cost for both first and second mortgages?

15. A mortgage of $150 000 is repaid by monthly payments of $1000 on the principal and quarterly interest payments of 9% on the unpaid balance.

(a) Calculate the first two interest payments if the mortgage is taken out March 1, and payments are due the first of every month.

(b) What is the total amount paid in the first 6 months?

16. Using the utility rates from section 13.9, calculate the bill for each of the following.

(a) consecutive water meter readings of 74 234 and 74 549

(b) consecutive electricity meter readings of 23 441 and 26 196

(c) consecutive gas meter readings of 2336.4 and 2460.6

17. Write up a statement of adjustments for the following sales and calculate the balance due on closing.

(a) Mr. and Mrs. O. Simpson are selling a house to Mr. and Mrs. P. Branson at 32 Plain Cres., Warwick.

Closing date — August 15
Sale price — $264 500
Deposit — $5000
Taxes — $1985, first instalment of $350 paid
Fire insurance — one-year premium — $317, expires November 18

(b) Mr. B. Wallace is selling a condominium to Miss W. Saxby at 12 Horton Place, Newtown.

Closing date — February 13
Sale price — $135 000
Deposit — $3000
Taxes — $1745, none paid to date, none in arrears
First mortgage — assumed by the purchaser, principal at the time of last payment $81 430; unpaid interest accrued from January 25 at $9\frac{1}{2}\%$
Monthly maintenance charge — $127/month, paid for February
Fire insurance — one-year premium — $185, expires April 4

18. How many kilowatt hours of electricity are used by ten 60 W bulbs in 8 h?

13.13 CHAPTER 13 TEST

1. A salesperson is paid a weekly salary of $250 plus a commission of 20% on sales over $2000.
Calculate the gross income for the week on sales of $3540.

2. Samantha is a computer operator. She makes $22.50/h, based on 35 h/week, 52 weeks per year. The estimated income tax deduction is 35% of gross income. C.P.P. is deducted at a rate of 2% of gross income, and U.I. is deducted at 0.8%.
What is her estimated monthly net income?

3. It is estimated that 8% to 12% of disposable income is necessary for clothing, depending on the job requirements.
What is the range of spending required for clothing by a person who has a net income of $286/week?

4. It is estimated that 20% to 30% of net income is required for housing costs.
What is the range of expenditure required for housing costs on a net salary of $65 280?

5. Determine the cash flow for each month in the chart.

Month	June	July	August
Net Income	$2465.50	$2105.16	$2541.25
Expenditures	$2106.75	$3246.82	$1989.67

6. What is the effective rate of interest on a loan of $1800 if the loan is to be paid off with 24 equal monthly payments of $100?

7. What is the highest monthly cost for housing that each of the following should consider?
(a) Phil Brazeau has a gross income of $52 750/a.
(b) Jackie McIntosh has an annual salary of $58 675, and her husband Ed earns $42 500.

8. Draw up a statement of adjustments and calculate the balance due on closing for Bruce Garret selling a house to Deborah Tooke.
The closing date is June 30. The selling price of the house is $185 000, and a deposit of $5000 was made with the offer to purchase. The first instalment of $392 has been paid on the annual taxes of $1845. The home-owners' insurance premium of $210 has been paid, and the expiry date is October 31.

MATHEMATICS OF SMALL BUSINESS

14

BUYING AND SELLING

Goods are bought and sold at either a profit or a loss. The following definitions apply to profit and loss in the buying and selling of goods:

Sales − cost of goods sold = $\begin{cases} \text{gross profit (if positive)} \\ \text{or} \\ \text{loss (if negative)} \end{cases}$
Cost of goods sold = $\begin{cases} \quad \text{(inventory at beginning of period)} \\ + \text{(purchases)} \\ - \text{(inventory at end of period)} \end{cases}$
Net profit = gross profit − operating expenses (A negative net profit is called a loss.)
Gross margin = selling price − cost price
Rate of margin = $\dfrac{\text{selling price} - \text{cost price}}{\text{selling price}} \times 100\%$
Selling price = cost price + markup
Markup = selling price − cost price
Rate of markup = $\dfrac{\text{selling price} - \text{cost price}}{\text{cost price}} \times 100\%$
Net price = list price − discount

EXERCISE 1

1. Find the missing quantities.

Number of Units Sold	50	15	144
Unit Cost Price	$1.25		$0.09
Unit Selling Price	$1.65		
Cost of Goods Sold		$82.50	
Total Sales		$131.70	$17.28
Profit (+) or Loss (−)			

2. What is the selling price of a leather jacket with a cost price of $876.40 and a rate of markup of 25%?

3. What is the selling price of a radio with a cost price of $53.65 and a rate of markup of 40%?

4. What is the markup on a lamp with cost price of $123.50 and a margin of 22%?

5. (a) If the margin is 24%, what is the rate of markup?
(b) If the rate of markup is 42%, what is the margin?

ORDER

EXERCISE 2

1. Express the following sets of numbers from smallest to largest and identify the median.
(a) 15, 22, 17, 46, 21, 9, 85, 11, 28, 20, 75
(b) 33, 24, 56, 33, 29, 85, 24, 47, 31, 83, 85, 9
(c) $\frac{1}{2}, \frac{3}{4}, \frac{5}{8}, \frac{7}{16}, \frac{1}{4}, \frac{3}{16}, \frac{5}{32}$

2. Express the following sets of numbers from largest to smallest and identify the median.
(a) 27, 39, 18, 124, 63, 35, 59, 61, 33, 44, 37, 26, 51, 109
(b) 25, 53, 26, 64, 22, 43, 37, 56, 22, 34, 54, 25, 63, 8, 20, 13
(c) $\frac{3}{4}, \frac{1}{2}, \frac{5}{8}, \frac{9}{16}, \frac{1}{4}, \frac{11}{32}, \frac{3}{8}, \frac{7}{16}$

AVERAGES

EXERCISE 3

1. Find the arithmetic mean of the following sets of numbers.
(a) 85, 71, 39, 49, 68, 53, 72, 65
(b) 58, 78, 47, 58, 63, 54, 79, 61
(c) 68.4, 21.3, 58.5, 63.2, 71.7, 58.5, 48.6
(d) 328, 527, 683, 425, 501, 575

2. Ingrid's first seven marks are

   78, 82, 67, 88, 75, 72, 79

What should her eighth mark be in order to have an average mark of 80?

3. Manny Rivero hit safely 119 times during 462 official "at bats."
Calculate his batting average to the nearest thousandth.

CALCULATOR AND ROUNDING

EXERCISE 4

Evaluate the following correct to 3 significant digits.

1. (a) 26.5 × 3.7
(b) 4.8 × 11.6
(c) 33.5 × 14.2
(d) 0.7 × 25.5
(e) 0.3 × 0.52
(f) 136 × 9.8

2. (a) 12.3 × 7.4 × 16.2
(b) 66.5 × 0.42 × 1.1
(c) 23.6 × 13.3 × 0.72
(d) 798 × 0.43 × 1.07
(e) 7.7 × 0.005 × 60
(f) 605 × 7.9 × 0.35

3. (a) 66.5 ÷ 32   (b) 127 ÷ 2.7
(c) 0.81 ÷ 3.2   (d) 0.073 ÷ 0.56
(e) 9.01 ÷ 27.3   (f) 4.6 ÷ 83.5

4. (a) $\dfrac{77.2 \times 11.3}{12.1}$
(b) $\dfrac{6.8 \times 7.25}{4.6}$
(c) $\dfrac{2.8 \times 9.65}{3.7 \times 12.2}$
(d) $\dfrac{0.76 \times 4.2}{0.083 \times 161}$
(e) $\dfrac{83.5 \times 124 \times 0.51}{6.3 \times 96.4}$
(f) $\dfrac{22.2 \times 871 \times 76.2}{4.3 \times 974}$

5. (a) $(26.3)^2$ (b) $(9.7)^2$
(c) $(11.5)^2$ (d) $(127)^2$
(e) $(0.52)^2$ (f) $(0.073)^2$
(g) $(4.65)^2$ (h) $(7.86)^2$

6. (a) $\sqrt{17.3}$ (b) $\sqrt{9.85}$
(c) $\sqrt{0.56}$ (d) $\sqrt{763}$
(e) $\sqrt{0.0017}$ (f) $\sqrt{0.000\,565}$

14.1 STARTING A SMALL BUSINESS

Starting and operating a small business is an option for young people who are looking for an exciting and rewarding career. According to Statistics Canada, over one-quarter of the revenue generated by the Canadian economy is from small business. Since these businesses are almost entirely owned by Canadians, it means that the revenues stay in Canada.

A business is considered small based on two criteria:
(i) the number of people employed, and
(ii) the total annual sales.

The Federal Department of Industry, Trade, and Commerce uses a working definition of 1 to 100 employees, depending on the type of business, and less than $2 million in annual sales. The department divides small business into six business sectors:

- Construction Sector
- Financial Sector
- Manufacturing Sector
- Service Sector
- Trade Sector (wholesale/retail)
- Transportation Sector

Starting a small business requires
- A good business idea
- A business plan
- Knowledge of the business
- Hard work
- Money

When you have decided to start a small business, it is important to discuss your plans with a lawyer, an accountant, and a banker.

A good business plan should consider the product or service, the potential customers, and the competition. The following chart can be used to develop a small business plan:

Planning a Small Business	
Product Service	1. Is the product or service unique? 2. Is it something people want or need? 3. Can it be priced competitively? 4. Does it exist now or must it be developed?
Potential Customers	1. Who are the customers? (sex, age, and income level) 2. What is the customer's lifestyle? Where do they live? 3. Why do they want to buy or use the product or service? 4. How often do they purchase the product or service?
Competition	1. How is their product/service different from yours? 2. What percentage of the market do they control? 3. How experienced and strong is the competition? 4. What is your advantage? What is their advantage?

Financial planning is essential for a small business. The essence of a business finance, as with personal finance, is cash flow. When the amount of money taken in is greater than the amount of money going out, we say that the business is in a position of positive cash flow.

> **Cash Flow**
> Net cash flow = cash inflow − cash outflow
>   = business revenues − expenses and taxes

When planning the financing of a small business, it is assumed that there are start-up costs, and these must be accounted for in the monthly cash flow. Start-up costs include the initial purchase of equipment, furniture, supplies, and other items peculiar to the type of business and the rental of space. Fixed costs are those expenses that occur whether or not any profit is made. Rent, heat, lighting, telephone, advertising, and wages for permanent staff are examples of fixed costs. Variable costs are those expenses that vary according to the level of sales. Extra staff, extra advertising, long distance telephone calls, and additional supplies are examples of variable costs.

Example. Two people start and operate a small software business called Soft Design Inc. The cash flow for the first year of operation is given in the graph below.
From the graph, determine the following.
(a) What were the start-up costs?
(b) What were the fixed costs per month?
(c) In which month did the business break even?

Solution:
(a) To find the start-up costs, read the amount from the intercept on the vertical axis. The start-up costs include the fixed costs for the first month.
Start-up costs are $3000.

(b) To find the fixed costs, extend the Fixed Costs line to the left and read the intercept on the vertical axis.
Fixed costs per month are $1500.

(c) To find the break-even point on the graph, locate the point where the Gross Profit line and Total Costs line intersect. The business reached its break-even point in January.

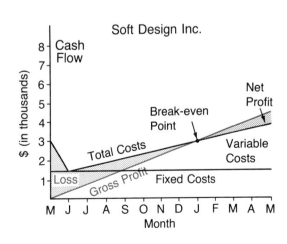

Soft Design Inc.

EXERCISE 14.1

A

1. Using a suitable reference, define the following terms as they relate to business.

(a) entrepreneur
(b) marketing
(c) consumer
(d) labour
(e) proprietor
(f) job market
(g) product
(h) wholesale
(i) service industry
(j) retail

2. List three businesses in your community that fall under the following business sectors.

(a) construction
(b) manufacturing
(c) financial
(d) trade
(e) service
(f) transportation

B

3. Calculate the net profit or loss for the first year of operation of each of the following small businesses.

(a) Diamond Distributors had start-up costs of $4895 and average monthly costs of $1789. The gross profit for each month averaged $2211.
   What is the profit or loss for the first year?
(b) Safeplay Toy Manufacturing had start-up costs of $120 211 and average monthly costs of $22 890. The average monthly gross profit was $27 100.
   What is the profit or loss for the first year?
(c) Anne's Designer Bridal Fashions had start-up costs of $34 755 and average monthly costs of $25 000. Gross monthly profits averaged $32 000.
   What is the profit or loss for the first year?

4. For each of the cash flow graphs below, answer the following.

(a) What are the fixed costs per month?
(b) During which months did the company reach a break-even point?
(c) What was the net profit or loss in January?
(d) Determine whether the company had a successful year.

(i)

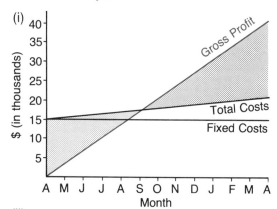

(ii)

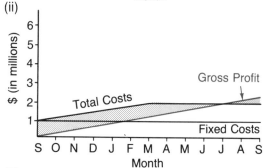

(iii)

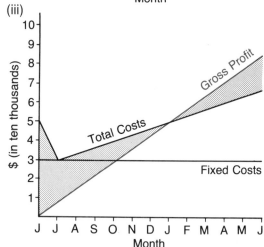

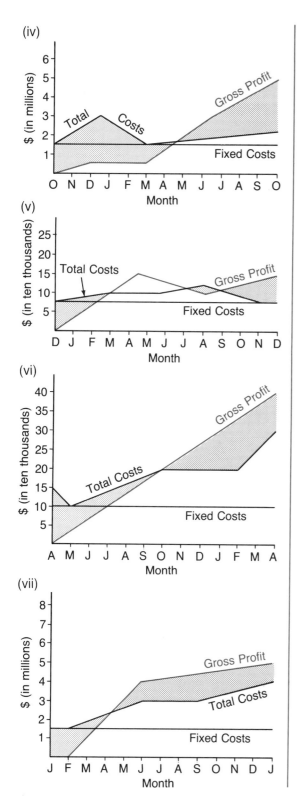

(iv)

(graph: y-axis $ (in millions) 1–6; x-axis Month O N D J F M A M J J A S O; labels "Total", "Costs", "Gross Profit", "Fixed Costs")

(v)

(graph: y-axis $ (in ten thousands) 5–25; x-axis Month D J F M A M J J A S O N D; labels "Total Costs", "Gross Profit", "Fixed Costs")

(vi)

(graph: y-axis $ (in ten thousands) 5–40; x-axis Month A M J J A S O N D J F M A; labels "Gross Profit", "Total Costs", "Fixed Costs")

(vii)

(graph: y-axis $ (in millions) 1–8; x-axis Month J F M A M J J A S O N D J; labels "Gross Profit", "Total Costs", "Fixed Costs")

C

5. Draw a yearly cash flow graph for the Cooper Business Products Company with monthly fixed costs of $3500 using the following information.

Month	Variable Costs	Gross Profit
June	$1500	$3000
July	$1000	$3500
Aug.	$1000	$3500
Sept.	$1500	$4500
Oct.	$2000	$5000
Nov.	$2500	$6000
Dec.	$3500	$6500
Jan.	$2000	$6000
Feb.	$1500	$5000
March	$1500	$4000
April	$1000	$3500
May	$1000	$3000

(a) What is the net profit or loss per month?
(b) What is the total net profit or loss for the year?
(c) When did the company reach the break-even point(s)?
(d) Write a statement that describes the company's profitability.

MIND BENDER

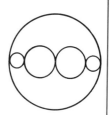

The diameter of the large circle has been divided into four parts in the ratio 1 : 2 : 2 : 1, and circles are drawn as shown.

Compare the circumference of the large circle with the sum of the circumferences of the four smaller circles.

14.2 OFFICE COSTS

Most small businesses require an office from which to operate. Consulting services, accounting services, and real estate are examples of businesses that require a business address, office, secretarial assistance, office machines, and paper supplies to operate. In this section we will examine the cost of maintaining an office.

Example 1. Two accountants start a small accounting firm. The space requirement is a 5 m by 5 m office for each partner and a secretarial/reception area 4 m by 6 m.

(a) What floor area is required?
(b) What is the monthly rent at $85/m² per year?

Solution:

(a) Floor area required $= 2(5 \times 5) + (4 \times 6)$
$$= 50 + 24$$
$$= 74$$

The floor area required is 74 m².

(b) Cost per year for space $= 74 \times \$85$
$$= \$6290$$

Cost per month $= \$6290 \div 12$
$$= \$524.17$$

∴ the monthly rent is $524.17.

> **625 m²**
> **OFFICE**
> One entire floor, free parking, new building. From $115/m². Ten minutes to downtown.

> **ATRIUM**
> **IN THE MARKET**
> Professional office to 750 m², 24 h security. For $125/m².

> **NICHOLAS STREET**
> 70 m² to 200 m². Will partition to suit. $95/m²

> **CITY CENTRE**
> Ample parking. Several offices and reception. Available Nov. 1. $85/m². 70 m² to 350 m².

Example 2. A consulting firm uses about 235 000 sheets of paper per year. Of the paper used, 19% is for preparing originals and 81% is used for photocopying. Paper costs $22 per 1000 sheets and photocopies cost an additional $0.035 per copy. What is the annual cost for paper and photocopying?

Solution: Cost per sheet of paper $= \$22 \div 1000$
$$= \$0.022$$

Number of sheets for originals $= 19\% \text{ of } 235\,000$
$$= 0.19 \times 235\,000$$
$$= 44\,650$$

Paper cost for originals $= \$0.022 \times 44\,650$
$$= \$982.30$$

Cost per sheet for photocopying $= \$0.022 + \$0.035$
$$= \$0.057$$

Cost for photocopying $= 81\% \text{ of } 235\,000 \times \$0.057$
$$= 0.81 \times 235\,000 \times \$0.057$$
$$= \$10\,849.95$$

Total cost of paper and photocopying $= \$982.30 + \$10\,948.95$
$$= \$11\,832.25$$

The total paper and photocopying costs are $11 832.25.

EXERCISE 14.2

A

1. Using the classified advertisements in a daily newspaper, determine the current

(a) lowest, (b) highest, (c) average

cost per square metre for office space.

2. Using the classified advertisements in a daily newspaper, determine the average salaries offered for secretarial assistance.

B

3. What are the monthly costs of maintaining an office for the Technical Consulting Company if it has the following fixed costs?

- 150 m² at $155/m² per year
- 17.5% of annual rent for utilities
- $1000 monthly for office supplies
- 600 000 photocopies per year at $0.41
- $75/month for a computer line
- $122/month for telephone
- $19 000 and $17 000 plus 11.3% for benefits for two secretaries

4. The Comtrack Lighting Company has monthly fixed costs of $22 725.

What must the minimum annual amount billed to customers be if after the fixed costs are deducted the company plans to have net earnings of $100 000/a?

5. Determine the cost of staffing and maintaining a work station per working day for the start-up of a small business given the following.

- The office is open 230 d each year.
- Floor space of 4 m by 5 m costs $109/m² per year.
- Furniture to equip a work station costs $2300.
- A computer for the work station costs $3500.
- Additional office supplies for a work station cost $14/d.
- Additional equipment for a work station costs $315/a.
- Secretarial staff earn $72 000/a plus 22% for employee benefits.

6. The daily cost of maintaining a work station at Designer Fashions headquarters is $138.75/d. The secretary at this work station prepares 80 pieces of written communication per day.

What is the average cost to the company to produce one piece of written communication?

7. Calculate the cost of producing a 20-page report, given the following information.

- The secretary earns $376 for a 40 h work week.
- The secretary types 55 words per minute using a word processor.
- The report averages 235 words per page.
- It takes 2 min to print a page.
- The consultant who prepared the report earns $32 000/a, based on 52 weeks and 36 h/week.
- It took the consultant 59 h, including data collection, to prepare the report.
- 500 sheets of paper costs $9.50.

MIND BENDER

1. Find a pattern and complete the tables.

(a)

2	12	10	25	20		16
3	7	7	10	9	6	

(b)

2	12	10	25	20		15
1	1	−3	0	1	3	

(c)

8	12	8	12	20		15
2	3	$\frac{1}{2}$	$\frac{1}{3}$	$\frac{4}{5}$	$\frac{3}{4}$	

14.3 COSTS OF MANUFACTURING

If a business is involved in manufacturing, then there will also be costs of manufacturing, selling, and distributing the product in addition to maintaining a business office. The following list shows some of the costs that are included in a business that manufactures a product.

Overhead
• Costs for design of the product
• Start-up and maintenance costs for the plant
• Equipment purchase and replacement
• Delivering the product to the customer
• Marketing and selling the product to the dealer
• Billing the customer
• Accounting costs to plan and maintain the cash flow
• Management costs

Labour Costs
• Employment costs for skilled and unskilled workers, management, and professional and clerical staff

Raw Materials
• Costs for supplies of raw materials and parts

When we purchase a manufactured product such as a pair of jeans, we are not only paying for the material that went into the production of the jeans but also for all of the above costs. The unit price of the jeans includes costs in overhead, labour costs, and raw materials and allows for a profit.

Example 1. What is the unit cost, to the nearest cent, for a pair of blue jeans, given the following information about the Good Looking Jean Company?
- Material costs for 1000 pairs are $1150.
- Manufacturing labour costs average $11/h.
- A time-motion study reveals that it takes 6 h to make 100 pairs of jeans.
- Total factory costs per day based on a daily output of 10 000 pairs are $12 000/d.
- The sales staff receives a commission of $0.32 per pair.
- Office, design, and management costs, including salaries of professional staff, are $5400/d.
- The company expects a profit of 20%.
- Shipping costs are charged to the customer.

Solution: Material costs per pair = $1150 ÷ 1000
$$= \$1.15$$

Labour costs per 100 pairs = $11 × 6
$$= \$66$$

Labour costs per pair = $66 ÷ 100
$$= \$6.60$$

Factory costs per pair = $12 000 ÷ 10 000
$$= \$1.20$$

Sales commission per pair = $0.32

Office costs per pair = $5400 ÷ 10 000
$$= \$0.54$$

Cost, not including the proft margin = $1.15 + $6.60 + $1.20 + $0.32 + $0.54
$$= \$9.81$$

Profit = $9.81 × 0.20
$$= \$1.96 \text{ (rounded to the nearest cent)}$$

Total unit cost = $9.81 + $1.96
$$= \$11.77$$

The unit cost is $11.77.

This is, of course, not the price that is paid by the customer in a department store. There are at least two more levels of profit — markup by the wholesaler and the retailer. The distribution of a product through various profit levels will be discussed later in this chapter.

Example 2. Using the information in Example 1, what are the expectations of the profit per day of the Good Looking Jean Company?

Solution: If the company manufactures 10 000 pairs per day,

Profit = $1.96 × 10 000
$$= \$19\ 600$$

The daily profit is $19 600.

EXERCISE 14.3

B

1. A manufacturer that produces computer keyboards has the following yearly costs:

Costs of Factory Building	$45 890
Utilities	$23 280
Wages for Labour	$428 762
Supplies/Parts	$89 120
Maintenance	$31 000
Insurance	$12 432
Professional Staff	$167 800
Sales/Advertising	$12 430
Clerical Staff	$58 120
Equipment Costs	$34 100

(a) Identify each of the above costs as overhead, labour, or raw materials.
(b) What are the yearly costs of overhead, raw materials, and labour?
(c) What are the daily costs of manufacturing, based on a five-day week, 52 weeks/a with seven statutory holidays during the year?
(d) If the company manufactures 35 keyboards each day, what is the cost of producing one unit?
(e) What is the percentage of profit if the keyboards are sold for $237 per unit?

2. (a) What is the unit cost of manufacturing a computer disk given the following information?
- The computer disk machine runs constantly stamping out 480 disks per hour 24 h/d.
- The cost of maintaining and running the disk machine is $78/h.
- The machine operator earns $17/h.
- The disk machine occupies 3.4 m² of floor space, which has a value of $289/m² per day.
- 40 disks can be stamped from a sheet of material, which costs $2.00 per sheet.
- Other overhead costs are 10% of the unit cost.

(b) What is the percentage of profit, based on the manufacturing costs, if the manufacturer sells a disk for $0.71?

3. Determine the overhead costs as a percent of the labour costs for each department of a small manufacturing firm if the company has the following six departments.

Management

The management department employs three executives. The president earns $85 000/a, and two vice-presidents earn $72 000/a.
Each executive office is 4 m by 6 m.

Clerical Department

The clerical department has four secretaries at an average salary of $29 000/a.
Each secretary has an office space of 3 m by 4 m.

Shipping and Receiving

The shipping and receiving department has five employees at an average salary of $30 000/a.
This department occupies a space of 12 m by 15 m.

Promotion and Sales

The promotion and sales department employs three salespeople at an average salary of $47 000/a and two public relations officers at $38 000/a.
Each salesperson has an office 4 m by 4 m, and each public relations officer has an office 4 m by 3 m.

Research and Development

In this department, there are two designers, each earning $49 000/a, and one draftsperson earning $37 000/a.
The designers share an office space 7 m by 8 m, and the draftsperson has an office 3 m by 2 m.

Manufacturing

The manufacturing department has 42 operators earning an average salary of $47 000/a.
The manufacturing floor is 34 m by 27 m. The average cost for utilities, rent, equipment, and supplies for the manufacturing department is $345/m². The average cost for the same items in the other five departments is $234/m².

4. The table below shows the costs related to the manufacture of seven products.

(a) Complete the table in your notebook, supplying the missing values.
(b) For each of the products in the table, find
   (i) the percentage of the unit cost that is overhead,
   (ii) the percentage of the unit cost that is labour,
   (iii) the percentage of the unit cost that is raw materials.
(c) Which of the given products are
   (i) labour intensive (labour costs make up the greatest part of unit cost),
   (ii) material intensive (material costs make up the greatest part of unit cost),
   (iii) overhead intensive (overhead costs make up the greatest part of unit cost)?
(d) Give three examples of products that would be
   (i) labour intensive,
   (ii) material intensive,
   (iii) overhead intensive.

5. Obtain an annual report from a small manufacturer and determine
(a) the products being manufactured (the product line),
(b) the costs for overhead,
(c) the labour costs,
(d) the cost of raw materials,
(e) the profit.

6. Obtain an annual report from a large national or international manufacturing company and determine
(a) the products being manufactured (the product line),
(b) the costs for overhead,
(c) the labour costs,
(d) the cost of raw materials,
(e) the profit.

Product	Overhead	Labour Costs	Raw Materials	Unit Cost	Profit	Price
Earrings	$81/100	$33/100	$1.80/100		12%	
Motorbike	$12 000/10	$4899/10	$29 897/10		34%	
Sticker	$143/10 000	$156/10 000	$1.78/10 000		119.5%	
Car Kit	$12 788/100	$123/10	$3121/10 000		23%	
Bicycle	$4578/100	$12 789/10	$78/1			$2348
Boat	$120 987/100	$89 983/10	$178 948/100			$20 200
Paper Clip	$438/10 000	$78/100 000	$348/10 000		16.7%	

14.4 DISTRIBUTION

Once the manufacturer has made a product, it is necessary to have the product reach the person who will buy it. The wholesale distributor is the link between the manufacturer and the purchaser. If the purchaser is closer to the manufacturer, then the cost of distribution will be less. Each time the product is handled in any way by a distributor, a percentage is added to the price of the product for distribution cost.

The manufacturer is the company that produces the product.

The wholesaler is the dealer who buys the product from the manufacturer and distributes it to the retailer, institutions, and other users.

The retailer is the dealer who sells directly to the public.

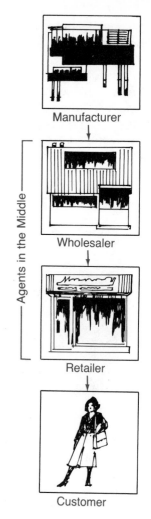

Manufacturer

Wholesaler

Retailer

Customer

Agents in the Middle

Example. A manufacturer of compact disc players ships 1000 units to the wholesale distributor. The wholesaler ships 200 units to Electronics City, who sells to the consumer.
What is the price of the CD player to the consumer given the following information?
• The unit price from the manufacturer is $98.
• Shipping charges from manufacturer to wholesaler are $23 500 per shipment.
• The wholesaler has a markup of 34% of the unit price to the retailer plus shipping charges.
• The retailer pays the wholesaler $3920 for shipping the 200 CD players.
• The retailer, Electronics City, has a markup of 55% to the consumer plus shipping charges.

Solution:

Shipping charges per unit (manufacturer to wholesaler)
= $23 500 ÷ 1000
= $23.50

Costs per unit after wholesale markup and shipping
= 134% of $98 + $23.50
= 1.34 × $98 + $23.50
= $131.32 + $23.50
= $154.82

Shipping charges per unit (wholesaler to retailer)
= $3920 ÷ 200
= $19.60

Cost per unit after retail markup and shipping
= 155% of $154.82 + $19.60
= 1.55 × $154.82 + $19.60
= $239.97 + $19.60
= $259.57

The consumer would pay $259.57 for the compact disc player.

EXERCISE 14.4

A

1. What services does the wholesaler provide for the manufactuer?

2. What services does the wholesaler provide for the retailer?

B

3. Complete the table below in your notebook, supplying the missing values.

Unit Cost (Manufacturer)	Markup (Wholesaler)	Markup (Retailer)	Retail Price
$458	42%	60%	
$1.23	30%	40%	
$1230	22%	55%	
	40%	70%	$240
	36%	45%	$1080
	18%	22%	$10.40
$500		50%	$900
$1200	30%		$2240

4. If a wholesaler has a choice of shipping by parcel post, courier service, commercial transport, or bus parcel express, what factors other than cost need to be considered when deciding on the method of shipment?

5. If a wholesaler has the following costs for handling a shipment of 100 desks. What percentage markup is necessary to cover the overhead and labour costs?
- Each desk costs the wholesaler $550.
- It costs $17 893 to ship 310 units.
- Storage charges are $45/m² per month, and each desk uses 1.2 m² of space.
- A desk stays in storage an average of two months prior to being shipped to the retailer.
- Sales and processing costs average $78 per unit.
- The company projects a profit of 14%.

6. A wholesaler has a choice of shipping goods from a manufacturer by postal service, courier service, or commercial transport.
Which method is most economical, given the following information?
Each unit has a mass of 4 kg and can be mailed individually according to the following postal chart.

Parcel Post Table	
Weight (kg)	Charge ($)
to 0.50	3.00
0.51 to 0.75	6.75
0.76 to 1.00	8.00
1.01 to 1.50	10.50
1.51 to 2.00	13.00
2.01 to 2.50	15.50
2.51 to 3.00	18.00
3.01 to 3.50	20.50
3.51 to 4.00	23.00
4.01 to 4.50	25.50
4.51 to 5.00	28.00
5.01 to 5.50	30.50
5.51 to 6.00	33.00

- A courier service would ship at $25 per unit.
- 245 units would fill one truck at a cost of $5345.

7. What would a school board pay for a desk from question 5 if the retailer paid shipping charges of $234 for 3 units, has a markup of 55%, and gives a 10% discount to non-profit institutions?

14.5 DEPRECIATION

Each piece of equipment is a business asset. Equipment that is purchased for use in a business, such as machines used in manufacturing, office equipment, cars, and trucks, depreciates in value when purchased. In this section we will look at two ways in which depreciation is calculated.

STRAIGHT LINE METHOD OF CALCULATING DEPRECIATION

This method is used when the value of an asset is depreciated by a fixed amount each year.

> **Straight Line Depreciation**
>
> $$\text{Depreciation per year} = \frac{\text{original cost of equipment}}{\text{number of years equipment may be used}}$$

Example 1. The Eastern Tire company purchased a computer that cost $8680. The computer has an equipment life of 8 a.
Find the depreciation for each year and the percentage that the equipment depreciates each year.
Prepare a Straight Line Depreciation Schedule for the computer system.

Solution: Depreciation per year = $8680 ÷ 8
= $1085

Percentage depreciation per year = 100% ÷ 8
= 12.5%

The computer system depreciates $1085 per year,
and the percentage depreciation is 12.5%.

Straight Line Depreciation Schedule for Computer System			
Year	Depreciation per year	Accumulated Depreciation	Undepreciated Costs
1	$1085	$1085	$8680
2	$1085	$2170	$7595
3	$1085	$3255	$6510
4	$1085	$4340	$5425
5	$1085	$5425	$4340
6	$1085	$6510	$3255
7	$1085	$7595	$2170
8	$1085	$8680	$1085

DIMINISHING-VALUE METHOD OF CALCULATING DEPRECIATION

This method is used when the actual amount of depreciation declines as years pass.

> Diminishing-Value Depreciation
>
> Depreciation per year = fixed percent × undepreciated cost
>
> where undepreciated cost is the new value each year after depreciation is subtracted.

Example 2. A company has manufacturing equipment with an original value of $45 000. Prepare a Diminishing-Value Depreciation Schedule over 10 a at a diminishing-value depreciation rate of 12.5%.

Solution: Percentage depreciation per year: 12.5%.

	Diminishing-Value Depreciation for Manufacturing Equipment		
Year	Undepreciated Costs	Depreciation per year	Diminishing-Value
1	$45 000	$5625	$39 375
2	$39 375	$4921.88	$34 453.12
3	$34 453.12	$4306.64	$30 146.48
4	$30 146.48	$3768.25	$26 378.23
5	$26 378.23	$3297.28	$23 080.95
6	$23 080.95	$2885.12	$20 195.83
7	$20 195.83	$2524.48	$17 671.35
8	$17 671.35	$2208.92	$15 462.43
9	$15 462.43	$1932.80	$13 529.63
10	$13 529.63	$1691.20	$11 838.43

Accurate records of depreciation are essential because all assets, including equipment costs, must be valued for income tax purposes. This will give your Capital Cost Allowance. Revenue Canada Taxation requires a business to use the Diminishing-Value Method for calculating depreciation.

Revenue Canada Taxation sets maximum percentages of depreciation of assets by class. An example is given in the table below.

Class	Description	Maximum Depreciation
3	Most buildings, including component parts	5%
7	Canoes, rowboats, scows, and equipment	15%
8	Furniture, fixtures, machinery	20%
10	Automotive equipment	30%
17	Roads, parking lots, sidewalks, runways	8%
22	Movable excavating equipment	50%

EXERCISE 14.5

A

1. Which kinds of company assets depreciate?

2. Why is it important that a business calculate depreciation?

3. Under what circumstances would a business not report depreciation for taxation during a business year?

4. State reasons why Revenue Canada requires diminished-value depreciation instead of straight line depreciation.

B

5. Complete the table below.

Undepreciated Costs	Depreciation	Amount Depreciation
$23 765	23%	
$123 000		$50 000
	45%	$78 900
$12 789	6%	
$34 200		$22 000
	15%	$3500
$3 489 782	23.2%	
$1780		$710
	31%	$78

6. For the following assets and undepreciated costs, find the maximum rate and the amount of depreciation per taxation year allowed by Revenue Canada Taxation.
(a) Bulldozer $345 100
(b) Manufacturing plant $1 893 300
(c) Van $27 800
(d) Fishing boat $123 457
(e) Stamping machine $78 232
(f) Computer network $19 345
(g) Small runway $102 001
(h) Company car $32 347

7. A small consulting business has the following assets.
The undepreciated costs are given for each asset.

Share of a building	$175 000
Company car	$11 890
Computer system	$7440
Filing cabinets	$158
Office furniture	$5430
Copy machine	$2389

Using the maximum amounts allowed by Revenue Canada, calculate the maximum capital cost allowance over the year.

8. The Hardware Supply Company has the following assets:

Building	$2 500 000
Computer system	$9400
Office furniture	$27 300
Trucks (3)	$39 700
Copy Machine	$5675
Fork-lift	$12 750
Front-end loader	$23 600

(a) Group the assets into classes according to the Revenue Canada chart given in this section.
(b) For each class, prepare a Diminishing-Value Depreciation Schedule over 5 a, using the maximum depreciation allowed.

9. A company has manufacturing equipment with an original value of $1 234 000.

(a) Prepare a Straight Line Depreciation Schedule based on 25% depreciation over the number of years it takes to reduce the undepreciated costs to $0.
(b) Draw a graph of the undepreciated costs.

10. A company has manufacturing equipment with an original value of $1 234 000.
(a) Prepare a Diminishing-Value Depreciation Schedule based on 25% depreciation over the number of years it takes to reduce the undepreciated costs to less than $1000.
(b) Draw a graph of the undepreciated costs.
(c) Extrapolating from the graph, can you determine how many years it will take for the value of the assets to be reduced to $0?

11. (a) Compare the graphs in questions 9 and 10.
(b) Which method causes the assets to depreciate faster?

12. A company has a van and two cars with an initial value of $120 000.
(a) Using straight line depreciation, prepare a schedule of depreciation based on 20% per year over a five-year life of the assets.
(b) Using diminishing-value depreciation and the maximum capital cost allowance for depreciation from Revenue Canada, prepare a schedule of depreciation over a five-year life of the assets.
(c) On the same set of axes, graph the undepreciated values for each method of calculating depreciation.
(d) In how many years will the straight line depreciation graph and the diminishing-value depreciation graph intersect?

C
13. A small, private airport has 450 ha of land. Under regulations established by Revenue Canada Taxation, land does not depreciate, but roads, sidewalks, parking lots, and runways do depreciate.
Prepare Diminishing-Value Depreciation Schedules over 5 a at the maximum rate allowed by Revenue Canada for the following assets of the small airport.

Yearly undepreciated costs are as follows:

Airplane hangar	$289 899
Runway	789 m by 50 m at $56/m²
Parking lot	120 m by 98 m at $23/m²
Van	$34 000
Snow plow	$48 990
Control tower	$98 489
Control tower equipment	$65 890
Office equipment	$17 892

14. Using the information in question 13, prepare an Accumulated Diminishing-Value Depreciation Schedule listing the total undepreciated values, depreciation, and diminishing value.

EXTRA

SMALL BUSINESS PROJECT

Using the information in this chapter, develop a plan to operate a small business for one year using the following outline.

1. Choose a business sector and product.
Develop a plan as described in section 14.1.

2. Prepare a cash flow statement that projects the fixed costs, profit, loss, and break-even point for the first year of operation.

3. Plan office support needed and project costs.

4. Plan manufacturing costs and unit costs for the product. Include overhead, labour costs, raw material costs, and a projected profit margin.

5. Plan your distribution network through a wholesaler and a retailer, including shipping costs.

14.6 PROBLEM SOLVING

1. There are 1000 students and 1000 lockers in a school, and all of the lockers are closed. The first student comes and opens all the lockers. The second student comes and closes every second locker. The third student goes to every third locker and opens the lockers that are closed and closes the lockers that are open. The fourth student goes to every fourth locker and opens it if it is closed and closes it if it is open, and so on. Finally, the 1000th student goes to the 1000th locker and opens or closes it, depending on its state. Which lockers are left open after the 1000th student changed the state of the 1000th locker?

2. Divide 100 into four parts so that when you add 4 to one part, you get the same result as when you subtract 4 from another part, or multiply 4 by another part, or divide the last part by 4.

3. It takes six days to cross the desert. A person can only carry enough food and water to last four days on the desert.
How many people would have to start out in order for one person to cross the desert and for the others to return to the starting point?
Map out the strategy.

4. The time is now 10:35:42.
How long will it be to the nearest second until the minute and hour hands are in a straight line?

5. How many times will the minute-hand and hour-hand be in a straight line during a 12 h period from 00:00 to 12:00?

6. The numbers 12 and 13 are consecutive numbers that add to 25.
What other consecutive whole numbers add to 25?

7. (a) Find the value of

$$33^2, 333^2, \text{ and } 3333^2.$$

(b) Use your results from part (a) to predict the value of $333\ 333^2$ without calculating.
(c) Check your answer to part (b).

8. Jessie, Tara, Brian, Shawn, and Mia have guidance appointments. Jessie's appointment is later in the week than Tara's, but earlier than Brian's. Shawn's guidance appointment is later in the week than Mia's, but earlier than Brian's. Shawn, Mia, and Brian do not have their appointments on Monday. Shawn cannot have an appointment on Thursday.
From the above information, determine on which day of the week each student has a guidance appointment.

9. A long-playing record is 30 cm in diameter. The outer non-playing margin is 0.5 cm wide, and the non-playing central area is 10 cm in diameter.

(a) How far does the needle travel during one playing of the record?
(b) What assumptions were made in solving this problem?

10. Compare the perimeter and area of the shaded portion of the figure with the other portion.

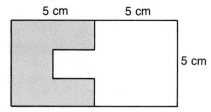

11. Find the sum of the angles in the five points of the star.

12. Four oil storage tanks are situated in a rectangular pattern as follows:

Find a way to connect the four tanks so that the least amount of pipe is required.

13. There are many 3-digit numbers that can be made with the digits

2, 3, 4, 5, 6, and 7

using a digit only once in each number. If you arrange all these numbers in order from the largest to the smallest, will the seventy-fifth number be even or odd?

14. The number 144 is a perfect square. The digits in 144 add up to another perfect square.

$$1 + 4 + 4 = 9$$

What is the smallest 3-digit perfect square whose digits do not total a perfect square?

15. Place 8 coins on a checkerboard so that no two coins lie in the same row, column, or diagonal.

CAREER

ACCOUNTANT

Bill Echevar and Sue Lam work as accountants in a small manufacturing company. In their work, they are required to keep and inspect records of debit and credit of moneys or services received and expended. Their work also entails planning and administering accounting systems to provide records of assets, liabilities, and financial transactions. They also assist in the preparation of budgets, corporate tax returns, and financial statements and analyse these statements in order to assist in planning financial management policies. Some accountants work in accounting systems and management positions in industry and government. Others work in public accounting firms or set up their own practice.

EXERCISE

1. A small business has the following expenditures and revenues for one month:

Telephone	$324.50
Heat	$156.87
Materials	$9235.00
Sales	$22 755.67
Interest	$806.24
Lighting	$45.36
Rent	$1250.00
Wages	$24 675.40
Service	$24 153.64

(a) Identify each of the above as an expenditure or revenue.
(b) Prepare a balance sheet for the month to determine the profit or loss.

14.7 REVIEW EXERCISE

1. Complete the table to determine the net profit per annum for the first year of each business.

	Start-up Costs	Average Costs per month	Average Gross Profit per month	Net Profit or Loss per annum
(a)	$1128	$912	$1897	
(b)	$2 245 102	$145 102	$87 100	
(c)	$167 389	$89 167	$89 342	

2. Draw a yearly cash flow graph for a company with fixed costs of $6100 per month using the following information.

Month	Variable Costs	Gross Profit
May	$7129	$8120
June	$6897	$9364
July	$5123	$7231
Aug.	$6123	$8100
Sept.	$7893	$7450
Oct.	$8234	$5389
Nov.	$9349	$8754
Dec.	$10 764	$9123
Jan.	$9120	$9001
Feb.	$8500	$8546
March	$7145	$7345
April	$6120	$5987

(a) What is the net profit or loss per month?
(b) During which months did the company reach a break-even point?
(c) What is the total net profit or loss for the year?
(d) Write a statement that describes the company's profitability.

3. What are the average costs of staffing and maintaining a work station per working day for the first year of a small business, given the following?
• The office is open 240 d/a.

• Floor space 8 m by 10 m costs $143/m² per year including utilities.
• Each area is equipped with furniture that costs $17 500.
• Each area has a computer that costs $23 765.
• Each area has miscellaneous office supplies that are used at an average cost of $543/d.
• Each area has miscellaneous equipment that costs $1265.
• The secretary earns $23 100/a plus 17% employee benefits.

4. If the secretary in question 3 prepares 101 pieces of written communication per day, what is the average cost to the company to produce each piece?

5. What is the cost to the nearest cent of producing a 100-page report given the following information?
• A secretary earns $23 400/a, based on 52 weeks and 40 h/week.
• The secretary types 60 words per minute using a word processor.
• The report averages 217 words per page.
• The printer prints at a rate 1.4 minutes per page.
• The consultant who prepared the report earns $45 000/a, based on 52 weeks and 36 h/week.
• It took the consultant 76 h, including collecting data, to prepare the report.
• 1000 sheets of special bond paper costs $27.

6. A manufacturer of compact discs ships 1 000 000 units to the wholesale distributor. The wholesaler ships 1000 units to Electronics City who sells to the customer. What is the final price of a compact disc to the customer, given the following information?
- The unit price from the manufacturer is $2.89.
- Shipping charge from manufacturer to wholesaler is $34 789 per shipment.
- The wholesaler has a markup of 54% of the unit price to the retailer plus shipping charges.
- The retailer pays the shipper $1198 for shipping the 500 compact discs.
- The retailer, Electronics City, has a markup of 67% to the customer plus shipping charges.

7. A company has manufacturing equipment with an original value of $123 892.
Prepare a Diminishing-Value Depreciation Schedule over 10 a at a diminishing-value depreciation rate of 9.5%.

8. For the company and equipment in question 7, compare the undepreciated values after 10 a for a straight line depreciation and a diminishing-value depreciation.

9. It costs $1.73 to manufacture a toy car. The following sequence of factors determines the price: manufacturer's markup 40%, federal sales tax 12%, retailer's markup 50%, sale discount 20%, and provincial sales tax 8%.
Find the cost to the consumer.

10. Complete the table below, supplying the missing values.

	Overhead	Labour Costs	Raw Materials	Unit Cost	Profit	Price
(a)	$123/1000	$1234/100	$77.80/100		42%	
(b)	$78 237/100	$9233/10	$76 891/10		23%	
(c)	$98/100 000	$123/100 000	$0.78/1000		16.3%	
(d)	$15 699/100	$213/10	$4211/10 000		25%	
(e)	$81 784/100	$45 789/10	$781/1			$12 786
(f)	$438/1000	$123/1000	$8482/1000			$13.89

11. Complete the table below, supplying the missing values.

	Unit Cost (Manufacturer)	Markup (Wholesaler)	Markup (Retailer)	Retail Price
(a)	$7689	37%	62%	
(b)	$12.11	32.8%	55.3%	
(c)		33%	67%	$1234
(d)		54%	67.3%	$568
(e)	$432.89		103%	$1589
(f)	$34 892	12%		$56 892

14.8 CHAPTER 14 TEST

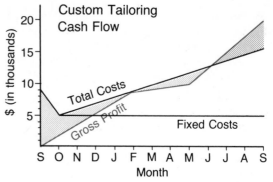

Custom Tailoring Cash Flow

1. The graph at the right shows the cash flow for the first year of operation of Custom Tailoring.
Read the following from the graph.
(a) What were the start-up costs?
(b) What were the monthly fixed costs?
(c) In which months did the business break even?

2. Calculate the monthly costs of maintaining an office with the following fixed costs.
• 224 m² of space at $325/m² per year
• 18.2% of space rent is for utilities
• $875 for supplies each month
• 720 000 photocopies per year at $0.036 each
• $120/month for a computer data line
• $216/month for telephone
• $24 000 and $21 500 plus 15.5% for benefits for 2 secretaries

3. Calculate the unit cost to the nearest cent to manufacture jackets at Gaetano Sportswear, given the following.
• Material for 500 jackets costs $1750.
• Labour costs average $12/h.
• It takes 4 h to make 50 jackets.
• Factory costs based on output of 5000 jackets daily are $8000/d.
• Sales staff commission is $0.50 per jacket.
• Office, design, and management costs, including executive salaries, are $8400/d.
• The company expects a profit of 12%.

4. A manufacturer of digital watches ships 2000 units to the wholesaler. The wholesaler ships 100 units to Friendly Jewellers who sells to consumers in a shopping mall.
Calculate the cost of a watch to a consumer, given the following information.
• The unit price from the manufacturer is $56 per unit.
• It costs $5000 per shipment to ship from the manufacturer to the wholesaler.
• The wholesaler's markup is 20% of the unit price to the retailer plus shipping charges.
• Friendly Jewellers pays $150 to the wholesaler for shipping.
• Friendly Jewellers has a markup of 40% to the consumer plus the shipping charges.

SPREADSHEETS IN
MATHEMATICS

REVIEW AND PREVIEW TO CHAPTER 15

ORDER OF OPERATIONS

EXERCISE 1

1. Simplify.
(a) $3(2 - 5) + 2(5 - 3)$
(b) $(5 + 3)(2 + 7) + (6 + 1)(7 + 2)$
(c) $(5 - 8)(3 - 7) - (2 + 5)(3 - 5)$
(d) $(2 + 3)(5 - 1)(4 + 2)(8 - 3)$
(e) $(2 + 6)(5 + 4) \div (8 - 2)(4 + 1)$
(f) $5(2 + 7) - 3(4 - 2) + 6(8 - 3)$
(g) $63 \div 9 \times 5 + 2 \times 3(4 - 1)$

2. Simplify.
(a) $3[4 - 2(3 + 2)] - 4[2 - (5 - 2)]$
(b) $[2 + (3 + 8)][2 - (3 + 8)]$
(c) $(100 + 2)(100 - 2)$
(d) $(3 + 5)(9 - 15 + 25)$
(e) $\sqrt{64} - 4 \times 2 + 7 \times 6$
(f) $-3(4 + 2) + 2(2 - 4)$
(g) $5[2(3 + 7) - 5] + 5$

3. Simplify.
(a) $\frac{2}{3} + \frac{5}{8}$

(b) $\frac{3}{4} - \frac{2}{3}$

(c) $\frac{5}{8} + 3\frac{3}{4}$

(d) $4\frac{2}{3} - 2\frac{1}{4}$

(e) $\frac{3}{4} \times \frac{2}{3} \div \frac{5}{8}$

(f) $3\frac{3}{4} + 2\frac{4}{5} - 4\frac{2}{5}$

(g) $2\frac{2}{3} \times 3\frac{3}{4} \div 4\frac{4}{5}$

4. Simplify.
(a) $3.125 + 2.586 - 3.265$
(b) $4.24 + 5.265 + 3.5 + 7.215$
(c) 45.3×21.6
(d) $2.55(4.16 - 1.27)$
(e) $6.25 \times 3.14 - 5.685$
(f) $24.65 - (4.85 + 11.375)$
(g) $24.75 + 12.2 \times 1.75$

GEOMETRY AND TRIGONOMETRY

EXERCISE 2

1. Find the length of the indicated side in each of the following pairs of triangles.
(a)

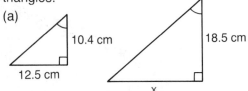

(b)

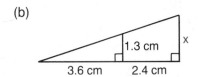

2. Find the length of the indicated side in each triangle.

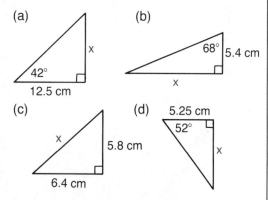

3. Solve the following triangles.

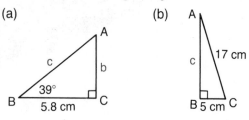

ALGEBRA

EXERCISE 3

1. Simplify.
(a) $3x + 5x - 2x + 6x$
(b) $2x + 7y - x + 5y$
(c) $3(x + 2y) - 2(x - 3y)$
(d) $5x + 2x - 5x + 4x$
(e) $3x(x + 2) - 5x(2x - 3)$
(f) $-2x(1 + 3x) + 2x(3 + x)$

2. Expand.
(a) $(x + y)(x + 2y)$
(b) $(2x - 5)(x + 3)$
(c) $(3x - 5)(2x + 3)$
(d) $(x - 5y)(x + 5y)$
(e) $(x + y)(x - y)$
(f) $(x + y)^2$
(g) $(2x - 5)(2x - 5)$
(h) $(3x - 2)^2$

3. Evaluate the following expressions for $x = 5$.
(a) $3x^2 - 5x + 7$
(b) $5x^3 + 3x^2 - 2x + 5$
(c) $-3x^3 + 2x^2 - 5x + 8$
(d) $5 + 2x - 3x^2 + 4x^3$
(e) $2x^2 + 5x - 7 + 8x^3$
(f) $3 + 7x - 2x^3 + x^2$
(g) $4x - 2x^2 + 6x^3 - x^4$
(h) $3(4x - 3) - 2(3 - 2x)$

4. Prepare tables of values and evaluate each expression for $x = 1, 2, 3, ..., 10$.
(a) $2x - 5$ (b) $x - 5$
(c) $3x + 4$ (d) $2 - x$
(e) $2x + 5$ (f) $4 + 3x$
(g) $x + 1$ (h) $(x + 1)$

5. Solve the following equations.
(a) $3x - 5 = 2x + 7$
(b) $4(2x + 3) - x = -3$
(c) $5x - 2(x + 3) = 2x + 7$
(d) $x^2 - 7x + 12 = 0$
(e) $x^2 + x - 20 = 0$

BUSINESS APPLICATIONS

EXERCISE 4

1. Using the formula
$$I = Prt$$
calculate the amount of simple interest on the following principals.
(a) $2500 for 200 d at 8% interest
(b) $5000 for 125 d at 8.9% interest
(c) $1250 for 6 months at 7.5% interest
(d) $3000 for 1 a at 9.9% interest
(e) $5000 for 30 d at 8.7% interest
(f) $2500 for 90 d at 16% interest

2. Using the formula
$$A = P(1 + i)^n$$
calculate the compound interest and the amount for each of the following principals.
(a) $5000 for 4 a at 9% compounded annually
(b) $10 000 for 8 a at 12% compounded annually
(c) $15 000 for 5 a at 10% compounded semi-annually
(d) $20 000 for 5 a at 12% compounded quarterly

3. Calculate the total value of the following stock portfolio.

Stock	Number of Shares	Share Value
Aluminum Can	200	$3.25
Bow Valley Inc.	500	$7.50
Cons Sud Basin	850	$5.75
Myron Exploration	1000	$0.88
Open Pit Resources	2000	$1.35
Queens Mining	5000	$2.75
Zencar Resources	750	$9.80

15.1 USING A SPREADSHEET

The electronic spreadsheet is a computer application that performs instant calculations and lets you work with numbers that are arranged in columns and rows. With a spreadsheet, it is possible to efficiently change format, project results, make calculations, and print almost anything that can be set up in a table. Using a spreadsheet eliminates the need to recalculate every number every time you enter a new number or change one that has already been entered. The spreadsheet recalculates the totals automatically.

It is possible to increase your problem solving ability by using a spreadsheet because you can play "what if" with the numbers. The spreadsheet allows you to make a variety of changes that would require hours of work, even with a calculator, if you were to do them by hand.

The vertical columns and the horizontal rows are combined and named to form a collection of cells. The following figure shows how the upper left portion of a spreadsheet appears on a computer screen.

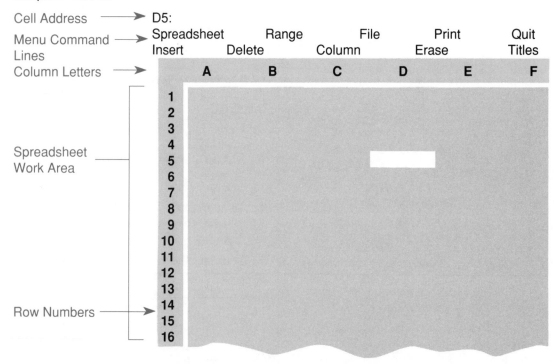

The columns are identified by letters, and the rows are identified by numbers. Each cell is identified by a column and a row. The highlighted cell above is cell D5 because it lies in column D and row 5. To reach a location in a spreadsheet, you enter the letter (A, B, C, ...) followed by the row number (1, 2, 3, ...). The cell in the upper left corner of the spreadsheet is in location A1.

When working with larger spreadsheets, it is necessary to move around in the spreadsheet, working on smaller segments until the spreadsheet is complete. The cursor can be moved by keystroke, trackball, or mouse. Check the manual for the spreadsheet software you are using to determine the specific methods required.

Example 1. From the partial display of the given computer screen, state the information in each of the following cells.

(a) E4 (b) B5 (c) F1 (d) A1 (e) C2 (f) E5

	A	B	C	D	E	F	G
1	Example 1: Locating information in a cell.						
2	Monday	Tuesday	Wednesday	Thursday	Friday	Saturday	
3	25.5	35.64	19.35	72.5	75.35	95.89	
4	35.95	64.73	12.85	62.37	45.75	25.64	
5	54.66	28.63	62.65	75.75	58.95	75.26	
6	36.45	82.43	62.49	29.55	75.59	95.15	
7	85.25	52.35	52.53	29.55	63.58	63.37	
8							

Solution:
(a) 45.75 (b) 28.63 (c) Blank (d) Example 1: Locating information in a cell. (e) Wednesday
(f) 58.95

In each cell, it is possible to enter data in the form of numerical expressions or letters and words. Numerical expressions can be simple numbers, a combination of simple numbers and cell locations (coordinates), mathematical operations and functions, or a range of coordinates. Numerical expressions must contain at least one of the following:
(i) a number or coordinate reference,
(ii) a mathematical function understood by the computer.

Where a cell, D7, contains a coordinate such as B5, the value that appears in D7 would be taken from B5 if it is entered $+$B5 or (B5), depending on the software.

Values can be entered in a variety of formats. The number of decimal places in a value can usually be fixed from zero to six. It is also possible to change the width of a column. This is especially helpful when a wider column is needed for headings. The commands for fixing the number of decimal places and changing the width of a column are accessed by means of the Menu Command Line across the top of the spreadsheet. Check your manual for instructions on using these two commands.

Example 2. Using the manual and spreadsheet software,
(a) change the width of column A to 16 characters,
(b) enter "Robert E. Smith" in cell A2 and 3275 in cell B2,
(c) change the format of the number in cell B2 to three decimal places.

Solution: First, call up the Menu Command Line across the top of the spreadsheet, then proceed as instructed in the manual.

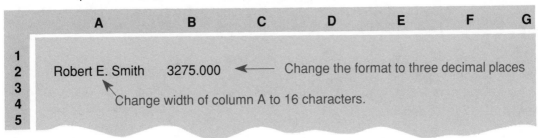

	A	B	C	D	E	F	G
1							
2	Robert E. Smith	3275.000	← Change the format to three decimal places				
3							
4	Change width of column A to 16 characters.						
5							

In the spreadsheet below, we see how to enter and work with formulas.
Enter the following data into a spreadsheet.

	A	B	C	D	E	F	G
1							
2		Jan.	Feb.	March	April		
3							
4		256.35	342.56	225.34	325.32		
5		257.34	314.15	255.44	423.75		
6		343.45	153.95	302.35	425.25		
7		203.75	423.54	315.35	253.56		
8							
9	Total:						
10	Monthly Average:						
11	Difference March – April:						
12	Four times Jan. total:						

Programming an Addition Formula

Enter the formula (B4 + B5 + B6 + B7) in cell B9.
Enter formulas to add the columns for February, March, and April.
Enter the formula (B9 + C9 + D9 + E9) in cell F9 to find the total.

Programming a Division Formula

To find the average monthly sum, enter the formula (F9/4) in cell F10.
Note that the symbol for division is the solidus, /.

Programming a Subtraction Formula

To find the difference between the totals in April and March, enter the formula (E9 – D9) in cell F11.

Programming a Multiplication Formula

To multiply the January total by 4, enter the formula (4∗B9) in cell F12. If the formula begins with a number, the parentheses can be omitted, and we can enter 4∗B9.

	A	B	C	D	E	F	G
1							
2		Jan.	Feb.	March	April		
3							
4		256.35	342.56	225.34	325.32		
5		257.34	314.15	255.44	423.75		
6		343.45	153.95	302.35	425.25	(B9+C9+D9+E9)	
7		203.75	423.54	315.35	253.56		
8							
9	Total:	1060.89	1234.2	1098.48	1427.88	4821.45	
10	Monthly Average:				(F9/4) →	1205.362	
11	Difference March – April:	(B4+B5+B6+B7)			(E9–D9) →	329.4	
12	Four times Jan. total:				4∗B9 →	4243.56	

The following table shows the sales for five bestsellers at H. Hill Bookstore. We can set up a spreadsheet to calculate the total value of the sales.

H. Hill Bookstore — Bestseller Sales					
Book	Lannie	Richard	Happiness	Rachel	Marathon
Number	124	375	263	832	512
Price	$9.95	$8.50	$11.95	$4.50	$4.95

	A	B	C	D	E	F	G
1	H. HILL BOOKSTORE: Bestseller Sales						
2							
3	Book Title	Sales	Price	Total			
4					To find totals,		
5	Lannie	124	9.95	1233.80 ← (B5*C5)			
6	Richard	375	8.50	3187.50 ← (B6*C6)			
7	Happiness	263	11.95	3142.85 ← (B7*C7)			
8	Rachel	832	4.50	3744.00 ← (B8*C8)			
9	Marathon	512	4.95	2534.40 ← (B9*C9)			
10							
11	Totals:	2106		13842.55 ← To find total sales, we add			
12				(D5+D6+D7+D8+D9).			

The formula in cell D5 can be copied to cells D6, D7, D8, and D9 using the COPY command. In spreadsheet terminology, copying a formula from a source cell to one or more destination cells is called replication. Check your manual to learn how to use the COPY command.

EXERCISE 15.1

B

1. Using spreadsheet software, check the manual for the method to do the following.
(a) move the cursor left, right, up, and down
(b) enter numeric data in a cell
(c) enter alpha data in a cell
(d) enter numeric data as if it were alpha data
(e) copy contents of one cell into another cell
(f) enter a formula that takes the contents of two cells and performs the operations of
  (i) + addition
  (ii) * multiplication
  (iii) − subtraction
  (iv) / division
(g) use the COPY command to replicate a formula

2. Move the cursor to the following cells.
(a) A7   (b) H20   (c) BB125   (d) D11

3. (a) Enter the following data into a spreadsheet.

	A	B	C	D
1	First	Second	Third	Fourth
2	125	425	263	4467
3	245	555	535	5263
4	142	154	332	4524
5	735	584	374	4852
6	562	256	626	5825
7				

(b) Enter formulas to find the sum of each column in row 8.
(c) Enter a formula to find the total of all the cells in cell E8.

4. (a) Enter the following data into a spreadsheet.

	A	B	C	D
1	Average			
2		4568		
3		7365		
4		8265		
5		3950		
6		8264		
7		2845		
8		9325		
9				
10	Total:			
11	Average:			
12				

(b) Enter a formula in cell B10 to find the sum of the figures.
(c) Enter a formula in cell B11 to find the average of the numbers.
(d) Write the formula that could be placed in cell C11 to find the average in one step.

5. (a) Enter the following data into a spreadsheet.

	A	B	C
1			
2	Revenue	Expenses	Profit/Loss
3			
4	135.75	98.56	
5	204.25	253.78	
6	326.61	425.98	
7	5375.25	4627.98	
8	7565.34	8004.25	
9			

(b) Enter a formula in cell C4 to find the profit or loss by subtracting the value in cell B4 from the value in cell A4.
(c) Replicate the formula in cells C5, C6, C7, and C8.
(d) In which cells is a loss indicated?

6. (a) Enter the following data into a spreadsheet.

	A	B	C
1			
2	Number	Price	Total
3			
4	5	4.96	
5	11	3.65	
6	14	7.49	
7	5	12.55	
8	12	9.99	
9			
10	Grand Total:		
11			
12			

(b) Enter a formula in cell C4 to find the product of the values in cells A4 and B4.
(c) Replicate the formula in cells C5, C6, C7, and C8.
(d) Enter a formula in cell C10 to add the numbers in column C.

7. A company pays its executives the following salaries:

President	$125 000
Vice-president	$102 000
Treasurer	$85 000
Manager	$85 000
Assistant Manager	$62 000

The company gave its executives an across-the-board increase in salary of 3.2%.

(a) Enter this information into a spreadsheet.
(b) Enter formulas to compute new salaries for these executives.
(c) Enter a formula to compute the total salary for executives
  (i) at the old rate,
  (ii) at the new rate.

8. (a) Design a spreadsheet to contain the information given with the numeric data showing two decimal places.

	A	B	C
1	ACE DISTRIBUTORS STATEMENT		
2			
3	Monthly Operating Profit/Loss		
4	Month of:	January	
5			
6	Department	Revenue	Expenses
7			
8	Toiletries	13527.00	11428.00
9	Software	10406.00	11308.00
10	Cosmetics	13896.00	10192.00
11	Magazines	14780.00	9362.00
12	Photography	12586.00	9264.00
13	Housewares	21482.00	16835.00
14			
15	Net Profit/Loss		

(b) Write and enter formulas in column D to compute profit or loss for each group.

(c) Enter a formula in cell D15 to compute the net profit or loss for the entire month.

9. (a) Design a spreadsheet with the following information to prepare an income statement for Marino's Auto Body Shop.

Revenues:
Labour	536 205.75
General supplies	28 645.75
Paint	33 526.00
Total Revenues:	

Expenses:
Wages	342 205.50
Insurance	2435.65
Advertising	4800.00
Telephone	1720.13
Building rental	21 234.00
Equipment rental	1825.00
Paint	17 885.50
Utilities	2250.00
Miscellaneous	2756.00
Total Expenses:	

(b) Find the total revenue, total expenses, and net income.

Net income = revenues − expenses

10. (a) Design a spreadsheet with the following information.
Include a spreadsheet title and a label for each column.

Monthly Tickets Issued by Four Police Officers				
Month	Jones	Kirk	Lima	Singh
Jan.	82	64	75	88
Feb.	77	88	64	74
March	96	72	86	61
April	104	121	94	112
May	62	71	82	68
June	87	92	96	84
July	90	69	87	91
Aug.	68	72	70	74
Sept.	72	81	75	63
Oct.	85	92	84	57
Nov.	71	82	91	94
Dec.	124	107	118	131

(b) Write and enter formulas to compute the total number of tickets issued by each officer for the year.

(c) Write and enter formulas to compute the average number of tickets per month issued by each officer.

(d) Write and enter a formula to compute the total number of tickets issued by the four officers during the year.

(e) Write and enter a formula to compute the total amount of fines if the average fine is $72.50.

15.2 SPREADSHEET FUNCTIONS

Most spreadsheet software packages have some built-in functions. A lot of time can be saved when writing the same formula by using an @function.

The following spreadsheet shows the number of cars sold at Dale's Car Lot in the first six months of the year. Using the method from the previous section, we could compute the total sales by entering the formula (B4+B5+B6+B7+B8+B9) in cell B11. Using @SUM, we will get the same result by entering the formula @SUM(B4..B9) in cell B11. By using @SUM in the formula, we avoid typing out all of the cell addresses separated by plus signs (+).

	A	B	C	D	E	F	G
1	DALE'S CAR LOT: Monthly Auto Sales						
2							
3	Month	Units					
4	Jan.	77					
5	Feb.	83					
6	Mar.	90					
7	Apr.	95					
8	May	94					
9	June	103					
10							
11	Total:	542	◄——— @SUM (B4..B9)				
12							
13	Mean:	90.33333	◄——— @AVG (B4..B9)				
14							
15	Integer:	90	◄——— @INT (B13)				
16							

In order to compute the average number of units sold each month, we can take the sum in cell C11 and divide it by 6 or use @AVG and the formula @AVG(B4..B9) in cell C13, which gives the result 90.33333.

Since we are interested in the integer part of the mean, we use @INT and enter the formula @INT(B13) in cell B15, which gives the desired result, 90.

The summary at the right shows the @functions that we will use in this book.
Consult your spreadsheet manual for the complete list of functions available.

Function	Outcome
@AVG(list)	the average of the values in the list
@INT(x)	the integer part of x
@SQRT(x)	the positive square root of x
@PI	the value of $\pi = 3.141\ 592\ 6$
@SUM(list)	the sum of the values in the list
@SIN(x)	the sine of the angle x (in radians)
@COS(x)	the cosine of the angle x (in radians)
@TAN(x)	the tangent of the angle x (in radians)

EXERCISE 15.2

B

1. Use @AVG to find the average of each of the following lists of numbers.

List	(a)	(b)	(c)	(d)
	125	1875	27 735	738 500
	926	3385	83 936	825 977
	557	9925	48 536	826 463
	264	5853	76 354	867 254
	586	7449	58 385	527 482
	884	3385	29 723	629 294
	773	2957	63 500	503 758
Average				

2. Use @INT to list the integer parts of the following numbers.
Place the numbers in column A and the integer parts in column B.

(a) 34.675 (b) 1.265 (c) 1.875
(d) 125.8 (e) 128.09 (f) 565.5
(g) 0.725 (h) 0.075 (i) 31.25

3. Use @SQRT to find the square roots of the following numbers.
Place the numbers in column A and the square roots in column B.

(a) 75.735 (b) 150.25 (c) 3.1416
(d) 0.2855 (e) 365.75 (f) 92.647
(g) 0.0064 (h) 0.064 (i) 6937

4. (a) Use @PI to list the value of π in cell C3.
(b) Use the π function to evaluate πd for d = 56.75.

5. Use the @SUM to find the sum of each of the following lists of numbers.

List	(a)	(b)	(c)	(d)
	345	8365	27 746	265 846
	476	2745	37 463	263 253
	557	9925	36 635	374 366
	365	4665	57 350	354 735
	683	4775	28 647	275 823
	376	2485	36 635	243 260
	476	8354	36 476	250 004
Sum				

6. Use @SIN, @COS, and @TAN to complete the following chart on a spreadsheet.

Degree Angle	Sine of Angle	Cosine of Angle	Tangent of Angle
30°			
45°			
60°			
90°			
120°			
135°			
150°			
180°			

7. The following chart shows NFL attendance for four teams for the months of September to November.

Team Location	Sept.	Oct.	Nov.
Candlestick Park	71 850	82 275	101 450
Soldier's Field	84 245	75 825	96 225
Los Angeles Coliseum	80 275	124 650	125 000
Arrowhead Stadium	78 350	103 925	118 300

(a) Set up a spreadsheet to find the
   (i) totals per location,
   (ii) totals per month.
(b) Check the spreadsheet manual to determine how to insert a column. Add the following information to your spreadsheet and complete a new calculation.

Attendance for the Month of December	
Candlestick Park	97 750
Soldier's Field	88 775
Los Angeles Coliseum	142 500
Arrowhead Stadium	96 250

15.3 ALGEBRA ON A SPREADSHEET

The following table shows the operators that are used in this book, and the order in which the operations are performed.

Operation	Operator			Order
Exponentiation	^	or	↑	1
Negative and Positive	−	and	+	2
Multiplication and Division	∗	and	/	3
Addition and Subtraction	+	and	−	4

It is possible to override this order by using parentheses around an operation. The following example shows how a spreadsheet program would perform a calculation according to the above order with parentheses.

$$350 + ((25.6\text{^}3 + 175)*4.85)/2.56$$

(order indicators: 5th, 1st, 3rd above; 2nd, 4th below)

Entering this calculation into a spreadsheet gives the result 32 466.50.

This order of operations is also followed when the formula contains a cell address. In the spreadsheet below, numbers have been entered in cells A2, B1, and C3. The indicated formula has been entered in cell A6.

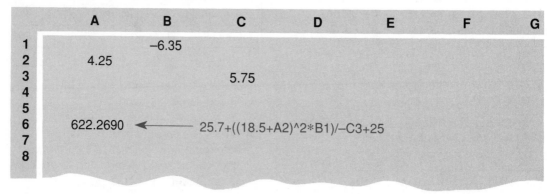

The operations were performed in the following order:

$$25.7 + ((18.5 + A2)\text{^}2*B1)/ - C3 + 25$$

(order indicators: 1st, 3rd above; 5th, 2nd, 4th, 6th below)

Substitute the cell entries to verify the order of operations using a computer or calculator.

The roots of the quadratic equation

$$ax^2 + bx + c = 0$$

can be found using the quadratic formulas

$$x = \frac{-b \pm \sqrt{b^2 - 4ac}}{2a}$$

For example, to find the roots of the quadratic equation

$$3x^2 - 2x - 8 = 0$$

the values $a = 3$, $b = -2$, and $c = -8$ are substituted into the quadratic formulas

$$x = \frac{-b + \sqrt{b^2 - 4ac}}{2a} \quad \text{and} \quad x = \frac{-b - \sqrt{b^2 - 4ac}}{2a}$$

When a spreadsheet is used, we place the formulas in two cells. The data for a, b, and c are entered in other cells, and the roots are calculated automatically.

In a spreadsheet, @SQRT is used to evaluate the radicals. The entry @SQRT(B^2−4*A*C) means $\sqrt{b^2 - 4ac}$. The formulas to be entered into the spreadsheet are written

$(-b + \sqrt{b^2 - 4ac})/2a$ and $(-b - \sqrt{b^2 - 4ac})/2a$

$(-B+@SQRT(B^2-4*A*C))/(2*A)$ $(-B-@SQRT(B^2-4*A*C))/(2*A)$

In the following spreadsheet, the quadratic formulas shown above are entered in cells D6 and D9, and the values $a = 3$, $b = -2$, and $c = -8$ are entered in cells B7, B8, and B9 respectively.

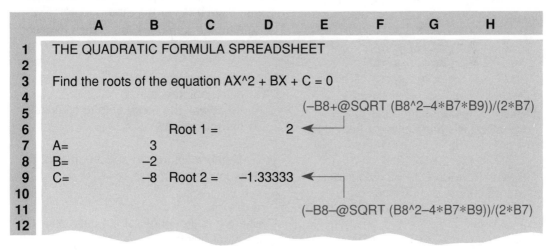

From cells D6 and D9, the roots are 2 and $-1.\overline{3}$.

Once the formulas are entered, any quadratic equation can be solved by entering new values for a, b, and c in cells B7, B8, and B9.

EXERCISE 15.3

B

1. Copy each of the following expressions and indicate the order in which a spreadsheet program would perform the operations.

(a) $4.56 + (1.75*2.6 - 3.75)$
(b) $(3.5 + 2.7)*(5.6 - 2.3)/(1.2*3.4)$
(c) $2.5\char`^2 + 3.6\char`^2$
(d) $(2.5 + 3.6)\char`^2$
(e) $(6.25 + 4.13)*(6.25 - 4.13)$
(f) $6.25\char`^2 - 4.13\char`^2$

2. Copy each of the following expressions and indicate the order in which a spreadsheet program would perform the operations.

(a) $+C7 - D8*D7$
(b) $(A1 + B1)*(A1 - B1)$
(c) $+A1\char`^2 - B1\char`^2$
(d) $+A2 - ((A3 + B5)*2 - 1.6)*E7$
(e) $+A3\char`^3 - B3\char`^3$
(f) $(A3 - B3)*(A3*A3 + A3*B3 + B3\char`^2)$

3. (a) Enter the following values into a spreadsheet.

1.65 in cell A2
−4.36 in cell B2
3.25 in cell C2

(b) Enter the following formulas in the indicated cells and compare the values.
(i) $(A2 + B2 + C2)\char`^2$ in cell D4 and $+A2\char`^2 + B2\char`^2 + C2\char`^2 + 2*(A2*B2 + A2*C2 + B2*C2)$ in cell E4
(ii) $(A2 + B2)\char`^3$ in cell D6 and $+A2\char`^3 + 3*(A2\char`^2*B2 + A2*B2\char`^2) + B2\char`^3$ in cell E6
(iii) $(B2 + C2)*(B2 - C2)$ in cell D8 and $+B2\char`^2 - C2\char`^2$ in cell E8
(iv) $+A2\char`^3 - C2\char`^3$ in cell D10 and $(A2 - C2)*(A2\char`^2 + A2*C2 + C2\char`^2)$ in cell E10
(v) $+A2 + B2 + C2$ in cell D12 and $@SQRT((A2 + B2 + C2)\char`^2)$ in cell E12

4. Set up a computer spreadsheet to solve quadratic equations and solve the following.

(a) $5x^2 + 2x - 7 = 0$
(b) $-3x^2 + x + 4 = 0$
(c) $-2x^2 + 3x + 5 = 0$
(d) $6x^2 - x - 5 = 0$
(e) $6x^2 - 5x + 1 = 0$
(f) $5x^2 + x - 4 = 0$
(g) $2.47x^2 - 3.65x - 1.25 = 0$
(h) $-3.2x^2 - 6.25x + 3.05 = 0$
(i) $5.75x^2 - 10.25x + 4.50 = 0$

C

5. A rectangular warehouse 200 m by 300 m, is to be built on a vacant lot with an area of 81 600 m². A uniform strip is to be left around the building for parking. Solve the following equation to find the width of the uniform strip.

$$4x^2 + 1000x - 21\ 600 = 0$$

6. The time to travel 540 km from Streetsville to Saginaw was 1 h greater than it took to return. The rate returning was 6 km/h faster than the rate going.
(a) Find the rate of travel in each direction by solving the equation

$$x^2 + 6x - 3240 = 0$$

using a spreadsheet.
(b) What was the travel time to complete the round trip?

7. The formula for the surface area of a rectangular pyramid is

$$S.A. = 4(0.5bs) + b^2$$

where b is the length of the base and s is the slant height.
The formula for the volume of a rectangular pyramid is

$$V = \tfrac{1}{3}b^2h$$

where b is the length of the base and h is the height of the pyramid.

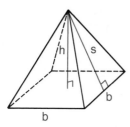

(a) Set up a spreadsheet to calculate the surface area and volume of a pyramid with b located in cell A6 and h located in cell A7.

The value for s is found using the formula

$$s = \sqrt{h^2 + (0.5b)^2}$$

The formula for s can be written

@SQRT(H^2+(0.5*B)^2)

Remember to express H and B in terms of their cell locations when you enter the formula into the spreadsheet so that you enter

@SQRT(A7^2+(.5*A6)^2)

(b) Find the surface area and volume of a rectangular pyramid whose base is 5.375 m long and height is 9.625 m using a spreadsheet.

8. The formulas for surface area and volume of a cylinder are

$$S.A. = 2\pi r(h + r)$$

$$V = \pi r^2 h$$

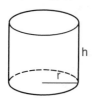

(a) Write spreadsheet formulas for the cylinder and set up a spreadsheet with the value for r in cell C4 and the value for h in cell C5.

(b) Find the surface area and volume of a cylinder with a radius of 5.25 cm and a height of 11.75 cm.

9. The formulas for surface area and volume of a cone are

$$S.A. = \pi r^2 + \pi rs$$
$$= \pi r(r + s)$$

$$V = \tfrac{1}{3}\pi r^2 h$$

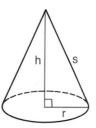

(a) Write spreadsheet formulas for the cone and set up a spreadsheet with the value for r in cell B6 and the value for h in cell B7.

The slant height, s, can be found using the formula

$$s = \sqrt{r^2 + h^2}$$

(b) Find the surface area and volume of a cone with a radius of 56.75 cm and a height of 125.75 cm.

10. The formula for the volume of the frustum of a cone is

$$V = \frac{\pi}{3}h(a^2 + ab + b^2)$$

where a is the smaller radius, b is the larger radius, and h is the height, as shown in the diagram.

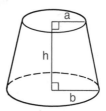

(a) Set up a spreadsheet to find the volume of the frustum of a cone.

(b) Use the spreadsheet to find the volume of the frustum of a cone with a smaller radius of 1.25 m, a larger radius of 1.68 m, and a height of 2.55 m.

15.4 DECISION MAKING WITH A SPREADSHEET

A spreadsheet is helpful in organizing information and performing calculations so that we can make intelligent decisions when solving problems. When making decisions, it is important to have an organized plan. In this section the PACED model for decision making is adapted for use with a spreadsheet. Setting up a spreadsheet in the following manner permits the user to assign values to the criteria and to rate each alternative based on each criterion. PACED is an acronym made up from the steps in the model:
Problem, Alternatives, Criteria, Evaluate, and Decide.

PROBLEM   Identify the problem in cell B4.

ALTERNATIVES   List each alternative under the numerals I, II, III, IV, ...

CRITERIA   List up to 8 criteria in cells A10 to A17.
Assign each criterion a value from 1 to 10 in cells B10 to B17, based on how important you think it is.
Enter the values in column B of the same row.

EVALUATE   Evaluate the alternatives based on each criterion and assign a value of 0, 1, 2, ... to the number of alternatives.
Multiply the value of each criterion by the corresponding value for each alternative.
Add the products for each alternative and place the sums in row 19.

DECIDE   Compare the sums in row 19 and decide.

	A	B	C	D	E	F
1						
2	THE PACED DECISION-MAKING MODEL					
3						
4	Decision:					
5						
6				Alternatives		
7						
8		Values	I	II	III	IV
9	Criteria	1 to 10				
10						
11	List	Assign		Assign values		
12	criteria	values		to the alternatives		
13	here	from		0, 1, 2, ...		
14		1 to 10				
15		to the				
16		criteria				
17						
18	Totals:		Sum	Sum	Sum	Sum

Example 1. Roman and Jane used the PACED model to assist in deciding which house to buy. As a result of working closely with a real estate agent, they were able to reduce their choices to 3 alternatives — a bungalow, a split-level house, and a two-storey house.

The criteria on which they planned to make their choice were the model, location, value priced, down payment, monthly payment, size, condition, and yard. They assigned values from 1 to 10 to the criteria and rated the alternatives in order (values 2, 1, 0) as follows:

Model: 9	bungalow, split-level, two-storey
Location: 10	split-level, bungalow, two-storey
Value Priced: 3	split-level, two-storey, bungalow
Down Payment: 6	split-level, two-storey, bungalow
Monthly Payment: 5	two-storey, bungalow, split-level
Size: 8	two-storey, split-level, bungalow
Condition: 4	two-storey, split-level, bungalow
Yard: 7	bungalow, two-storey, split-level

Complete a spreadsheet to rate each property based on the criteria.

Solution:

P: Identify the decision needed in cell B4.

A: List the alternatives in cells C9, D9, and E9.

C: List the criteria in cells A10 to A17. List the assigned values in column B.

E: Assign values 2, 1, or 0 to the alternatives and list in columns C, D, and E.
Multiply the assigned value by the alternative value. (B10∗C10, B11∗C11,...,B17∗C17)
Place the sum for each alternative in row 19. (B10∗C10+B11∗C11+...+B17∗C17)

D: Examine the totals in row 19 and decide.

	A	B	C	D	E	F
1						
2	THE PACED DECISION-MAKING MODEL					
3						
4	Decision: Selecting and buying a house.					
5						
6				Alternatives		
7						
8		Values	I	II	III	IV
9	Criteria	1 to 10	Bungalow	Split-Level	Two-storey	
10	Model	9	2	1	0	
11	Location	10	1	2	0	
12	Value priced	3	1	2	0	
13	Down Payment	6	0	2	1	
14	Monthly Payment	5	1	0	2	
15	Size	8	0	1	2	
16	Condition	4	0	1	2	
17	Yard	7	2	0	1	
18						
19	Totals:		50	59	47	

The best alternative is the split-level house (59).

Example 2. A sportscaster uses the PACED model and a spreadsheet to forecast the results of upcoming baseball games. Note that some criteria are given negative values.

The criteria used and their values are won–lost (3), runs (4), doubles (-5), triples (7), home runs (10), batting average (-3), errors (-4), double plays (7), walks by (8), shutouts (9), ERA (6), and head-to-head record (7). In the alternative column, the teams are assigned a value of 1 or 2 based on the criteria.

The following chart shows the team records for the Toronto Blue Jays and the Detroit Tigers before a three-game series.

Criteria	Toronto Blue Jays	Detroit Tigers	Criteria	Toronto Blue Jays	Detroit Tigers
Won–Lost	92–59	90–60	Errors	104	117
Runs	798	837	Double plays	133	133
Doubles	259	249	Walks By	521	512
Triples	34	28	Shutouts	8	8
Home Runs	206	211	ERA	3.79	4.13
Batting Average	0.272	0.273	Head-to-Head	4–3	3–4

Set up a spreadsheet as follows and compute a score to forecast the winner of the next game.

	A	B	C	D	E	F	G	H	I
1	SPORTS INDICATOR SPREADSHEET				BASEBALL				
2									
3	Criteria	Value	Team				Team		
4		to 10	Record	Points	Score		Record	Points	Score
5	Won–Lost	3	D	1	(B5*D5)		D	1	(B5*H5)
6	Runs	4	a	or	(B6*D6)		a	or	(B6*H6)
7	Doubles	–5	t	2	(B7*D7)		t	2	(B7*H7)
8	Triples	7	a		.		a		.
9	Home Runs	10			.				
10	Batting Avg.	–3			.				
11	Errors	–4							
12	Double Plays	7							
13	Walks By	8							
14	Shutouts	9							
15	ERA	6							
16	Head-to-Head	7							
17									
18	Totals:				Sum				Sum
19									

Solution:

Step 1. Enter the team records in columns C and G.

Step 2. Compare team records and enter a 1 or 2 in the points columns (D and H) with the team with the better record getting a 2.

Step 3. Enter the score formulas in columns E and I.
Column E: Multiply the values in column B by the values in column D.
Column I: Multiply the values in column B by the values in column H.

Step 4. Add the score columns using the @SUM function.
In cell E18, enter @SUM(E5..E16).
In cell I18, enter @SUM(I5..I16).

Step 5. Add the scores in column E.

Step 6. Add the scores in column I.

	A	B	C	D	E	F	G	H	I
1	SPORTS INDICATOR SPREADSHEET				BASEBALL				
2									
3	Criteria	Value	Team	Toronto			Team	Detroit	
4		to 10	Record	Points	Score		Record	Points	Score
5	Won–Lost	3	92–59	2	6		90–60	1	3
6	Runs	4	798	1	4		837	2	8
7	Doubles	–5	259	2	–10		249	1	–5
8	Triples	7	34	2	14		28	1	7
9	Home Runs	10	206	1	10		211	2	20
10	Batting Avg.	–3	.272	1.5	–4.5		.273	1.5	–4.5
11	Errors	–4	104	1	–4		117	2	–8
12	Double Plays	7	133	1.5	10.5		133	1.5	10.5
13	Walks By	7	521	1	7		512	2	14
14	Shutouts	9	8	1.5	13.5		8	1.5	13.5
15	ERA	6	3.79	2	12		4.13	1	6
16	Head-to-Head	7	4–3	2	14		3–4	1	7
17									
18	Totals:				72.5				71.5
19									

Using this forecasting system, Toronto has a score of 72.5 and Detroit has a score of 71.5. Toronto should win the next game.

EXERCISE 15.4

B1. Complete the following charts to determine which alternatives have the highest score.

(a) Decision: Kind of vehicle.

Criteria	Value	I Truck	II Wagon	III Van
Cost	4	1	2	0
Work	5	1	0	2
Hauling	2	2	0	1
Vacation	1	0	2	1
Camping	3	0	1	2
Pleasure	7	0	2	1
Resale	4	1	0	2
Totals				

(b) Decision: Select a math team.

Criteria	Value	I Marie	II Tom	III Hal	IV Ann
Algebra	3	3	2	1	0
Geometry	5	0	2	1	3
Trigonometry	4	3	0	2	1
Logic	8	1	3	2	0
Arithmetic	6	2	0	1	3
History	2	1	3	0	2
Totals					

(c) Decision: Select a book to read.

Criteria	Value	I Mystery	II Sport	III Romance
Pleasure	10	0	2	1
Length	5	2	0	1
Author	7	2	1	0
Popularity	4	0	1	2
Price	8	0	1	2
Cover	2	0	1	2
Reviews	3	1	2	0
Totals				

(d) Decision: Buying a used car.

Criteria	Value	I Sedan	II Coupe	III Convert.
Model	8	0	2	1
Colour	7	2	0	1
Year	5	2	1	0
Condition	10	0	1	2
Price	2	0	1	2
Metrage	4	0	1	2
Down Pay't.	6	1	2	0
Totals				

2. Complete the following chart to determine the method of travel to Calgary with the highest score.

Decision: Method of travel to Calgary.

Criteria	Value	I Road	II Rail	III Air
Cost	6	2	1	0
Tiring	8	0	1	2
Time	4	1	0	2
Pleasure	9	0	1.	2
Schedules	3	2	1	0
Stopovers	8	2	1	0
Sightseeing	7	2	1	0
Totals				

3. Complete the following chart to determine which accommodations are best suited for a school trip. The choices for accommodation are
(i) motel on the edge of town at $47 per person,
(ii) hotel downtown at $54 per person,
(iii) tourist home in midtown at $38 per person.

Most of the places to visit are in the downtown area. The hotel has a heated pool. The tourist home does not have private bathrooms. Extra transportation costs from the edge of town and from midtown would be $6 per person for the whole trip.

Use the PACED model with a spreadsheet.

(a) Assign values from 1 to 10 to each criterion.

(b) Assign the values 0, 1, or 2 to the alternatives based on each criterion.

Decision: Accommodations for school trip.				
		I	II	III
Criteria	Value	Motel	Hotel	Tourist Home
Distance				
Pool				
Price				
Comfort				
Privacy				
Totals				

4. Set up a spreadsheet as in Example 2 to predict the outcome when two baseball teams with the following records play.

Criteria	Montreal Expos	New York Mets
Won–Lost	88–53	90–51
Runs	827	737
Doubles	223	218
Triples	33	31
Home Runs	179	176
Batting Average	0.301	0.306
Errors	104	101
Double Plays	117	123
Walks By	493	488
Shutouts	7	7
ERA	3.12	3.45
Head-to-Head	5–2	2–5

5. A college basketball scout ranks prospective players according to the "Six H's":
- Height (The scout looks for size.)
- Head (The scout looks for ability to think.)
- Heart (The scout looks for desire to play.)
- Hands (The scout wants ball handling.)
- Heel (The scout looks for speed.)
- Hustle (The scout looks for quickness.)

(a) Use the PACED model to rank three basketball players of your choice based on the "six H's."

(b) Assign values from 1 to 10 to each of the six criteria.

(c) Evaluate each player in terms of each criterion and assign a value of 0, 1, or 2.

(d) Complete the computation to rank the players.

6. Set up a spreadsheet to determine your choice of college upon completion of high school.

(a) Use the following criteria.

(b) Assign your own criteria values.

(c) Select three colleges you would like to attend.

Decision: Choose a college.				
		I	II	III
Criteria	Value			
Distance				
Cost				
Programs				
Standards				
Residence				
Athletics				
Size				
Totals				

15.5 TRIGONOMETRY ON A SPREADSHEET

Many spreadsheets have the trigonometric functions, sine, cosine, and tangent, built in as @functions. In order to use these @functions, the angle must be entered in radian measure, rather than degree measure. The diagram below shows an angle equal in measure to one radian, where r is the length of the radius. This means that

$$180° = \pi \text{ rad}$$

$$1° = \frac{\pi}{180} \text{ rad}$$

We use the following formula to change degrees to radians in a spreadsheet.

$$N° = N\left(\frac{\pi}{180}\right) \text{ rad}$$

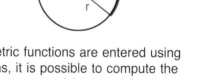

A spreadsheet enters π using @PI. The primary trigonometric functions are entered using @SIN(...), @COS(...), and @TAN(...). Using these functions, it is possible to compute the values of the trigonometric functions for any angle, N°, using a spreadsheet and the following formulas.

@SIN(N*@PI/180),   @COS(N*@PI/180),   @TAN(N*@PI/180)

When entering the formulas in a spreadsheet, the value for the angle in degree measure is placed in the appropriate cell location.

Example. Set up a spreadsheet to calculate the values of the primary trigonometric functions, sine, cosine, and tangent, for the following angle measures.

0°,   15°,   30°,   45°,   60°,   75°,   90°,   105°,   120°,   ...,   360°

Solution:

Place the title for the spreadsheet in cell A1.

Place headings in columns A, B, D, and F. Locate the measure of the angle, N, in column A, starting in cell A4.

Locate the function formulas in cells B4, D4, and F4.

Format column A with zero decimal places and columns B, D, and F with five decimal places.

	A	B	C	D	E	F	G
1	TRIGONOMETRIC FUNCTIONS: SINE, COSINE, TANGENT						
2							
3	Angle N	@SIN(A4*@PI/180)		@COS(A4*@PI/180)		@TAN(A4*@PI/180)	
4	0	0.00000		1.00000		0.00000	
5	15	0.25882		0.96593		0.26795	
6	30	0.50000		0.86603		0.57735	
7	45	0.70711		0.70711		1.00000	
8	60	0.86603		0.50000		1.73205	
9	75	0.96593		0.25882		3.73205	
10	90	1.00000		0.00000		*********	
26	3..	..0000.					
27	345	−0.25882		0.96593		−0.26795	
28	360	0.00000		1.00000		0.00000	

Tan 90° and tan 270° are undefined and are represented by *********.

EXERCISE 15.5

B

1. (a) Using your spreadsheet, print the complete table from the example.
(b) Use your table to draw the graphs of
   (i) Y = SIN N
   (ii) Y = COS N
   (iii) Y = TAN N,
   for 0° ⩽ N ⩽ 360°.

2. (a) Set up a spreadsheet as shown to find the lengths of the sides of right triangles.

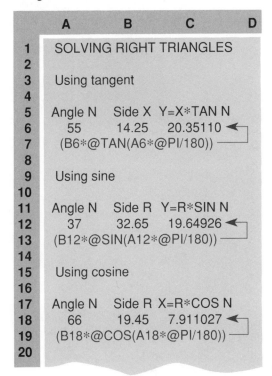

	A	B	C	D
1	SOLVING RIGHT TRIANGLES			
2				
3	Using tangent			
4				
5	Angle N	Side X	Y=X*TAN N	
6	55	14.25	20.35110 ◀	
7	(B6*@TAN(A6*@PI/180))			
8				
9	Using sine			
10				
11	Angle N	Side R	Y=R*SIN N	
12	37	32.65	19.64926 ◀	
13	(B12*@SIN(A12*@PI/180))			
14				
15	Using cosine			
16				
17	Angle N	Side R	X=R*COS N	
18	66	19.45	7.911027 ◀	
19	(B18*@COS(A18*@PI/180))			
20				

Test your formulas using the example numbers given below.
(b) Use your spreadsheet to find the length of the indicated side.

(i)   (ii)

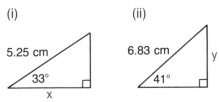

3. (a) Set up a spreadsheet as shown to find the lengths of the sides in oblique triangles.
Test your formulas using the example numbers given below.

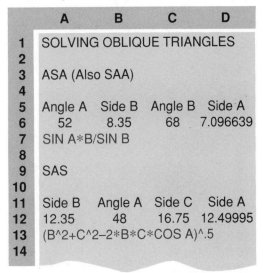

	A	B	C	D
1	SOLVING OBLIQUE TRIANGLES			
2				
3	ASA (Also SAA)			
4				
5	Angle A	Side B	Angle B	Side A
6	52	8.35	68	7.096639
7	SIN A*B/SIN B			
8				
9	SAS			
10				
11	Side B	Angle A	Side C	Side A
12	12.35	48	16.75	12.49995
13	(B^2+C^2–2*B*C*COS A)^.5			
14				

(b) Use your spreadsheet to find the length of the indicated side.

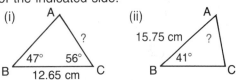

(i)   (ii)

4. (a) Set up a spreadsheet to generate a table of values in 10° intervals for
Y = SIN N + COS N, 0° ⩽ N ⩽ 360°.
(b) Use your table to draw the graph of
   Y = SIN N + COS N.

5. (a) Prepare a spreadsheet to generate a table of values in 10° intervals with the following columns.
ANGLE N, SIN(N), 2*SIN(N), and 3*SIN(N), 0° ⩽ N ⩽ 360°
(b) Using the same axes and the values in the table, draw the graphs of
   Y = SIN(N),
   Y = 2*SIN(N), and
   Y = 3*SIN(N).

15.6 STANDARD DEVIATION ON A SPREADSHEET

A spreadsheet provides a quick and accurate method of calculating the standard deviation of a set of values. In the following example, data on poplar trees will be used to show how to compute standard deviation using the formula from section 9.3 and the $@$ STD function in the software. Check your spreadsheet manual for greater detail in using $@$ functions.

Example. The heights of eight young poplar trees on an experimental farm are 124 cm, 143 cm, 118 cm, 108 cm, 127 cm, 96 cm, 112 cm, and 136 cm.
Find the standard deviation using a spreadsheet and the formula

$$\sigma = \sqrt{\frac{(x_1 - \bar{x})^2 + (x_2 - \bar{x})^2 + \ldots + (x_n - \bar{x})^2}{n}}$$

Solution:

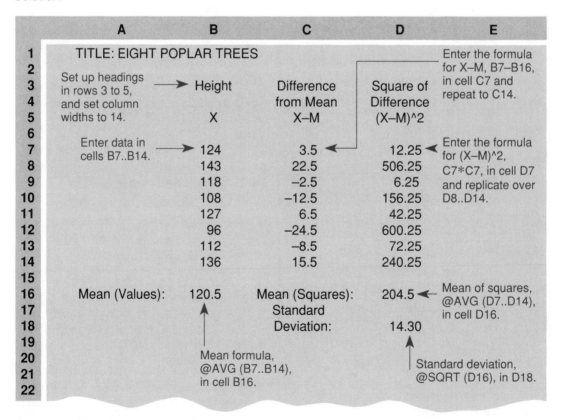

We can compute the standard deviation directly using the $@$ STD function as follows:
Enter the heading "STANDARD DEVIATION" in cell A20.
Enter the formula $@$ STD(B7..B14) in cell C20.

	A	B	C	D	E
1	TITLE: EIGHT POPLAR TREES				
2					
3		Height	Difference from Mean	Square of Difference	
4					
18					
19				Standard deviation, @STD (B7..B14), is in cell C20.	
20	Standard Deviation:		14.3003496461 ←		

From the spreadsheet, we read that the mean height of the trees is 120.5 cm and the standard deviation is 14.3 cm.

Using the @AVG and @STD functions enables us to find the mean and standard down deviation quickly.

EXERCISE 15.6

B

1. Design a spreadsheet to find the mean and the standard deviation of the given times in seconds for the following groups of people to run the 40 m dash.

(a) Grade 9 students:
6.8, 7.0, 5.6, 5.8, 6.3, 7.1, 5.7, 6.5, 6.3, 5.9, 6.8, 6.9, 6.3, 5.9, 7.2, 6.1, 5.8, 6.2, 6.7, 6.3, 6.4, 6.5, 5.9, 7.0, 6.8, 6.7, 6.3, 6.5, 5.7, 6.2, 6.8, 6.3, 6.1, 6.7, 6.4

(b) Grade 12 students:
5.6, 6.3, 6.7, 4.9, 5.5, 5.8, 4.8, 5.0, 5.7, 5.2, 6.6, 6.1, 5.9, 5.3, 5.7, 4.9, 6.0, 5.4, 5.8, 5.9, 6.2, 6.1, 5.7, 6.6, 5.9, 5.2, 5.8, 5.7, 6.2, 5.5, 5.9, 6.3, 6.5, 5.7, 5.4, 6.2, 5.8, 5.9, 6.4, 6.2, 5.7, 5.2, 6.0, 4.9, 5.0, 5.6, 5.8, 6.2, 6.7, 4.8, 5.8, 5.4, 5.9, 6.3, 6.2, 6.6, 5.5, 5.8, 6.4, 5.7, 6.5, 6.2, 5.9, 5.2, 6.1, 6.2, 6.3, 6.1, 5.8, 5.6

(c) Grade 12 boys:
5.4, 6.1, 5.7, 4.9, 5.2, 6.0, 5.7, 5.3, 5.9, 4.9, 5.3, 5.7, 4.8, 6.1, 5.5, 5.2, 4.9, 6.0, 5.6, 5.3, 5.1, 5.0, 5.3, 6.1, 4.9, 5.2, 5.4, 5.8, 5.2, 5.2, 5.1, 5.6, 5.8, 6.0, 5.2, 5.6, 5.7, 4.9, 5.9, 5.4, 5.3, 5.2

2. For each part of question 1, sketch a frequency distribution graph and interpret the data as described in section 9.4.

3. The price of grapes was surveyed in stores across the country, and the prices per kilogram were found to be as follows:
$3.85, $4.50, $4.07, $4.12, $3.95, $3.25, $3.75, $4.00, $3.90, $3.65, $3.69, $4.35, $3.99, $3.89, $4.19, $3.49, $3.55, $4.00, $3.65, $3.99, $4.05, $3.59, $4.95, $3.35

(a) Use a spreadsheet to find the mean and the standard deviation of the data.

(b) Make a sketch of a frequency diagram and interpret the data.

4. An autoshop class conducted a survey of three-year-old cars and recorded the odometer readings as follows:
32 126, 43 657, 75 835, 46 637, 77 446, 63 385, 63 756, 33 869, 73 863, 37 764, 64 364, 76 463, 47 756, 84 768, 48 857, 74 633, 74 665, 67 554, 35 664, 57 754, 35 547, 55 365, 57 405, 50 064, 47 758, 65 774, 47 586, 48 675, 87 685, 74 366, 55 874, 64 875, 38 746, 83 677, 75 647, 73 468, 77 876, 67 874, 66 476, 73 465

(a) Use a spreadsheet to find the mean and the standard deviation of the data.

(b) Make a sketch of a frequency diagram and interpret the data.

15.7 COMPOUND INTEREST ON A SPREADSHEET

A spreadsheet can be used to calculate compound interest and to prepare a table to show how funds are increasing. A compound interest table can be generated using the formula

$$A = P(1 + I)^N$$
where A is the amount,
P is the principal,
I is the interest rate for one interest period, and
N is the number of interest periods.

Example. Set up a spreadsheet to generate compound interest tables for $1(1 + I)^N$, giving 40 interest periods for the following interest rates: 4.0%, 4.5%, 5.0%, 5.5%, and 6.0%.

Solution: Set $P = 1$ in the formula $A = P(1 + I)^N$.
Enter the title in cell A1, Amount of $1(1 + I)^\wedge N$.
Format column A with a width of 3 spaces and zero fixed decimal places.
Enter the following headings in row 3.

	A	B	C	D	E	F
3	N	4.0%	4.5%	5.0%	5.5%	6.0%

Enter the numbers 1, 2, 3, 4, ..., 40 in cells A5 to A44.
To begin the table, enter the following formulas in row 5.

	A	B	C	D	E	F
5	1	1.04^A5	1.045^A5	1.05^A5	1.055^A5	1.06^A5

Use the COPY command to replicate the formulas in each column.

	A	B	C	D	E	F	G	H
1	AMOUNT OF 1(1+I)^N							
2						⌐1.06^A5	Using the COPY command,
3	N	4.0%	4.5%	5.0%	5.5%	6.0%	replicate the
4							formula.
5	1	1.04	1.045	1.05	1.055	└▸1.06	FROM: F5
6	2	1.0816	1.092025	1.1025	1.113025	1.1236	TO: F6..F44
7	3	1.124864	1.141166	1.157625	1.174241	1.191016	
8	4	1.169858	1.192518	1.215506	1.238824	1.262476	
9	5	1.216652	1.246181	1.276281	1.306960	1.338225	
		1.2~~	302260	~~~5	1.2~~	418519	
43	39	4.616365	5.5~~~9	6.704751	8.069486	9.7~~~~	
44	40	4.801020	5.816364	7.039988	8.513308	10.28571	

The values produced in the example can be used as accumulation factors. To evaluate $1500(1.055)^{14}$, or $1500*(1.055)^\wedge 14$, multiply the value in cell E18 by 1500, or $1500*E18$, and the result is 3174.14.

EXERCISE 15.7

B

1. (a) Print out the complete table for the example.
(b) Extend the table to include accumulation factors for N up to 50.

2. The following spreadsheet shows the growth of $100 invested for 7.5 a at 9% compounded semi-annually.

	A	B	C	D
1	GROWTH OF $100 AT 9%			
2	SEMI-ANNUALLY			
3	N	100(1+.045)^N		
4	1	104.50	← 100*(1+.045)	
5	2	109.20	← B4*1.045	
6	3	114.12		
7	4	119.25		
8	5	124.62		
9	6	130.23		
10	7	136.09	Use the	
11	8	142.21	COPY	
12	9	148.61	command.	
13	10	155.30		
14	11	162.29		
15	12	169.59		
16	13	177.22		
17	14	185.19		
18	15	193.53	← Check this	
19			figure using	
20			100*(1.045)^15.	

Use the COPY command to complete the table for N = 3 to 15.

3. Set up a spreadsheet to print out a table of accumulation factors for 1(1 + I)^N, giving 40 interest periods for the following interest rates:
0.5%, 1.0%, 1.5%, 2.0%, 2.5%, and 3.0%.

4. Set up a spreadsheet to print out a table of accumulation factors for 1(1 + I)^N, giving 40 interest periods for the following interest rates:
6.5%, 7.0%, 7.5%, 8.0%, 8.5%, and 9.0%.

5. Prepare a table on a spreadsheet to show how long it will take an investment of $1 at 1% interest per month to double.

6. The present value, PV, of an amount, A, is found using the formula

$$PV = A(1 + I)^{-N}$$

or

$$PV = \frac{A}{(1 + I)^N}$$

Design a spreadsheet to generate a table of present values of 1, giving values for N = 1, 2, 3, ..., 40 and using the interest rates 0.5%, 1.0%, 1.5%, 2.0%, 2.5%, and 3.0%.

C

7. Set up a spreadsheet to generate a table of present values of 1, using $1/(1 + I)^N$ and giving 40 interest periods for the following interest rates.
(a) 3.5%, 4.0%, 4.5%, 5.0%, 5.5%, and 6.0%
(b) 6.5%, 7.0%, 7.5%, 8.0%, 8.5%, and 9.0%

8. Use a spreadsheet to generate a table to compare the present values of an amount of $1000 over a period of 36 months if the monthly interest rates are 0.5%, 0.75%, 1%, and 1.25%.

9. Use a spreadsheet to generate a table to compare how a principal of $1000 increases over a period of 36 months if the monthly interest rates are 0.5%, 0.75%, 1%, and 1.25%.

10. Use a spreadsheet to show the number of interest periods it would take for an amount of $1 to double at each of the following interest rates:
3%, 4%, 5%, and 6%.

15.8 INVESTMENT TRACKING WITH SPREADSHEETS

The list of investments such as bonds, investment certificates, treasury bills, and shares on the stock market held by an investor is called a portfolio. A spreadsheet can be used to keep track of the value of a portfolio at any given moment.

Example. The following chart shows an investment portfolio on March 4.

Number of Shares	Name of Company	Share Prices	Cash Deposits Value	Item	Interest Rate	Term
500	Emco Ltd.	13.25	$75 000	Treasury Bill	9.9%	319 d
200	Federal Industries Inc.	24.50	$20 000	Savings Bonds	9.0%	1 a
3500	IPSCO Inc.	7.75	$12 500	Term Deposits	8.7%	120 d
100	Leon's Furniture Ltd.	24.00				
750	Noma Industries Ltd., A	18.25				
150	Torstar Corporation, B	29.50				

Use a spreadsheet to compute the value of the stocks on the given date and the value of the term deposits when they come due.

Solution:

Set up convenient column widths in the spreadsheet: column B at 22 spaces to contain the company and item names, columns C and D at 10 spaces, and E at 12 spaces to contain the portfolio values.

Enter the data and formulas to complete the spreadsheet as shown.

	A	B	C	D	E
1	INVESTMENT PORTFOLIO: MARCH 4				
2					
3	Number	Name of Company	Share		Share
4	of Shares		Prices		Value
5					
6	500.00	Emco Ltd.	13.25	(A6*C6) ➤	6625.00
7	200.00	Federal Industries Inc.	24.50		4900.00
8	3500.00	IPSCO Inc.	7.75		27125.00
9	100.00	Leon's Furniture	24.00		2400.00
10	750.00	Noma Industries Ltd., A	18.25		13687.50
11	150.00	Torstar Corporation, B	29.50		4425.00
12		Total Value:		@SUM (E6..E11) ➤	59162.50
13					
14	Cash	Item	Interest	Term in	Value at
15	Deposits		Rate	Days	Maturity
16	75000.00	Treasury Bill	0.099	319.00 ➤	81554.79
17	20000.00	Savings Bonds	0.09	365.00	21800.00
18	12500.00	Term Deposits	0.087	120.00	12857.53
19		Total Value:			116212.32

$(A16*(1+C16*D16/365))$ Replicate

@SUM (E16..E18)

EXERCISE 15.8

B 1. Use a spreadsheet to calculate the total value of each of the following portfolios.

(a) Portfolio for Joe Morin

Company Name	Price per Share	Number of Shares
AT&T	27.75	200
Colgate-Palmolive	51.75	50
Firestone Tire	39.25	100
C C L Industries Ltd. A	15.25	350
C C L Industries Ltd. B	14.50	500
Pepsico	37.25	250
Sterling Drugs	43.75	150

(b) Portfolio for Tamara Brazeau

Company Name	Price per Share	Number of Shares
American Express	58.50	75
Bank of Montreal	25.50	125
Bank of British Columbia	22.50	110
Cominco Ltd.	17.75	500
Great Lakes Forest Ltd.	45.25	200
Magna International Inc.	24.25	525
Shepherd Products Ltd.	14.75	700

(c) Portfolio for Clint and Maria Marco

Company Name	Price per Share	Number of Shares
Alco	$11\frac{5}{8}$	500
Bombardier A	$23\frac{3}{4}$	400
Bow Valley	$18\frac{7}{8}$	1200
Campeau	23	300
Chieftain	$14\frac{5}{8}$	200
Comtech	3.90	3000
Denison A	7.50	1000

Cash Deposit	Principal	Rate	Term
Term Deposit	$7000	8%	120 d
Treasury Bill	$20 000	9.9%	300 d
Savings Bonds	$17 000	9%	365 d

2. Helen and Lincoln Roberts have a portfolio consisting of the following mutual funds. Share prices quoted are correct as of the same base date.

Name of Mutual Fund	Price per Share	Number of Shares
Bolton Tremblay Canadian	16.83	250
Canada Trust Income	9.71	325
First City Growth	5.32	2300
Investors Group Mutual	9.00	340
Montreal Trust Equity	29.72	200
Royfund Equity	22.43	725
Templeton Canadian	6.41	2100

Use a spreadsheet to calculate the value of the portfolio using the share prices given above.

C 3. The following chart lists the high, low, and closing prices for a group of stocks in the portfolio of Gerry Mortinson.

Stock	Bid or High	Ask or Low	Last Price
Alcan	$40\frac{3}{4}$	$40\frac{1}{8}$	$40\frac{1}{2}$
Bell	25	$24\frac{3}{4}$	$24\frac{3}{4}$
Fleet Aero	$10\frac{1}{2}$	10	$10\frac{1}{4}$
Hemlo	$22\frac{3}{4}$	$22\frac{1}{4}$	$22\frac{1}{2}$
LAC Mnrls	$16\frac{1}{2}$	$15\frac{3}{4}$	$16\frac{1}{2}$
M Lf Gard	$30\frac{1}{2}$	30	$30\frac{1}{2}$
Nabisco	35	$34\frac{1}{4}$	35
Placer	$21\frac{5}{8}$	$20\frac{3}{4}$	$21\frac{1}{2}$

Gerry's holdings include 75 shares of Alcan, 100 shares of Bell, 150 shares of Fleet, 125 shares of Hemlo, 250 shares of LAC, 20 shares of M Lf Gard, 50 shares of Nabisco, and 100 shares of Placer. Prepare a spreadsheet to compute the value of Gerry's portfolio on the given day.

15.9 SPREADSHEETS IN SMALL BUSINESS

A computer with spreadsheet software can be used in a small business to do a variety of tasks such as timekeeping, payroll, expense accounts, billing, and inventory. In this section we will examine and develop some spreadsheet applications involving the Old Country Cheese Company and its 13 employees.

In the following spreadsheet, the hourly rates and the hours worked during the month of February are given for the 13 employees.

Enter this information in a spreadsheet and compute the column for gross pay.

	A	B	C	D	E	F
	OLD COUNTRY CHEESE COMPANY			TIMESHEET		
2				Month: February		
3	Name	Rate/Hour	Hours	Gross Pay		
4						
5	Adamo, Julio	7.50	160	(B5*C5)		
6	Davis, Janis	7.50	128			
7	Gibb, Mary	8.85	145			
8	Howie, Anne	12.63	160			
9	Innes, Pat	8.85	134			
10	Kirk, Dennis	7.50	140			
11	Marson, James	8.85	155			
12	Nelson, Cory	8.85	160			
13	Olsen, Sweyn	12.63	158			
14	Patt, Jane	8.85	148			
15	Singh, Louis	12.63	160			
16	Thoms, John	8.85	144			
17	Venn, Edward	7.50	160			
18						
19	Total:		1952			

What are the total number of hours worked by the employees during the month of February?

What is the total amount earned in gross pay?

The above spreadsheet can be extended to include the payroll computation.

Deductions from gross income are made at the following rates:

Canada Pension Plan (C.P.P.)	2%
Unemployment Insurance (U.I.)	0.8%
Income Tax (based on hourly rate) $\left\{ \begin{array}{l} \\ \\ \\ \end{array} \right.$	$7.50/h 16%
	$8.85/h 18%
	$12.63/h 20%

	A	B	C	D	E	F	G
1	OLD COUNTRY CHEESE COMPANY			PAYROLL		(B5–C5–D5–E5)	
2				Month: February			
3	Name	Gross Pay	C.P.P.	U.I.	Inc. Tax	Net Pay	
4			.02*B5	.008*B5			
5	Adamo, Julio	1200.00	24.00 ←	9.60 ←	192.00 ←	974.40 ←	.16*B5
6	Davis, Janis	960.00	19.20	7.68	153.60	779.52	
7	Gibb, Mary	1283.45	25.67	10.27	231.02 ←	1016.49	.18*B7
8	Howie, Anne	2020.80	40.42	16.17	404.16 ←	1560.06	.2*B8
9	Innes, Pat	1185.90	23.72	9.49	213.46	939.23	
10	Kirk, Dennis	1050.00	21.00	8.40	168.00	852.60	
11	Marson, James	1371.75	27.44	10.97	246.92	1086.43	
12	Nelson, Cory	1416.00	28.32	11.33	254.88	1121.47	
13	Olsen, Sweyn	1995.54	39.91	15.96	399.11	1540.56	
14	Patt, Jane	1309.80	26.20	10.48	235.76	1037.36	
15	Singh, Louis	2020.80	40.42	16.17	404.16	1560.06	
16	Thoms, John	1274.40	25.49	10.20	229.39	1009.32	
17	Venn, Edward	1200.00	24.00	9.60	192.00	974.40	
18							
19	Totals:	18288.44	365.77	146.31	3324.46	14451.90	
20							

@SUM (C5..C17)

EXERCISE 15.9

B

1. Read the following from the completed spreadsheet above.

(a) What is the total amount of Canada Pension Plan premiums paid by the 13 employees?

(b) What is the total amount of Unemployment Insurance premiums paid by the employees?

(c) What is the total amount of income tax withheld by the company on behalf of the government?

(d) Complete the summary at the right of employee deductions that a company must forward on behalf of its employees.

	A	B	C
20			
21	SUMMARY:		
22			
23	TOTAL C.P.P.		(C19)
24			
25	TOTAL U.I.		(D19)
26			
27	TOTAL INC. TAX		(E19)
28			
29	TOTAL DEDUCTIONS		(C19+D19+E19)
30			

2. Set up a spreadsheet to make up the bills for stores buying cheese from the Old Country Cheese Company.
Use the following headings and prices.

Old Country Cheese Company			
Customer:			
Kind	Quantity	Price per Kilogram	Cost
Mild Cheddar		7.20	
Medium Cheddar		7.40	
Old Cheddar		7.65	
Brick Cheese		7.20	
Mozzarella		6.80	
Total			
Previous Bill			
Balance Due			

Use the spreadsheet to prepare bills for each of the following purchases.
(a) Joe's Meat Market
    45 kg of mild cheddar
    50 kg of medium cheddar
    20 kg of old cheddar
    75 kg of brick cheese
    100 kg of mozzarella
(b) Molly's Convenience Store
    30 kg of mild cheddar
    40 kg of medium cheddar
    10 kg of old cheddar
    50 kg of brick cheese
    60 kg of mozzarella
(c) Bob's Corner Store
    20 kg of mild cheddar
    25 kg of medium cheddar
    10 kg of old cheddar
    30 kg of brick cheese
    25 kg of mozzarella
    Bob's has a previous balance of $128.25.

3. Production costs are determined by adding fixed costs such as rent and variable costs such as raw materials. The following table shows the production costs for making cheese at the Old Country Cheese Factory.

Old Country Cheese Factory		
Kilograms Output	Fixed Costs	Variable Costs
0	1075.00	0.00
50	1075.00	75.00
100	1075.00	150.0
150	1075.00	225.00
200	1075.00	300.00
250	1075.00	375.00
300	1075.00	450.00
375	1075.00	525.00
450	1075.00	600.00
500	1200.00	675.00
550	1200.00	750.00
600	1200.00	825.00
650	1200.00	900.00
700	1200.00	975.00
750	1200.00	1050.00
800	1200.00	1125.00
850	1200.00	1200.00

(a) Set up a spreadsheet to find the total costs for each of the given outputs up to 850 kg.
(b) Extend the spreadsheet with three new columns to compute
    (i) average fixed cost,
    (ii) average variable cost,
    (iii) average total cost.
(c) Reading from your spreadsheet, determine the number of kilograms of cheese production that has the lowest average total cost.

15.10 AMORTIZATION SCHEDULES

Amortization refers to the repayment of debts by a series of payments, usually equal in size and made at regular time intervals. Mortgages and consumer loans are repaid by this method. Each payment that the consumer makes is blended. First, the interest due is paid, and then the balance is used to reduce the principal. A problem arises in the calculation of amortization in determining the size of the equal payment that will reduce the balance to 0 over a period of time. Once the monthly payment has been determined, an amortization schedule can be produced as in the following example.

Example. A debt of $4000 is to be repaid by making equal blended payments at the end of each month for two years. Interest is charged at a rate of 15% per annum compounded monthly.

Construct an amortization schedule.

Solution:
Set up the spreadsheet as shown.
Enter titles and column headings in rows 1 to 6.
Enter zeros in cells A7, B7, C7, and D7, and enter the principal sum to be borrowed, the Outstanding Balance, in cell E7.

	A	B	C	D	E
1	AMORTIZATION SCHEDULE				
2			The monthly		
3	$4000 for 2 a at 15% per annum		payment is $193.95	0.0125*E7	(B8–C8)	(E7–D8)
4					
5	Payment	Amount	Interest	Principal	Outstanding
6	Number	Paid	Paid	Repaid	Balance
7	0	$0.00	$0.00	$0.00	$4000.00
8	1	$193.95 ←	$50.00 ←	$143.95 ←	$3856.05 ←
	Payment	2	~193.95	$48.20	$1.75	$3710.20
29	Numbers 22	$19.	$7.09	$186.80	.65
30	1 to 24 23	$193.95	$4.76	$189.19	$191.46
31	24	$193.85	$2.39	$191.46	($0.00)

▲ Why is the
final payment $193.85?

EXERCISE 15.10

B

1. Enter the spreadsheet given in the example and print the complete table.

2. Using the spreadsheet in the example as a model, determine the monthly payment if the interest rate had been the following.

(a) 12% per annum
(b) 8% per annum
(c) 18% per annum

3. (a) Set up an amortization schedule for a loan of $12 000 at 12% per annum compounded monthly with a monthly payment of $500.
(b) How long will it take to repay the loan?
(c) How much is the last payment?
(d) What should the monthly payment be in order to repay the loan in 3 a?

15.11 MORE APPLICATIONS OF SPREADSHEETS

In the previous sections we used the capabilities of the spreadsheet to assist in making decisions and to solve problems. The spreadsheet incorporates many of the other problem solving strategies with the strategy Make a table. In this section additional applications are presented.

EXERCISE 15.11

B

1. The Elmvale Secondary School Students' Council treasurer prepares all statements for bank deposits.

(a) Set up a spreadsheet for the treasurer with the following headings to perform the calculations.

ELMVALE SECONDARY SCHOOL
Account Number:
Deposited by:

Event:

Bills   Amount
_____ × $50.00
_____ × $20.00
_____ × $10.00
_____ × $5.00
_____ × $2.00
_____ × $1.00

Coins
_____ × $1.00
_____ × $0.50
_____ × $0.25
_____ × $0.10
_____ × $0.05
_____ × $0.01

Total Deposit

(b) Use your spreadsheet to prepare the following deposits.
 (i) School Dance:
    3 fifty dollar bills, 14 twenties,
    45 tens, 56 fives, 22 twos, 72 ones,
    18 one-dollar coins, 124 quarters,
    50 dimes, 30 nickels, and
    172 pennies

 (ii) Drama Festival:
    11 twenty dollar bills, 1012 tens,
    537 fives, 218 twos, 532 ones,
    71 one-dollar coins, 3 half-dollar
    coins, 63 quarters, 132 dimes,
    56 nickels, and 256 pennies

2. Set up a spreadsheet to find your choice of camera equipment. The choices are a disc camera, an automatic-focus compact camera, and an automatic-focus single lens reflex camera (SLR). The criteria are price, ease of use, quality of picture, flexibility, carrying ease, and cost of film.

(a) Assign values from 1 to 10 to each criterion.
(b) Assign the value 0, 1, or 2 to each model of camera based on each criterion.

3. The Hi-tech Auto Centre keeps track of its customers' cars using a computer. Design a spreadsheet to compute the amount of service that Edna and Joe MacLean purchased from November 4 until July 18, including 7% sales tax.

November 4
    4 tires at $129.95 each
    Front-end alignment at $40

January 31
    Tune-up at $69.95
    Six spark plugs at $4.18 each
    Set of wires at $39.95

March 7
    Muffler at no charge
    Exhaust pipe at $44.50
    3 clamps at $1.50
    Service charge $9.50

July 18
    Flush radiator at $19.95
    Overhaul on air-conditioner for $144

4. Anne Howie travels for the Old Country Cheese Company and is reimbursed for her travel expenses.
Set up a spreadsheet to calculate Anne's expense account using the headings Date, Place, Travel, Meals, Accommodation, and Other and find the total for each column and the grand total.

Feb. 3: Grand Fork, $35.20 for travel, $32.65 for meals, no accommodation, $6 for parking.
Feb. 6: Almater, $45.20 for travel, $43.18 for meals, $82.60 for motel
Feb. 12: Rochville, $56.25 for travel, $37.15 for meals, $75.86 for hotel
Feb. 13: Grand Fork, $35.20 for travel, $29.82 for meals, no accommodation, $6 for parking
Feb. 17: Retton, $88.62 for travel, $142.50 for meals, $243.75 for motel
Feb. 22: Grand Fork, 35.20 for travel, $36.05 for meals, no accommodation, $6 for parking

5. Set up a spreadsheet to determine your choice of a bicycle. The choices are a red 10-speed for $549.50, a black mountain bike for $599.95, and a silver motocross for $375. The criteria are price, general road use, colour, durability, and resale value.

(a) Assign values from 1 to 10 to each criterion.
(b) Assign the values 0, 1, or 2 to each model based on each criterion.

Criteria	Value	I 10-speed	II Mountain Bike	III Motocross
Price				
General				
Colour				
Durability				
Resale				
Totals				

15.12 REVIEW EXERCISE

1. Prepare a summary for the following operations on a spreadsheet.
(a) moving the cursor
(b) entering numeric data
(c) entering alpha data
(d) entering numeric data as alpha data
(e) copying the contents from one cell to another
(f) entering formulas that perform operations with the contents of two or more cells
(g) using the built-in @ functions
(h) using the COPY command to replicate a formula
(i) using the PRINT command to print the contents of a spreadsheet
(j) using the FILE command to save and retrieve a file

2. (a) Enter the following values in a spreadsheet.
    (i) 24.3 in cell A2
    (ii) 6.4 in cell B2
    (iii) 35.2 in cell C2
    (iv) 5.7 in cell D2
(b) Set the format for column F to give the answer to one decimal place.
    Enter each of the following formulas in the indicated cell.
    (i) ((A2*B2) − C2)/D2 in cell F2
    (ii) ((A2 + B2) − (C2 − D2))*3.5 in cell F3
    (iii) (A2/B2 + C2/D2 − A2/C2) in cell F4
    (iv) (F2 + F3 + F4) in cell F5

3. The following list gives times in seconds for a professional football team to run the 40 m dash.

5.0, 4.8, 4.5, 4.2, 4.7, 4.7, 5.3, 5.0, 4.2, 4.3, 4.4, 4.7, 4.6, 4.8, 4.6, 5.0, 4.9, 4.5, 4.8, 5.1, 4.9, 5.4, 4.5, 4.8, 4.9, 5.0, 5.1, 5.4, 4.3, 4.4, 4.6, 4.8, 4.7, 4.8, 5.2, 4.9, 4.6, 5.0, 4.5, 4.8, 5.0, 4.7, 4.6, 5.1, 4.9, 5.4, 4.5, 4.7

(a) Use a spreadsheet to find the mean.
(b) Find the standard deviation.
(c) Illustrate these results on a graph.

4. The following list shows the number of suits sold in a clothing store each month for one year.

Month	Number Sold	Month	Number Sold
Jan.	68	July	62
Feb.	75	Aug.	77
March	84	Sept.	83
April	74	Oct.	88
May	69	Nov.	93
June	65	Dec.	112

(a) Find the average number of suits sold each month.
(b) Find the standard deviation.
(c) Illustrate the above results on a graph.

5. Set up a spreadsheet to compute a table of square roots, squares, cubes, and fourth powers for the positive integers from 1 to 25 with the following headings:

N,   N^.5,   N^2,   N^3,   and   N^4.

6. The following chart lists the number of monthly phone calls made by each of 4 salespersons.

Month	James	Burk	Hicks	Spence
Jan.	124	136	118	134
Feb.	152	144	123	108
March	122	135	166	132
April	143	165	156	155
May	134	142	115	143
June	132	152	144	167
July	145	154	162	156
Aug.	144	113	102	156
Sept.	153	154	145	173
Oct.	152	172	139	161
Nov.	153	155	172	148
Dec.	152	169	182	130

Prepare a spreadsheet to do the following calculations.
(a) Find the total number of phone calls made by each person.
(b) Find the average number of phone calls per person made each month.
(c) Find the standard deviation and determine the range within which two-thirds of the values lie.

7. (a) Set up a spreadsheet to generate a table of values in 10° intervals for each of the following, $0° \leqslant N \leqslant 360°$.
 (i) $Y = 2 \sin N + \cos N$
 (ii) $Y = \sin N + 2 \cos N$
 (iii) $Y = 0.5 \sin N + \cos N$
 (iv) $Y = 1.5 \sin N - 1.5 \cos N$
(b) Use the values in the above tables to draw graphs of each function.

8. (a) Set up a spreadsheet as shown to find the measure of the angles of a right triangle when the lengths of the three sides are known.
The @ATAN(...) function gives the measure of an angle in radians when the tangent value is entered.
To change radians to degrees, we multiply by $\dfrac{180}{\pi}$.
Test your formula using the example numbers given below.

	A	B	C
1	SOLVING FOR ANGLES		
2			Angle
3	Side X	Side Y	Opposite Y
4	5.25	3.75	54.46232
5			▲
6		180/@PI*@ATAN (B4/A4)	
7			

(b) Use your spreadsheet to find the measures of the acute angles in each of the following triangles.

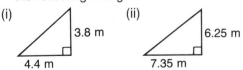
(i) 3.8 m, 4.4 m   (ii) 6.25 m, 7.35 m

9. Solve the following equations using a spreadsheet.
Give the roots to one decimal place.
(a) $2x^2 + 5x - 7 = 0$
(b) $-3x^2 - 4x + 6 = 0$
(c) $6.25x^2 - 5.35x - 6.75 = 0$
(d) $1.35x^2 = 5.14x + 6.14$

10. Prepare a table on a spreadsheet to show how long it will take an investment of $1000 to amount to $2500 at 12% compounded monthly.

11. Set up a spreadsheet to generate a compound interest table for $P(1 + I)\verb|^|N$, giving 25 interest periods at an interest rate of 4.5%.

12. Compute the value of the following portfolio of cash deposits upon maturity.

Cash Deposit	Principal	Rate	Term
Term Deposits	$12 000	9.5%	180 d
Savings Bonds	$25 000	9.3%	365 d
Treasury Bill	$80 000	9.9%	319 d

13. The following table gives the list of employees, their hourly rates, and the number of hours worked.
Use a spreadsheet to compute the gross pay for each employee and the total amount to be paid out by the company.

Barr, H.	$14.75	142 h
Cote, W.	$18.80	162 h
Hume, H.	$21.15	135 h
Lim, L.	$21.15	142 h
Marin, F.	$14.75	148 h
Matte, C.	$14.75	154 h
Page, H.	$14.75	150 h
Piche, J.	$18.80	120 h
Rivard, S.	$18.80	136 h
Speck, B.	$14.75	148 h
Toth, J.	$14.75	156 h

APPENDIX

Table I   SQUARE ROOTS

n	$\sqrt{n}$	n	$\sqrt{n}$	n	$\sqrt{n}$	n	$\sqrt{n}$
1	1.000	51	7.141	101	10.050	151	12.288
2	1.414	52	7.211	102	10.010	152	12.329
3	1.732	53	7.280	103	10.149	153	12.369
4	2.000	54	7.349	104	10.198	154	12.410
5	2.236	55	7.416	105	10.247	155	12.450
6	2.450	56	7.483	106	10.296	156	12.490
7	2.646	57	7.550	107	10.344	157	12.530
8	2.828	58	7.616	108	10.392	158	12.570
9	3.000	59	7.681	109	10.440	159	12.610
10	3.162	60	7.746	110	10.488	160	12.649
11	3.317	61	7.810	111	10.536	161	12.689
12	3.464	62	7.874	112	10.583	162	12.728
13	3.606	63	7.937	113	10.630	163	12.767
14	3.742	64	8.000	114	10.677	164	12.806
15	3.873	65	8.062	115	10.724	165	12.845
16	4.000	66	8.124	116	10.770	166	12.884
17	4.123	67	8.185	117	10.817	167	12.923
18	4.243	68	8.246	118	10.863	168	12.961
19	4.359	69	8.307	119	10.909	169	13.000
20	4.472	70	8.367	120	10.954	170	13.038
21	4.583	71	8.426	121	11.000	171	13.077
22	4.690	72	8.485	122	11.045	172	13.115
23	4.796	73	8.544	123	11.091	173	13.153
24	4.899	74	8.602	124	11.136	174	13.191
25	5.000	75	8.660	125	11.180	175	13.229
26	5.099	76	8.718	126	11.225	176	13.266
27	5.196	77	8.775	127	11.269	177	13.304
28	5.292	78	8.832	128	11.314	178	13.342
29	5.385	79	8.888	129	11.358	179	13.379
30	5.477	80	8.944	130	11.402	180	13.416
31	5.568	81	9.000	131	11.446	181	13.454
32	5.657	82	9.055	132	11.489	182	13.491
33	5.745	83	9.110	133	11.533	183	13.528
34	5.831	84	9.165	134	11.576	184	13.565
35	5.916	85	9.220	135	11.619	185	13.601
36	6.000	86	9.274	136	11.662	186	13.638
37	6.083	87	9.327	137	11.705	187	13.675
38	6.164	88	9.381	138	11.747	188	13.711
39	6.245	89	9.434	139	11.790	189	13.748
40	6.325	90	9.487	140	11.832	190	13.784
41	6.403	91	9.539	141	11.874	191	13.820
42	6.481	92	9.592	142	11.916	192	13.856
43	6.557	93	9.644	143	11.958	193	13.892
44	6.633	94	9.695	144	12.000	194	13.928
45	6.708	95	9.747	145	12.042	195	13.964
46	6.782	96	9.798	146	12.083	196	14.000
47	6.856	97	9.849	147	12.124	197	14.036
48	6.928	98	9.900	148	12.166	198	14.071
49	7.000	99	9.950	149	12.207	199	14.107
50	7.071	100	10.000	150	12.247	200	14.142

Table II TRIGONOMETRIC RATIOS

0°	sin θ	cos θ	tan θ	cot θ	sec θ	cosec θ
0	0.0000	1.0000	0.0000	—	1.0000	—
1	0.0175	0.9999	0.0175	57.290	1.0001	57.299
2	0.0349	0.9994	0.0349	28.636	1.0006	28.654
3	0.0523	0.9986	0.0524	19.081	1.0014	19.107
4	0.0698	0.9976	0.0699	14.301	1.0024	14.335
5	0.0872	0.9962	0.0875	11.430	1.0038	11.474
6	0.1045	0.9945	0.1051	9.5144	1.0055	9.5668
7	0.1219	0.9926	0.1228	8.1443	1.0075	8.2055
8	0.1392	0.9903	0.1405	7.1154	1.0098	7.1853
9	0.1564	0.9877	0.1584	6.3137	1.0125	6.3924
10	0.1737	0.9848	0.1763	5.6713	1.0154	5.7588
11	0.1908	0.9816	0.1944	5.1445	1.0187	5.2408
12	0.2079	0.9782	0.2126	4.7046	1.0223	4.8097
13	0.2250	0.9744	0.2309	4.3315	1.0263	4.4454
14	0.2419	0.9703	0.2493	4.0108	1.0306	4.1336
15	0.2588	0.9659	0.2680	3.7320	1.0353	3.8637
16	0.2756	0.9613	0.2867	3.4874	1.0403	3.6279
17	0.2924	0.9563	0.3057	3.2708	1.0457	3.4203
18	0.3090	0.9511	0.3249	3.0777	1.0515	3.2361
19	0.3256	0.9455	0.3443	2.9042	1.0576	3.0715
20	0.3420	0.9397	0.3640	2.7475	1.0642	2.9238
21	0.3584	0.9336	0.3839	2.6051	1.0711	2.7904
22	0.3746	0.9272	0.4040	2.4751	1.0785	2.6695
23	0.3907	0.9025	0.4245	2.3558	1.0864	2.5593
24	0.4067	0.9136	0.4452	2.2460	1.0946	2.4586
25	0.4226	0.9063	0.4663	2.1445	1.1034	2.3662
26	0.4384	0.8988	0.4877	2.0503	1.1126	2.2812
27	0.4540	0.8910	0.5095	1.9626	1.1223	2.2027
28	0.4695	0.8830	0.5317	1.8807	1.1326	2.1300
29	0.4848	0.8746	0.5543	1.8040	1.1433	2.0627
30	0.5000	0.8660	0.5774	1.7320	1.1547	2.0000
31	0.5150	0.8572	0.6009	1.6643	1.1666	1.9416
32	0.5299	0.8481	0.6249	1.6003	1.1792	1.8871
33	0.5446	0.8387	0.6494	1.5399	1.1924	1.8361
34	0.5592	0.8290	0.6745	1.4826	1.2062	1.7883
35	0.5736	0.8192	0.7002	1.4281	1.2208	1.7434
36	0.5878	0.8090	0.7265	1.3764	1.2361	1.7013
37	0.6018	0.7986	0.7536	1.3270	1.2521	1.6616
38	0.6157	0.7880	0.7813	1.2799	1.2690	1.6243
39	0.6293	0.7772	0.8098	1.2349	1.2867	1.5890
40	0.6428	0.7660	0.8391	1.1917	1.3054	1.5557
41	0.6561	0.7547	0.8693	1.1504	1.3250	1.5242
42	0.6691	0.7431	0.9004	1.1106	1.3456	1.4945
43	0.6820	0.7314	0.9325	1.0724	1.3673	1.4663
44	0.6947	0.7193	0.9657	1.0355	1.3902	1.4395
45	0.7071	0.7071	1.0000	1.0000	1.4142	1.4142

Table II   (*Continued*)

0°	sin θ	cos θ	tan θ	cot θ	sec θ	cosec θ
46	0.7193	0.6947	1.0355	0.9657	1.4395	1.3902
47	0.7314	0.6820	1.0724	0.9325	1.4663	1.3673
48	0.7431	0.6691	1.1106	0.9004	1.4945	1.3456
49	0.7547	0.6561	1.1504	0.8693	1.5242	1.3250
50	0.7660	0.6428	1.1917	0.8391	1.5557	1.3054
51	0.7772	0.6293	1.2349	0.8098	1.5890	1.2867
52	0.7880	0.6157	1.2799	0.7813	1.6243	1.2690
53	0.7986	0.6018	1.3270	0.7536	1.6616	1.2521
54	0.8090	0.5878	1.3764	0.7265	1.7013	1.2361
55	0.8192	0.5736	1.4281	0.7002	1.7434	1.2208
56	0.8290	0.5592	1.4826	0.6745	1.7883	1.2062
57	0.8387	0.5446	1.5399	0.6494	1.8361	1.1924
58	0.8481	0.5299	1.6003	0.6249	1.8871	1.1792
59	0.8572	0.5150	1.6643	0.6009	1.9416	1.1666
60	0.8660	0.5000	1.7320	0.5774	2.0000	1.1547
61	0.8746	0.4848	1.8040	0.5543	2.0627	1.1433
62	0.8830	0.4695	1.8807	0.5317	2.1300	1.1326
63	0.8910	0.4540	1.9626	0.5095	2.2027	1.1223
64	0.8988	0.4384	2.0503	0.4877	2.2812	1.1126
65	0.9063	0.4226	2.1445	0.4663	2.3662	1.1034
66	0.9136	0.4067	2.2460	0.4452	2.4586	1.0946
67	0.9205	0.3907	2.3558	0.4245	2.5593	1.0864
68	0.9272	0.3746	2.4751	0.4040	2.6695	1.0785
69	0.9336	0.3584	2.6051	0.3839	2.7904	1.0711
70	0.9397	0.3420	2.7475	0.3640	2.9238	1.0642
71	0.9455	0.3256	2.9042	0.3443	3.0715	1.0576
72	0.9511	0.3090	3.0777	0.3249	3.2361	1.0515
73	0.9563	0.2924	3.2708	0.3057	3.4203	1.0457
74	0.9613	0.2756	3.4874	0.2867	3.6279	1.0403
75	0.9659	0.2588	3.7320	0.2680	3.8637	1.0353
76	0.9703	0.2419	4.0108	0.2493	4.1336	1.0306
77	0.9744	0.2250	4.3315	0.2309	4.4454	1.0263
78	0.9782	0.2079	4.7046	0.2126	4.8097	1.0223
79	0.9816	0.1908	5.1445	0.1944	5.2408	1.0187
80	0.9848	0.1737	5.6713	0.1763	5.7588	1.0154
81	0.9877	0.1564	6.3137	0.1584	6.3924	1.0125
82	0.9903	0.1392	7.1154	0.1405	7.1853	1.0098
83	0.9926	0.1219	8.1443	0.1228	8.2005	1.0075
84	0.9945	0.1045	9.5144	0.1051	9.5668	1.0055
85	0.9962	0.0872	11.430	0.0875	11.474	1.0038
86	0.9976	0.0698	14.301	0.0699	14.335	1.0024
87	0.9986	9.0523	19.081	0.0524	19.107	1.0014
88	0.9994	0.0349	28.636	0.0349	28.654	1.0006
89	0.9999	0.0175	57.290	0.0175	57.299	1.0001
90	1.0000	0.0000	—	0.0000	—	1.0000

Table III THE NUMBER OF EACH DAY OF THE YEAR

Day of Month	Jan.	Feb.	Mar.	Apr.	May	Jun.	Jul.	Aug.	Sept.	Oct.	Nov.	Dec.	Day of Month
1	1	32	60	91	121	152	182	213	244	274	305	335	1
2	2	33	61	92	122	153	183	214	245	275	306	336	2
3	3	34	62	93	123	154	184	215	246	276	307	337	3
4	4	35	63	94	124	155	185	216	247	277	308	338	4
5	5	36	64	95	125	156	186	217	248	278	309	339	5
6	6	37	65	96	126	157	187	218	249	279	310	340	6
7	7	38	66	97	127	158	188	219	250	280	311	341	7
8	8	39	67	98	128	159	189	220	251	281	312	342	8
9	9	40	68	99	129	160	190	221	252	282	313	343	9
10	10	41	69	100	130	161	191	222	253	283	314	344	10
11	11	42	70	101	131	162	192	223	254	284	315	345	11
12	12	43	71	102	132	163	193	224	255	285	316	346	12
13	13	44	72	103	133	164	194	225	256	286	317	347	13
14	14	45	73	104	134	165	195	226	257	287	318	348	14
15	15	46	74	105	135	166	196	227	258	288	319	349	15
16	16	47	75	106	136	167	197	228	259	289	320	350	16
17	17	48	76	107	137	168	198	229	260	290	321	351	17
18	18	49	77	108	138	169	199	230	261	291	322	352	18
19	19	50	78	109	139	170	200	231	262	292	323	353	19
20	20	51	79	110	140	171	201	232	263	293	324	354	20
21	21	52	80	111	141	172	202	233	264	294	325	355	21
22	22	53	81	112	142	173	203	234	265	295	326	356	22
23	23	54	82	113	143	174	204	235	266	296	327	357	23
24	24	55	83	114	144	175	205	236	267	297	328	358	24
25	25	56	84	115	145	176	206	237	268	298	329	359	25
26	26	57	85	116	146	177	207	238	269	299	330	360	26
27	27	58	86	117	147	178	208	239	270	300	331	361	27
28	28	59	87	118	148	179	209	240	271	301	332	362	28
29	29		88	119	149	180	210	241	272	302	333	363	29
30	30		89	120	150	181	211	242	273	303	334	364	30
31	31		90		151		212	243		304		365	31

Table IV DAYS EXPRESSED IN DECIMAL EQUIVALENTS OF A YEAR — 365 d BASIS

For Figuring Interest, Cancellation of Insurance Premiums, Etc.

Day of Month	January Decimal Equivalent	February Day of Year	February Decimal Equivalent	March Day of Year	March Decimal Equivalent	April Day of Year	April Decimal Equivalent	May Day of Year	May Decimal Equivalent	June Day of Year	June Decimal Equivalent	July Day of Year	July Decimal Equivalent	August Day of Year	August Decimal Equivalent	September Day of Year	September Decimal Equivalent	October Day of Year	October Decimal Equivalent	November Day of Year	November Decimal Equivalent	December Day of Year	December Decimal Equivalent	Day of Month
1	0.0027	32	0.0877	60	0.1644	91	0.2493	121	0.3315	152	0.4164	182	0.4986	213	0.5836	244	0.6685	274	0.7507	305	0.8356	335	0.9178	1
2	0.0055	33	0.0904	61	0.1671	92	0.2521	122	0.3342	153	0.4192	183	0.5014	214	0.5863	245	0.6712	275	0.7534	306	0.8384	336	0.9205	2
3	0.0082	34	0.0932	62	0.1699	93	0.2548	123	0.3370	154	0.4219	184	0.5041	215	0.5890	246	0.6740	276	0.7562	307	0.8411	337	0.9233	3
4	0.0110	35	0.0959	63	0.1726	94	0.2575	124	0.3397	155	0.4247	185	0.5068	216	0.5918	247	0.6767	277	0.7589	308	0.8438	338	0.9260	4
5	0.0137	36	0.0986	64	0.1753	95	0.2603	125	0.3425	156	0.4274	186	0.5096	217	0.5945	248	0.6795	278	0.7616	309	0.8466	339	0.9288	5
6	0.0164	37	0.1014	65	0.1781	96	0.2630	126	0.3452	157	0.4301	187	0.5123	218	0.5973	249	0.6822	279	0.7644	310	0.8493	340	0.9315	6
7	0.0192	38	0.1041	66	0.1808	97	0.2658	127	0.3479	158	0.4329	188	0.5151	219	0.6000	250	0.6849	280	0.7671	311	0.8521	341	0.9342	7
8	0.0219	39	0.1068	67	0.1836	98	0.2685	128	0.3507	159	0.4356	189	0.5178	220	0.6027	251	0.6877	281	0.7699	312	0.8548	342	0.9370	8
9	0.0247	40	0.1096	68	0.1863	99	0.2712	129	0.3534	160	0.4384	190	0.5205	221	0.6055	252	0.6904	282	0.7726	313	0.8575	343	0.9397	9
10	0.0274	41	0.1123	69	0.1890	100	0.2740	130	0.3562	161	0.4411	191	0.5233	222	0.6082	253	0.6932	283	0.7753	314	0.8603	344	0.9425	10
11	0.0301	42	0.1151	70	0.1918	101	0.2767	131	0.3589	162	0.4438	192	0.5260	223	0.6110	254	0.6959	284	0.7781	315	0.8630	345	0.9452	11
12	0.0329	43	0.1178	71	0.1945	102	0.2795	132	0.3616	163	0.4466	193	0.5288	224	0.6137	255	0.6986	285	0.7808	316	0.8658	346	0.9479	12
13	0.0356	44	0.1205	72	0.1973	103	0.2822	133	0.3644	164	0.4493	194	0.5315	225	0.6164	256	0.7014	286	0.7836	317	0.8685	347	0.9507	13
14	0.0384	45	0.1233	73	0.2000	104	0.2849	134	0.3671	165	0.4521	195	0.5342	226	0.6192	257	0.7041	287	0.7863	318	0.8712	348	0.9534	14
15	0.0411	46	0.1260	74	0.2027	105	0.2877	135	0.3699	166	0.4548	196	0.5370	227	0.6219	258	0.7068	288	0.7890	319	0.8740	349	0.9562	15
16	0.0438	47	0.1288	75	0.2055	106	0.2904	136	0.3726	167	0.4575	197	0.5397	228	0.6247	259	0.7096	289	0.7918	320	0.8767	350	0.9589	16
17	0.0466	48	0.1315	76	0.2082	107	0.2932	137	0.3753	168	0.4603	198	0.5425	229	0.6274	260	0.7123	290	0.7945	321	0.8795	351	0.9616	17
18	0.0493	49	0.1342	77	0.2110	108	0.2959	138	0.3781	169	0.4630	199	0.5452	230	0.6301	261	0.7151	291	0.7973	322	0.8822	352	0.9644	18
19	0.0521	50	0.1370	78	0.2137	109	0.2986	139	0.3808	170	0.4658	200	0.5479	231	0.6329	262	0.7178	292	0.8000	323	0.8849	353	0.9671	19
20	0.0548	51	0.1397	79	0.2164	110	0.3014	140	0.3836	171	0.4685	201	0.5507	232	0.6356	263	0.7205	293	0.8027	324	0.8877	354	0.9699	20
21	0.0575	52	0.1425	80	0.2192	111	0.3041	141	0.3863	172	0.4712	202	0.5534	233	0.6384	264	0.7233	294	0.8055	325	0.8904	355	0.9726	21
22	0.0603	53	0.1452	81	0.2219	112	0.3068	142	0.3890	173	0.4740	203	0.5562	234	0.6411	265	0.7260	295	0.8082	326	0.8932	356	0.9753	22
23	0.0630	54	0.1479	82	0.2247	113	0.3096	143	0.3918	174	0.4767	204	0.5589	235	0.6438	266	0.7288	296	0.8110	327	0.8959	357	0.9781	23
24	0.0658	55	0.1507	83	0.2274	114	0.3123	144	0.3945	175	0.4795	205	0.5616	236	0.6466	267	0.7315	297	0.8137	328	0.8986	358	0.9808	24
25	0.0685	56	0.1534	84	0.2301	115	0.3151	145	0.3973	176	0.4822	206	0.5644	237	0.6493	268	0.7342	298	0.8164	329	0.9014	359	0.9836	25
26	0.0712	57	0.1562	85	0.2329	116	0.3178	146	0.4000	177	0.4849	207	0.5671	238	0.6521	269	0.7370	299	0.8192	330	0.9041	360	0.9863	26
27	0.0740	58	0.1589	86	0.2356	117	0.3205	147	0.4027	178	0.4877	208	0.5699	239	0.6548	270	0.7397	300	0.8219	331	0.9068	361	0.9890	27
28	0.0767	59	0.1616	87	0.2384	118	0.3233	148	0.4055	179	0.4904	209	0.5726	240	0.6575	271	0.7425	301	0.8247	332	0.9096	362	0.9918	28
29	0.0795			88	0.2411	119	0.3260	149	0.4082	180	0.4932	210	0.5753	241	0.6603	272	0.7452	302	0.8274	333	0.9123	363	0.9945	29
30	0.0822			89	0.2438	120	0.3288	150	0.4110	181	0.4959	211	0.5781	242	0.6630	273	0.7479	303	0.8301	334	0.9151	364	0.9973	30
31	0.0849			90	0.2466			151	0.4137			212	0.5808	243	0.6658			304	0.8329			365	1.0000	31

Table V   AMOUNT OF I $(1 + i)^n$

i/n	½%	1%	1½%	2%	2½%	3%	3½%	i/n
1	1.005 00	1.010 00	1.015 00	1.020 00	1.025 00	1.030 00	1.035 00	1
2	1.010 03	1.020 10	1.030 23	1.040 40	1.050 63	1.060 90	1.071 23	2
3	1.015 08	1.030 30	1.045 68	1.061 21	1.076 89	1.092 73	1.108 72	3
4	1.020 15	1.040 60	1.061 36	1.082 43	1.103 81	1.125 51	1.147 52	4
5	1.025 25	1.051 01	1.077 28	1.104 08	1.131 41	1.159 27	1.187 69	5
6	1.030 38	1.061 52	1.093 44	1.126 16	1.159 69	1.194 05	1.229 26	6
7	1.035 53	1.072 14	1.109 84	1.148 69	1.188 69	1.229 87	1.272 28	7
8	1.040 71	1.082 86	1.126 49	1.171 66	1.218 40	1.266 77	1.316 81	8
9	1.045 91	1.093 69	1.143 39	1.195 09	1.248 86	1.304 77	1.362 90	9
10	1.051 14	1.104 62	1.160 54	1.218 99	1.280 08	1.343 92	1.410 60	10
11	1.056 40	1.115 67	1.179 95	1.243 37	1.312 09	1.384 23	1.459 97	11
12	1.061 68	1.126 83	1.195 62	1.268 24	1.344 89	1.425 76	1.511 07	12
13	1.066 99	1.138 09	1.213 55	1.293 61	1.378 51	1.468 53	1.563 96	13
14	1.072 32	1.149 47	1.231 76	1.319 48	1.412 97	1.512 59	1.618 69	14
15	1.077 68	1.160 97	1.250 23	1.345 87	1.448 30	1.557 97	1.675 35	15
16	1.083 07	1.172 58	1.268 99	1.372 79	1.484 51	1.604 71	1.733 99	16
17	1.088 49	1.184 30	1.288 02	1.400 24	1.521 62	1.652 85	1.794 68	17
18	1.093 93	1.196 15	1.307 34	1.428 25	1.559 66	1.702 43	1.857 49	18
19	1.099 40	1.208 11	1.326 95	1.456 81	1.598 65	1.753 51	1.922 50	19
20	1.104 90	1.220 19	1.346 86	1.485 95	1.638 62	1.806 11	1.989 79	20
21	1.110 42	1.232 39	1.367 06	1.515 67	1.679 58	1.860 29	2.059 43	21
22	1.115 97	1.244 72	1.387 56	1.545 98	1.721 57	1.916 10	2.131 51	22
23	1.121 55	1.257 16	1.408 38	1.576 90	1.764 61	1.973 59	2.206 11	23
24	1.127 16	1.269 73	1.429 50	1.608 44	1.808 73	2.032 79	2.283 33	24
25	1.132 80	1.282 43	1.450 95	1.640 61	1.853 94	2.093 78	2.363 24	25
26	1.138 46	1.295 26	1.472 71	1.673 42	1.900 29	2.156 59	2.445 96	26
27	1.144 15	1.308 21	1.494 80	1.706 89	1.947 80	2.221 29	2.531 57	27
28	1.149 87	1.321 29	1.517 22	1.741 02	1.997 50	2.287 93	2.620 17	28
29	1.155 62	1.334 50	1.539 98	1.775 84	2.046 41	2.356 57	2.711 88	29
30	1.161 40	1.347 85	1.563 08	1.811 36	2.097 57	2.427 26	2.806 79	30
31	1.167 21	1.361 33	1.586 53	1.847 59	2.150 01	2.500 08	2.905 03	31
32	1.173 04	1.374 94	1.610 32	1.884 54	2.203 76	2.575 08	3.006 71	32
33	1.178 91	1.388 69	1.634 48	1.922 23	2.258 85	2.652 34	3.111 94	33
34	1.184 80	1.402 58	1.659 00	1.906 68	2.315 32	2.731 91	3.220 86	34
35	1.190 73	1.416 60	1.683 88	1.999 89	2.373 21	2.813 86	3.333 59	35
36	1.196 68	1.430 77	1.709 14	2.039 89	2.432 54	2.898 28	3.450 27	36
37	1.202 66	1.445 08	1.734 78	2.080 69	2.493 35	2.985 23	3.571 03	37
38	1.208 68	1.459 53	1.760 80	2.122 30	2.555 68	3.074 78	3.696 01	38
39	1.214 72	1.474 12	1.787 21	2.164 74	2.619 57	3.167 03	3.825 37	39
40	1.220 79	1.488 86	1.814 02	2.208 04	2.685 06	3.264 04	3.959 26	40

Table V (Continued)

i / n	4%	4½%	5%	5½%	6%	7%	8%	i / n
1	1.040 00	1.045 00	1.050 00	1.055 00	1.060 00	1.070 00	1.080 00	1
2	1.081 60	1.092 03	1.102 50	1.113 03	1.123 60	1.144 90	1.166 40	2
3	1.124 86	1.141 17	1.157 63	1.174 24	1.191 02	1.225 04	1.259 71	3
4	1.169 86	1.192 52	1.215 51	1.238 82	1.262 48	1.310 80	1.360 49	4
5	1.216 65	1.246 18	1.276 28	1.306 96	1.338 23	1.402 55	1.469 33	5
6	1.265 32	1.302 26	1.340 10	1.378 84	1.418 52	1.500 73	1.586 87	6
7	1.315 93	1.360 86	1.407 10	1.454 68	1.503 63	1.605 78	1.713 82	7
8	1.368 57	1.422 10	1.477 46	1.534 69	1.593 85	1.718 19	1.850 93	8
9	1.423 31	1.486 10	1.551 33	1.619 09	1.689 48	1.838 46	1.999 00	9
10	1.480 24	1.552 97	1.628 89	1.708 14	1.790 85	1.967 15	2.158 93	10
11	1.539 45	1.622 85	1.710 34	1.802 09	1.898 30	2.104 85	2.331 64	11
12	1.601 03	1.695 88	1.795 86	1.901 21	2.012 20	2.252 19	2.518 17	12
13	1.665 07	1.772 20	1.885 65	2.005 77	2.132 93	2.409 85	2.719 62	13
14	1.731 68	1.851 94	1.979 93	2.116 09	2.260 90	2.578 53	2.937 19	14
15	1.800 94	1.935 28	2.078 93	2.232 48	2.396 56	2.759 03	3.172 17	15
16	1.872 98	2.022 37	2.182 87	2.355 26	2.540 35	2.952 16	3.425 94	16
17	1.947 90	2.113 38	2.292 02	2.484 80	2.692 77	3.158 81	3.700 02	17
18	2.025 82	2.208 48	2.406 62	2.621 47	2.854 34	3.379 93	3.996 02	18
19	2.106 85	2.307 86	2.526 95	2.765 65	3.025 60	3.616 53	4.315 70	19
20	2.191 12	2.411 71	2.653 30	2.917 76	3.207 14	3.869 68	4.660 96	20
21	2.278 77	2.520 24	2.785 96	3.078 23	3.399 56	4.140 56	5.033 83	21
22	2.369 92	2.633 65	2.925 26	3.247 54	3.603 54	4.430 40	5.436 54	22
23	2.464 72	2.752 17	3.071 52	3.426 15	3.819 75	4.740 53	5.871 46	23
24	2.563 30	2.876 01	3.225 10	3.614 59	4.048 93	5.072 37	6.341 18	24
25	2.665 84	3.005 43	3.386 35	3.813 39	4.291 87	5.427 43	6.848 48	25
26	2.772 47	3.140 68	3.555 67	4.023 13	4.549 38	5.807 35	7.396 35	26
27	2.883 37	3.282 01	3.733 46	4.244 40	4.822 35	6.213 87	7.988 06	27
28	2.998 70	3.429 70	3.920 13	4.477 84	5.111 69	6.648 84	8.627 11	28
29	3.118 65	3.584 04	4.116 14	4.724 12	5.418 39	7.114 26	9.317 27	29
30	3.243 40	3.745 32	4.321 94	4.983 95	5.743 49	7.612 26	10.062 66	30
31	3.373 13	3.913 86	4.538 04	5.258 07	6.088 10	8.145 11	10.867 67	31
32	3.508 06	4.089 98	4.764 94	5.547 26	6.453 39	8.715 27	11.737 08	32
33	3.648 38	4.274 03	5.003 19	5.852 36	6.840 59	9.325 34	12.676 05	33
34	3.794 32	4.446 36	5.253 35	6.174 24	7.251 03	9.978 11	13.690 13	34
35	3.946 09	4.667 35	5.516 02	6.513 83	7.686 09	10.676 58	14.785 34	35
36	4.130 93	4.877 38	5.791 82	6.872 09	8.147 25	11.423 94	15.968 17	36
37	4.268 09	5.096 86	6.081 41	7.250 05	8.636 09	12.223 62	17.245 63	37
38	4.438 81	5.326 22	6.385 48	7.648 80	9.154 25	13.079 27	18.625 28	38
39	4.616 37	5.565 90	6.704 75	8.069 49	9.703 51	13.994 82	20.115 30	39
40	4.801 02	5.816 36	7.039 99	8.513 31	10.285 72	14.974 46	21.724 52	40

Table VI   PRESENT VALUE OF I $\dfrac{1}{(1+i)^n}$

$\frac{i}{n}$	$\frac{1}{2}$%	1%	$1\frac{1}{2}$%	2%	$2\frac{1}{2}$%	3%	$3\frac{1}{2}$%	$\frac{i}{n}$
1	0.995 02	0.990 10	0.985 22	0.980 39	0.975 61	0.970 87	0.966 18	1
2	0.990 07	0.980 30	0.970 66	0.961 17	0.951 81	0.942 60	0.933 51	2
3	0.985 15	0.970 59	0.956 32	0.942 32	0.928 60	0.915 14	0.901 94	3
4	0.980 25	0.960 98	0.942 18	0.923 85	0.905 95	0.888 49	0.871 44	4
5	0.975 37	0.951 47	0.928 26	0.905 73	0.883 85	0.862 61	0.841 97	5
6	0.970 52	0.942 05	0.914 54	0.887 97	0.862 30	0.837 48	0.813 50	6
7	0.965 69	0.932 72	0.901 03	0.870 56	0.841 27	0.813 09	0.785 99	7
8	0.960 89	0.923 48	0.887 71	0.853 49	0.820 75	0.789 41	0.759 41	8
9	0.956 10	0.914 34	0.874 59	0.836 76	0.800 73	0.766 42	0.733 73	9
10	0.951 35	0.905 29	0.861 67	0.820 35	0.781 20	0.744 09	0.708 92	10
11	0.946 61	0.896 32	0.848 93	0.804 26	0.762 14	0.722 42	0.684 95	11
12	0.941 91	0.887 45	0.836 39	0.788 49	0.743 56	0.701 38	0.661 78	12
13	0.937 22	0.878 66	0.824 03	0.773 03	0.725 42	0.680 95	0.639 40	13
14	0.932 56	0.869 96	0.811 85	0.757 88	0.707 73	0.661 12	0.617 78	14
15	0.927 92	0.861 35	0.799 85	0.743 01	0.690 47	0.641 86	0.596 89	15
16	0.923 30	0.852 82	0.788 03	0.728 45	0.673 62	0.623 17	0.576 71	16
17	0.918 71	0.844 38	0.776 39	0.714 16	0.657 20	0.605 02	0.557 20	17
18	0.914 14	0.836 02	0.764 91	0.700 16	0.641 17	0.587 39	0.538 36	18
19	0.909 59	0.827 74	0.753 61	0.686 43	0.625 53	0.570 29	0.520 16	19
20	0.905 06	0.819 54	0.742 47	0.672 97	0.610 27	0.553 68	0.502 57	20
21	0.900 56	0.811 43	0.731 50	0.659 78	0.595 39	0.527 55	0.485 57	21
22	0.896 08	0.803 40	0.720 69	0.646 84	0.580 86	0.521 89	0.469 15	22
23	0.891 62	0.795 44	0.710 04	0.634 16	0.566 70	0.506 69	0.453 29	23
24	0.887 19	0.787 57	0.699 54	0.621 72	0.552 88	0.491 93	0.437 96	24
25	0.882 77	0.779 77	0.689 21	0.609 53	0.539 39	0.477 61	0.423 15	25
26	0.878 38	0.772 05	0.679 02	0.597 58	0.526 23	0.463 69	0.408 84	26
27	0.874 01	0.764 40	0.668 99	0.585 86	0.513 40	0.450 19	0.395 01	27
28	0.869 66	0.756 84	0.659 10	0.574 37	0.500 88	0.437 08	0.381 65	28
29	0.865 33	0.749 34	0.649 36	0.563 11	0.488 66	0.424 35	0.368 75	29
30	0.861 03	0.741 92	0.639 76	0.552 07	0.476 74	0.411 99	0.356 28	30
31	0.856 75	0.734 58	0.630 31	0.541 25	0.465 11	0.399 99	0.344 23	31
32	0.852 48	0.727 30	0.620 99	0.530 63	0.453 77	0.388 34	0.332 59	32
33	0.848 24	0.720 10	0.611 82	0.520 23	0.442 70	0.377 03	0.321 34	33
34	0.844 02	0.712 97	0.602 77	0.510 03	0.431 91	0.366 04	0.310 48	34
35	0.839 82	0.705 91	0.593 87	0.500 03	0.421 37	0.355 38	0.299 98	35
36	0.835 64	0.698 92	0.585 09	0.490 22	0.411 09	0.345 03	0.289 83	36
37	0.831 49	0.692 00	0.576 44	0.480 61	0.401 07	0.334 98	0.280 03	37
38	0.827 35	0.685 15	0.567 92	0.471 19	0.391 28	0.325 23	0.270 56	38
39	0.823 23	0.678 37	0.559 53	0.461 95	0.381 74	0.315 75	0.261 41	39
40	0.819 14	0.671 65	0.551 26	0.452 89	0.372 43	0.306 56	0.252 57	40

Table VI   (*Continued*)

i\n	4%	4½%	5%	5½%	6%	7%	8%	i/n
1	0.961 54	0.956 94	0.952 38	0.947 87	0.943 40	0.934 58	0.925 93	1
2	0.924 56	0.915 73	0.907 03	0.898 45	0.890 00	0.873 44	0.857 34	2
3	0.889 00	0.876 30	0.863 84	0.851 61	0.839 62	0.816 30	0.793 83	3
4	0.854 80	0.838 56	0.822 70	0.807 22	0.792 09	0.762 90	0.735 03	4
5	0.821 93	0.802 45	0.783 53	0.765 13	0.747 26	0.712 99	0.680 58	5
6	0.790 31	0.767 90	0.746 22	0.725 25	0.704 96	0.666 34	0.630 17	6
7	0.759 92	0.734 83	0.710 68	0.687 44	0.665 06	0.622 75	0.583 49	7
8	0.730 69	0.703 19	0.676 84	0.651 60	0.627 41	0.582 01	0.540 27	8
9	0.702 59	0.672 90	0.644 61	0.617 63	0.591 90	0.543 93	0.500 25	9
10	0.675 56	0.643 93	0.613 91	0.585 43	0.558 39	0.508 35	0.463 19	10
11	0.649 58	0.616 20	0.584 68	0.554 91	0.526 79	0.475 09	0.428 88	11
12	0.624 60	0.589 66	0.556 84	0.525 98	0.496 97	0.444 01	0.397 11	12
13	0.600 57	0.564 27	0.530 32	0.498 56	0.468 84	0.414 96	0.367 70	13
14	0.577 48	0.539 97	0.505 07	0.472 57	0.442 30	0.387 82	0.340 46	14
15	0.555 26	0.516 72	0.481 02	0.447 93	0.417 27	0.362 45	0.315 24	15
16	0.533 91	0.494 47	0.458 11	0.424 58	0.393 65	0.338 73	0.291 89	16
17	0.513 37	0.473 18	0.436 30	0.402 45	0.371 36	0.316 57	0.270 27	17
18	0.493 63	0.452 80	0.415 52	0.381 47	0.350 34	0.295 86	0.250 25	18
19	0.474 64	0.433 30	0.395 73	0.361 58	0.330 51	0.276 51	0.231 71	19
20	0.456 39	0.414 64	0.376 89	0.342 73	0.311 80	0.258 42	0.214 55	20
21	0.438 83	0.396 79	0.358 94	0.324 86	0.294 16	0.241 51	0.198 66	21
22	0.421 96	0.379 70	0.341 85	0.307 93	0.277 51	0.225 71	0.183 94	22
23	0.405 73	0.363 35	0.325 57	0.291 87	0.261 80	0.210 95	0.170 32	23
24	0.390 12	0.347 70	0.310 07	0.276 66	0.246 98	0.197 15	0.157 70	24
25	0.375 12	0.332 73	0.295 30	0.262 23	0.233 00	0.184 25	0.146 02	25
26	0.360 69	0.318 40	0.281 24	0.248 56	0.219 81	0.172 20	0.135 20	26
27	0.346 82	0.304 69	0.267 85	0.235 60	0.207 37	0.160 93	0.125 19	27
28	0.333 48	0.291 57	0.255 09	0.223 32	0.195 63	0.150 40	0.115 91	28
29	0.320 65	0.279 02	0.242 95	0.211 68	0.184 56	0.140 56	0.107 33	29
30	0.308 32	0.267 00	0.231 38	0.200 64	0.174 11	0.131 37	0.099 38	30
31	0.296 46	0.255 50	0.220 36	0.190 18	0.164 25	0.122 77	0.092 02	31
32	0.285 06	0.244 50	0.209 87	0.180 27	0.154 96	0.114 74	0.085 20	32
33	0.274 09	0.233 97	0.199 87	0.170 87	0.146 19	0.107 23	0.078 89	33
34	0.263 55	0.223 90	0.190 35	0.161 96	0.137 91	0.100 22	0.073 05	34
35	0.253 42	0.214 25	0.181 29	0.153 52	0.130 11	0.093 66	0.067 63	35
36	0.243 67	0.205 03	0.172 66	0.145 52	0.122 74	0.087 54	0.062 62	36
37	0.234 30	0.196 20	0.164 44	0.137 93	0.115 79	0.081 81	0.057 99	37
38	0.225 29	0.187 75	0.156 61	0.130 74	0.109 24	0.076 46	0.053 69	38
39	0.216 62	0.179 67	0.149 15	0.123 92	0.103 06	0.071 46	0.049 71	39
40	0.208 29	0.171 93	0.142 05	0.117 46	0.097 22	0.066 78	0.046 03	40

Table VII AMOUNT OF AN ANNUITY OF 1 $S_{\overline{n}|}i$

n	$\frac{1}{2}$%	1%	$1\frac{1}{2}$%	2%	$2\frac{1}{2}$%	3%
1	1.000 000	1.000 000	1.000 000	1.000 000	1.000 000	1.000 000
2	2.005 000	2.010 000	2.015 000	2.020 000	2.025 000	2.030 000
3	3.015 025	3.030 100	3.045 225	3.060 400	3.075 625	3.090 900
4	4.030 100	4.060 401	4.090 903	4.121 608	4.152 516	4.183 627
5	5.050 251	5.101 005	5.152 267	5.204 040	5.256 329	5.309 136
6	6.075 502	6.152 015	6.229 551	6.308 121	6.387 737	6.468 410
7	7.105 879	7.213 535	7.322 994	7.434 283	7.547 430	7.662 462
8	8.141 409	8.285 671	8.432 839	8.582 969	8.736 116	8.892 336
9	9.182 116	9.368 527	9.559 332	9.754 628	9.954 519	10.159 106
10	10.228 026	10.462 213	10.702 722	10.949 721	11.203 382	11.463 879
11	11.279 167	11.566 835	11.863 262	12.168 715	12.483 466	12.807 796
12	12.335 562	12.682 503	13.041 211	13.412 090	13.795 553	14.192 030
13	13.397 240	13.809 328	14.236 830	14.680 332	15.140 442	15.617 790
14	14.464 226	14.947 421	15.450 382	15.973 938	16.518 953	17.086 324
15	15.536 548	16.096 896	16.682 138	17.293 417	17.931 927	18.598 914
16	16.614 230	17.257 864	17.932 370	18.639 285	19.380 225	20.156 881
17	17.697 301	18.430 443	19.201 355	20.012 071	20.864 730	21.761 588
18	18.785 788	19.614 748	20.489 376	21.412 312	22.386 349	23.414 435
19	19.879 717	20.810 895	21.796 716	22.840 559	23.946 007	25.116 868
20	20.979 115	22.019 004	23.123 667	24.297 370	25.544 658	26.870 374
21	22.084 011	23.239 194	24.470 522	25.783 317	27.183 274	28.676 486
22	23.194 431	24.471 586	25.837 580	27.298 984	28.862 856	30.536 780
23	24.310 403	25.716 302	27.225 144	28.844 963	30.584 427	32.452 884
24	25.431 955	26.973 465	28.633 521	30.421 862	32.349 038	34.426 470
25	26.559 115	28.243 200	30.063 024	32.030 300	34.157 764	36.459 264
26	27.691 911	29.525 632	31.513 969	33.670 906	36.011 708	38.553 042
27	28.830 370	30.820 888	32.986 679	35.344 324	37.912 001	40.709 634
28	29.974 522	32.129 097	34.481 479	37.051 210	39.859 801	42.930 923
29	31.124 395	33.450 388	35.998 701	38.792 235	41.856 296	45.218 850
30	32.280 017	34.784 892	37.538 681	40.568 079	43.902 703	47.575 416
31	33.441 417	36.132 740	39.101 762	42.379 441	46.000 271	50.002 678
32	34.608 624	37.494 068	40.688 288	44.227 030	48.150 278	52.502 759
33	35.781 667	38.869 009	42.298 612	46.111 570	50.354 034	55.077 841
34	36.960 575	40.257 699	43.933 092	48.033 802	52.612 885	57.730 177
35	38.145 378	41.660 276	45.592 088	49.994 478	54.928 207	60.462 082
36	39.336 105	43.076 878	47.275 969	51.994 367	57.301 413	63.275 944
37	40.532 785	44.507 647	48.985 109	54.034 255	59.733 948	66.174 223
38	41.735 449	45.952 724	50.719 885	56.114 940	62.227 297	69.159 449
39	42.944 127	47.412 251	52.480 684	58.237 238	64.782 979	72.234 233
40	44.158 847	48.886 373	54.267 894	60.401 983	67.402 554	75.401 260
41	45.379 642	50.375 237	56.081 912	62.610 023	70.087 617	78.663 298
42	46.606 540	51.878 989	57.923 141	64.862 223	72.839 808	82.023 196
43	47.839 572	53.397 779	59.791 988	67.159 468	75.660 803	85.483 892
44	49.078 770	54.931 757	61.688 868	69.502 657	78.552 323	89.048 409
45	50.324 164	56.481 075	63.614 201	71.892 710	81.516 131	92.719 861
46	51.575 785	58.045 885	65.568 414	74.330 564	84.554 034	96.501 457
47	52.833 664	59.626 344	67.551 940	76.817 176	87.667 885	100.396 501
48	54.097 832	61.222 608	69.565 219	79.353 519	90.859 582	104.408 396
49	55.368 321	62.834 834	71.608 698	81.940 590	94.131 072	108.540 648
50	56.645 163	64.463 182	73.682 828	84.579 401	97.484 349	112.796 867

Table VII (Continued)

n	3½%	4%	4½%	5%	5½%	6%
1	1.000 000	1.000 000	1.000 000	1.000 000	1.000 000	1.000 000
2	2.035 000	2.040 000	2.045 000	2.050 000	2.055 000	2.060 000
3	3.106 225	3.121 600	3.137 025	3.152 500	3.168 025	3.183 600
4	4.214 943	4.246 464	4.278 191	4.301 125	4.342 266	4.374 616
5	5.362 466	5.416 323	5.470 710	5.525 631	5.581 091	5.637 093
6	6.550 152	6.632 975	6.716 892	6.801 913	6.888 051	6.975 319
7	7.779 408	7.898 294	8.019 152	8.142 008	8.266 894	8.393 838
8	9.051 687	9.214 226	9.380 014	9.549 109	9.721 573	9.897 468
9	10.368 496	10.582 795	10.802 114	11.026 564	11.256 260	11.491 316
10	11.731 393	12.006 107	12.288 209	12.577 893	12.875 354	13.180 795
11	13.141 992	13.486 351	13.841 179	14.206 787	14.583 498	14.971 643
12	14.601 962	15.025 805	15.464 032	15.917 127	16.385 591	16.869 941
13	16.113 030	16.626 838	17.159 913	17.712 983	18.286 798	18.882 138
14	17.676 986	18.291 911	18.932 109	19.598 632	20.292 572	21.015 066
15	19.295 681	20.023 588	20.784 054	21.578 564	22.408 664	23.275 970
16	20.971 030	21.824 531	22.719 337	23.657 492	24.641 140	25.672 528
17	22.705 016	23.697 512	24.741 707	25.840 366	26.996 403	28.212 880
18	24.499 691	25.645 413	26.855 084	28.132 385	29.481 205	30.905 653
19	26.357 181	27.671 229	29.063 562	30.539 004	32.102 671	33.759 992
20	28.279 682	29.778 079	31.371 423	33.065 954	34.868 318	36.785 591
21	30.269 471	31.969 202	33.783 137	35.719 252	37.786 076	39.992 727
22	32.328 902	34.247 970	36.303 378	38.505 214	40.864 310	43.392 290
23	34.460 414	36.617 889	38.937 030	41.430 475	44.111 847	46.995 828
24	36.666 528	39.082 604	41.689 196	44.501 999	47.537 998	50.815 577
25	38.949 857	41.645 908	44.565 210	47.727 099	51.152 588	54.864 512
26	41.313 102	44.311 745	47.570 645	51.113 454	54.965 981	59.156 383
27	43.759 060	47.084 214	50.711 324	54.669 126	58.989 109	63.705 766
28	46.290 627	49.967 583	53.993 333	58.402 583	63.233 510	68.528 112
29	48.910 799	52.966 286	57.423 033	62.322 712	67.711 354	73.639 798
30	51.622 677	56.084 938	61.007 070	66.438 848	72.435 478	79.058 186
31	54.429 471	59.328 335	64.752 388	70.760 790	77.419 429	84.801 677
32	57.334 502	62.701 469	68.666 245	75.298 829	82.677 498	90.889 778
33	60.341 210	66.209 527	72.756 226	80.063 771	88.224 760	97.343 165
34	63.453 152	69.857 909	77.030 256	85.066 959	94.077 122	104.183 755
35	66.674 013	73.652 225	81.496 618	90.320 307	100.251 364	111.434 780
36	70.007 603	77.598 314	86.163 966	95.836 323	106.765 189	119.120 867
37	73.457 869	81.702 246	91.041 344	101.628 139	113.637 274	127.268 119
38	77.028 895	85.970 336	96.138 205	107.709 546	120.887 324	135.904 206
39	80.724 906	90.409 150	101.464 424	114.095 023	128.536 127	145.058 458
40	84.550 278	95.025 516	107.030 323	120.799 774	136.605 614	154.761 966
41	88.509 537	99.826 536	112.846 688	127.839 763	145.118 923	165.047 684
42	92.607 371	104.819 598	118.924 789	135.231 751	154.100 464	175.950 545
43	96.848 629	110.012 382	125.276 404	142.993 339	163.575 989	187.507 577
44	101.238 331	115.412 877	131.913 842	151.143 006	173.572 669	199.758 032
45	105.781 673	121.029 392	138.849 965	159.700 156	184.119 165	212.743 514
46	110.484 031	126.870 568	146.098 214	168.685 164	195.245 719	226.508 125
47	115.350 973	132.945 390	153.672 633	178.119 422	206.984 234	241.098 612
48	120.388 257	139.263 206	161.587 902	188.025 393	219.368 367	256.564 529
49	125.601 846	145.833 734	169.859 357	198.426 663	232.433 627	272.958 401
50	130.997 910	152.667 084	178.503 028	209.347 996	246.217 476	290.335 905

Table VIII PRESENT VALUE OF AN ANNUITY OF 1 $a_{\overline{n}|}i$

n	$\frac{1}{2}$%	1%	$1\frac{1}{2}$%	2%	$2\frac{1}{2}$%	3%
1	0.995 025	0.990 099	0.985 222	0.980 392	0.975 610	0.970 874
2	1.985 099	1.970 395	1.955 883	1.941 561	1.927 424	1.913 470
3	2.970 248	2.940 985	2.912 200	2.883 883	2.856 024	2.828 611
4	3.950 496	3.901 966	3.854 385	3.807 729	3.761 974	3.717 098
5	4.925 866	4.853 431	4.782 645	4.713 460	4.645 829	4.579 707
6	5.896 384	5.795 476	5.697 187	5.601 431	5.508 125	5.417 191
7	6.862 074	6.728 195	6.598 214	6.471 991	6.349 391	6.230 283
8	7.822 959	7.651 678	7.485 925	7.325 481	7.170 137	7.019 692
9	8.779 064	8.566 018	8.360 517	8.162 237	7.970 866	7.786 109
10	9.730 412	9.471 305	9.222 185	8.982 585	8.752 064	8.530 203
11	10.677 027	10.367 628	10.071 118	9.786 848	9.514 209	9.252 624
12	11.618 932	11.255 077	10.907 505	10.575 341	10.257 765	9.954 004
13	12.556 151	12.133 740	11.731 532	11.348 374	10.983 185	10.634 955
14	13.488 708	13.003 703	12.543 382	12.106 249	11.690 912	11.296 073
15	14.416 625	13.865 053	13.343 233	12.849 264	12.381 378	11.937 935
16	15.339 925	14.717 874	14.131 264	13.577 709	13.055 003	12.561 102
17	16.258 632	15.562 251	14.907 649	14.291 872	13.712 198	13.166 118
18	17.172 768	16.398 269	15.672 561	14.992 031	14.353 364	13.753 513
19	18.082 356	17.226 009	16.426 168	15.678 462	14.978 891	14.323 799
20	18.987 419	18.045 553	17.168 639	16.351 433	15.589 162	14.877 475
21	19.887 979	18.856 983	17.900 137	17.011 209	16.184 549	15.415 024
22	20.784 059	19.660 379	18.620 824	17.658 048	16.765 413	15.936 917
23	21.675 681	20.455 821	19.330 861	18.292 204	17.332 110	16.443 608
24	22.562 866	21.243 387	20.030 405	18.913 926	17.884 986	16.935 542
25	23.445 638	22.023 156	20.719 611	19.523 456	18.424 376	17.413 148
26	24.324 018	22.795 204	21.398 632	20.121 036	18.950 611	17.876 842
27	25.198 028	23.559 608	22.067 617	20.706 898	19.464 011	18.327 031
28	26.067 689	24.316 443	22.726 717	21.281 272	19.964 889	18.764 108
29	26.933 024	25.065 785	23.376 076	21.844 385	20.453 550	19.188 455
30	27.794 054	25.807 708	24.015 838	22.396 456	20.930 293	19.600 441
31	28.650 800	26.542 285	24.646 146	22.937 702	21.395 407	20.000 428
32	29.503 284	27.269 589	25.267 139	23.468 335	21.849 178	20.388 766
33	30.351 526	27.989 693	25.878 954	23.988 563	22.291 881	20.765 792
34	31.195 548	28.702 666	26.481 728	24.498 592	22.723 786	21.131 837
35	32.035 371	29.408 580	27.075 595	24.998 619	23.145 157	21.487 220
36	32.871 016	30.107 505	27.660 684	25.488 842	23.556 251	21.832 253
37	33.702 504	30.799 510	28.237 127	25.969 453	23.957 318	22.167 235
38	34.529 854	31.484 663	28.805 052	26.440 641	24.348 603	22.492 462
39	35.353 089	32.163 033	29.364 583	26.902 589	24.730 344	22.808 215
40	36.172 228	32.834 686	29.915 845	27.355 479	25.102 775	23.114 772
41	36.987 291	33.499 689	30.458 961	27.799 489	25.466 122	23.412 400
42	37.798 300	34.158 108	30.994 050	28.234 794	25.820 607	23.701 359
43	38.605 274	34.810 008	31.521 232	28.661 562	26.166 446	23.981 902
44	39.408 232	35.455 454	32.040 622	29.079 963	26.503 849	24.254 274
45	40.207 196	36.094 508	32.552 337	29.490 160	26.833 024	24.518 713
46	41.002 185	36.727 236	33.056 490	29.892 314	27.154 170	24.775 449
47	41.793 219	37.353 699	33.553 192	30.286 582	27.467 483	25.024 708
48	42.580 318	37.973 959	34.042 554	30.673 120	27.773 154	25.266 707
49	43.363 500	38.588 079	34.524 683	31.052 078	28.071 369	25.501 657
50	44.142 786	39.196 118	34.999 688	31.423 606	28.362 312	25.729 764

Table VIII   (*Continued*)

n	$3\frac{1}{2}$%	4%	$4\frac{1}{2}$%	5%	$5\frac{1}{2}$%	6%
1	0.966 184	0.961 538	0.956 938	0.952 381	0.947 867	0.943 396
2	1.899 694	1.886 095	1.872 668	1.859 410	1.846 320	1.833 393
3	2.801 637	2.775 091	2.748 964	2.723 248	2.697 933	2.673 012
4	3.673 079	3.629 895	3.587 526	3.545 951	3.505 150	3.465 106
5	4.515 052	4.451 822	4.389 977	4.329 477	4.270 284	4.212 364
6	5.328 553	5.242 137	5.157 872	5.075 692	4.995 530	4.917 324
7	6.114 544	6.002 055	5.892 701	5.786 373	5.682 967	5.582 381
8	6.873 955	6.732 745	6.595 886	6.463 213	6.334 566	6.209 794
9	7.607 687	7.435 332	7.268 791	7.107 822	6.952 195	6.801 692
10	8.316 605	8.110 896	7.912 718	7.721 735	7.537 626	7.360 087
11	9.001 551	8.760 477	8.528 917	8.306 414	8.092 536	7.886 875
12	9.663 334	9.385 074	9.118 581	8.863 252	8.618 518	8.383 844
13	10.302 738	9.985 648	9.682 852	9.393 573	9.117 079	8.852 683
14	10.920 520	10.563 123	10.222 825	9.898 641	9.589 648	9.294 984
15	11.517 411	11.118 387	10.739 546	10.379 658	10.037 581	9.712 249
16	12.094 117	11.652 296	11.234 015	10.837 770	10.462 162	10.105 895
17	12.651 321	12.165 669	11.707 191	11.274 066	10.864 609	10.477 260
18	13.189 682	12.659 297	12.159 992	11.689 587	11.246 074	10.827 603
19	13.709 837	13.133 939	12.593 294	12.085 321	11.607 654	11.158 116
20	14.212 403	13.590 326	13.007 936	12.462 210	11.950 382	11.469 921
21	14.697 974	14.029 160	13.404 724	12.821 153	12.275 244	11.764 077
22	15.167 125	14.451 115	13.784 425	13.163 003	12.583 170	12.041 582
23	15.620 410	14.856 842	14.147 775	13.488 574	12.875 042	12.303 379
24	16.058 368	15.246 963	14.495 478	13.798 642	13.151 699	12.550 358
25	16.481 515	15.622 080	14.828 209	14.093 945	13.413 933	12.783 356
26	16.890 352	15.982 769	15.146 611	14.375 185	13.662 495	13.003 166
27	17.285 365	16.329 586	15.451 303	14.643 034	13.898 100	13.210 534
28	17.667 019	16.663 063	15.742 874	14.898 127	14.121 422	13.406 164
29	18.035 767	16.983 715	16.021 889	15.141 074	14.333 101	13.590 721
30	18.392 045	17.292 033	16.288 889	15.372 451	14.533 745	13.764 831
31	18.736 276	17.588 494	16.544 391	15.592 811	14.723 929	13.929 086
32	19.068 865	17.873 552	16.788 891	15.802 677	14.904 198	14.084 043
33	19.390 208	18.147 646	17.022 862	16.002 549	15.075 069	14.230 230
34	19.700 684	18.411 198	17.246 758	16.192 904	15.237 033	14.368 141
35	20.000 661	18.664 613	17.461 012	16.374 194	15.390 552	14.498 246
36	20.290 494	18.908 282	17.666 041	16.546 852	15.536 068	14.620 987
37	20.570 525	19.142 579	17.862 240	16.711 287	15.673 999	14.736 780
38	20.841 087	19.367 864	18.049 990	16.867 893	15.804 738	14.846 019
39	21.102 500	19.584 485	18.229 656	17.017 041	15.928 662	14.949 075
40	21.355 072	19.792 774	18.401 584	17.159 086	16.046 125	15.046 297
41	21.599 104	19.993 052	18.566 109	17.294 368	16.157 464	15.138 016
42	21.834 883	20.185 627	18.723 550	17.423 208	16.262 999	15.224 543
43	22.062 689	20.370 795	18.874 210	17.545 912	16.363 032	15.306 173
44	22.282 791	20.548 841	19.018 383	17.662 773	16.457 851	15.381 182
45	22.495 450	20.720 040	19.156 347	17.774 070	16.547 726	15.455 832
46	22.700 918	20.884 654	19.288 371	17.880 067	16.632 915	15.524 370
47	22.899 438	21.042 936	19.414 709	17.981 016	16.713 664	15.589 028
48	23.091 244	21.195 131	19.535 607	18.077 158	16.790 203	15.650 027
49	23.276 565	21.341 472	19.651 298	18.168 722	16.862 751	15.707 572
50	23.455 618	21.482 185	19.762 008	18.255 925	16.931 518	15.761 861

Table IX POWERS OF N

n	n^2	n^3	n^4	n^5	n^6	n^7	n^8	n^9	n^{10}	n^{11}	n^{12}
1	1	1	1	1	1	1	1	1	1	1	1
1.01	1.0201	1.030301	1.040604	1.0510101	1.0615202	1.0721354	1.0828567	1.0936853	1.1046221	1.1156683	1.126825
1.0125	1.0251562	1.0379707	1.0509453	1.0640822	1.0773832	1.0908505	1.1044861	1.1182922	1.1322708	1.1464242	1.1607545
1.015	1.030225	1.0456784	1.0613636	1.077284	1.0934433	1.1098449	1.1264926	1.14339	1.1605408	1.1779489	1.1956182
1.0175	1.0353063	1.0534241	1.071859	1.0906166	1.1097024	1.1291221	1.1488818	1.1689872	1.1894445	1.2102598	1.2314393
1.02	1.0404	1.061208	1.0824322	1.1040808	1.1261624	1.1486857	1.1716594	1.1950926	1.2189944	1.243374	1.2682418
1.0225	1.0455062	1.0690301	1.0930833	1.1176777	1.1428254	1.168539	1.1948311	1.2217148	1.2492034	1.2773105	1.30605
1.025	1.050625	1.0768906	1.1038129	1.1314082	1.1596934	1.1886858	1.2184029	1.248863	1.2800845	1.3120867	1.3448888
1.0275	1.0557563	1.0847895	1.1146213	1.1452733	1.1767684	1.2091295	1.2423806	1.276546	1.311651	1.3477214	1.3847838
1.03	1.0609	1.092727	1.1255088	1.1592741	1.1940523	1.2298739	1.2667701	1.3047732	1.3439164	1.3842339	1.4257609
1.0325	1.0660562	1.1007031	1.1364759	1.1734114	1.2115473	1.2509226	1.2915775	1.3335538	1.3768943	1.4216434	1.4678468
1.035	1.071225	1.1087179	1.147523	1.1876863	1.2292553	1.2722793	1.316809	1.3628974	1.4105988	1.4599697	1.5110687
1.0375	1.0764063	1.1167715	1.1586504	1.2020998	1.2471785	1.2939477	1.3424708	1.3928134	1.4450439	1.4992331	1.5554543
1.04	1.0816	1.124864	1.1698586	1.2166529	1.265319	1.3159318	1.3685691	1.4233118	1.4802443	1.5394541	1.6010322
1.0425	1.0868062	1.1329955	1.1811478	1.2313466	1.2836788	1.3382352	1.3951102	1.4544024	1.5162145	1.5806536	1.6478314
1.045	1.092025	1.1411661	1.1925186	1.2461819	1.3022601	1.3608618	1.4221006	1.4860951	1.5529694	1.622853	1.6958814
1.0475	1.0972563	1.1493759	1.2039713	1.2611599	1.321065	1.3838156	1.4495468	1.5184003	1.5905243	1.6660742	1.7452128
1.05	1.1025	1.157625	1.2155063	1.2762816	1.3400956	1.4071004	1.4774554	1.5513282	1.6288946	1.7103394	1.7958563
1.0525	1.1077562	1.1659135	1.2271239	1.2915479	1.3593542	1.4307203	1.5058331	1.5848893	1.668096	1.7556711	1.8478438
1.055	1.113025	1.1742414	1.2388247	1.30696	1.3788428	1.4546792	1.5346865	1.6190943	1.7081445	1.8020924	1.9012075
1.0575	1.1183063	1.1826089	1.2506089	1.3225189	1.3985637	1.4789811	1.5640225	1.6539538	1.7490562	1.8496269	1.9559805
1.06	1.1236	1.191016	1.262477	1.3382256	1.4185191	1.5036303	1.5938481	1.689479	1.7908477	1.8982986	2.0121965
1.0625	1.1289062	1.1994629	1.2744293	1.3540812	1.4387112	1.5286307	1.6241701	1.7256807	1.8335358	1.9481318	2.06989
1.065	1.134225	1.2079496	1.2864664	1.3700867	1.4591423	1.5539865	1.6549957	1.7625704	1.8771375	1.9991514	2.1290962
1.0675	1.1395562	1.2164763	1.2985884	1.3862432	1.4798146	1.5797021	1.686332	1.8001594	1.9216701	2.0513829	2.1898512
1.07	1.1449	1.225043	1.310796	1.4025517	1.5007304	1.6057815	1.7181862	1.8384592	1.9671514	2.104852	2.2521916
1.0725	1.1502562	1.2336498	1.3230894	1.4190134	1.5218919	1.6322291	1.7505657	1.8774817	2.0135991	2.159585	2.316155
1.075	1.155625	1.2422969	1.3354691	1.4356293	1.5433015	1.6590491	1.7834778	1.9172387	2.0610316	2.2156089	2.3817796
1.0775	1.1610062	1.2509842	1.3479355	1.4524005	1.5649616	1.6862461	1.8169301	1.9577422	2.1094673	2.272951	2.4491047
1.08	1.1664	1.259712	1.360489	1.4693281	1.5868743	1.7138243	1.8509302	1.9990046	2.158925	2.331639	2.5181701
1.0825	1.1718062	1.2684803	1.3731299	1.4864131	1.6090422	1.7417882	1.8854857	2.0410383	2.2094239	2.3917014	2.5890168
1.085	1.177225	1.2772891	1.3858587	1.5036567	1.6314675	1.7701422	1.9206043	2.0838557	2.2609834	2.453167	2.6616862
1.0875	1.1826562	1.2861387	1.3986758	1.5210599	1.6541527	1.798891	1.956294	2.1274697	2.3136233	2.5160654	2.7362211
1.09	1.1881	1.295029	1.4115816	1.538624	1.6771001	1.8280391	1.9925626	2.1718933	2.3673637	2.5804264	2.8126648
1.0925	1.1935563	1.3039602	1.4245765	1.5563499	1.7003122	1.8575911	2.0294183	2.2171395	2.4222249	2.6462807	2.8910616
1.095	1.199025	1.3129324	1.437661	1.5742387	1.7237914	1.8875516	2.066869	2.2632216	2.4782276	2.7136592	2.9714569
1.0975	1.2045062	1.3219456	1.4508353	1.5922917	1.7475402	1.9179254	2.1049231	2.3101531	2.535393	2.7825938	3.0538967
1.1	1.21	1.331	1.4641	1.61051	1.771561	1.9487171	2.1435888	2.3579477	2.5937425	2.8531167	3.1384284
1.1025	1.2155063	1.3400956	1.4774554	1.6288946	1.7958563	1.9799316	2.1828746	2.4066192	2.6532977	2.9252607	3.2250999
1.105	1.221025	1.3492326	1.4909021	1.6474468	1.8204287	2.0115737	2.2227889	2.4561818	2.7140808	2.9990593	3.3139606
1.1075	1.2265562	1.358411	1.5044402	1.6661676	1.8452806	2.0436482	2.2633404	2.5066495	2.7761143	3.0745466	3.4050604
1.11	1.2321	1.367631	1.5180704	1.6850582	1.8704146	2.0761602	2.3045378	2.5580369	2.839421	3.1517573	3.4984506
1.1125	1.2376563	1.3768926	1.531793	1.7041197	1.8958332	2.1091144	2.3463898	2.6103586	2.904024	3.2307267	3.5941834
1.115	1.243225	1.3861959	1.5456084	1.7233534	1.921539	2.142516	2.3889053	2.6636294	2.9699468	3.3114907	3.6923121
1.1175	1.2488062	1.395541	1.5595171	1.7427603	1.9475346	2.17637	2.4320934	2.7178644	3.0372135	3.3940861	3.7928912
1.12	1.2544	1.404928	1.5735194	1.7623417	1.9738227	2.2106814	2.4759632	2.7730788	3.1058482	3.47855	3.895976
1.1225	1.2600063	1.414357	1.5876158	1.7820987	2.0004058	2.2454555	2.5205238	2.8292879	3.1758757	3.5649205	4.0016232
1.125	1.265625	1.4238281	1.6018066	1.8020325	2.0272865	2.2806973	2.5657845	2.8865076	3.247321	3.6532362	4.1098907
1.1275	1.2712562	1.4333414	1.6160925	1.8221442	2.0544676	2.3164123	2.6117548	2.9447536	3.3202096	3.7435364	4.2208372
1.13	1.2769	1.442897	1.6304736	1.8424352	2.0819518	2.3526055	2.6584442	3.0040419	3.3945674	3.8358612	4.3345231
1.1325	1.2825563	1.452495	1.6449505	1.8629065	2.1097416	2.3982823	2.7058623	3.064389	3.4704206	3.9302513	4.4510096
1.135	1.288225	1.4621354	1.6595237	1.8835593	2.1378399	2.4264482	2.7540187	3.1258113	3.5477958	4.0267482	4.5703592
1.1375	1.2939062	1.4718184	1.6741934	1.904395	2.1662493	2.4641086	2.8029235	3.1883255	3.6267202	4.1253942	4.692636
1.14	1.2996	1.481544	1.6889602	1.9254146	2.1949726	2.5022688	2.8525864	3.2519485	3.7072213	4.2262323	4.8179048
1.1425	1.3053063	1.4913124	1.7038244	1.9466194	2.2240126	2.5409344	2.9030176	3.3166976	3.789327	4.3293061	4.9462323
1.145	1.311025	1.5011236	1.7187866	1.9680106	2.2533721	2.5801111	2.9542272	3.3825902	3.8730657	4.4346603	5.077686
1.1475	1.3167562	1.5109778	1.733847	1.9895895	2.2830539	2.6198044	3.0062255	3.4496438	3.9584662	4.54234	5.2123351
1.15	1.3225	1.520875	1.7490062	2.0113572	2.3130608	2.6600199	3.0590229	3.5178763	4.0455577	4.6523914	5.3502501

ANSWERS

REVIEW AND PREVIEW TO CHAPTER 1

EXERCISE 1
1. (a) 6   (b) 11   (c) 72   (d) 28   (e) 64   (f) 50
  (g) 18   (h) -5 (i) 18   (j) -18 (k) 5   (l) 19
  (m) 30
2. (a) 35   (b) 10   (c) 40   (d) 9   (e) 22.9   (f) 41
  (g) 19   (h) 14   (i) 26   (j) 115   (k) 48   (l) 30
  (m) 4   (n) 10   (o) 25   (p) 9   (q) 11
3. (a) A = 150 mm, B = 250 mm, C = 375 mm, D = 450 mm
  (b) A = 5.2 m, B = 6.2 m, C = 4.2 m, D = 10.4 m
  (c) A = 6.2 m, B = 4.5 m, C = 6.6 m, D = 4.1 m
4. (a) 0.6   (b) 6   (c) 0.63   (d) 0.82   (e) 1.2   (f) 96
  (g) 0.68   (h) 115   (i) 20   (j) 4.5   (k) 12   (l) 45
  (m) 21 700   (n) 1680   (o) 816   (p) 1520   (q) 12 400   (r) 7049
5. (a) 346   (b) 211   (c) 156   (d) 208
6. 3.0984   7. 1.1766   8. 49.06   9. 4980   10. 1033   11. 6310
12. (a) $\frac{7}{12}$ (b) $\frac{11}{24}$ (c) $\frac{15}{32}$ (d) $1\frac{1}{3}$
  (e) $5\frac{11}{20}$ (f) $3\frac{1}{6}$ (g) $8\frac{2}{3}$ (h) $\frac{35}{48}$
  (i) $11\frac{1}{5}$ (j) $\frac{5}{56}$ (k) 0.24   (l) 0.995
  (m) 0.86   (n) 0.88   (o) 3.5   (p) 1.6

EXERCISE 2
1. (a) rational   (b) irrational   (c) rational
  (d) rational   (e) rational   (f) rational
  (g) irrational   (h) rational   (i) irrational
2. (a) 0.5   (b) $0.\overline{3}$ (c) 0.75   (d) 0.375   (e) 0.6 (f) $0.\overline{09}$
  (g) $0.8\overline{3}$ (h) 2.625   (i) 3.8
3. (a) $0.\overline{142\ 857}$ (b) $0.\overline{285\ 714}$ (c) $0.\overline{230\ 769}$ (d) $0.\overline{5}$ (e) $0.\overline{238\ 095}$
  (f) $0.\overline{27}$ (g) $1.1\overline{6}$ (h) $1.\overline{428\ 571}$ (i) $3.5\overline{4}$
4. (a) 1.732 050 808   (b) 2.236 067 977   (c) 3.605 551 275
  (d) 4.123 105 626   (e) 4.358 898 944   (f) 4.898 979 486
5. (a) 89.57   (b) 2604.8   (c) 30.125   (d) 256.9   (e) 25.457   (f) 0.212
6. (a) 436.8   (b) 210.6   (c) 0.253   (d) 0.5494   (e) 46.55   (f) 0.3168
  (g) 2.367
7. (a) 2.3   (b) 560   (c) 23   (d) 0.057   (e) 0.78   (f) 0.85

EXERCISE 3
1. (a) 12 300   (b) 98   (c) 450   (d) 11 000   (e) 5   (f) 2300
2. (a) 30   (b) 0.54   (c) 1.25   (d) 0.006   (e) 1200   (f) 0.007
3. (a) 45.6   (b) 0.023   (c) 0.76   (d) 0.067   (e) 0.0009   (f) 8
4. (a) 6700   (b) 9900   (c) 69   (d) 50   (e) 0.7   (f) 600 000
5. (a) 670   (b) 8450   (c) 3   (d) 120   (e) 4   (f) 555
  (g) 1.9   (h) 60   (i) 100 000   (j) 0.034   (k) 3450   (l) 202
6. (a) 4.5   (b) 0.062   (c) 3.8   (d) 0.04   (e) 40.8

EXERCISE 4
1. (a) 0.23   (b) 0.46   (c) 0.87   (d) 0.05   (e) 0.99   (f) 0.01
2. (a) $\frac{1}{2}$ (b) $\frac{1}{4}$ (c) $\frac{1}{10}$ (d) $\frac{1}{100}$ (e) $\frac{9}{20}$ (f) $1\frac{1}{2}$
  (g) $1\frac{1}{10}$ (h) $\frac{3}{40}$ (i) $\frac{12}{125}$
3. (a) 1 : 2   (b) 3 : 5   (c) 3 : 20   (d) 1 : 5   (e) 3 : 10   (f) 7 : 10
  (g) 1 : 10   (h) 2 : 25   (i) 1 : 20
4. (a) 50%   (b) 25%   (c) 70%   (d) 20%   (e) 60%   (f) 12.5%
5. (a) 50%   (b) 35%   (c) 86%   (d) 2%   (e) 17%   (f) 90%

EXERCISE 5
1. (a) 60   (b) 161   (c) 484   (d) 60   (e) 87.5   (f) 220.5
   (g) 637   (h) 10
2. 240   3. $67.50   4. $2000   5. $3000   6. $12

EXERCISE 6
1. (a) 25%   (b) 25%   (c) 5%   (d) 20%   (e) 5%
2. 62.5%   3. 20%   4. 77.8%   5. 200%   6. (a) 50%   (b) 75%

EXERCISE 7
1. (a) 75   (b) 20   (c) 80   (d) 150   (e) 87.5
2. 20 000   3. 1250   4. 600   5. 85 000

EXERCISE 8
1. (a) 30   (b) 40   (c) 140
2. (a) 14.2   (b) 0.8   (c) 1.0
3. (a) 3.12   (b) 5.14   (c) 72.87
4. (a) 36 000   (b) 36 000   (c) 2300   (d) 0.6   (e) 0.4   (f) 0.38
   (g) 3.48   (h) 7.49   (i) 880 000   (j) 900   (k) 73.6   (l) 8.72
   (m) 54 000   (n) 750
5. (a) 465.99   (b) 2.3   (c) 270   (d) 74   (e) 98   (f) 2271
   (g) 6.0

EXERCISE 1.1

1. 971 km   2. 1584 km   3. 1902 km   4. $108 or $89.10 (via Detroit)
5. (a) 625 km   (b) 7.8 h   6. approximately 12 h
7. (a) 312 km   (b) 37.4 L   (c) Answers will vary.
8. Val-d'Or, 103 km
9. (a) 1686 km   (b) 22.5 h   (c) 151.7 L   (d) Answers will vary.
10. 15:45   11. 275 km
12. (a) 31 740 km   (b) 793.5 h   (c) 3174 L   (d) Answers will vary.

EXERCISE 1.2

1. (a) -49 (b) 118   (c) 647   (d) 239   (e) 107
2. (a) 1060   (b) 623   (c) 656   (d) 7   (e) 338
3. (a) 68   (b) 29   (c) 67   (d) 29   (e) 166
4. (a) 96   (b) 128   (c) 2484   (d) 434   (e) 147
5. (a) 74.75   (b) 45   (c) 50.75   (d) 131.25   (e) 256.5
6. (a) 300 cm²   (b) 41 m²   (c) 53.0 m²   (d) 3 333 000 m²

EXERCISE 1.3

1. (a) 6   (b) -12 (c) -9 (d) -9 (e) -7 (f) -15
2. (a) 13   (b) -8 (c) -22 (d) 46   (e) -21 (f) 2
3. (a) 20   (b) -42 (c) -64 (d) 72   (e) -8 (f) -5
   (g) -28 (h) 7
4. (a) 17   (b) 17   (c) 2   (d) -3 (e) -120 (f) -7
   (g) 5   (h) -20 (i) -6 (j) -29
5. (a) 4   (b) -8 (c) 14
6. (a) -6 (b) 17   (c) 11   (d) -14
7. (a) 9   (b) -9 (c) 16   (d) -16 (e) -1 (f) 1

EXERCISE 1.4

1. $8\frac{7}{8}$ 2. (a) $18   (b) $17\frac{1}{8}$ (c) $437.50   3. $750

4. (a) $\frac{1}{2}$ (b) $\frac{3}{8}$ 5. $420   6. (a) $525 000   (b) $140

7. $1\frac{7}{8}$ 8. $42 000   9. Sandra ($328.12 more)

10. (a) $162 462.50   (b) $147 406.25   11. $12 150

12. (a) $\frac{2}{5}$ (b) $5\frac{1}{4}$ (c) $5\frac{7}{12}$ (d) $6\frac{11}{12}$ (e) $\frac{1}{12}$ (f) $1\frac{11}{16}$

(g) $2\frac{2}{3}$ (h) 2   (i) 5   (j) $4\frac{2}{3}$ (k) $2\frac{11}{32}$ (l) $7\frac{1}{3}$

13. $2089.50

EXERCISE 1.5

1. (a) 81   (b) 32   (c) 25   (d) -8 (e) -1 (f) 36
(g) 36   (h) 16   (i) -16

2. (a) x^{11} (b) b (c) m^6 (d) s^7 (e) t^5 (f) r^{10}

(g) b^9 (h) m^{20} (i) r^2 (j) a^4b^6 (k) $\frac{a^{12}}{b^{14}}$ (l) $\frac{m^9}{n^6}$

3. (a) $12m^8$ (b) $-21x^6$ (c) $24t^6$ (d) $56a^5$ (e) $-4b^2$ (f) $-2s^4$

(g) $36x^4y^6$ (h) $8a^6b^3c^{12}$ (i) $\frac{16m^4}{9n^6}$ (j) $\frac{8x^6y^3}{27z^9}$

4. (a) $20x^6y^4$ (b) $18m^4n^7$ (c) $4ab^2$ (d) $-5x^2z$ (e) $-42x^5y^6$
5. (a) $-a^6b^4$ (b) $-3r^4s^5t^{12}$ (c) $9xyz^3$ (d) $2a^3b^3$
6. (a) 3^{a+b+c} (b) 4^y

EXERCISE 1.6

1. (a) 1   (b) 2   (c) $\frac{1}{4}$ (d) 16   (e) 1   (f) $\frac{8}{9}$
(g) $\frac{1}{10\,000}$ (h) 1   (i) -1 (j) -8 (k) $\frac{1}{9}$ (l) -1

2. (a) 3   (b) 4   (c) 2   (d) 2   (e) 4   (f) 9
(g) 27   (h) 2   (i) 8   (j) -2 (k) -3 (l) -25

3. (a) $\frac{1}{2}$ (b) $\frac{1}{6}$ (c) $\frac{1}{9}$ (d) $\frac{1}{4}$ (e) $\frac{1}{8}$ (f) $\frac{1}{4}$

(g) $\frac{1}{10}$ (h) $-\frac{1}{2}$ (i) $\frac{1}{2}$ (j) $\frac{1}{25}$ (k) $-\frac{1}{16}$ (l) $\frac{1}{16}$

4. (a) $\frac{8}{27}$ (b) $\frac{9}{25}$ (c) 4   (d) $\frac{256}{81}$ (e) $\frac{5x^2}{m^8}$ (f) $\frac{3a^2}{b^4}$

(g) $b^{\frac{3}{4}}$ (h) $a^{\frac{7}{6}}$ (i) $b^{\frac{1}{4}}$

5. (a) a (b) $\frac{1}{b^{10}}$ (c) $\frac{1}{x^8}$ (d) $\frac{y}{x^2}$ (e) a^2b (f) $\frac{1}{b^7}$

(g) $\frac{a}{2}$ (h) $\frac{3xy^{10}}{4}$ (i) x^6y^9 (j) 8   (k) 6   (l) 7

EXERCISE 1.8

1. (a) $\frac{3}{4}$ (b) $3:4$ (c) 2 to 1   (d) $5:7:3$ (e) $\frac{4}{1}$ (f) 7 to 8

(g) $3:1$ (h) $2:4:3$ (i) $\frac{2}{1}$ (j) $14:11$

2. (a) 6   (b) 12.5   (c) 8.125   (d) 4.9
(e) $x = 2.5$, $y = 2$ (f) $m = 3.5$, $t = 15.4$ (nearest tenth)
3. 30   4. Cheryl: $3800, Brian: $5700
5. 5.7 km   6. Rod: 75, Barbara: 150
7. 76 sailboats, 38 power boats, 95 fishing boats
8. $38.28   9. Magic Car Wax (by $0.02/L)
10. (a) 90 km/h   (b) 5.5 h   (c) 112.5 km
11. (a) $3710   (b) $3745   (c) $3815
12. $537.50   13. 42 words/min   14. $217   15. 5   16. 39

EXERCISE 1.9

1. (a) $2\sqrt{2}$ (b) $2\sqrt{3}$ (c) $3\sqrt{2}$ (d) $2\sqrt{5}$ (e) $4\sqrt{2}$ (f) $5\sqrt{2}$
   (g) $2\sqrt{7}$ (h) $3\sqrt{3}$ (i) $10\sqrt{2}$ (j) $3\sqrt{5}$ (k) $3\sqrt{6}$ (l) $6\sqrt{2}$

2. (a) $\sqrt{18}$ (b) $\sqrt{20}$ (c) $\sqrt{27}$ (d) $\sqrt{32}$ (e) $\sqrt{96}$ (f) $\sqrt{250}$
   (g) $\sqrt{175}$ (h) $\sqrt{44}$ (i) $\sqrt{45}$

3. (a) $\sqrt{21}$ (b) $2\sqrt{15}$ (c) $\sqrt{10}$ (d) $\sqrt{33}$ (e) $\sqrt{78}$ (f) $\sqrt{30}$
   (g) $2\sqrt{7}$ (h) $3\sqrt{2}$

4. (a) $6\sqrt{14}$ (b) $6\sqrt{15}$ (c) $16\sqrt{3}$ (d) 105 (e) $16\sqrt{5}$ (f) $12\sqrt{6}$

5. (a) $2\sqrt{10}$ (b) $3\sqrt{6}$ (c) $2\sqrt{15}$ (d) $4\sqrt{3}$ (e) 9 (f) $4\sqrt{10}$
   (g) $3\sqrt{30}$ (h) 14

6. (a) $8\sqrt{7}$ (b) $4\sqrt{3}$ (c) $\sqrt{13}$ (d) $5\sqrt{5}$ (e) $14\sqrt{11}$ (f) $5\sqrt{3}$
   (g) $4\sqrt{7}$ (h) $\sqrt{15}$ (i) $6\sqrt{5}$ (j) $12\sqrt{3}$ (k) $2\sqrt{5}$ (l) $2\sqrt{3}$
   (m) $12\sqrt{3}$ (n) $3\sqrt{7}$

7. (a) $4\sqrt{3} - 2\sqrt{11}$ (b) $11\sqrt{17} - 3\sqrt{15}$ (c) $8\sqrt{2} + 4\sqrt{3}$
   (d) $10\sqrt{5} + 3\sqrt{7}$ (e) $10\sqrt{3} + 6\sqrt{5}$ (f) $7\sqrt{7} - 16\sqrt{3}$

8. (a) $8 + 5\sqrt{2}$ (b) $4 + 8\sqrt{3}$ (c) $16 - 8\sqrt{2}$
   (d) $4\sqrt{3} + 4\sqrt{5}$ (e) $3\sqrt{7}$ (f) $-5 - \sqrt{2}$

9. (a) $5\sqrt{2}$ (b) $5\sqrt{3}$ (c) $8\sqrt{2}$ (d) $3\sqrt{2}$ (e) $5\sqrt{5}$
   (f) $\sqrt{3}$ (g) $11\sqrt{2}$ (h) $13\sqrt{3}$ (i) $2\sqrt{6} - 3\sqrt{2}$ (j) $\sqrt{2}$
   (k) $23\sqrt{3}$ (l) $-\sqrt{2}$ (m) $11\sqrt{2}$ (n) $4\sqrt{2}$ (o) $15\sqrt{2}$
   (p) $18\sqrt{2} + 2\sqrt{3}$

EXERCISE 1.10

1. (a) $\sqrt{5}$ (b) 5 (c) $4\sqrt{3}$ (d) 2 (e) $\frac{3}{2}$ (f) 6

2. (a) 2.6 (b) 2.4 (c) 2.6 (d) 33.5 (e) 28.3 (f) 2.3
   (g) 2.6 (h) 15 (i) 6.7

EXERCISE 1.11

1. (a) $\sqrt{6} + \sqrt{10}$ (b) $5\sqrt{3} + \sqrt{21}$ (c) $6\sqrt{5} - 9\sqrt{2}$ (d) $5\sqrt{3} - 10\sqrt{5}$
   (e) $3 + \sqrt{3}$ (f) $4 - 2\sqrt{3}$ (g) $2\sqrt{3} - 2\sqrt{6}$ (h) $3\sqrt{10} + 3\sqrt{30}$
   (i) $2\sqrt{3} + 3\sqrt{6}$ (j) $6\sqrt{2} + 6\sqrt{6}$

2. (a) $17 + 7\sqrt{5}$ (b) $27 + 7\sqrt{21}$
   (c) $8 + 3\sqrt{6}$ (d) $16 - 17\sqrt{2}$
   (e) $142 + 32\sqrt{21}$ (f) $-22 - 52\sqrt{15}$
   (g) $108 + 10\sqrt{15}$ (h) $-163 - 9\sqrt{11}$
   (i) $36 - 18\sqrt{10}$ (j) $12\sqrt{21} - 8\sqrt{15} + 15\sqrt{14} - 10\sqrt{10}$

3. (a) $8 + 2\sqrt{15}$ (b) $9 - 2\sqrt{14}$ (c) $8 - 4\sqrt{3}$ (d) $13 - 2\sqrt{42}$
   (e) $19 + 6\sqrt{2}$ (f) $3 - 2\sqrt{2}$ (g) $82 - 8\sqrt{10}$ (h) $342 + 240\sqrt{2}$
   (i) $372 + 24\sqrt{30}$ (j) $8 + 4\sqrt{3}$ (k) $42 + 24\sqrt{3}$ (l) $116 - 48\sqrt{5}$

4. (a) 3 (b) 1 (c) 2 (d) 8 (e) -5
   (f) 78 (g) 146 (g) 148 (i) 94 (j) 31

5. (a) $82 - 17\sqrt{6}$ (b) $-73 - 62\sqrt{3}$ (c) 18

EXERCISE 1.12

1. 25 m   2. 10 356   3. 93

5. $1 + 1 + 1 + 1 + 1 + 1 + 1 + 13 = 20$, $1 + 1 + 1 + 1 + 1 + 3 + 3 + 9 = 20$,
   $1 + 1 + 1 + 1 + 1 + 1 + 7 + 7 = 20$, $1 + 1 + 1 + 1 + 1 + 3 + 5 + 7 = 20$,
   $1 + 1 + 1 + 1 + 3 + 3 + 3 + 7 = 20$, $1 + 1 + 1 + 1 + 1 + 5 + 5 + 5 = 20$,
   $1 + 1 + 1 + 3 + 3 + 3 + 3 + 5 = 20$, $1 + 1 + 3 + 3 + 3 + 3 + 3 + 3 = 20$.

6. A, B, and E   7. 51   8. 6 210 001 000   11. 21

1.13 REVIEW EXERCISE

1. (a) 4.12   (b) 36 700   (c) 15.2   (d) 6000   (e) 8000   (f) 0.051
2. (a) 4935   (b) 2661   (c) 2.0×10^3 (d) 9.0   (e) 5837   (f) 2014
   (g) 13 000   (h) 750
3. (a) 7.9   (b) 4.230   (c) 0.91   (d) 9.2
   (e) 2.37   (f) 2.75   (g) 0.46   (h) 5.2
4. A = 2.2 cm, B = 1.5 cm, C = 5.5 cm, D = 1.3 cm
5. (a) 298   (b) 469   (c) 23   (d) 130
   (e) -22 (f) 15   (g) 1316   (h) 49
6. (a) 23   (b) 20   (c) 107   (d) 209   (e) 81
7. (a) 52   (b) 45   (c) 51   (d) 241
8. (a) -1 (b) 28   (c) -22 (d) -56 (e) 3   (f) -9
9. (a) -7 (b) 21   (c) 31   (d) 49   (e) -10
10. (a) $\frac{17}{60}$ (b) $1\frac{1}{20}$ (c) $12\frac{1}{2}$ (d) $2\frac{2}{3}$ (e) $7\frac{1}{8}$ (f) $\frac{2}{15}$
   (g) $15\frac{7}{20}$ (h) $10\frac{1}{12}$
11. (a) $28x^5$ (b) $-16y^3$ (c) $3y$ (d) $8x^6y^9$
   (e) $3x^3y$ (f) $18a^2b^3$ (g) $-54a^4b^2c^2$ (h) $20m^7n^5$
12. (a) 4   (b) 3   (c) -2 (d) $\frac{1}{5}$ (e) $\frac{1}{25}$ (f) -4
   (g) $\frac{1}{1000}$ (h) $-\frac{1}{8}$ (i) 1   (j) $\frac{2}{5}$ (k) $\frac{2}{3}$ (l) $a^{\frac{5}{6}}$
13. (a) 0.84   (b) x = 1.25, y = 0.5   14. \$736   15. \$71.28
16. (a) $5\sqrt{2}$ (b) $4\sqrt{2}$ (c) $3\sqrt{3}$ (d) $2\sqrt{5}$ (e) $2\sqrt{6}$ (f) $4\sqrt{3}$
17. (a) $\sqrt{45}$ (b) $\sqrt{28}$ (c) $\sqrt{54}$ (d) $\sqrt{32}$ (e) $\sqrt{75}$ (f) $\sqrt{1000}$
18. (a) $24\sqrt{3}$ (b) $2\sqrt{5}$ (c) $45\sqrt{2}$ (d) $120\sqrt{6}$ (e) 3   (f) $\sqrt{3}$
19. (a) $7\sqrt{3}$ (b) $12\sqrt{2} + \sqrt{5}$ (c) $11\sqrt{7} - 2\sqrt{10}$ (d) $23\sqrt{3}$
   (e) $-7\sqrt{7}$ (f) $4\sqrt{5} + 23\sqrt{6}$ (g) $10\sqrt{5}$ (h) $3 - 21\sqrt{2}$
   (i) $17\sqrt{2}$
20. (a) 5   (b) 2   (c) 3
21. (a) $\sqrt{10} - 4$ (b) $6 + 3\sqrt{2}$ (c) $6\sqrt{5} + 15\sqrt{10}$ (d) $\frac{2 + \sqrt{10} -}{\sqrt{6} - \sqrt{15}}$
   (e) $1 + \sqrt{35}$ (f) 4   (g) $5 + 2\sqrt{6}$ (h) $9 - 4\sqrt{5}$
22. 21 and 29   23. 6

1.14 CHAPTER 1 TEST

1. (a) 542.4   (b) 129   (c) 115   (d) 8.4
2. (a) 26   (b) 29   (c) 13   (d) -14
3. (a) $-20x^5y^6$ (b) $27m^9s^6t^{12}$ (c) $4ab$
4. (a) 9   (b) $\frac{1}{8}$ (c) 1   (d) -4 (e) -8 (f) $\frac{27}{8}$
5. x = 2.625, y = 2.25   6. \$236   7. (a) $11\sqrt{2}$ (b) $\sqrt{5}$

REVIEW AND PREVIEW TO CHAPTER 2

EXERCISE 1

1. (a) $\frac{4}{5}$ (b) $\frac{5}{8}$ (c) $\frac{17}{20}$ (d) $5\frac{1}{2}$ (e) $5\frac{1}{10}$ (f) $4\frac{7}{9}$
   (g) $1\frac{1}{16}$ (h) $2\frac{1}{10}$ (i) $\frac{11}{12}$
2. (a) $\frac{1}{4}$ (b) $\frac{5}{8}$ (c) $\frac{1}{2}$ (d) $\frac{1}{2}$ (e) $\frac{1}{12}$ (f) $\frac{5}{8}$
   (g) $2\frac{2}{5}$ (h) $1\frac{1}{8}$ (i) $\frac{5}{12}$
3. (a) $\frac{1}{6}$ (b) $\frac{3}{20}$ (c) $\frac{1}{2}$ (d) $\frac{2}{7}$ (e) $\frac{4}{15}$ (f) 1
   (g) $1\frac{13}{32}$ (h) $5\frac{1}{4}$ (i) 55

4. (a) 3   (b) $1\frac{1}{8}$ (c) $2\frac{1}{2}$ (d) $\frac{5}{9}$ (e) $\frac{1}{2}$ (f) 3

    (g) $1\frac{1}{3}$ (h) $1\frac{1}{15}$ (i) 9

EXERCISE 2

1. (a) $\frac{1}{4}$ (b) $-\frac{1}{3}$ (c) $\frac{1}{4}$ (d) $-1\frac{1}{10}$ (e) $-1\frac{3}{10}$ (f) $2\frac{7}{10}$

    (g) $-6\frac{7}{8}$ (h) $-1\frac{3}{20}$

2. (a) $-\frac{3}{8}$ (b) $-1\frac{1}{2}$ (c) $-\frac{2}{5}$ (d) $-3\frac{1}{3}$ (e) $\frac{1}{6}$ (f) $\frac{2}{3}$

    (g) $-\frac{3}{8}$ (h) $-\frac{2}{5}$ (i) $6\frac{2}{3}$ (j) $\frac{1}{2}$ (k) $-3\frac{5}{9}$ (l) $1\frac{1}{20}$

    (m) $-6\frac{2}{5}$ (n) $-1\frac{1}{2}$

3. A $= 2\frac{3}{4}$ cm, B $= 2\frac{3}{5}$ cm, C $= 1\frac{21}{40}$ cm

EXERCISE 3

1. (a) $10x + 2$ (b) $2a + 2b$ (c) $3m - n$
    (d) $4x - 4y - 7$ (e) $5x^2 + 2x$ (f) $a^2 - 4a - 5$
    (g) $t^2 + t - 10$ (h) $ab + 11ac - 4bc$ (i) $3x^2 + 5x - 24$
    (j) $-6t^2 + 5t - 4$ (k) $-2m^2 + 3mn - 8n^2$ (l) $-2a^2 - 3ab + b^2$
    (m) $-2x^2 - 2x + 1$
2. (a) $4x - 20$ (b) $2x^2 + 2x - 14y$

EXERCISE 4

1. (a) $15xy$ (b) $18m^2$ (c) $6t^2$ (d) $-32b^2$ (e) $-55y^3$ (f) $45abcd$
    (g) $18t^6$ (h) $84a^3$ (i) $140m^2n^2$ (j) $-30a^7$ (k) $-96c^2d$ (l) $150x^3y^5$
    (m) $-6m^2nt$ (n) $-44r^5s^3$

EXERCISE 5

1. (a) $3x - 12$ (b) $8x - 12y$ (c) $-2x^2 + 2x + 2$
    (d) $-3a + 4b + c$ (e) $8 - 24y - 8y^2$ (f) $84x - 21xy + 28y$
2. (a) $7x + 4$ (b) $3x - 3$ (c) $6x + 15$
    (d) $9x - 9y$ (e) $-16x + 24$ (f) $-10x^2 + 9x + 2$
    (g) $3a - 17b - 4$ (h) $-8r^2 + 16r - 22$ (i) $-14a + 6ab + 26b$
    (j) $3x^2 - 3y^2$ (k) $5m^2 - 14$ (l) $3a + 3b$
    (m) $-5x - y - 7$ (n) $x - 3y + 7$
3. (a) $14x^2 - 7x - 21$ (b) $4a + 8b + 24c$

EXERCISE 2.1

1. (a) $12x^2 + 3x$ (b) $6t^2 - 10t$ (c) $6m - 18m^2$
    (d) $2x^3y - 2x^2y$ (e) $4x^2y + 12xy^2$ (f) $6st - 18s^2t^2$
2. (a) $2x^2 + 6x + 20$ (b) $9y^2 - y$ (c) $21t^2 - 17st$
    (d) $7a^2b - 21ab^2$
3. (a) $4x^3 - 4x^2 - 4x$ (b) $6a^3 - 6a^2 - 15a$ (c) $5t^4 - 5t^3 + 20t^2$
    (d) $6a^2 + 30a^3 + 36a^4$ (e) $2xy - 6xy^2 + 8x^2y$ (f) $-14m^3 + 21m^2 + 7m$
4. (a) $2x^2 - 15x + 28$ (b) $4a^2 - 2ab - 2b^2$ (c) $6m^2 + 11mn - 7n^2$
    (d) $x^2 - 7xy + 12y^2$ (e) $35t^2 - 11st - 6s^2$ (f) $1 + 9a - 9b - 81ab$
5. (a) $x^2 - 6x + 9$ (b) $x^2 + 14x + 49$ (c) $16a^2 - 40ab + 25b^2$
    (d) $4t^2 + 4t + 1$ (e) $25m^2 - 60mn + 36n^2$ (f) $64x^2 + 48xy + 9y^2$
6. (a) $x^3 - 4x - 15$ (b) $6y^3 + 11y^2 - 10y - 7$ (c) $6t^3 - 11t^2 - 2t + 8$
    (d) $8a^3 - 30a^2 - 37a - 30$ (e) $3t^3 - 4t^2 - 6t + 15$
7. (a) $3x^3 + 25x^2 + 28x$ (b) $5\pi x^3 - \pi x^2$
8. (a) 2000 cm³, 20 cm by 20 cm by 5 cm   (b) 1944 cm³, 18 cm by 18 cm by 6 cm

EXERCISE 2.2

1. (a) $3x$ (b) $-3t$ (c) $4x^3$ (d) $-4ab$ (e) $-4x^2y$ (f) $-9m^2t$

2. (a) $2a + 4$ (b) $3x - 9$ (c) $2t - 4$ (d) $-3 + 2r$ (e) $3x - 2y$ (f) $x - y$
3. (a) $2y + x, x \neq 0$ (b) $3a^2 - 2a, a \neq 0$ (c) $6x - 5y, y \neq 0$ (d) $-4x + 2, x \neq 0$
4. (a) $-3x^2 + x - 4, x \neq 0$ (b) $-3y^2 - 2y + 4, y \neq 0$
   (c) $8ab - 4b + 2a, a \neq 0, b \neq 0$ (d) $6m^2n - 4mn + 2m^2, m \neq 0, n \neq 0$
   (e) $1 - 2xt - 5x^2t^2, x \neq 0, t \neq 0$
5. (a) $-4x^6 + 3x^4 - 2x^2$ (b) $4a^5 + 5a^3 - 6$
   (c) $-t^4 + t^3 + t^2 + t$ (d) $x^2y - xy + y^2$

EXERCISE 2.3

1. (a) $3(x + 2)$ (b) $x(3x + 5)$ (c) $x(x^2 + 7)$
   (d) $x^2(x^2 + 7x + 5)$ (e) $pm(pm - n)$ (f) $3y(2y - 1)$
2. (a) $x(31y - 3)$ (b) $3a(2a - 3b + 8ab^2)$
   (c) $x(x^4 + 5x^3 + 3x + 2)$ (d) $3xy(x^2 + 3y + 12)$
   (e) $3r(14st - 4rs^2 + rt^2)$ (f) $7a^3(2x + 3y + z)$
   (g) $6x(4ab + 2ax + x^2)$ (h) $4r^2t^2(20t - 6r + 9rt^2)$
3. (a) $(x + 3)(3x + 4)$ (b) $(a - 7)(2a - 3)$ (c) $(x - 1)(3x^2 - 4)$
   (d) $(a + 3)(5a + 1)$ (e) $(t + 7)(5 + 6t)$ (f) $(x + 5)(2x - 1)$
4. (a) $(x + 2)(x + y)$ (b) $(x + 5)(x + t)$ (c) $(2x - 5)(x + y)$
   (d) $(5a + 4)(t + 1)$ (e) $(x + 3)(x - y)$ (f) $(3y - 2)(x - 1)$

EXERCISE 2.4

1. (a) $(x + 3)(x + 4)$ (b) $(t + 2)(t + 4)$ (c) $(a - 2)(a - 3)$ (d) $(x - 2)(x + 4)$
   (e) $(y - 5)(y + 2)$ (f) $(x + 6)(x + 6)$ (g) $(x - 2)(x + 1)$ (h) $(s - 4)(s + 3)$
   (i) $(x - 3)(x + 4)$ (j) $(x + 2)(x + 10)$
2. (a) $(a + 2)(a + 6)$ (b) $(x - 4)(x - 9)$ (c) $(x - 4)(x + 9)$ (d) $(t + 2)(t + 8)$
   (e) $(x - 6)(x + 5)$ (f) $(x - 3)(x + 9)$ (g) $(b + 7)(b + 10)$ (h) $(m - 20)(m + 10)$
   (i) $(x - 6)(x - 8)$ (j) $(t - 5)(t + 9)$
3. (a) $(x + 3y)(x + 4y)$ (b) $(x - 4y)(x + 3y)$ (c) $(a - 4b)(a + b)$ (d) $(p + q)(p - 9q)$
   (e) $(s + t)(s + 2t)$ (f) $(c - 3d)(c + 4d)$ (g) $(x - 3y)(x - 4y)$ (h) $(ab - 1)(ab - 1)$
4. (a) $4(a - 5)(a + 3)$ (b) $3(b - 2)(b + 7)$ (c) $6(c - 1)(c - 1)$ (d) $5(d - 5)(d - 5)$
   (e) $2(e - 3)(e + 8)$ (f) $x(1 - 2x)(1 - 3x)$ (g) $3(x + 1)(x + 1)$ (h) $2(x + 6)(x + 6)$
   (i) $4(t - 5)(t + 3)$ (j) $a(x - 5)(x + 6)$
5. (a) $(x + \frac{1}{2})(x + \frac{1}{2})$ (b) $(x - \frac{1}{2})(x - \frac{1}{2})$ (c) $(x + \frac{1}{4})(x + \frac{1}{4})$ (d) $(x - \frac{1}{2})(x + \frac{1}{4})$

EXERCISE 2.5

1. (a) $(t + 6)^2$ (b) $(y + 7)^2$ (c) $(x - 9)^2$ (d) $(p - 6)^2$
   (e) $(s - 10)^2$ (f) $(a + 5)^2$ (g) $(2x + 3)^2$ (h) $(3a - 1)^2$
2. (a) $(3x + 4y)^2$ (b) $(2a - 3b)^2$ (c) $(2c - 5d)^2$ (d) $(5p + 3q)^2$
   (e) $(5s + 2t)^2$ (f) $(8x - 5y)^2$
3. (a) $(x - 3)(x + 3)$ (b) $(x - 5)(x + 5)$ (c) $(t - 4)(t + 4)$
   (d) $(a - 10)(a + 10)$ (e) $(m - 8n)(m + 8n)$ (f) $(a - 6b)(a + 6b)$
   (g) $(7t - s)(7t + s)$ (h) $(11x - y)(11x + y)$ (i) $(3x - 2y)(3x + 2y)$
   (j) $(5p - 4q)(5p + 4q)$

EXERCISE 2.6

1. (a) $(x + 7)(x - 3)$ (b) $(2t + 1)(3t + 2)$ (c) $(3m - 1)(2m - 4)$
   (d) $(y - 3)(5y - 1)$ (e) $(5x + 4)(4x + 3)$ (f) $(4m - 5)(3m + 6)$
2. (a) $(x + 1)(2x + 5)$ (b) $(x + 2)(3x + 1)$ (c) $(3x + 2)(2x + 5)$
   (d) $(x + 3)(2x - 1)$ (e) $(x - 3)(5x - 2)$ (f) $(x + 2)(2x - 7)$
   (g) $(2x + 3)(3x + 5)$ (h) $(2x + 3)(3x + 2)$ (i) $(x - 1)(8x + 9)$
   (j) $(2x - 5)(5x + 2)$
3. (a) $(x + 3)(2x - 1)$ (b) $(m - 3)(5m - 2)$ (c) $(3x + 1)(2x - 5)$

(d) (3a − 2b)(3a − 4b) (e) (3r − 2)(5r − 7) (f) (2x + y)(2x + 3y)
(g) (4y − x)(7y − 8x) (h) (3x − 2y)(4x + y) (i) (m − 7n)(3m + 2n)
(j) (2a − 5b)(5a + 6b)

EXERCISE 2.7

1. (a) $x \neq 0$ (b) $m \neq 0, n \neq 0$ (c) $w \neq 0$ (d) $x \neq -5$ (e) $t \neq 0, 3$
  (f) $m \neq 0$ (g) $x \neq -1$ (h) $x \neq 3, 4$ (i) $x \neq -2, -1$ (j) $x \neq \frac{1}{2}$
  (k) $x \neq 3$ (l) $x \neq -1, 4$

2. (a) $\frac{1}{3a}$; $a \neq 0$ (b) $2y$; $x \neq 0$ (c) $4ab$; $a \neq 0, b \neq 0$

  (d) $2x + 3y$ (e) $2b − 3c$; $a \neq 0$ (f) $\frac{x}{y − 4t}$; $y \neq 4t$

  (g) $\frac{x}{2y + 3t}$; $a \neq 0, 2y \neq -3t$ (h) 3; $x \neq -2$ (i) $\frac{a}{3}$; $c \neq 2b$

  (j) $\frac{1}{x − 2}$; $x \neq -2, 0, 2$ (k) $\frac{1}{x − 2}$; $x \neq -2, 2$ (l) $\frac{a}{a − 7}$; $a \neq -7, 7$

3. (a) $\frac{1}{t + 2}$; $t \neq -5, -2$ (b) $\frac{1}{m + 1}$; $m \neq -6, -1$ (c) $\frac{1}{x − 5}$; $x \neq 4, 5$

  (d) $\frac{1}{r + 7}$; $r \neq -7, 2$ (e) $\frac{s + 3}{s + 2}$; $s \neq -4, -2$ (f) $\frac{t − 4}{t − 3}$; $t \neq -2, 3$

  (g) $y + 5$; $y \neq -3$ (h) $\frac{x + 10}{x + 2}$; $x \neq -2, 2$ (i) $\frac{a + 4}{a + 5}$; $a \neq -5, 3$

  (j) $\frac{6x}{x + 4}$; $x \neq -4$ (k) $\frac{x + 3}{x + 1}$; $x \neq -3, -1$ (l) $\frac{m − 1}{m − 2}$; $m \neq 2$

  (m) $\frac{r − 1}{r − 2}$; $r \neq -5, 2$ (n) $\frac{x + 2}{x − 4}$; $x \neq 3, 4$ (o) $\frac{a − 1}{a − 4}$; $a \neq 1, 4$

  (p) $\frac{x + 3}{x − 1}$; $x \neq 1, 3$

4. (a) $\frac{2t − 3}{3t − 2}$; $t \neq \frac{2}{3}, 1$ (b) $\frac{3a − 1}{6a − 1}$; $a \neq -3, \frac{1}{6}$ (c) $\frac{2m − 1}{m − 4}$; $m \neq -\frac{4}{3}, 4$

  (d) $\frac{3x + 1}{2x − 3}$; $x \neq -\frac{3}{2}, \frac{3}{2}$ (e) $\frac{3k + 4}{3k − 4}$; $k \neq \frac{4}{3}, \frac{3}{2}$ (f) $\frac{3}{5}$

EXERCISE 2.8

1. (a) $\frac{2}{5}$ (b) $\frac{4}{27}$ (c) $\frac{10}{7}$ (d) $\frac{1}{4}$ (e) $\frac{2}{7}$ (f) -4

2. (a) 2 (b) 10 (c) $\frac{1}{10}$ (d) 18 (e) 2 (f) $-\frac{9}{7}$

3. (a) $\frac{2b}{3}$; $a \neq 0$ (b) $\frac{10}{3}$; $x, y \neq 0$ (c) -1; $a, b \neq 0$

  (d) 2; $m, x \neq 0$ (e) $\frac{2b}{3}$; $a, b \neq 0$ (f) -1; $m, t \neq 0$

  (g) $\frac{a^2}{bd}$; $b, c, d \neq 0$ (h) s; $s, t \neq 0$

4. (a) $\frac{4a^3}{5}$; $a, x \neq 0$ (b) $\frac{4a^4}{15b^2}$; $a, b, s \neq 0$

  (c) $\frac{4cb^2}{3a}$; $a, b, c \neq 0$ (d) $\frac{3pq}{8s}$; $p, q, r, s \neq 0$

5. (a) 2; $x \neq -3$ (b) 10; $t \neq 1$

  (c) $2m$; $m \neq -1, 0$ (d) $\frac{x + 2}{x + 1}$; $x \neq -4, -2, -1$

6. (a) $\dfrac{(x + 1)(x - 1)}{2}$; $x \neq -1$

(b) $\dfrac{1}{(m + 4)(m + 5)}$; $m \neq -5, -4, 3$

(c) $\dfrac{2(x - 2)}{x + 4}$; $x \neq -6, -4, -3$

(d) $\dfrac{(a - 2)^2}{a(a + 1)}$; $a \neq -2, -1, 0, 2, 4$

(e) $\dfrac{x + 2}{x - 3}$; $x \neq -5, -1, 2, 3$

(f) $\dfrac{a - 6}{a - 3}$; $a \neq 0, 3, 5$

7. (a) $\dfrac{x}{x - 1}$; $x \neq -5, -4, -1, 0, 1, 2, 5$

(b) $\dfrac{(x - 2)(x - 3)}{(x + 3)(x - 1)}$; $x \neq -3, 1, 2, 3$

(c) $\dfrac{a + 1}{a - 2}$; $a \neq -\frac{2}{3}, \frac{1}{2}, 1, \frac{3}{2}, 2, 3$

(d) 1; $x \neq -3, -2, -\frac{1}{2}, \frac{1}{3}, \frac{1}{2}, \frac{5}{2}$

EXERCISE 2.9

1. (a) $\frac{5}{7}$

(b) $\frac{3}{13}$

(c) $2x$

(d) $\dfrac{4}{x}$; $x \neq 0$

(e) $\dfrac{5}{2a}$; $a \neq 0$

(f) $\dfrac{10m}{3}$

(g) $\dfrac{6a}{5}$

(h) $\dfrac{6}{y - 1}$; $y \neq 1$

(i) $\dfrac{4}{x + 1}$; $x \neq -1$

(j) $\dfrac{10}{a + 3}$; $a \neq -3$

(k) $\dfrac{4}{a + b}$; $a \neq -b$

(l) $\dfrac{a - b}{x + y}$; $x \neq -y$

2. (a) $\dfrac{23x}{21}$

(b) $\dfrac{19a}{10}$

(c) m

(d) $\dfrac{-13x}{24}$

(e) $\dfrac{13x}{30}$

(f) $\dfrac{4a - 33b}{22}$

(g) $\dfrac{6c + 35d}{14}$

(h) $\dfrac{9a + 8b - 10c}{12}$

3. (a) $\dfrac{3y + 4x}{xy}$; $x, y \neq 0$

(b) $\dfrac{5b + 2a}{ab}$; $a, b \neq 0$

(c) $\dfrac{7n - 3m}{mn}$; $m, n \neq 0$

(d) $\dfrac{4n + 15m}{6mn}$; $m, n \neq 0$

(e) $\dfrac{9b - 20a}{12ab}$; $a, b \neq 0$

(f) $\dfrac{x^2 + y^2}{xy}$; $x, y \neq 0$

(g) $\dfrac{az + bx}{xyz}$; $x, y, z \neq 0$

(h) $\dfrac{xbc + yac - zab}{abc}$; $a, b, c \neq 0$

4. (a) $\dfrac{7x + 29}{12}$

(b) $\dfrac{7x + 9}{10}$

(c) $\dfrac{2a - 27}{15}$

(d) $\dfrac{-m + 47}{30}$

(e) $\dfrac{-b}{6}$

(f) $\dfrac{22a + 3}{20}$

(g) $\dfrac{-5x - 30y}{18}$

(h) $\dfrac{-b + 9c}{6}$

5. (a) $\dfrac{7x + 8}{x(x + 2)}$; $x \neq -2, 0$

(b) $\dfrac{4m + 3}{m(m - 1)}$; $m \neq 0, 1$

(c) $\dfrac{a + 6}{a(a + 1)}$; $a \neq -1, 0$

(d) $\dfrac{2r + 5}{r(r + 5)}$; $r \neq -5, 0$

(e) $\dfrac{m^2 + 5m + 15}{m(m + 3)}$; $m \neq -3, 0$

(f) $\dfrac{2x^2 - 3x + 12}{x(x - 4)}$; $x \neq 0, 4$

6. (a) $\dfrac{7x + 16}{(x + 3)(x + 2)}$; $x \neq -3, -2$

(b) $\dfrac{8a + 1}{(a + 2)(a - 1)}$; $a \neq -2, 1$

(c) $\dfrac{m - 13}{(m + 3)(m - 1)}$; $m \neq -3, 1$

(d) $\dfrac{3b - 23}{(b + 4)(b - 3)}$; $b \neq -4, 3$

(e) $\dfrac{2x^2 + x - 5}{(x + 1)(x - 1)}$; $x \neq -1, 1$

(f) $\dfrac{2m^2 - 9m + 7}{(m + 1)(m - 2)}$; $m \neq -1, 2$

(g) $\dfrac{6}{(x - 2)(x - 5)}$; $x \neq 2, 5$

(h) $\dfrac{12a - 6}{(a - 3)(a + 3)}$; $a \neq -3, 3$

7. (a) $\dfrac{2x + 7}{(x + 3)(x + 2)}$; $x \neq -3, -2$

(b) $\dfrac{-3a + 11}{(a - 5)(a - 2)}$; $a \neq 2, 5$

(c) $\dfrac{m + 5}{(m - 7)(m + 1)}$; $m \neq -1, 7$

(d) $\dfrac{6t + 34}{(t + 6)(t + 5)}$; $t \neq -6, -5$

(e) $\dfrac{3x - 16}{(x + 4)(x - 5)}$; $x \neq -4, 5$

(f) $\dfrac{x - 1}{(x - 3)(x - 3)}$; $x \neq 3$

8. (a) $\dfrac{5x + 5}{(x - 4)(x + 3)(x - 2)}$; $x \neq -3, 2, 4$

(b) $\dfrac{x - 27}{(x + 5)(x + 2)(x - 3)}$; $x \neq -5, -2, 3$

(c) $\dfrac{3a + 7}{(a + 4)(a + 3)(a + 3)}$; $a \neq -4, -3$

9. (a) $\dfrac{R_1 R_2}{R_1 + R_2}$

(b) $\dfrac{R_1 R_2 R_3}{R_2 R_3 + R_1 R_3 + R_1 R_2}$

EXERCISE 2.11

1. 400 km
2. 19, 28, 37, 46, 55, 64, 73, 82, 91
3. The scores any team may achieve can be written in the form $3m + 7n$ where $m = 0, 1, 2, ...$ and $n = 0, 1, 2, ... $. All others are impossible.
4. 8 m, 8 m, and 11 m
5. 5 packages of 15, 2 packages of 25
6. A,A,A,F,F; A,A,B,D,F; A,A,C,C,F; A,A,C,D,D; A,B,B,C,F; A,B,B,D,D; A,B,C,C,D; A,C,C,C,C; B,B,B,B,F; B,B,B,C,D; B,B,C,C,C
7. 13
8. 9
9. 33, 66, and 99
10. 40 cm²
11. 91 min
12. 20.5 cm² (nearest tenth)
13. 12
14. 510 cm
15. 1024
16. Adams: female trucker; Beam: male editor; Cliffe: male dentist; Dalton: female artist
17. Fill the 7 L container and pour water from it to fill the 4 L container. Empty the 4 L container and pour the remaining 3 L from the 7 L container into the 4 L container. Fill the 7 L container and use it to fill the 4 L container. There is now 6 L of water in the 7 L container.

2.12 REVIEW EXERCISE

1. (a) $2x^2 - 3x - 35$
   (b) $4m^2 - 8m$
   (c) $7t^2 + t$
   (d) $6x^2 - 12x - 24$
   (e) $6t^2 - 15t + 3$
   (f) $2x^3 - 2x^2 - 2x$
   (g) $-2m^3 + 3m^2 + 3m$
   (h) $-2t + 6t^2 + 4t^3$

2. (a) $2x^2 + 7x + 3$
   (b) $15t^2 - 17t + 4$
   (c) $6m^2 + 5ms - 4s^2$
   (d) $x^2 - 2x + 1$
   (e) $x^2 - 49$
   (f) $3a^2 - 14ab + 8b^2$
   (g) $36a^2 - 1$
   (h) $4m^2 - 4mn + n^2$
   (i) $x^2 - 7xy + 12y^2$
   (j) $20s^2 - 7st - 6t^2$

3. (a) $x^3 + 3x^2 + 5x + 3$
   (b) $t^3 - 7t^2 + 14t - 8$
   (c) $6a^3 + 7a^2 + 12a - 5$
   (d) $2m^3 - 13m^2 - 8m + 7$

4. (a) $4xy$
   (b) $-4s^2t^2$
   (c) $2a - 4b - c$
   (d) $-x^2 + 2x - 6$
   (e) $2 - 3a$
   (f) $-4a^2 + a - 2$
   (g) $6ab - 5a^2b^2 - 8ab^3$
   (h) $-2ac^3 + 5c - 3$

5. (a) $2x(2x - 3)$
   (b) $5xy(5y - 6x)$
   (c) $9rst(2 + 3rst - s)$
   (d) $5a^2bc^2(abc^2 - 2c - a^2b^2)$
   (e) $(x - 1)(4x - 3)$
   (f) $(t + 3)(2t + 5)$
   (g) $(1 - 3a)(5a - 1)$
   (h) $6ab(4a - b)$
   (i) $5mnt(1 + 2m - 6mnt)$
   (j) $(2a - 3)(b - x)$
   (k) $(2x - 1)(2mx + 1)$

6. (a) $(x - 3)(x - 4)$
   (b) $(a - 4)(a + 3)$
   (c) $(x - 4)(x + 9)$
   (d) $(x + 7)(x + 5)$
   (e) $(t + 7)(t + 5)$
   (f) $(b + 1)(b - 9)$
   (g) $(x - 12)(x + 12)$
   (h) $(m - 4)(m - 4)$
   (i) $(t - 7)(t + 6)$
   (j) $(a - 8)(a - 9)$
   (k) $(x - 6)(x - 9)$
   (l) $(m - 3)(m - 5)$
   (m) $(s - 6)(s + 5)$
   (n) $(t + 10)(t + 6)$
   (o) $(p - 2)(p - 8)$
   (p) $(r + 5)(r + 7)$
   (q) $(x + 8)(x - 5)$
   (r) $(x + 3y)(x + 6y)$
   (s) $(a - 5b)(a + 3b)$
   (t) $(x + \frac{1}{2})(x - 1)$
   (u) $(x + \frac{1}{6})(x - 1)$

7. (a) $(x - 5)(x + 5)$
   (b) $(a + 7)^2$
   (c) $(m - 11)^2$
   (d) $(2t + 5)^2$
   (e) $(7y - 10)(7y + 10)$
   (f) $(9b - 2c)^2$
   (g) $(5t + 2)^2$
   (h) $(4m - 3)^2$

8. (a) $(m + 5)(3m + 4)$
   (b) $(x + 4)(3x - 1)$
   (c) $(3t - 2)(2t - 5)$
   (d) $(a - 1)(7a - 5)$
   (e) $(3t + 4)(2t + 5)$
   (f) $(3y - 2)(3y - 4)$

9. (a) $6y$; $x, y \neq 0$ (b) $4ab^2$; $a, b, c \neq 0$ (c) $a - 2$; $a \neq 0$

    (d) $\frac{4}{3}$; $x \neq 2y$ (e) $\frac{x + 2}{x + 3}$; $x \neq -4, -3$ (f) $\frac{x + 3}{x - 3}$; $x \neq 3$

10. (a) $\frac{a}{b}$; $a, b \neq 0$ (b) $\frac{3x^3}{2y}$; $x, y \neq 0$

    (c) 2; $a, b \neq 0$ (d) $\frac{x - 4}{x + 5}$; $x \neq -5,. -4, 4, 2$

    (e) $\frac{x - 4}{x + 2}$; $x \neq -6, -5, -2, 4$ (f) $\frac{5(x + 5)}{(x + 1)(x - 2)}$; $x \neq -2, 1, 2, 5$

11. (a) $\frac{9x + 8y}{6}$ (b) $\frac{10a - 3b}{6}$

    (c) $\frac{3n - 2m}{mn}$; $m, n \neq 0$ (d) $\frac{2bc + 3ac - 2ab}{abc}$; $a, b, c \neq 0$

    (e) $\frac{19x + 1}{6}$ (f) $\frac{13b}{12}$

    (g) $\frac{6x^2 + 22x + 18}{(x + 1)(x + 2)(x + 3)}$; $x \neq -3, -2, -1$ (h) $\frac{x - 4}{(x - 1)(x - 2)}$; $x \neq 1, 2$

    (i) $\frac{2x^2 + 8x + 7}{(x + 3)(x + 2)}$; $x \neq -3, -2$ (j) $\frac{x - 12}{(x - 4)(x + 3)(x - 2)}$; $x \neq -3, 2, 4$

    (k) $\frac{-x^2 + 30}{(x - 5)^2}$; $x \neq 5$ (l) $\frac{x + 2}{x - 1}$; $x \neq -2, 1$

2.13 CHAPTER 2 TEST

1. (a) $3x^2 - 20x + 20$ (b) $6t^2 - 13t + 5$ (c) $a^2 - 8a + 16$
    (d) $x^3 - 4x^2 - 2x + 5$
2. (a) $6ab$; $a, b, c \neq 0$ (b) $-4x + 2y - 1$; $x, y \neq 0$
3. (a) $3x(2x - 3)$ (b) $(a - 3)(a - 4)$ (c) $(m + 2)(m + 7)$
    (d) $(2t - 1)(t + 4)$ (e) $(2b - 3)^2$
4. (a) $\frac{x + 4}{x - 4}$; $x \neq 4$ (b) $\frac{9m^2}{5}$; $n \neq 0$ (c) $\frac{4y + 3x}{xy}$; $x, y \neq 0$

    (d) $\frac{x + 1}{x - 4}$; $x \neq -5, -3, 2, 4$ (e) $\frac{x + 1}{x - 1}$; $x \neq -3, 1$ (f) $\frac{-24}{(x + 4)(x - 4)}$; $x \neq -4, 4$

    (g) $\frac{2x^2 + x + 2}{(x - 2)(x + 2)}$; $x \neq -2, 2$

REVIEW AND PREVIEW TO CHAPTER 3

EXERCISE 1

1. (a) 2 (b) -6 (c) 5 (d) 2 (e) 6 (f) $\frac{21}{2}$

    (g) $\frac{5}{2}$

2. (a) -6 (b) 12 (c) 12 (d) $\frac{19}{11}$ (e) -2 (f) -2

    (g) $-\frac{6}{13}$ (h) $-\frac{7}{3}$ (i) $\frac{13}{3}$

EXERCISE 2

1. (a) 7 (b) 9 (c) $\frac{24}{5}$ (d) $-\frac{70}{11}$ (e) 2 (f) $-\frac{19}{27}$

    (g) -17 (h) $\frac{23}{9}$

EXERCISE 3

1. (a) $-x - 6$ (b) $7t + 35$ (c) $-5t - 20$ (d) $x^2 - x - 12$
    (e) $6a^2 - 19a - 7$ (f) $16b^2 - 9$ (g) $7m^2 - 54m + 35$ (h) $x^2 - 6xy + 9y^2$

(i) $2x^2 + 8x - 34$ (j) $10t - 27$ (k) $8x^2 - 39x - 32$ (l) $8t^2 - 39t + 67$
(m) $12x^2 - 5x - 2$ (n) $13a^2 + 72a - 50$ (o) $3 - 12x + 17x^2$

2. (a) $-\frac{5}{2}$ (b) $-\frac{1}{16}$ (c) -1 (d) $-\frac{5}{6}$ (e) $-\frac{2}{5}$ (f) 7

(g) $\frac{1}{2}$ (h) $\frac{7}{8}$

3. (a) $7 - b$ (b) $t + m$ (c) $\frac{m}{a}$ (d) $-\frac{a}{2}$ (e) $\frac{m - t}{b}$ (f) $\frac{w + m}{a}$

(g) $\frac{t}{2b}$ (h) $\frac{9}{3c}$ (i) $c - a - b$ (j) $-\frac{b}{a}$

EXERCISE 4

1. (a) 14.1   (b) 5.35   (c) 7.44   (d) 27.6   (e) 4530   (f) 0.226
(g) 1.91   (h) 275   (i) 0.0671   (j) 28.8   (k) 8.16   (l) 181
(m) 0.0462   (n) 0.0188   (o) 5.36   (p) 56.2
2. (a) 40.63   (b) 0.5439   (c) 43 990 000   (d) 0.000 543   (e) 154.3
(f) 0.1889   (g) -58.95 (h) 5.386   (i) 80 500 000   (j) 2.120
3. (a) 57.72   (b) 4.264   (c) 0.0908   (d) 46.05   (e) 2.301   (f) 2.5306
(g) 3.570   (h) 2.428   (i) 40.29

EXERCISE 3.1

1. (a) $A = \dfrac{50M}{S}$ (b) $225\ m^2$ (c) $175\ m^2$

2. (a) $b = \dfrac{2A}{h} - a$ (b) (i) 8 m   (ii) 13 cm

3. (a) 55   (b) 61   4. (a) $b = \dfrac{F - r}{t}$ (b) 8.2 t   (c) 47.5 t

5. (a) $t = \dfrac{P}{4}$ (b) $w = \dfrac{V}{lh}$ (c) $v = \dfrac{d}{t}$ (d) $R = \dfrac{PV}{t}$

EXERCISE 3.2

1. (a) $(2, -1)$ (b) $(4, 0)$ (c) $(-1, 3)$ (d) $(2, -2)$ (e) $(5, -7)$ (f) $(-5, 5)$
(g) $(3, 1)$
2. (a) $(-2, -5)$ (b) $(5, 2)$ (c) $(2, -3)$ (d) $(\frac{3}{2}, \frac{1}{2})$ (e) $(1, 1)$ (f) $(2, -1)$
(g) $(\frac{31}{11}, \frac{8}{11})$
3. (a) $(-3, 5)$ (b) $(\frac{2}{5}, -\frac{3}{4})$ (c) $(-\frac{1}{2}, -\frac{1}{3})$ (d) $(2, 3)$ (e) $(-\frac{1}{2}, 1)$ (f) $(5, 1)$
4. (a) $(4, 2)$ (b) $(12, -9)$ (c) $(10, -6)$ (d) $(1, 1)$ (e) $(-\frac{4}{7}, -\frac{1}{7})$

EXERCISE 3.3

1. (a) $2, -3$ (b) $-1, -2$ (c) $3, 4$ (d) $-5, 4$ (e) $0, -4$ (f) $0, 3$
2. (a) $-3, -4$ (b) $-2, 3$ (c) $-1, -3$ (d) $-5, 2$ (e) $-3, 5$ (f) $-3, -3$
(g) $4, 5$ (h) $4, 4$ (i) $-7, 3$ (j) $-6, 5$
3. (a) $-2, 2$ (b) $-7, 7$ (c) $-8, 8$ (d) $-10, 10$ (e) $-6, 6$ (f) $-3, 3$
4. (a) $4, \frac{2}{3}$ (b) $-\frac{3}{2}, -\frac{2}{3}$ (c) $-4, -\frac{1}{2}$ (d) $-\frac{3}{2}, \frac{1}{3}$ (e) $-7, \frac{5}{2}$ (f) $4, -\frac{7}{3}$

EXERCISE 3.4

1. (a) $2, 3, 4$ (b) $3, -5, 2$ (c) $1, 7, -1$ (d) $4, -1, -3$ (e) $5, -3, 0$ (f) $1, 0, -25$
(g) $1, 5, 16$ (h) $2, -3, -4$ (i) $2, -5, 3$ (j) $3, 0, 17$

2. (a) $3, 4$ (b) $\dfrac{3 + \sqrt{6}}{3}, \dfrac{3 - \sqrt{6}}{3}$ (c) $7, -1$

(d) $11, -8$ (e) $1, \frac{2}{3}$ (f) $\dfrac{3 + \sqrt{11}}{2}, \dfrac{3 - \sqrt{11}}{2}$

(g) $\dfrac{-3 + \sqrt{15}}{3}, \dfrac{-3 - \sqrt{15}}{3}$ (h) $\dfrac{1 + 2\sqrt{2}}{7}, \dfrac{1 - 2\sqrt{2}}{7}$ (i) $\dfrac{-5 + \sqrt{17}}{4}, \dfrac{-5 - \sqrt{17}}{4}$

(j) $1, 1$ (k) $\dfrac{-1 + \sqrt{22}}{3}, \dfrac{-1 - \sqrt{22}}{3}$ (l) $7, \frac{11}{2}$

(m) $3, -3$ (n) $0, 5$

3. (a) $-0.38, -2.62$ (b) $4.19, -1.19$ (c) $4.79, 0.21$ (d) $2.35, -0.85$

(e) $1.58, -1.58$ (f) $2.14, -0.47$ (g) $1.88, 0.32$ (h) $1, 0.17$

4. (a) $3, 2$ (b) $3, -1$ (c) $1 + \sqrt{3}, 1 - \sqrt{3}$

(d) $\dfrac{-1 + \sqrt{1201}}{40}, \dfrac{-1 - \sqrt{1201}}{40}$

(e) $-\frac{3}{2}, 5$ (f) $4, 7$

(g) $\dfrac{-3 + \sqrt{39}}{3}, \dfrac{-3 - \sqrt{39}}{3}$ (h) $\dfrac{1 + \sqrt{2}}{2}, \dfrac{1 - \sqrt{2}}{2}$ (i) $\dfrac{2 + \sqrt{14}}{2}, \dfrac{2 - \sqrt{14}}{2}$

(j) $\dfrac{15 + 3\sqrt{5}}{10}, \dfrac{15 - 3\sqrt{5}}{10}$ (k) $0, -3.5$ (l) $\sqrt{5}, -\sqrt{5}$

(m) $2, -5$ (n) $-0.27, -3.73$

5. (a) $2, -\frac{1}{2}$ (b) $-\frac{5}{2}, -\frac{1}{2}$ (c) $-1 + \sqrt{10}, -1 - \sqrt{10}$

(d) $0.5, -1$

EXERCISE 3.5

1. (a) $10i$ (b) $11i$ (c) $13i$ (d) $-6i$ (e) $-8i$

(f) $3i$ (g) $-5i$ (h) $-12i$ (i) $-i$ (j) $2 - 2i$

2. (a) $-1 + i, -1 - i$ (b) $-\frac{1}{2} + \frac{3}{2}i, -\frac{1}{2} - \frac{3}{2}i$ (c) $4i, -4i$

EXERCISE 3.6

1. (a) $x + (x + 1) + (x + 2)$ (b) $x + x^2$ (c) $x^2 - 2x$

(d) $x^2 + (x + 1)^2$

2. $7, 8$ and $-7, -8$ 3. $9, 10, 11$ and $-9, -10, -11$

4. $14, 15, 16, 17$ and $-14, -15, -16, -17$

5. 6 m, 8 m   6. 12 m, 16 m, 20 m   7. 16 m by 12 m   8. 14 cm

9. 36 m²   10. $3, 11$ and $-3, -11$ 11. 0 and 7 12. 8 cm by 5.5 cm

13. 0.5 cm   14. 5 m   15. 4.5 m

EXERCISE 3.7

1. (a) 9 (b) 1 (c) 15 (d) 2 (e) 0 (f) 4

(g) 1 (h) 1

2. (a) 16 (b) 9 (c) 22 (d) 33 (e) 2 (f) $\frac{9}{2}$

(g) 9 (h) no solution

3. (a) 13 (b) 1 (c) 3 (d) $\frac{3}{2}$

4. (a) 7 (b) 0 (c) 5 (d) 3 (e) $1, 4$ (f) 8

(g) 7

5. (a) 7.41 (b) 5 (c) $\frac{16}{9}$

EXERCISE 3.8

2. 4 3. $67, 68, 69, 70$ 4. $10{:}30$ 5. $st + 2(r - t)$

6. $24\ 000$ cm³   7. Shelly, Marie, Kim, Peter, Bob

8. 05:45
10. 2024, 3024, 4224
14. 150 h

9. 1185 ÷ 79, 1785 ÷ 119
11. 3^{200}

3.9 REVIEW EXERCISE

1. (a) -11 (b) 2   (c) 8   (d) -9 (e) -1 (f) -1
   (g) 22   (h) 6   (i) 2

2. (a) $\frac{9}{4}$ (b) -6 (c) 7   (d) 8   (e) -1 (f) -8
   (g) 5   (h) 5

3. (a) 15   (b) 10   (c) 10   (d) 5   (e) 10   (f) $\frac{2000}{7}$

   (g) $h = \dfrac{2A}{b}$ (h) $y = \dfrac{xz}{x-z}$ (i) $r = \sqrt{\dfrac{V}{\pi h}}$

4. (a) $(2, -1)$ (b) $(-1, -1)$ (c) $(1, -3)$ (d) $(6, 3)$ (e) $(2, -1)$

5. (a) $(1, 1)$ (b) $\left(\frac{23}{7}, \frac{34}{7}\right)$ (c) $(-2, -2)$ (d) $(2, -1)$ (e) $(1, 0)$ (f) $(2, -3)$
   (g) $(10, 6)$ (h) $(3, -1)$ (i) $(-5, 2)$ (j) $(4, 5)$

6. (a) $(-3, 4)$ (b) $(2.5, 3.5)$ (c) $(1.4, 0.9)$

7. (a) $-2, -4$ (b) $4, 5$ (c) $-3, 7$ (d) $-8, 5$ (e) $-2, -2$
   (f) $6, 6$ (g) $-9, 3$ (h) $-4, -3$ (i) $-3, 7$ (j) $3, 3$

8. (a) $-1, -\frac{3}{2}$ (b) $-\frac{3}{2}, 3$ (c) $3, -\frac{1}{4}$ (d) $-5, \frac{2}{3}$ (e) $\frac{1}{4}, 4$

   (f) $-\frac{3}{2}, \frac{1}{3}$ (g) $9, -2$ (h) $6, -6$ (i) $7, -6$ (j) $-\frac{1}{2}, 2$

   (k) $-\frac{3}{2}, -4$ (l) $\frac{2}{3}, 1$ (m) $-\frac{4}{3}, \frac{1}{2}$ (n) $\frac{1}{5}, -\frac{3}{2}$ (o) $-6, -\frac{1}{6}$

9. (a) $-4, 7$ (b) $\dfrac{-3+\sqrt{65}}{4}, \dfrac{-3-\sqrt{65}}{4}$ (c) $-\frac{5}{3}, 4$

   (d) $\dfrac{-3+\sqrt{3}}{2}, \dfrac{-3-\sqrt{3}}{2}$ (e) $\dfrac{-1+\sqrt{33}}{8}, \dfrac{-1-\sqrt{33}}{8}$ (f) $\dfrac{5+\sqrt{13}}{2}, \dfrac{5-\sqrt{13}}{2}$

   (g) $-1, \frac{4}{3}$ (h) $\dfrac{-3+\sqrt{29}}{10}, \dfrac{-3-\sqrt{29}}{10}$ (i) $3 + 2\sqrt{2}, 3 - 2\sqrt{2}$

   (j) $\dfrac{-5+\sqrt{17}}{2}, \dfrac{-5-\sqrt{17}}{2}$ (k) $\dfrac{-1+\sqrt{13}}{4}, \dfrac{-1-\sqrt{13}}{4}$

10. (a) $-1 + \sqrt{5}i, -1 - \sqrt{5}i$ (b) $\dfrac{3+\sqrt{11}i}{2}, \dfrac{3-\sqrt{11}i}{2}$ (c) $\sqrt{2}i, -\sqrt{2}i$

11. 27, 28 and $-27, -28$ 12. 10 m

13. (a) 25   (b) 51   (c) 21
   (d) 17   (e) 7   (f) no solution
   (g) 8   (h) 8   (i) 12
   (j) $\dfrac{15+3\sqrt{5}}{2}, \dfrac{15-3\sqrt{5}}{2}$ (k) 5

3.10 CHAPTER 3 TEST

1. 700   2. $m = \dfrac{y-b}{x}$ 3. $g = \dfrac{2(S-ut)}{t^2}$

4. (a) $(3, -4)$ (b) $(600, 400)$ (c) $(5, -2)$

5. (a) $3, 5$ (b) $-3, 3$ (c) $-3, \frac{1}{2}$

6. (a) $\dfrac{-5+\sqrt{17}}{4}, \dfrac{-5-\sqrt{17}}{4}$ (b) $\dfrac{3+\sqrt{33}}{2}, \dfrac{3-\sqrt{33}}{2}$

7. 8, 9, 10, 11 and $-8, -9, -10, -11$

8. (a) 8   (b) 5

REVIEW AND PREVIEW TO CHAPTER 4

EXERCISE 1

1. (a) $\frac{4}{3}$　　　　(b) $\frac{1}{3}$　　　　(c) 0　　　　(d) not defined

　(e) $\frac{4}{5}$　　　　(f) $\frac{9}{8}$　　　　(g) $-\frac{10}{9}$　　　　(h) not defined

　(i) $\frac{3}{13}$　　　　(j) $\frac{5}{3}$　　　　(k) $\frac{2}{3}$　　　　(l) 1

EXERCISE 2

1. (a) 7.6 m　　　　(b) 13.5 m　　　　(c) 8.9 cm　　　　(d) 8.5 cm

EXERCISE 3

1. (a) 8, 25　　　　(b) 10, 64　　　　(c) 7, 35　　　　(d) 21, 56
　(e) 1, 5　　　　(f) 4, 7　　　　(g) 6, 24　　　　(h) 4, 18
2. (a) 10^{12}　　　　(b) 10^3　　　　(c) 10^{-8}　　　　(d) 10^8
　(e) 10^{25}　　　　(f) 10^{15}　　　　(g) 10^2　　　　(h) 10^7
　(i) 10^{15}　　　　(j) 10^{-6}　　　　(k) 10^{-6}　　　　(l) 10^{-12}

EXERCISE 4

1. (a) 25.1 cm, 50.3 cm²　　　　(b) 28.3 cm, 63.6 cm²　　　　(c) 15.4 cm, 14.1 cm²
　(d) 8.9 cm, 4.9 cm²　　　　(e) 11.9 cm, 9.8 cm²　　　　(f) 17.9 cm, 17.0 cm²

EXERCISE 5

1. (a) 1.042　　(b) 1.292　　(c) 1.111　　(d) 0.2222　　(e) 1.947
　(f) -2.726　　(g) 6.044　　(h) -3.853　　(i) 22.25　　(j) 0.4197

EXERCISE 4.1

2. (a) $y = -\frac{2}{3}x + 3$　　　　(b) $y = -x + 7$　　　　(c) $y = x + 3$

　(d) $y = 2x - \frac{3}{2}$　　　　(e) $y = -2x - 1$　　　　(f) $y = -\frac{1}{4}x - 1$

3. Intercepts:
　(a) (6, 0), (0, 4)　　(b) (8, 0), (0, −2)　　(c) (2, 0), (0, −10)　　(d) (−3, 0), (0, −4)
　(e) (6, 0), (0, 6)　　(f) (−2, 0), (0, 1)　　(g) (5, 0), (0, 4)　　(h) (−7, 0), (0, 2)

4. (a) 7, $-\frac{6}{7}$, 6　　　　(b) −2, $\frac{1}{2}$, 1　　　　(c) $\frac{3}{2}$, $-\frac{8}{3}$, 4

　(d) $-\frac{1}{2}$, 6, 3　　　　(e) −1, −4, −4　　　　(f) $\frac{3}{2}$, $-\frac{7}{6}$, $\frac{7}{4}$

EXERCISE 4.2

1. (a) $3x - y - 9 = 0$　　　　(b) $2x + y + 8 = 0$
　(c) $x - 2y + 8 = 0$　　　　(d) $x + 3y + 6 = 0$
　(e) $2x - 3y - 18 = 0$　　　　(f) $4x + 5y + 7 = 0$
　(g) $3x - 4y - 28 = 0$　　　　(h) $x + y - 10 = 0$
　(i) $y = 0$　　　　(j) $x - 2y - 9 = 0$
2. (a) $5x + 2y - 32 = 0$　　　　(b) $2x - 11y + 6 = 0$
　(c) $13x - y - 58 = 0$　　　　(d) $2x - 5y - 3 = 0$
　(e) $5x - 2y + 36 = 0$　　　　(f) $4x + 3y - 20 = 0$
　(g) $12x + 5y - 16 = 0$

EXERCISE 4.3

1. (a) 7　　　　(b) 5　　　　(c) 11　　　　(d) 10
2. (a) 5.1　　　　(b) 10.0　　　　(c) 14.0　　　　(d) 10.6
　(e) 19.6　　　　(f) 8.1　　　　(g) 5.7　　　　(h) 5.4

EXERCISE 4.4

1. (a) $x^2 + y^2 = 25$ (b) $x^2 + y^2 = 81$ (c) $x^2 + y^2 = 16$ (d) $x^2 + y^2 = 144$
   (e) $x^2 + y^2 = 49$ (f) $x^2 + y^2 = 64$ (g) $x^2 + y^2 = 3$ (h) $x^2 + y^2 = 2$
   (i) $x^2 + y^2 = a^2$ (j) $x^2 + y^2 = r^2$
2. (a) 4   (b) 10   (c) 5   (d) $\sqrt{5}$
   (e) 6   (f) 7   (g) $2\sqrt{3}$ (h) r
3. (a) 4   (b) $x^2 + y^2 = 16$ 4. (a) 13   (b) $x^2 + y^2 = 169$
5. (a) $x^2 + y^2 = 25$ (b) $x^2 + y^2 = 625$ (c) $x^2 + y^2 = 10$ (d) $x^2 + y^2 = 49$
7. (a) (ii)   (b) (v)   (c) (i)   (d) (iii)   (e) (iv)
8. (a) (1, 4), (−1, −4)   (b) (5, 5), (−5, 5)   (c) (2, 4), (2, −4)   (d) (0, 9), (9, 0)

EXERCISE 4.5

1. (a) (4, 7), 11   (b) (−5, 2), 5   (c) (2, 3), 6   (d) (2, −3), 7
2. (a) $x^2 + (y − 3)^2 = 16$ (b) $(x − 1)^2 + (y − 2)^2 = 64$
   (c) $(x − 4)^2 + y^2 = 36$ (d) $(x − 3)^2 + (y − 6)^2 = 49$
   (e) $(x − 2)^2 + (y − 4)^2 = 81$ (f) $(x − 5)^2 + (y − 2)^2 = 144$
   (g) $(x − 5)^2 + (y − 2)^2 = 5$
3. (a) $(x − 4)^2 + (y − 5)^2 = 9$ (b) $(x + 1)^2 + (y − 4)^2 = 25$
   (c) $(x − 3)^2 + (y + 4)^2 = 49$ (d) $(x − 6)^2 + y^2 = 64$
4. $(x − 3)^2 + (y − 3)^2 = 17$ 5. $(x + 4)^2 + (y + 5)^2 = 61$ 6. $x^2 + (y + 6)^2 = 85$

EXERCISE 4.7

1. (a) (2, 4), (−1, 1)   (b) (4, 12), (−1, −3)   (c) (4, 3), (−3, −4)
   (d) (2, 3), (4, 1)   (e) (−3, 5), (1, 1)   (f) (2, −4), (−1, −1)
   (g) $(3, \frac{7}{3})$, (−2, 4)   (h) (2, −3), (4, 3)   (i) (2, 4), (−4, −2)
   (j) (0, −5), (4, 3)   (k) (1, 2), (−1, −2)
2. (a) (3, −4), (−3, 4)   (b) (4, 3)   (c) no solution
3. (a) (2, 1)   (b) (3, 5), (5, 3)
   (c) $(4, −7)$, $(\frac{2}{3}, −2)$ (d) (4, −3), (−52, 11)
4. 2, 7   5. 9 m by 5 m

EXERCISE 4.9

1. 625   2. 0.125 m   3. 8.7 m (nearest tenth)
4. $\frac{1}{32}$ 5. 2.5%   6. 2816   7. 16n   8. 256

EXERCISE 4.10

1. $(4 + 4) − (4 + 4)$, $4 ÷ 4 × 4 ÷ 4$, $4 ÷ 4 + 4 ÷ 4$, $(4 + 4 + 4) ÷ 4$, $4 × (4 − 4) + 4$,
   $(4 × 4 + 4) ÷ 4$, $4 + (4 + 4) ÷ 4$, $4 + 4 − 4 ÷ 4$, $(4 + 4) ÷ 4 × 4$, $4 + 4 + 4 ÷ 4$,
   $(4 − 4 ÷ 4) × 4$
2. 2, 5, 8, 10, 13, 17, 20, 25, 26, 29, 34, 37, 40, 41, 45
3. 6   4. (a) 6   (b) 15   (c) 28
6. Thursday (Friday if a leap year)   7. 82.5°   8. 60 cm   9. 42   10. 40 L
11. approximately 7380   12. 93%   13. 19   15. 2 h 24 min
16. 12 h   17. 28.3 cm square (nearest tenth)
18. 84.7 km/h (nearest tenth)   19. 8 units

4.11 REVIEW EXERCISE

1. (a) $-\frac{4}{3}$　　(b) $\frac{1}{2}$　　(c) $-\frac{7}{3}$　　(d) 3　　(e) $\frac{9}{2}$　　(f) $\frac{1}{2}$
2. (a) yes　　(b) no　　(c) yes　　(d) no　　(e) no
3. (a) $x - 2y + 10 = 0$　　(b) $2x + y - 5 = 0$　　(c) $3x - 4y - 6 = 0$
   (d) $2x + 3y + 11 = 0$　　(e) $2x - 5y - 29 = 0$
4. $y = -x + 4$　　　　5. $x + 4y - 9 = 0$　　6. $5x + 3y + 19 = 0$　7. $3x - 5y - 15 = 0$
8. $-\frac{3}{2}, \frac{7}{2}$　　　　　　　　9. (a) $\frac{4}{3}$　　　　　　　(b) -3
10. 1　　　　　　　　11. $6x - 7y - 23 = 0$
12. (a) $\sqrt{17}$　　　　(b) $\sqrt{53}$　　　　(c) $2\sqrt{13}$　　　　(d) 4
    (e) $\sqrt{85}$　　　　(f) $4\sqrt{2}$　　　　(g) $3\sqrt{2}$　　　　(h) 6
13. (a) $(0, -4), (4, 0), (-1, -1)$　　(b) $\sqrt{10}, 4\sqrt{2}, \sqrt{26}$　　(c) $-3, 1, \frac{1}{5}$
14. (a) $x^2 + y^2 = 36$　　(b) $x^2 + y^2 = 81$　　(c) $x^2 + y^2 = 25$
    (d) $x^2 + y^2 = 25$　　(e) $x^2 + y^2 = 49$　　(f) $x^2 + y^2 = 2$
15. (a) $(x - 1)^2 + (y - 2)^2 = 9$　　　　(b) $(x - 2)^2 + (y - 3)^2 = 25$
    (c) $x^2 + (y - 4)^2 = 36$　　　　(d) $x^2 + (y - 1)^2 = 16$
    (e) $(x - 7)^2 + (y + 2)^2 = 53$　　　　(f) $(x - 4)^2 + y^2 = 25$
16. $x^2 + y^2 = 5$　　　　　　17. $x^2 + y^2 = 13$
19. (a) $(0, 3)$, 3, no x-intercepts　　(b) $(0, 8)$, 8, -2 and 2
    (c) $(0, -4)$, -4, $-2\sqrt{2}$ and $2\sqrt{2}$
22. $(x - 1)^2 + (y + 3)^2 = 45$　　　　23. $(x - 3)^2 + (y + 5)^2 = 5$
24. (b) $(x - 3)^2 + (y - 2)^2 = 25$
25. (a) $6x - 5y - 30 = 0$　　　　(b) $7x + 5y + 11 = 0$
26. (a) $(8, 6), (-6, -8)$　　　　(b) $(-3, 2), (4, -\frac{3}{2})$

27. (a) (i) 2.25 m　　(ii) 0.9 m　　　　(b) $\frac{1}{4}$

4.12 CHAPTER 4 TEST

1. $2x - 3y - 8 = 0$　　　　　　2. $11x - 4y + 24 = 0$
4. (a) $2\sqrt{10}$　　　　(b) $2\sqrt{17}$　　　　　　(c) 8
5. (a) $3x - 2y - 6 = 0$　　　　(b) $x + y - 3 = 0$
6. (a) $(-1, 1), (2, 4)$　　　　(b) $(-3, -4), (-4, -3)$

REVIEW AND PREVIEW TO CHAPTER 5

EXERCISE 1
1. (a) 10.0 cm　　(b) 9.4 cm　　(c) 7.1 cm　　(d) 6.7 cm　　(e) 3.9 cm　　(f) 13 cm
2. (a) 8.9 cm　　(b) 7.9 cm　　(c) 17.0 cm　　(d) 3.0 m　　(e) 3.6 m　　(f) 6.4 m
3. 5.8 m　　　　4. 6.2 m　　　　5. 13.2 m　　6. 4.7 m　　7. 150 km

EXERCISE 2
1. (a) -3　　(b) 26　　(c) 109　　(d) 35　　(e) -33
2. (a) -3　　(b) 23　　(c) 5　　(d) 54　　(e) -152
3. (a) 29　　(b) 49　　(c) 133　　(d) 133　　(e) 119
4. (a) -5　　(b) 25　　(c) -11　　(d) 5　　(e) 52
5. (a) $\frac{5}{6}$　　(b) $\frac{13}{36}$　　(c) $\frac{25}{36}$　　(d) $\frac{7}{36}$　　(e) $\frac{13}{6}$
   (f) 5　　(g) $\frac{1}{36}$　　(h) $\frac{11}{6}$　　(i) $\frac{29}{6}$　　(j) $-\frac{1}{6}$

EXERCISE 5.1

1. (a) 15 cm　　(b) 16.0 m　　(c) 9.5 cm　　(d) 32 m　　(e) 68.0 cm　　(f) 12.0 m
2. (a) 5.2 cm　　　　(b) 5.2 cm　　　　(c) 17 cm　　　　(d) 0.7 m

3. (a) $2x + 2y + z$ (b) $4a + 2b$ (c) $8x + 2y$ (d) $2a + b$
4. 9.25 cm   5. 6   6. 9.7 cm   7. 76 cm   8. 140.0 cm

9. (a) $b = \dfrac{P - a}{2}$ (b) $w = \dfrac{P - 2l}{2}$

   (c) $d = P - a - b - c$ (d) $s = \dfrac{P}{4}$

10. (a) perimeter is doubled   (b) perimeter is doubled

EXERCISE 5.2

1. (a) 16.7 cm²   (b) 12.7 cm²   (c) 16.8 cm²   (d) 42.3 m²   (e) 7.4 m²   (f) 146.4 cm²
2. (a) 4.1 cm   (b) 6.7 cm   (c) 3.2 cm   (d) 3 cm
3. (a) $2x^3y^3$ (b) $x^2y + xy^2$ (c) $3x^2y^3$ (d) $4x^4$
4. 3.7 cm   5. 41.5 cm²   6. 8.4 cm   7. 96 cm²   8. 43 cm²
9. (a) $4x^4$ (b) $5xy$ (c) $24x$ (d) $3x + 5y$

EXERCISE 5.3

1. (a) 219.9 m, 3848.5 m²   (b) 37.7 cm, 113.1 cm²
   (c) 94.2 cm, 706.9 cm²   (d) 113.1 cm, 1017.9 cm²
2. (a) 39.2 cm, 68.7 cm²   (b) 175.9 m, 9852.0 m²
   (c) 22.7 m, 226.9 m²   (d) 146.6 m, 7330.4
3. 16 m (nearest one)   4. 11 m (nearest one)   5. 63 m (nearest one)
6. (a) approximately 2 453 000 km   (b) 3650 km/h
7. 53.4 cm, 844.5 cm

EXERCISE 5.4

1. (a) 350 cm², 300 cm³   (b) 376 cm², 480 cm³   (c) 350 cm², 375 cm³
   (d) 800 cm², 1200 cm³
2. 30.5 cm (nearest tenth)   3. 5 cm   4. 245 cm³
5. 6 cm by 6 cm by 6 cm   6. 30 cm by 30 cm by 30 cm
7. (a) 21.3 m³   (b) 46.0 m³   8. 832   9. 10 cm

EXERCISE 5.5

1. (a) 471.2 cm², 785.4 cm³   (b) 227.8 cm², 235.6 cm³
   (c) 296.9 cm², 384.8 cm³   (d) 1156.1 cm², 3015.9 cm³
2. 5.2 cm (nearest tenth)   3. 5.6 cm (nearest tenth)   4. 4.3 cm (nearest tenth)
5. (a) 28 274 cm³   (b) 3695 cm³   (c) 24 579 cm³
6. 10.9 cm (nearest tenth)   7. 17.4 m²
8. (a) 94.2 m²   (b) 4   9. 10 cm

EXERCISE 5.6

1. (a) 314.2 cm³   (b) 720 cm³   (c) 95.4 cm³   (d) 2513.3 cm³
2. (a) 735.1 cm²   (b) 240.0 cm²   (c) 125.8 m²   (d) 202.4 m²
3. (a) 703.7 cm²   (b) 3300.0 cm²   4. 5.6 cm   5. 35.7 cm
6. (a) 5 cm by 5 cm   (b) 360 cm²   (c) 400 cm³   (d) 5.6 cm
7. 1306.4 cm³   8. 231.7 cm³

EXERCISE 5.7

1. neither   3. 25.7 (nearest tenth)
5. 3.75 m   6. 6.7 m (nearest tenth)
7. 8 km along the shore from the perpendicular from A, 16 km from the perpendicular from B

8. 30 minestrone, 20 veal, 45 Caesar salad   9. 9 a and 16 a
10. approximately 11:27:16.5   11. 02:45
12. 16   13. 82

5.8 REVIEW EXERCISE

1. (a) 27.4 cm   (b) 26 cm   (c) 56 cm   (d) 24 cm   (e) 16.0 cm   (f) 22.8 cm
2. (a) 24 cm²   (b) 96 cm²   (c) 6.2 cm²   (d) 60 cm²   (e) 120 cm²   (f) 126 cm²
3. (a) 1.2 m   (b) 11 cm   (c) 50 cm   (d) 5.0 cm   (e) 20 cm   (f) 17 cm
4. (a) 22.0 m, 38.5 m²   (b) 11.0 cm, 9.6 cm²   (c) 30.3 cm, 37.7 cm²
   (d) 10.5 cm, 26.2 cm²   (e) 85.7 cm, 401.1 cm²
5. (a) 138 cm², 90 cm³   (b) 678.6 cm², 1357.2 cm³   (c) 282.7 cm², 314.2 cm³
   (d) 96 cm², 48 cm³   (e) 310 cm², 350 cm³   (f) 596.9 cm², 1099.6 cm³
6. 7.5 cm (nearest tenth)   7. 31.8 cm (nearest tenth)
8. (a) 26 cm, 20 cm   (b) 1131 cm² (nearest one)   (c) 2513 cm³ (nearest one)
   (d) 3200 cm³   (e) 687 cm³ (nearest one)
9. 333.3 cm³
10. (a) 1696.5 cm³ (nearest tenth)   (b) 2120.6 cm³ (nearest tenth)
11. (a) 1560 m²   (b) 3400 m³
12. (a) 56.5 m² (nearest tenth)   (b) 58.7 m³ (nearest tenth)

5.9 CHAPTER 5 TEST

1. (a) 40.0 cm   (b) 38 cm (nearest one)   (c) 34 cm
2. (a) 91.2 cm² (nearest tenth)   (b) 154 cm² (nearest one)   (c) 45.8 cm² (nearest tenth)
3. 35.3 cm (nearest tenth), 51.3 cm² (nearest tenth)
4. 722.6 cm² (nearest tenth)   5. 1500 cm³
6. 40 cm   7. 10 cm

REVIEW AND PREVIEW TO CHAPTER 6

EXERCISE 1
1. (a) 60°, 60°   (b) 80°, 80°   (c) 27.3°   (d) 70°, 110°   (e) 40°, 100°
   (f) 60°, 70°   (g) 118°, 118°   (h) 70°, 35°   (i) 120°, 25°   (j) 90°, 40°

EXERCISE 2
1. (a) 5   (b) 13   (c) 15   (d) 25   (e) 8   (f) 24
2. 3.9 m

EXERCISE 3
1. (a) 2   (b) 7   (c) 20   (d) 16   (e) −24, 24   (f) −25, 25
2. 95   3. 345
4. (a) 16.16   (b) 83.29   (c) 2.15   (d) 96.21
   (e) 16.81   (f) 5.136   (g) 55.36   (h) 0.6618

EXERCISE 4
1. (a) 12 m   (b) 5.25 m   (c) 75 cm (nearest one)   (d) 16 cm

EXERCISE 6.1

1. (a) p—hypotenuse, r—opposite, q—adjacent
   (b) z—hypotenuse, y—opposite, x—adjacent
2. (a) 0.6691   (b) 0.9063   (c) 1.3270   (d) 0.2588   (e) 0.9903   (f) 0.3584
   (g) 2.1445   (h) 3.7321   (i) 0.9613   (j) 0.9613   (k) 0.2679   (l) 0.2756
3. (a) 2.4586   (b) 1.7883   (c) 1.0000   (d) 3.8637   (e) 0.7265   (f) 1.0515
   (g) 1.6003   (h) 0.6249   (i) 1.4396   (j) 5.7588   (k) 1.1034   (l) 3.7321

4. (a) 31°   (b) 82°   (c) 14°   (d) 44°   (e) 45°
   (f) 36°   (g) 14°   (h) 45°   (i) 72°   (j) 85°
5. (a) 0.600, 0.800, 0.750   (b) 0.500, 0.850, 0.588
   (c) 0.707, 0.707, 1.000   (d) 0.806, 0.591, 1.364
6. (a) 1.133, 2.125, 1.875   (b) 1.514, 1.325, 0.875
   (c) 1.414, 1.414, 1.000   (d) 1.667, 1.250, 0.750
7. (a) 67°   (b) 46°   (c) 72°   (d) 22°
8. (a) ∠ABC = 30°, ∠BAC = 60°   (b) ∠ABC = 37°, ∠BAC = 53°
   (c) ∠ABC = 54°, ∠BAC = 36°   (d) ∠ABC = 36°, ∠BAC = 54°

EXERCISE 6.2

1. (a) 55°36'   (b) 21°45'   (c) 16°22'12"   (d) 9°10'12"   (e) 45°9'   (f) 24°50'24"
   (g) 65°14'24"   (h) 18°39'   (i) 53°28'12"   (j) 45°27'   (k) 73°30'   (l) 20°51'
2. (a) 25.6°   (b) 18.7°   (c) 63.8°   (d) 35.3°
   (e) 31.9°   (f) 15.1°   (g) 75.2°   (h) 57.5°
   (i) 49.35°   (j) 20.3° (nearest tenth)
3. (a) 16.42°   (b) 24.41°   (c) 65.43°   (d) 66.36°
   (e) 52.54°   (f) 64.66°   (g) 64.34°   (h) 56.27°
   (i) 83.86°   (j) 71.47°

EXERCISE 6.3

1. (a) 127 cm   (b) 3.01 cm   (c) 182 m   (d) 5.96 m   (e) 11.5 m   (f) 707 m
2. (a) 38.7°   (b) 63.4°   (c) 36.9°   (d) 50.2°   (e) 30.0°   (f) 48.6°
3. (a) a = 205 cm, b = 143 cm, ∠A = 55°   (b) b = 14 cm, c = 33.1 cm, ∠B = 24.3°
   (c) a = 12 m, c = 7 m, ∠C = 34.7°   (d) c = 61.8 m, ∠A = 62.7°, ∠C = 27.3°
4. (a) b = 54.7 cm, ∠A = 50.2°, ∠C = 39.8°   (b) d = 37.6 cm, ∠D = 38.1°, ∠F = 51.9°
   (c) q = 33.5 cm, ∠Q = 30.0°, ∠R = 60.0°   (d) b = 528.0 cm, ∠B = 38.0°, ∠C = 52.0°
   (e) s = 711.0 cm, ∠T = 43.2°, ∠U = 46.8°   (f) ∠X = 16.3°, ∠Y = 73.7°, ∠Z = 90°
5. (a) 130 m   (b) 37.7 m

EXERCISE 6.4

1. 606 m   2. 530 m   3. (a) 40 m   (b) 23 m
4. 259 m   5. 203 m   6. (a) 98.0 m   (b) 6.9 m
7. (a) 401 m   (b) 272 m   8. (a) 52°   (b) 4.6 m
9. 21.7 m   10. (a) 47.5°   (b) 22.2°   11. 3040 m   12. 50 m
13. 2.5 m   14. 233 m   15. 40 m   16. 28.6 m

EXERCISE 6.5

1. 0.433 cm   2. 10.26 cm   3. a = 4.99 cm, b = 5.54 cm
4. 18.2°   5. ∠A = 9°, ∠B = 18°   6. 14.8 cm
7. 20.0 cm   8. 4.4 cm

EXERCISE 6.7

1. (a) 6.6 cm   (b) 5.9 cm   (c) 7.9 cm   (d) 12.9 m
2. (a) 34.5 cm   (b) 28.0 cm   (c) 90.2 cm   (d) 39.0 m
3. (a) ∠C = 62°, b ≐ 121 cm, c ≐ 115 cm   (b) ∠A = 66°, b ≐ 7.69 cm, c ≐ 10.9 cm
   (c) ∠A = 18°, a ≐ 10.1 cm, c ≐ 30.3 cm   (d) ∠C = 104.8°, a ≐ 6.6 cm, b ≐ 14.6 cm
   (e) ∠A = 69°, a ≐ 41.9 cm, b ≐ 33.4 cm

EXERCISE 6.8

1. (a) 12.9 cm　　　　(b) 14.8 cm　　　　(c) 18.2 cm　　　　(d) 10.83 m
2. (a) 77.6°　　　　(b) 113.6°　　　3. (a) 38.9 cm　　(b) 81.0°　　　(c) 172.7 cm

EXERCISE 6.9

1. 8°　　　　　　　2. 7°　　　　　　3. 8.7 cm　　　　　4. 4.2 m, 8.7 m

EXERCISE 6.11

1. 1.9 km　　　　　2. 40.6 m　　　　　3. 70.6 m　　　　　4. 265 m

EXERCISE 6.12

1. 157.5°　　　　　　　　　2. −40°　　　　　　3. approximately 16 000 km
4. 14 or 15　　　　　　　　6. 61　　　　　　　　7. 19.4 m
8. 3.2 km from the perpendicular from A, 4.8 km from the perpendicular from B
9. 0, 1, 3, 8　　　　　　10. 250 m　　　　11. approximately 35.3° 12. $9^3 + 10^3$

6.13 REVIEW EXERCISE

1. (a) 91.9 cm　　　　(b) 9.06 cm　　　　(c) 740 cm　　　　(d) 20.6 cm
2. (a) 56°　　　(b) 38°　　　(c) 55°　　　(d) 61°　　　3. 34 m
4. (a) b = 31.6 cm, ∠B = 35.1°, ∠C = 54.9°　(b) f = 43.8 cm, ∠E = 47.6°, ∠F = 42.4°
　(c) ∠H = 38°, g = 43.3 cm, h = 33.9 cm　(d) ∠J = 30°, k = 400 cm, l = 346 cm
5. (a) ∠A = 80°, a = 41.9 m, b = 21.3 m　(b) ∠B = 85°, b = 5.18 m, c = 2.98 m
　(c) a = 76.2 cm, ∠B = 54.2°, ∠C = 40.8°　(d) a = 57.6 cm, ∠B = 40.7°, ∠C = 29.3°
　(e) a = 202 cm, ∠A = 81.9°, ∠C = 36.1°　(f) ∠A = 35°, a = 299 cm, b = 451 cm
6. (a) b = 6.82 cm, ∠A = 100.8°, ∠C = 53.6°　(b) ∠B = 53°, a = 35.2 cm, c = 91.3 cm
　(c) ∠A = 43.1°, ∠B = 81.2°, ∠C = 55.7°　(d) ∠C = 41.2°, a = 21.9 cm, c = 14.8 cm
7. 61 m　　　　　8. 29 m　　　　9. 115 m　　　　10. 15.1 m
11. 128 m　　　12. 14.5 m　　　13. 7.7 m　　　14. (a) 112.5 cm　(b) $3.00
15. 8.1 km and 8.9 km　　　　　16. 5.4 km and 6.6 km

6.14 CHAPTER 6 TEST

1. 6.33 cm　　　　　2. 79.4°　　　　　3. (a) 17.9 cm　　　(b) 17.4 m
4. (a) 36.3°　　　　(b) 32.0°　　　　5. 106 m

REVIEW AND PREVIEW TO CHAPTER 7

EXERCISE 1
1. (a) △ABC ≅ △EDC (ASA)　　　(b) △ABD ≅ △CBD (SSS)　　　(c) △ABE ≅ △DCE (SAS)

EXERCISE 2
1. (a) 38.7°　　　　　(b) 30.3°　　　　2. (a) 6.25 m　　　(b) 7.66 m
3. (a) a = 20.6 cm, c = 25.1 cm, ∠C = 50.6°　(b) b = 19.2 m, ∠A = 38.7°, ∠C = 51.3°

EXERCISE 3
1. (a) 35.2 m, 98.5 m²　　(b) 15.1 m, 18.1 m²
2. (a) 5.0 m, 20.1 m²　　(b) 75.4 cm, 603.2 cm² (c) 5.2 cm, 13.1 cm²　(d) 25.6 m, 65.4 m²

EXERCISE 4
1. (a) (0, −5), (1, −2), (2, 1)　　(b) (0, 3), (1, 1), (2, −1)　　(c) (0, −3), (1, −7), (2, −11)
　(d) (0, 3), (1, 2), (2, 1)　　(e) (0, 6), (1, 4), (2, 2)　　(f) (1, 2), (4, 4), (7, 6)
　(g) (1, 5), (3, 8), (5, 11)　　(h) (1, 0), (3, 1), (5, 2)
2. (a) x − y + 2 = 0　　(b) 3x − y + 2 = 0　　(c) 4x − y + 6 = 0

(d) $x - y - 1 = 0$ (e) $3x - y = 0$ (f) $y - 5 = 0$
3. (a) $(-4, -3)$ (b) $(\frac{7}{3}, \frac{1}{9})$ (c) $(1, 3)$ (d) $(1, 1)$

EXERCISE 7.1

1. (a) $540°$ (b) $135°$ (c) $240°$ (d) $150°$ (e) $270°$ (f) $225°$
2. (a) $\dfrac{2\pi}{3}$ (b) $\dfrac{11\pi}{6}$ (c) $\dfrac{\pi}{2}$ (d) $\dfrac{5\pi}{4}$ (e) $\dfrac{\pi}{6}$ (f) $\dfrac{4\pi}{3}$
3. $57.2958°$ 4. $0.017\,453$ rad
5. (a) $172°$ (b) $140°$ (c) $298°$ (d) $659°$ (e) $8.42°$ (f) $26\,200°$
6. (a) 0.712 rad   (b) 1.23 rad   (c) 2.80 rad
   (d) 3.50 rad   (e) 7.16 rad   (f) 5.68 rad

EXERCISE 7.2

1. 192 cm/s   2. $\dfrac{8\pi}{5} \doteq 5.03$ rad/s

3. (a) $\dfrac{\pi}{30} \doteq 0.105$ rad/s   (b) $\dfrac{\pi}{30} \doteq 0.105$ rad/min   (c) $\dfrac{\pi}{6} \doteq 0.524$ rad/h
4. 4.71 rad/s   5. (a) 262 rad/s   (b) 1310 cm/s
6. (a) 1.3 cm/s   (b) 107 m/s   (c) 85 cm/s   (d) 21 cm/s

EXERCISE 7.3

1. (a) $90°$ (b) $450°$ (c) $180°$ (d) $-270°$ (e) $270°$ (f) $-300°$
   (g) $330°$ (h) $-220°$ (i) $190°$ (j) $225°$ (k) $400°$ (l) $490°$
2. (i) (a) $\sqrt{2}$
       (b) $\sin \theta = \frac{12}{13}$, $\cos \theta = \frac{5}{13}$, $\tan \theta = \frac{12}{5}$, $\csc \theta = \frac{13}{12}$, $\sec \theta = \frac{13}{5}$, $\cot \theta = \frac{5}{12}$
   (ii) (a) $\sqrt{2}$
       (b) $\sin \theta = \frac{-1}{\sqrt{2}}$, $\cos \theta = \frac{-1}{\sqrt{2}}$, $\tan \theta = \frac{-1}{-1}$, $\csc \theta = \frac{\sqrt{2}}{-1}$, $\sec \theta = \frac{\sqrt{2}}{-1}$, $\cot \theta = \frac{-1}{-1}$
   (iii) (a) 1
       (b) $\sin \theta = \frac{1}{1}$, $\cos \theta = \frac{0}{1}$, $\tan \theta$ is undefined, $\csc \theta = \frac{1}{1}$, $\sec \theta$ is undefined, $\cot \theta = \frac{0}{1}$
   (iv) (a) 2
       (b) $\sin \theta = \frac{-\sqrt{3}}{2}$, $\cos \theta = \frac{1}{2}$, $\tan \theta = \frac{-\sqrt{3}}{1}$, $\csc \theta = \frac{2}{-\sqrt{3}}$, $\sec \theta = \frac{2}{1}$, $\cot \theta = \frac{1}{-\sqrt{3}}$
   (v) (a) 5
       (b) $\sin \theta = \frac{4}{5}$, $\cos \theta = \frac{-3}{5}$, $\tan \theta = \frac{4}{-3}$, $\csc \theta = \frac{5}{4}$, $\sec \theta = \frac{5}{-3}$, $\cot \theta = \frac{-3}{4}$
   (vi) (a) $\sqrt{2}$
       (b) $\sin \theta = \frac{1}{\sqrt{2}}$, $\cos \theta = \frac{-1}{\sqrt{2}}$, $\tan \theta = \frac{1}{-1}$, $\csc \theta = \frac{\sqrt{2}}{1}$, $\sec \theta = \frac{\sqrt{2}}{-1}$, $\cot \theta = \frac{-1}{1}$

3. $(-4, 3)$, $\sin \theta = 0.6$ 4. $(-1, -1)$, $\cos \theta = \dfrac{-1}{\sqrt{2}}$
5. (a) $-12, 12$
   (c) $x = -12$: $\cos \theta = \frac{-12}{13}$, $\tan \theta = \frac{5}{-12}$, $\csc \theta = \frac{13}{5}$, $\sec \theta = \frac{13}{-12}$, $\cot \theta = \frac{-12}{5}$
       $x = 12$: $\cos \theta = \frac{12}{13}$, $\tan \theta = \frac{5}{12}$, $\csc \theta = \frac{13}{5}$, $\sec \theta = \frac{13}{12}$, $\cot \theta = \frac{12}{5}$

EXERCISE 7.4

1. (a) $\sin 60° = \dfrac{\sqrt{3}}{2}$, $\cos 60° = \frac{1}{2}$, $\tan 60° = \sqrt{3}$, $\csc 60° = \dfrac{2}{\sqrt{3}}$, $\sec 60° = 2$, $\cot 60° = \dfrac{1}{\sqrt{3}}$

(b) $\sin 150° = \frac{1}{2}$, $\cos 150° = -\frac{\sqrt{3}}{2}$, $\tan 150° = -\sqrt{3}$, $\csc 150° = 2$, $\sec 150° = -\frac{2}{\sqrt{3}}$,

   $\cot 150° = -\frac{1}{\sqrt{3}}$

(c) $\sin 45° = \frac{1}{\sqrt{2}}$, $\cos 45° = \frac{1}{\sqrt{2}}$, $\tan 45° = 1$, $\csc 45° = \sqrt{2}$, $\sec 45° = \sqrt{2}$, $\cot 45° = 1$

(d) $\sin 225° = \frac{-1}{\sqrt{2}}$, $\cos 225° = -\frac{1}{\sqrt{2}}$, $\tan 225° = 1$, $\csc 225° = -\sqrt{2}$, $\sec 225° = -\sqrt{2}$,

   $\cot 225° = 1$

(e) $\sin 120° = \frac{\sqrt{3}}{2}$, $\cos 120° = -\frac{1}{2}$, $\tan 120° = -\sqrt{3}$, $\csc 120° = \frac{2}{\sqrt{3}}$, $\sec 120° = -2$,

   $\cot 120° = -\frac{1}{\sqrt{3}}$

(f) $\sin 30° = \frac{1}{2}$, $\cos 30° = \frac{\sqrt{3}}{2}$, $\tan 30° = \frac{1}{\sqrt{3}}$, $\csc 30° = 2$, $\sec 30° = \frac{2}{\sqrt{3}}$, $\cot 30° = \sqrt{3}$

(g) $\sin 135° = \frac{1}{\sqrt{2}}$, $\cos 135° = -\frac{1}{\sqrt{2}}$, $\tan 135° = -1$, $\csc 135° = \sqrt{2}$, $\sec 135° = -\sqrt{2}$,

   $\cot 135° = -1$

(h) $\sin 315° = -\frac{1}{\sqrt{2}}$, $\cos 315° = \frac{1}{\sqrt{2}}$, $\tan 315° = -1$, $\csc 315° = -\sqrt{2}$, $\sec 315° = \sqrt{2}$,

   $\cot 315° = -1$

(i) $\sin 240° = -\frac{\sqrt{3}}{2}$, $\cos 240° = -\frac{1}{2}$, $\tan 240° = \sqrt{3}$, $\csc 240° = -\frac{2}{\sqrt{3}}$, $\sec 240° = -2$,

   $\cot 240° = \frac{1}{\sqrt{3}}$

(j) $\sin 210° = -\frac{1}{2}$, $\cos 210° = -\frac{\sqrt{3}}{2}$, $\tan 210° = \frac{1}{\sqrt{3}}$, $\csc 210° = -2$, $\sec 210° = -\frac{2}{\sqrt{3}}$

   $\cot 210° = \sqrt{3}$

2. (a) $\sin \theta = 0$, $\cos \theta = 1$, $\tan \theta = 0$, $\csc \theta$ is undefined, $\sec \theta = 1$, $\cot \theta$ is undefined
   (b) $\sin \theta = 1$, $\cos \theta = 0$, $\tan \theta$ is undefined, $\csc \theta = 1$, $\sec \theta$ is undefined, $\cot \theta = 0$
   (c) $\sin \theta = 0$, $\cos \theta = -1$, $\tan \theta = 0$, $\csc \theta$ is undefined, $\sec \theta = -1$, $\cot \theta$ is undefined
   (d) $\sin \theta = -1$, $\cos \theta = 0$, $\tan \theta$ is undefined, $\csc \theta = -1$, $\sec \theta$ is undefined, $\cot \theta = 0$

3. (a) $\sin \frac{3\pi}{2} = -1$, $\cos \frac{3\pi}{2} = 0$, $\tan \frac{3\pi}{2}$ is undefined, $\csc \frac{3\pi}{2} = -1$, $\sec \frac{3\pi}{2}$ is undefined, $\cot \frac{3\pi}{2} = 0$

   (b) $\sin \frac{11\pi}{6} = -\frac{1}{2}$, $\cos \frac{11\pi}{6} = \frac{\sqrt{3}}{2}$, $\tan \frac{11\pi}{6} = -\frac{1}{\sqrt{3}}$, $\csc \frac{11\pi}{6} = -2$, $\sec \frac{11\pi}{6} = \frac{2}{\sqrt{3}}$,

   $\cot \frac{11\pi}{6} = -\sqrt{3}$

   (c) $\sin \frac{7\pi}{3} = \frac{\sqrt{3}}{2}$, $\cos \frac{7\pi}{3} = \frac{1}{2}$, $\tan \frac{7\pi}{3} = \sqrt{3}$, $\csc \frac{7\pi}{3} = \frac{2}{\sqrt{3}}$, $\sec \frac{7\pi}{3} = 2$, $\cot \frac{7\pi}{3} = \frac{1}{\sqrt{3}}$

   (d) $\sin \frac{5\pi}{2} = 1$, $\cos \frac{5\pi}{2} = 0$, $\tan \frac{5\pi}{2}$ is undefined, $\csc \frac{5\pi}{2} = 1$, $\sec \frac{5\pi}{2}$ is undefined, $\cot \frac{5\pi}{2} = 0$

   (e) $\sin \frac{7\pi}{6} = -\frac{1}{2}$, $\cos \frac{7\pi}{6} = -\frac{\sqrt{3}}{2}$, $\tan \frac{7\pi}{6} = \frac{1}{\sqrt{3}}$, $\csc \frac{7\pi}{6} = -2$, $\sec \frac{7\pi}{6} = -\frac{2}{\sqrt{3}}$, $\cot \frac{7\pi}{6} = \sqrt{3}$

   (f) $\sin \frac{7\pi}{4} = \frac{-1}{\sqrt{2}}$, $\cos \frac{7\pi}{4} = \frac{1}{\sqrt{2}}$, $\tan \frac{7\pi}{4} = -1$, $\csc \frac{7\pi}{4} = -\sqrt{2}$, $\sec \frac{7\pi}{4} = \sqrt{2}$, $\cot \frac{7\pi}{4} = -1$

EXERCISE 7.5

1. A(1, 0), B(0.97, 0.26), C(0.87, 0.50), D(0.71, 0.71), E(0.50, 0.87), F(0.26, 0.97), G(0, 1),
   H(-0.26, 0.97), I(-0.50, 0.87), J(-0.71, 0.71), K(-0.87, 0.50), L(-0.97, 0.26), M(-1, 0),
   N(-0.97, -0.26), O(-0.87, -0.50), P(-0.71, -0.71), Q(-0.50, -0.87), R(-0.26, -0.97),
   S(0, -1), T(0.26, -0.97), U(0.50, -0.87), V(0.71, -0.71), W(0.87, -0.50), X(0.97, -0.26)

3. (c) (i) 1   (ii) − 1   4. (b) 45°, 225°
6. (b) (i) 45°   (ii) 225°   (iii) 135°, 315°

EXERCISE 7.6

1. (a) 2   (b) 0.8   (c) 1
2. (a) 3   (b) 7   (c) 24   (d) m   (e) 3   (f) $\frac{1}{3}$

EXERCISE 7.7

1. (a) 2π or 360°   (b) $\frac{4\pi}{5}$ or 144°

2. (a) 2π or 360°   (b) $\frac{2\pi}{3}$ or 120°   (c) π or 180°

   (d) 4π or 720°   (e) $\frac{\pi}{2}$ or 90°   (f) π or 180°

EXERCISE 7.8

1. (a) 0°   (b) 30° (left)   (c) 90° (right)   (d) 360° (left)
2. (a) 30° (left)   (b) 45° (right)   (c) 180° (left or right)

EXERCISE 7.10

1. (b) 15, 360°, 0°   (c) y = 15 sin θ
2. (a) (i) 1578 km (above)   (ii) 1303 km (below)   (iii) 560 km (above)
   (b) 1578 km
3. (b) y = 5 sin (θ − 90°) + 5   4. (b) y = 3 sin θ + 2.5

EXERCISE 7.12

1. $\frac{1}{5844}$ (consider leap years)   2. −2°, − 1°, 1°, 2°, 3°   3. 1.04 L
4. 555 555, 222 222, 777 777, 333 333, 888 888, 42
5. 50 valve caps, 41 jugs windshield cleaner, 9 inner tubes
6. 100 km/h   7. approximately 470 m/s
8. fan: 1800 r/min, alternator: 1894.7 r/min
11. (a) approximately 4 × 10⁻⁸ cm 12. approximately 32   13. approximately 0.04 cm/s
15. (a) 45°   (b) approximately 27.8 m

7.13 REVIEW EXERCISE

1. (a) 45°   (b) 30°   (c) 270°   (d) 200.5°   (e) 154.7°   (f) 179.9°
2. (a) $\frac{3\pi}{4}$ rad   (b) $\frac{7\pi}{4}$ rad   (c) π rad   (d) 0.449 rad   (e) 1.90 rad   (f) 3.49 rad
3. 187.5 cm/s   4. 0.6 rad/s   5. 698 km/min
6. (i) (a) 13
        (b) sin θ = $\frac{12}{13}$, cos θ = $\frac{5}{13}$, tan θ = $\frac{12}{5}$, csc θ = $\frac{13}{12}$, sec θ = $\frac{13}{5}$, cot θ = $\frac{5}{12}$
   (ii) (a) $\sqrt{2}$
        (b) sin θ = $\frac{1}{\sqrt{2}}$, cos θ = $\frac{-1}{\sqrt{2}}$, tan θ = − 1, csc θ = $\sqrt{2}$, sec θ = − $\sqrt{2}$, cot θ = − 1
   (iii) (a) 5
        (b) sin θ = − $\frac{4}{5}$, cos θ = − $\frac{3}{5}$, tan θ = $\frac{4}{3}$, csc θ = − $\frac{5}{4}$, sec θ = − $\frac{5}{3}$, cot θ = $\frac{3}{4}$

(iv) (a) $\sqrt{34}$

    (b) $\sin\theta = \dfrac{-5}{\sqrt{34}}$, $\cos\theta = \dfrac{3}{\sqrt{34}}$, $\tan\theta = -\frac{5}{3}$, $\csc\theta = -\dfrac{\sqrt{34}}{5}$, $\sec\theta = \dfrac{\sqrt{34}}{3}$, $\cot\theta = -\frac{3}{5}$

7. $\tan\theta = -\dfrac{1}{\sqrt{3}}$, $\cos\theta = -\dfrac{\sqrt{3}}{2}$

12. (b) 45°, 225°

14. (a) $y = 2\sin\theta$ (b) $y = 3\sin 2\theta$ (c) $y = \frac{1}{2}\sin\frac{1}{2}\theta$ (d) $y = \sin(\theta + 90°)$

7.14 CHAPTER 7 TEST

1. 135°   2. $\dfrac{5\pi}{4}$ 3. 150 cm/s

4. (a) $\sin\theta = \frac{3}{5}$, $\cos\theta = \frac{4}{5}$, $\tan\theta = \frac{3}{4}$, $\csc\theta = \frac{5}{3}$, $\sec\theta = \frac{5}{4}$, $\cot\theta = \frac{4}{3}$

    (b) $\sin\theta = \frac{12}{13}$, $\cos\theta = \frac{-5}{13}$, $\tan\theta = -\frac{12}{5}$, $\csc\theta = \frac{13}{12}$, $\sec\theta = -\frac{13}{5}$, $\cot\theta = -\frac{5}{12}$

5. (a) $y = 2\sin\theta$ (b) $y = \sin 2\theta$

REVIEW AND PREVIEW TO CHAPTER 8

EXERCISE 1
1. (a) 20.0 cm   (b) 14.4 cm   (c) 7.5 cm   (d) 8.0 cm
   (e) 29.7 cm   (f) 16.0 cm   (g) 13.3 cm   (h) 9.9 cm

EXERCISE 2
1. (a) a = 163.8 m, b = 114.7 m (b) a = 80.3 m, b = 89.2 m   (c) a = 31.5 m, b = 45.1 m
   (d) a = 97.1 m, b = 51.6 m   (e) a = 35.2 m, b = 66.2 m   (f) a = 999.8 m, b = 999.8 m

EXERCISE 3
1. $40.00   2. 570 750 J   3. 58 641
4. 125   5. 147.7 L   6. $2.48

EXERCISE 4
1. 227.5 km   2. 2.5 h   3. 57 km/h
4. 54 min 33 s   5. 340 km   6. 98 km/h
7. 75 h   8. (a) 127.5 km   (b) 7.5 km

EXERCISE 8.1

1. 375 N   2. 0.15 kg   3. 2.5 m/s²   4. 9.8 N   5. 12 kg

EXERCISE 8.2

1. (a) 125 N·m   (b) 3.4 N·m   (c) 10 N·m   (d) 20 N·m   (e) 10 N·m   (f) 50 N·m
2. (a) 15 N   (b) 1.33 m   (c) 17 N   (d) 40 cm   (e) 3 m   (f) 62.5 N
  (g) 2.4 m   (h) 3 N   (i) 0.67 m   (j) 20 N
3. (a) 15 N   (b) 1.5 kg   4. 37.5 kg
5. 270 kg   6. 1000 N   7. (a) 680 N   (b) 68 kg

EXERCISE 8.3

1. (a) second, 20 N   (b) first, $53\frac{1}{3}$ N   (c) third, 6 cm   (d) first, 22.5 cm

2. 375 N, $\frac{8}{3}$ 3. 35 N   4. (a) 3 m   (b) 4

5. (a) $98\frac{1}{3}$ N   (b) 1.22   6. (a) 150 N   (b) 5

7. (a) $41\frac{2}{3}$ N   (b) $\frac{5}{24}$ 8. (a) $166\frac{2}{3}$ (b) 6

9. 1500 N   10. 30 N   11. 0.8 N
12. (i) (a) 3   (b) $266\frac{2}{3}$ N   (ii) (a) 6   (b) $133\frac{1}{3}$ N
13. $233\frac{1}{3}$ N   14. 4 m   15. 64 N   17. 3000 N   18. 0.075 m   19. 0.32 m

EXERCISE 8.4

1. (a) 6 N (right)   (b) 4 N (right)   (c) 7 N (right)
   (d) 4 N (right)   (e) 28 N (left)   (f) 25 N (right)
3. (a) 24.2 N   (b) 16.5 N   (c) 36.1 N   (d) 8.5 N   (e) 14.4 N   (f) 7.0 N
   (g) 22.4 N   (h) 13.9 N   (i) 3.0 N   (j) 17.6 N
4. (b) 185 N   (c) 31°   5. (b) 11.6 kN   (c) 12°

EXERCISE 8.5

1. (a) 50 N, 53°   (b) 25 N, 53°   (c) 13 N, 67°   (d) 13.5 N, 17°   (e) 15.7 N, 37°
   (f) 14.4 N, 56°   (g) 12.5 N, 76°   (h) 8.4 N, 83°   (i) 20.4 N, 47°   (j) 26.2 N, 41°
2. 14.1 N, 45°   3. 169.7 N   4. 6.3 kN
5. 180.3 N, 162° (measured counter-clockwise with the smaller force)
6. (a) 8.9 kN   (b) 7°   7. (a) 14.6 kN   (b) 30°
8. 44.7 N, 89.4 N   9. 72.1 N   10. 372 N, 54°

EXERCISE 8.6

1. (a) 342 N, 940 N   (b) 150 N, 260 N   (c) 86.8 N, 492 N
   (d) 386 N, 460 N   (e) 104 N, 60.0 N
2. (a) 193 N   (b) 230 N   3. (a) 164 N   (b) 115 N
4. 376 N, 137 N   5. 134 N, 112 N   6. 86.6 N, 50.0 N

EXERCISE 8.7

1. 7.5 L   2. 9.4 m² (nearest tenth)   3. 8.5 cm
4. (a) 31.4 rad/s   (b) 38 km/h   5. 237   6. 20   7. 234 r/min
8. 160.3 cm (nearest tenth)   9. 3.25 cm
10. (a) 150 km   (b) 3 h   11. (a) 150 N   (b) 55 N   (c) 81 n

8.8 REVIEW EXERCISE

1. (a) 70 N   (b) 20 N   (c) 3 m   (d) 250 N   (e) $3333\frac{1}{3}$ N
2. 18.6 N
3. (a) 2.33   (b) 2.5   (c) 3   (d) 4   (e) 5   (f) 5
   (g) 2199   (h) 3.08   (i) 2513   (j) 26.7
4. (a) 127.2 N, 29°   (b) 57.9 N, 89°   5. 3.6 km/h   6. 46.0 N, 38.6 N

8.9 CHAPTER 8 TEST

1. 800 N   3. 2.54   4. (a) 240 N   (b) 6
5. (a) (i) 3   (ii) $333\frac{1}{3}$ N   6. 122.9 N, 39°   7. 13.7 N, 71°   8. (b) 136.7 N, 14°

REVIEW AND PREVIEW TO CHAPTER 9

EXERCISE 1
1. (a) Superior   (b) 10 km²   (c) Michigan and Huron
2. (a) $2.75   (b) $0.75   (c) $200.00
3. (a) 7 800 000 km²   (b) 1 200 000 km²

4. (a) British Columbia　　　　　(b) Prince Edward Island　　　(c) 1200

EXERCISE 9.1

1. Determining the quality of a certain product by testing until failure results in a non-saleable product.
   (i) determining the lifespan of a brand of battery
   (ii) determining the strength of a certain glue
   (iii) determining upper or lower temperature or pressure limits of a product (for example, aerosol cans)
2. Statistics Canada brochures, journals, text books, news articles (magazines)
3. calculating an average examination mark for a class; checking all cars in a parking lot for a valid parking permit; checking the engine, after installation, in all new cars at an automobile manufacturing plant.
4. Answers will vary.
5. Carson: 35 100, Clash: 40 050, Dianini: 42 750, Santana: 30 150, Trevelli: 31 950
6. Answers will vary.　　　　　　　　　　　　7. Answers will vary.
8. Grade 9: 32, Grade 10: 29, Grade 11: 21, Grade 12: 18　　9. Answers will vary.
10. When sampling a population that is spread out over a large area, a mail survey would avoid long distance telephone charges.
11. 1700

EXERCISE 9.2

1. (a) 5.4　　　(b) 4.6　　　(c) 5.2　　　(d) 0.2　　　(e) 0.3　　　(f) 175.2
   (g) 8.4　　　(h) 3861.5
2. (a) 7　　　　(b) 5.5　　　(c) 15　　　(d) 3　　　(e) 4　　　(f) 87
3. (a) 36　　　(b) 21　　　(c) 4 and 9　　(d) 27　　(e) −5 and 0　(f) no mode
   (g) 14 and 17
4. $18.65, $19.00, $20.00　　　　　　5. 17.4, 17.5, 18
6. 78.3, 77.5, 75　　　　　　　　　　7. 65.7, 58.3, 44.3, 36.3, 36.7

EXERCISE 9.3

1. (a) 6　　　　(b) 5.9　　　(c) 10　　　(d) 7　　　(e) 29
2. (a) 1.4　　　(b) 1.4　　　(c) 2　　　(d) 12.2　　(e) 1.3
3. 2.2 cm^3　　　4. 16, 3.9

EXERCISE 9.4

1. (a) 16%　　　(b) 98%　　　(c) 4900　　　(d) 2400
2. (a) 84%　　　(b) 2720　　　(c) 160
3. (a) 960　　　(b) 16%　　　(c) 5880
4. (a) 84%　　　(b) 82%　　　(c) 980　　　(d) 680

EXERCISE 9.5

1. (a) 45%　　(b) 55%　　2. (a) 176　　(b) 104　　3. 90　　　4. 78
5. 81.5　　6. (a) 78.9　　(b) 38.6

EXERCISE 9.6

1. 31.7 a　　　　　　　　　　　2. 177 cm by 176 cm
3. 1 + 1 + 1 + 1 + 1 + 1 + 1 + 13, 1 + 1 + 1 + 1 + 1 + 1 + 5 + 9,
   1 + 1 + 1 + 1 + 1 + 1 + 7 + 7, 1 + 1 + 1 + 1 + 1 + 3 + 3 + 9,
   1 + 1 + 1 + 1 + 1 + 3 + 5 + 7, 1 + 1 + 1 + 1 + 3 + 3 + 3 + 7,
   1 + 1 + 3 + 3 + 3 + 3 + 3 + 3

4. 0.75 km   5. (a) 0.5 km and 1 km   (b) 0.25 km
6. 4881.3   7. none   10. 1536 m³
11. 263 (using quarters, dimes, nickels, and pennies)
13. 19%

9.7 REVIEW EXERCISE

1. Answers will vary.
2. CHAM: 8900, CHAT: 14 500, CHIN: 7500, WPTR: 4100
3. Answers will vary.
4. (a) 55.7   (b) 105.8   (c) 8.2
5. (a) 44   (b) 217   6. 32, 32, 33
7. 24.25, 23.50, 20.75, 16.75, 14.75, 12.75, 12.25, 13.50, 15.5
8. 194, 170, 206, 206   9. (a) 1.7   (b) 1.4
10. 2.2 kg   11. (a) 84%   (b) 82%
12. (a) 84%   (b) 164 000   (c) 4000
13. (a) 26%   (b) 74%   14. 60.5

9.8 CHAPTER 9 TEST

1. 52, 53, 55   2. $81 590.91, $50 000, $50 000
3. 33.0, 12.2
4. (a) 82%   (b) 50 400   (c) 20 400   5. 66.7

REVIEW AND PREVIEW TO CHAPTER 10

EXERCISE 1
1. (a) $0.69 (b) $5.04 (c) $39.12 (d) $75.92 (e) $2.87 (f) $54.74
  (g) $6.03 (h) $90.93 (i) $961.86 (j) $34.96 (k) $56.07 (l) $3.51
  (m) $105.48 (n) $80.87 (o) $22.58 (p) $40.45 (q) $299.46 (r) $70.88
  (s) $342.00 (t) $10.77 (u) $16.86 (v) $2931.25 (w) $293.12 (x) $29.31
2. (a) 50% (b) 25% (c) 12.5% (d) 25% (e) 50% (f) 125%
  (g) 40%

EXERCISE 2
1. (a) 0.0932 a (b) 0.1753 a (c) 0.2658 a (d) 0.6575 a (e) 0.1644 a (f) 0.5753 a
  (g) 0.2301 a (h) 0.5178 a (i) 0.1644 a (j) 0.2466 a (k) 0.3288 a (l) 0.0630 a
  (m) 0.1397 a (n) 0.2110 a (o) 0.8219 a (p) 2.4932 a (q) 0.1014 a (r) 0.1288 a
  (s) 0.0055 a (t) 0.0082 a (u) 0.0096 a (v) 0.0151 a (w) 0.0274 a (x) 0.0329 a

EXERCISE 3
1. (a) 69 d, 0.1890 a (b) 169 d, 0.4630 a (c) 113 d, 0.3096 a (d) 60 d, 0.1644 a
  (e) 190 d, 0.5205 a (f) 45 d, 0.1233 a (g) 170 d, 0.4658 a (h) 118 d, 0.3233 a
  (i) 201 d, 0.5507 a (j) 364 d, 0.9973 a
2. (a) June 5 (b) May 18 (c) August 22 (d) December 9 (e) July 3
  (f) July 5 (g) January 27 (h) July 23 (i) November 7 (j) October 21

EXERCISE 4
1. (a) $t = \dfrac{I}{pr}$ (b) $r = \dfrac{I}{pt}$ (c) $p = \dfrac{I}{rt}$ (d) $c = \dfrac{a - 3b}{4}$

  (e) $f = \dfrac{a^2 + ab}{4r}$ (f) $b = \dfrac{4rf - a^2}{a}$ (g) $c = \sqrt{a^2 + b^2}$ (h) $b^2 = c^2 - a^2$

  (i) $b = \sqrt{c^2 - a^2}$

EXERCISE 5
1. (a) 105.90   (b) 0.13   (c) 3.78   (d) 0.01
2. (a) 0.01   (b) 190.86   (c) 13.42   (d) 0.02

EXERCISE 10.2

1. (a) $41.02, $1934.02
   (c) $1670.21, $1748.71
   (e) 9.9%, $7975
   (g) 5 months, $92.25
   (i) $914.11, $44 835.89

   (b) $84.12, $797.01
   (d) $4211.12, $4301.12
   (f) 8%, $19 839
   (h) 1 a, $53 750
   (j) $243.82, $956.18

2. $P = \dfrac{I}{rt}, t = \dfrac{I}{Pr}, r = \dfrac{I}{Pt}$

3. (a) $1175.28, $6072.28
   (d) $65.75, $854.75
   (b) $6.98, $192.98
   (e) $9.68, $733.57
   (c) $33.65, $1161.54
   (f) $450.11, $25 340.11

4. $10 000   5. $657.98   6. $518.90

EXERCISE 10.3

1. (a) 2   (b) 3   (c) not geometric   (d) $\frac{1}{2}$

   (e) not geometric   (f) not geometric   (g) $-\frac{1}{3}$

2. (a) 32, 2^{n-1} (b) 405, $5(3)^{n-1}$ (c) 192, $3(2)^{k-1}$ (d) $\frac{1}{4}, 64(\frac{1}{2})^{k-1}$

   (e) 64, $4(-2)^{n-1}$ (f) $\frac{1}{9}, 81(-\frac{1}{3})^{n-1}$

3. (a) 8   (b) 7   (c) 6   (d) 7   (e) 8   (f) 7
4. (a) $105, $110.25, $115.76, $121.55, $100(1.05)^n$, a = $100(1.05), r = 1.05
   (b) $108, $116.64, $125.97, $136.05, $100(1.08)^n$, a = $100(1.08), r = 1.08
5. (a) 4, 3, $4(3)^{n-1}$ (b) 3, 2, $3(2)^{n-1}$ (c) 7, 4, $7(4)^{n-1}$

   (d) 256, $\frac{1}{2}, 256(\frac{1}{2})^{n-1}$ (e) $-243, \frac{1}{3}, -243(\frac{1}{3})^{n-1}$ (f) 3, 4, $3(4)^{n-1}$

6. 1023

EXERCISE 10.4

1. (a) 40, 5%   (b) 40, 3%   (c) 8%, semi-annually   (d) 15 a, 4%
   (e) 18%, 6 a   (f) 9%, monthly   (g) 4 a, 6%   (h) 8%, 1.5 a
2. (a) $9054.88   (b) $796.02   (c) $69 914.36   (d) $5391.74   (e) $964.54
3. (a) $5049.91   (b) $1049.91   4. (a) $1418.52   (b) $1425.76   (c) $1430.77
5. 17.5 a   6. $11 436.33   7. (a) $20.70   (b) $1225.70   8. (a) $51 052.30
9. 4.4%   10. $23 377.14

EXERCISE 10.5

1. (a) 12.36%   (b) 16.64%   (c) 16.986%   (d) 6.152%   (e) 18%   (f) 26.824%
2. $450.65, 9.203%
3. (a) 8%   (b) 8.16%   (c) 8.243%   (d) 8.286%   (e) 8.307%
5. (a) 8.31%   (b) 8.32%
6. The effective rate increases as m increases to the limit 8.329% (nearest thousandth).

EXERCISE 10.6

1. (a) $565.33   (b) $218.11   (c) $667.50   (d) $811.98   (e) $8427.42
2. $212 675.64   3. $128 785.54   4. (a) $704.96   (b) $701.38   (c) $698.92
5. $478.47   6. $923.16   7. $58 823.31   8. $54 288.36   9. $52 032.84
10. $5238.36   11. $750.00

EXERCISE 10.7

3. (a) 2.37   (b) 1.27   (c) 2.56   (d) 1.34
4. (a) 1.08   (b) 1.06   (c) 1.14   (d) 1.14

5. (a) 36.2% (b) 19.2% (c) 8.5% (d) 19.2%
6. the second 7. 10.3%

EXERCISE 10.8

1. (a) 5 (b) 6 (c) 1 2. Don 3. 276, 277
5. A, B, and D 6. 6 7. 17
8. (a) yes (b) 211 cm (c) 930 L
   (d) 555 (e) approximately 95 m
9. The first player should begin by picking up 2 toothpicks. After the second player has moved, the first player should pick up enough toothpicks to leave exactly 5 behind. Whatever move the second player now makes, the first player can subsequently arrange to leave behind exactly 1 toothpick.
11. $\frac{5}{8}$ 12. 20 13. 10:01, 11:11

10.9 REVIEW EXERCISE

3. (a) 12.36% (b) 12.55% (c) 12.68% (d) 12.72%
4. (a) 6.75 m (b) 3.80 m
5. (a) $3564.40 (b) $556.54 (c) $8857.80 (d) $11 284.79 (e) $9673.36
6. (a) $3667.50 (b) $6131.14 (c) $19 783.14 (d) $13 293.30 (e) $21 985.31
7. (a) $29.49, $1375.27 (b) $1925.53, $2016.03 (c) 3.8%, $9320
   (d) 20 months, $102.00 (e) $1585.09, $53 564.91 (f) $711.16, $2788.84
8. $171 928.70 9. 6.5% 10. $14 554.38
11. $523 859.90 12. $100[1.01 + (1.01)^2 + (1.01)^3 + ... + (1.01)^{12}]$

10.10 CHAPTER 10 TEST

1. $76, $1026 2. $2000, $1600 3. 640, $5(2)^{n-1}$ 4. $51 266.08
5. $90 436.30 6. 8.24% 7. $9722.22 8. $44 100.99 9. 8.9%

REVIEW AND PREVIEW TO CHAPTER 11

EXERCISE 1

1. (a) $2.74 (b) $33.00 (c) $66.52 (d) $600.00 (e) $204.01 (f) $62.77
   (g) $313.50 (h) $24.37 (i) $10.88 (j) $171.50 (k) $0.44 (l) $64.00
2. (a) $\frac{1}{10}$% (b) 5% (c) $\frac{1}{20}$% (d) $\frac{1}{8}$% (e) 20% (f) 12%
   (g) $2\frac{1}{2}$% (h) $\frac{3}{4}$% (i) 16% (j) $1\frac{1}{2}$% (k) 150% (l) 215%
   (m) $5\frac{1}{2}$% (n) $\frac{4}{5}$% (o) $\frac{7}{8}$% (p) $1\frac{5}{16}$% (q) 110% (r) 89%
   (s) $3\frac{3}{4}$%

EXERCISE 2

1. (a) 1, 2, 4, 8, 16 (b) 32, 16, 8, 4, 2 (c) 27, 18, 12, 8, $\frac{16}{3}$
   (d) 4, −12, 36, −108, 324 (e) $\frac{1}{2}$, 1, 2, 4, 8 (f) $\frac{5}{8}$, $\frac{5}{2}$, 10, 40, 160
   (g) $\frac{1}{9}$, $\frac{1}{3}$, 1, 3, 9 (h) 1, −2, 4, −8, 16
2. (a) 128 (b) −10 935 (c) 64 (d) $\frac{32}{27}$ (e) 32
3. (a) 1023 (b) 6560 (c) 215 (d) $-\frac{40}{3}$

EXERCISE 3

1. (a) $270, $4770 (b) $54.15, $814.15 (c) $1225, $1249.50 (d) $240, $244.80
   (e) $50.40, 18% (f) $37.80, 24% (g) 0.337 a, $51 179.50 (h) $16.50, 0.600 a

(i) $45.25, $1020.25   (j) $50.70, 8%   (k) 0.082, $352.87   (l) $944.92, $966.28
(m) $0.37, $24.60   (n) $128.42, $1900

EXERCISE 11.1

1. With compound interest, interest is charged on any outstanding interest.
2. (a) $200 000   (b) $259 374.25   (c) $265 329.77   (d) $268 506.38
4. (a) $0.27   (b) $24.66   (c) $76.16
5. (a) $839.62   (b) $17 069.81   (c) $61 391.33   (d) $44 372.46
6. (a) $50 413.57   (b) $54 446.66   (c) $58 802.39   (d) $63 506.58
   (e) $68 587.11   (f) $74 074.07
7. (a) 8   (b) $56.41   (c) $456.41

EXERCISE 11.2

3. $8620.25   4. (a) $8582.96

EXERCISE 11.3

1. (a) 2550   (b) 59 048   (c) 2343   (d) 16 380   (e) 27 305   (f) 100
2. (a) −3280   (b) 504   (c) 726   (d) −341   (e) 0

EXERCISE 11.4

1. (a) 40.568 079   (b) 110.484 031   (c) 31.513 969   (d) 24.641 140
   (e) 209.347 996   (f) 119.120 867   (g) 40.568 079   (h) 6.716 892
2. (a) $381.04   (b) $49 520.51   (c) $43 053.14   (d) $83 779.88
3. (a) $8933.42   (b) $17 213.24   (c) $4307.69   (d) $52 723.18
   (e) $210.47   (f) $174.28   (g) $127.46   (h) $515.55
4. $370.73   5. $104 819.60   6. $10 654.50   7. $974.62
8. $1362.33   9. $14 789.23

EXERCISE 11.5

1. (a) 22.723 786   (b) 16.046 125   (c) 5.697 187   (d) 16.890 352
   (e) 18.255 925   (f) 11.652 296   (g) 27.794 054   (h) 7.485 925
2. (a) $353.83   (b) $2924.78   (c) $36 551.46   (d) $35 571.35
   (e) $2042.04   (f) $14.62   (g) $978 684.80   (h) $923.16
3. (a) $4077.10   (b) $8467.77   (c) $3010.75   (d) $29 440.35
   (e) $1010.47   (f) $354.28   (g) $152.46   (h) $1235.55
4. $2766.07   5. $398.57
6. (a) $9818.67   (b) $5920.16   (c) $5531.51   (d) $1793.87
7. $8674.52   8. (a) $10 815.59 (b) $3677.54   (c) in one month
9. (a) $209 243.24   (b) $220 751.62   10. $2504.39   11. $127 217.68

EXERCISE 11.6

1. (a) $6795.16   (b) $2889.14   (c) $15 046.30   (d) $21 848.34
   (e) $425.01   (f) $6344.43   (g) $393.42   (h) $787.68
2. (a) 2%, 48, 30.673 120   (b) 6%, 20, 11.469 921   (c) 3.5%, 20, 14.212 403
   (d) 1.5%, 36, 27.660 684   (e) 0.5%, 6, 5.896 384   (f) 1.5%, 1, 0.985 222
3. $28 387.04   4. $36 825.06   5. $1129.51   6. $3799.44
7. (a) $88.85   (b) $47.07   (c) $33.21   (d) $26.33
   (e) $41.78, $13.86, $6.88   (f) no
8. (a) $47.07   (b) $70.61   (c) $94.15   (d) $117.68
   (e) $141.22   (f) $23.54, $23.54, $23.53, $23.54 (g) yes
9. (a) $26 262.37   (b) $26 581.79

(c) $26 902.71
(e) $27 549.01
(g) no

(d) $27 225.12
(f) $319.42, $320.92, $322.41, $323.89

EXERCISE 11.7

1. (a) $2500, 12.7%   (b) $613, 7.9%   (c) $28 000, 22.8%   (d) $8435.32, 27.4%
2. 6.1%   3. (a) 6.7%   (b) 14.5%   (c) 22.9%
4. (a) $100 000, $200 00, $300 000   (b) $100 000   (c) 100%, 50%
5. (a) $1619   (b) 21.9%
6. (a) $1283   (b) 25.7%
   (c) the three-year term by $336   (d) the two-year term by 3.8%
7. $8133.33, $668.89

EXERCISE 11.8

1. (a) $74 763.25   (b) $59 735.45   (c) 249.2%   (d) 199.1%
4. 98.2%   5. (a) $110.37

EXERCISE 11.9

1. (a) $2397   (b) $7560   (c) $3922.60   (d) $8183   (e) $1949
2. (a) $2973.02   (b) $245.10   (c) $1203.14
3. (a) The policy will pay $43 000 cash or deliver payments in the form of an annuity.
   (b) The policy is no longer in force.
   (c) The policy is worth $43 000 at his or her death.
4. (a) $43 000   (b) $43 000   (c) $43 000
5. (a) nothing   (b) nothing   (c) $43 000
6. $422.30   7. $2331.10   8. $9896.39

EXERCISE 11.10

1. 40   2. 14.6   3. 2 a, 2 a, and 9 a   4. 12
5. 17 576 000   6. no   8. 1   10. 10 s
11. 496 m²   12. 24 km/h   13. 12 L   14. 14

11.11 REVIEW EXERCISE

1. $96 095.00   2. $325 778.93   3. $7089.19   4. $16 548.65
5. (a) 1456   (b) 511   (c) 86
6. (a) $3564.40 (b) $556.54   7. (a) $3667.50 (b) $6131.14
8. (a) $5630.80 (b) $9196.40
9. (a) $815.57   (b) $24.48   (c) $802.16   (d) $2616.29
10. $12 772.33   11. $150 597.66 12. $1131.41   13. $339.16
14. $10 594.10   15. $8223.69   16. $42 275.14   17. $1950
18. 16.5%   19. $16 045.74   20. $11 345.55

11.12 CHAPTER 11 TEST

1. $160 844   2. $3731.10   3. (a) 1275   (b) −1023
4. $25 672.53   5. $1138.02   6. $3680.04   7. $4723.79   8. $3669.50   9. 18.5%

REVIEW AND PREVIEW TO CHAPTER 12

EXERCISE 1
1. (a) $35   (b) $51.48   (c) $33.60   (d) $0.23   (e) $396   (f) $762.50

(g) $2315.16   (h) $463.68   (i) $1208.92   (j) $4929.75   (k) $2922.75   (l) $4119.50
(m) $4936.99   (n) $5062.33

2. (a) 20%   (b) $6\frac{1}{4}$%   (c) $14\frac{2}{7}$%   (d) $6\frac{1}{4}$%   (e) 20%   (f) $15\frac{3}{5}$%

3. $487.92   4. $1038.80   5. $297.50

EXERCISE 2
1. (a) $1200   (b) $6200   2. (a) $812.50   (b) $3312.50   3. (a) $270   (b) $6270
4. (a) $115.29   (b) $8615.29   5. (a) $977.90   (b) $100 977.90
6. $7000   7. 3 a   8. 7%

EXERCISE 3
1. $11 996.77   2. $1273.09   3. $13 517.91
4. $14 533.57   5. $16 439.28   6. $3524.80
7. $6508.01   8. $2691.89   9. $620 992.92
10. $2791.17   11. Answers will vary.

EXERCISE 4
1. $14 889.04   2. $17 888.45   3. $57 267.04   4. $1507.62
5. $1116.47   6. $4212.36   7. $3585.07   8. $8530.20

EXERCISE 12.1

3. $5000   4. $4388.10   5. $63 750
6. (a) $1 080 000   (b) $2700   (c) 2.25%   7. (a) $0.65   (b) $325

EXERCISE 12.2

4. (a) $92.50   (b) $38.75   5. $200, 2.35%
6. (a) $832.05   (b) $2733.88   (c) $478.80   (d) $1500.19   (e) $4055.00   (f) $10 740.90
7. (a) $932.05   (b) $504.71   (c) $2733.70   (d) $1034.99

EXERCISE 12.3

1. (a) 12.0%   (b) 11.7%   (c) 12.5%   (d) 10.7%   (e) 9.5%
2. (a) 10.8%   (b) 10.6%   (c) 9.1%   (d) 11.3%
3. (a) (i) 11.5%   (ii) 10.8%   (b) risk
4. (a) (i) 10.3%   (ii) 9.6%   (iii) 11.5%   (iv) 11.8%

EXERCISE 12.4

2. (a) less   (b) more
3. (a) $81.76   (b) $86.85   (c) $86.45   (d) $83.06   (e) $67.14
4. (a) $111.87   (b) $117.48   (c) $106.53   (d) $107.81   (e) $104.56
5. $395.10   6. $5895   7. $7526   8. $114.55

EXERCISE 12.5

1. (a) $5800   (b) $24 750   (c) $4050   (d) $1212.50   (e) $5162.50   (f) $1095
   (g) $450
2. (a) $87.50   (b) $325   (c) $33.12   (d) $74.90   (e) $43.25   (f) $255.54
   (g) $1279.20   (h) $81.59   (i) $728.16
3. (a) $1332.50   (b) $3331.25   (c) $8258.25   (d) $4607.10   (e) $26 201.06   (f) $6555.78
4. (a) $1072.50   (b) $4387.50   (c) $42 540.70 (d) $38 455.06   (e) $18 663.33   (f) $18 073.65
5. (a) $1255.62   (b) $7935.98   (c) $5996.25   (d) $16 315.92   (e) $18 164.21
6. (a) $47.50 (profit)   (b) $221.25 (loss)   (c) $1434.60 (profit)   (d) $2201.82 (loss)
   (e) $7320.14 (profit)

EXERCISE 12.6

1. $1150   2. $525   3. $600   4. $576   5. none   6. $3860

EXERCISE 12.7

1. 3.5%   2. 2.85%   3. 1.4%   4. Tricorp   5. 20 : 1
6. (a) 21.7 : 1   (b) 41.6 : 1   (c) 26.1 : 1   (d) 9.3 : 1   7. 17.1 : 1

EXERCISE 12.8

4. (a) $1 765 310 000   (b) $1 692 611 000   (c) $50 400   (d) $660
   (e) 1.7%   (f) 1.7%   (g) 7.5 : 1   (h) 7.6 : 1
   (i) National Investments   (j) National Investments
5. (a) (i) 96.9%   (ii) 95.1%   (iii) 74.0%   (iv) 96.2%
   (b) (i) 3.1%   (ii) 4.9%   (iii) 26.0%   (iv) 3.8%

EXERCISE 12.9

1. (a) 1.100, 0.902   (b) 1.144, 0.862   (c) 1.213, 0.802   (d) 1.262, 0.762
   (e) 1.306, 0.727   (f) 1.384, 0.667   (g) 1.481, 0.597   (h) 1.540, 0.557
4. loss of $0.03   5. $3 424 238   6. loss of $1110   7. $130

EXERCISE 12.10

1. 43   3. May 13   5. (a) $1.25 billion/min 6. 25
8. 2352   10. 10   12. 145   14. $\frac{1}{5}$ 15. 16
16. 21   18. 24   19. 3

12.11 REVIEW EXERCISE

1. $166.67   2. (a) $5 500 000   (b) $12 375   (c) 6.875%
3. (a) $1.80   (b) $3600   (c) 7.2%   4. (a) $250   (b) $10 250
5. $920   6. $4512.69   7. $945   8. 9.3%   9. 10.7%   10. 8.7%
11. 9.9%   12. $72.40   13. $86.22   14. $105.62   15. $5806.62   16. $18 217.05
17. $222 337.50   18. $14 968.45   19. $279 194.86   20. $849.37 (loss)
21. $815.30 (loss)
22. (a) $2100   (b) $2546   (c) $1095
    (d) $1941.25 (profit)   (e) $315.86 (profit)
23. 7.0%   24. 1.025 : 1   25. decreased by $2350

12.12 CHAPTER 12 TEST

1. (a) $5 750 000   (b) 10.3%   2. $950   3. 7.9%   4. 11.4%
5. $112.66   6. $14 229.60   7. $14 706.60   8. 5.3%   9. 13.75 : 1

REVIEW AND PREVIEW TO CHAPTER 13

EXERCISE 1
1. (a) $1683.24   (b) $1001.57   (c) $2129.58   (d) $11 263.32
2. (a) $16.44   (b) $270.23   (c) $205.68   (d) $1633.77
3. (a) $6114.74   (b) $723.59   (c) $47.47   (d) $123.07
4. (a) $15 998.72   (b) $65.15   (c) $605.47   (d) $16 625.20
5. (a) 63.7%   (b) 3.9%   (c) 93.8%   (d) 219.6%
6. (a) −$42.67   (b) $90.90   (c) $35.48   (d) $546.16
7. (a) $7.41   (b) $3.08   (c) $8.61   (d) $148.65

(e) $338.80   (f) $64.12   (g) $42 132.39   (h) $18.77

EXERCISE 2
1. (a) $22 489.29   (b) $6753.34   (c) $94 699.24   (d) $119 077.68
   (e) $109 477.80   (f) $4557.35   (g) $1064.32   (h) $3754.47
   (i) $3966.96   (j) $1206.68   (k) $1860.26

EXERCISE 3
1. (a) $3300, $58 300   (b) $112.43, $901.43   (c) $346.64, $1584.64   (d) $70.47, $305.36
2. (a) $1225, $1249.5   (b) $240, $244.80   3. (a) $0.37, $24.60   (b) $128.42, $1900
4. (a) 0.337 a, $51 179.50 (b) 0.082 a, $352.87
5. (a) $3469.50, $33 469.50   (b) $12 152.88, $132 152.88   (c) $5060, $15 060
   (d) $5864.37, $30 864.37
6. (a) $10 501.37   (b) $9522.57

EXERCISE 13.1

1. $947.20   2. $1950.05   3. (a) $59 514 (b) $1144.50   (c) $228.90   (d) 28.61\frac{1}{4}$
6. (a) $575, $556   (b) the first   (c) $29 900
7. (a) $2625, $3000, $3125   (c) $15 000
8. $1778.50   9. $576.56   10. (a) $80.55

EXERCISE 13.2

2. $20 699.57   3. $529.20   4. $20 185.72/a
5. (a) $67 840   6. (a) 1.8%   (b) 0.9%   (c) 1.5%   (d) 4.0%
7. (a) 2.9%   (b) 4.0%   (c) 1.7%   (d) 4.6%
8. (a) $21 787.50, $182.40, $1245, $498   (b) $2000, $93.38, $504
   (c) $64.12   (d) $35 875.60

EXERCISE 13.3

4. (a) and (d)
5. $42 160 − $63 240   6. (a) yes   (b) 12.9%
7. yes   8. (a) 42.7%, 28.1%   9. (a) 39.0%, 25.4%

EXERCISE 13.5

1. (a) 14.5%   (b) 14.9%   (c) 9.9%
2. (a) $1086.81, $1113.19   (b) 36.9%
3. 262%   4. $428
7. (a) $556.80   (b) $9.74   (c) $200   (d) $169.35   (e) $91.68   (f) $458.38

EXERCISE 13.6

1. (a) $1091.25   (b) $1046.33   (c) $1726.88   (d) $1873.35   (e) $1833.47
2. (a) $691 111.11   (b) $43 777.78   (c) $33 333.33   (d) $111 111.11
3. Answers will vary.   4. $41 680   5. Answers will vary.   6. $40 444.44
7. (a) $83 688.89   (b) $63 938.89   (c) $2600
8. (a) $92 902.22   (b) $75 402.22   9. $2454.24   10. $4429.14

EXERCISE 13.7

4. (a) $944.13   (b) $602.71   (c) $797.97   (d) $990.18   (e) $1479.09   (f) $1001.83
5. (a) $47 000   (b) $36 000   (c) $102 000   (d) $158 000
6. First interest payment: $5835.34
7. First interest payment: $2109.02   8. (b) $3251.07

EXERCISE 13.8

1. (a) vendor   (b) purchaser   (c) vendor   (d) purchaser
   (e) vendor   (f) vendor   (g) purchaser
2. (a) $45.18, vendor   (b) $93.81, vendor   (c) $230.93, purchaser (d) $185.88, vendor
   (e) $96 665.33, purchaser   (f) $85 041.73, purchaser
3. $86 291.61   4. $67 046.65

EXERCISE 13.9

1. (a) $70.90   (b) $86.66   (c) $223.37   (d) $68.12
2. (a) $123.90   (b) $178.33   (c) $732.42   (d) $1984.86
3. (a) $316.14   (b) $24.16   4. Answers will vary.
6. (a) $2060.94   (b) $206.09   7. $62.63

EXERCISE 13.11

1. 60°   2. 3 628 800   3. 164, 166   4. 165, 167
5. (a) 6   (b) 6   (c) 6   (d) 3   (e) 3   (f) 1
   (g) 7   (h) 5   (i) 9
6. (a) $3 \div 3 + 3 - 3 = 1$ (b) $3 \div 3 + 3 \div 3 = 2$ (c) $(3 + 3 + 3) \div 3 = 3$,
   (d) $(3 \times 3 + 3) \div 3 = 4$ (e) $3 + 3 - 3 \div 3 = 5$ (f) $3 + 3 + 3 - 3 = 6$
7. (a) 6, 5.8, 6   (b) Answers will vary.   8. 6.7 kg   9. approximately 601 m³
10. (a) 12.5 kg   (b) 1200 kg   11. (a) C : 264, G : 396   12. 18.7 cm

13.12 REVIEW EXERCISE

1. $2320
2. $1650.45, $380.87, $761.75, $4951.36, $3300.91
3. $517.86
7. Housing: $6200 to $9300, Food: $4650 to $7750, Transportation: $3100 to $6200,
   Clothing: $2480 to $3720, Personal and Medical: $2170 to $3100
8. (a) $152.96, 40.3%   (b) $640, 30.7%   (c) $10 800, 25.9%   (d) $856, 10.1%
13. (a) $1421.30   (b) $63 169   14. (a) $1774.49   (b) $2208.14
15. (a) $3380.06, $3311.76   (b) $12 691.82
16. (a) $88.48   (b) $132.96   (c) $281.02
17. (a) $258 698   (b) $50 050.33   18. 4.8 kW·h

13.13 CHAPTER 13 TEST

1. $558   2. $2122.58
3. $1189.76 to $1784.64
4. $13 056 to $19 584
5. (+)$358.75, (−)$1141.66, (+)$551.58
6. 32%
7. (a) $1186.88   (b) $1798.31   8. $179 547.85

REVIEW AND PREVIEW TO CHAPTER 14

EXERCISE 1
2. $1095.50   3. $75.11   4. 31.6%   5. 29.6%

EXERCISE 2
1. (a) 9, 11, 15, 17, 20, 21, 22, 28, 46, 75, 85; 21
   (b) 9, 24, 24, 29, 31, 33, 33, 47, 56, 83, 85, 85; 33
   (c) $\frac{5}{32}, \frac{3}{16}, \frac{1}{4}, \frac{7}{16}, \frac{1}{2}, \frac{5}{8}, \frac{3}{4}, \frac{7}{16}$
2. (a) 124, 109, 63, 61, 59, 51, 44, 39, 37, 35, 33, 27, 26, 18; 41.5

(b) 64, 63, 56, 54, 53, 43, 37, 34, 26, 25, 25, 22, 22, 20, 13, 8; 30

(c) $\frac{3}{4}, \frac{5}{8}, \frac{9}{16}, \frac{1}{2}, \frac{7}{16}, \frac{3}{8}, \frac{11}{32}, \frac{1}{4}, \frac{15}{32}$

EXERCISE 3
1. (a) 62.75   (b) 62.25   (c) 55.74   (d) 506.5   2. 99   3. 0.258

EXERCISE 4
1. (a) 98.1   (b) 55.7   (c) 476   (d) 17.8   (e) 0.156   (f) 1330
2. (a) 1470   (b) 30.7   (c) 226   (d) 367   (e) 2.31   (f) 1670
3. (a) 2.08   (b) 47.0   (c) 0.253   (d) 0.130   (e) 0.330   (f) 0.0551
4. (a) 72.1   (b) 10.7   (c) 0.599   (d) 0.239   (e) 8.69   (f) 352
5. (a) 692   (b) 94.1   (c) 132   (d) 16 100   (e) 0.270   (f) 0.005 33
   (g) 21.6   (h) 61.8
6. (a) 4.16   (b) 3.14   (c) 0.748   (d) 27.6   (e) 0.0412   (f) 0.0238

EXERCISE 14.1
3. (a) $169 profit   (b) $69 691 loss   (c) $49 245 profit
5. (a) $2000 (loss), $1000 (loss), $1000 (loss), $500 (loss), $500 (loss), break even, $500 (loss), $500 (profit), break even, $1000 (loss), $1000 (loss), $1500 (loss)
   (b) $8500 (loss)   (c) November, February

EXERCISE 14.2
3. $27 312.56   4. $372 700   5. $3637.98   6. $1.73   7. $1028.43

EXERCISE 14.3
1. (b) $902 934   (c) $3568.91   (d) $101.97   (e) 132.4%
2. (a) $0.37   (b) 91.9%
3. Management: 7.4%, Clerical Department: 9.7%, Shipping and Receiving: 28.1%, Promotion and Sales: 7.8%, Research and Development: 10.7%, Manufacturing: 16.0%
4. (c) (i) Sticker, Bicycle, Boat   (ii) Motorbike   (iii) Earrings, Car kit, Paper clip

EXERCISE 14.4
5. 58.3%   6. truck   7. $1284.76

EXERCISE 14.5
6. (a) 50%, $172 550   (b) 5%, $94 665   (c) 30%, $8340   (d) 15%, $18 518.55
   (e) 20%, $15 646.40   (f) 20%, $3869   (g) 8%, $8160.08   (h) 30%, $9704.10
7. $15 400.40
8. (a) Class 3: Building; Class 8: Computer system, Office furniture, Copy machine, Fork-lift; Class 10: Trucks; Class 22: Front-end loader
11. (b) Straight Line Depreciation   12. (d) 1

EXERCISE 14.6
1. the lockers numbered by perfect squares
2. 4, 12, 20, 64   3. 3   4. 18 min 51 s   5. 12
6. 3, 4, 5, 6, 7   7. (a) 1089, 110 889, 11 108 889   (b) 111 110 888 889
8. Monday: Tara, Tuesday: Mia, Wednesday: Shawn, Thursday: Jessie, Friday: Brian
9. (a) 9.5 cm   (b) the needle moves in a straight line
10. Perimeters are equal, shaded area is smaller.
11. 180°   13. odd   14. 256

14.7 REVIEW EXERCISE

1. (a) $10 692 profit   (b) $2 941 126 loss   (c) $165 289 loss
2. (a) $5109 (loss), $3633 (loss), $3992 (loss), $4123 (loss), $6543 (loss), $8945 (loss), $6695 (loss), $7741 (loss), $6219 (loss), $6054 (loss), $5900 (loss), $6233 (loss)
    (b) never   (c) $71 187 (loss)
3. $880.49   4. $8.72   5. $1923.68   6. $9.88   9. $3.52
10. (a) $13.24, $18.80   (b) $9394.77, $11 555.57   (c) $0.003, $0.0035
    (d) $178.71, $223.39   (e) $6177.74, 107.0%   (f) $9.04, 53.7%
11. (a) $17 064.97   (b) $24.97   (c) $555.58   (d) $220.46   (e) 80.8%   (f) 45.6%

14.8 CHAPTER 14 TEST

1. (a) $9000   (b) $5000   (c) February and June
2. $14 921.18   3. $9.23   4. $99.08

REVIEW AND PREVIEW TO CHAPTER 15

EXERCISE 1
1. (a) -5 (b) 135   (c) 26   (d) 600   (e) 60   (f) 69
    (g) 53
2. (a) -14 (b) -117 (c) 9996   (d) 152   (e) 42   (f) -22
    (g) 80
3. (a) $1\frac{7}{24}$ (b) $\frac{1}{12}$ (c) $4\frac{3}{8}$ (d) $2\frac{5}{12}$ (e) $\frac{4}{5}$ (f) $2\frac{3}{20}$
    (g) $2\frac{1}{12}$
4. (a) 2.446   (b) 20.22   (c) 978.48   (d) 7.3695   (e) 13.94   (f) 8.425
    (g) 46.1

EXERCISE 2
1. (a) 22.2 cm   (b) 2.2 cm
2. (a) 11.3 cm   (b) 13.4 cm   (c) 8.6 cm   (d) 6.72 cm
3. (a) $\angle A = 51°$, $b = 4.7$ cm, $c = 7.5$ cm   (b) $\angle A = 17.1°$, $\angle C = 72.9°$, $c = 16.2$ cm

EXERCISE 3
1. (a) 12x   (b) $x + 12y$ (c) $x + 12y$ (d) 6x
    (e) $-7x^2 + 21x$ (f) $-4x^2 + 4x$
2. (a) $x^2 + 3xy + 2y^2$ (b) $2x^2 + x - 15$ (c) $6x^2 - x - 15$ (d) $x^2 - 25y^2$
    (e) $x^2 - y^2$ (f) $x^2 + 2xy + y^2$ (g) $4x^2 - 20x + 25$ (h) $9x^2 - 12x + 4$
3. (a) 57   (b) 695   (c) -342 (d) 440
    (e) 1068   (f) -187 (g) 95   (h) 65
5. (a) 12   (b) $-\frac{15}{7}$ (c) 13   (d) 3 and 4   (e) -5 and 4

EXERCISE 4
1. (a) $109.59   (b) $152.40   (c) $46.88   (d) $297   (e) $35.75   (f) $98.63
2. (a) $7057.91   (b) $24 759.63   (c) $24 433.42   (d) $36 122.22
3. $33 967.50

EXERCISE 15.1

3. (b) (A2 + A3 + A4 + A5 + A6), (B2 + B3 + B4 + B5 + B6), (C2 + C3 + C4 + C5 + C6), (D2 + D3 + D4 + D5 + D6)
    (c) (A8 + B8 + C8 + D8)
4. (b) (B2 + B3 + ... + B8)   (c) (B10/7)   (d) (B2 + B3 + ... + B8)/7
5. (b) (A4 − B4)   (d) C5, C6, and C8
6. (b) (A4 * B4)   (d) (C4 + C5 + C6 + C7 + C8)
8. (b) (B8 − C8), (B9 − C9), ..., (B13 − C13)   (c) (D8 + D9 + ... + D13)
9. (b) $598 377.50, $397 111.78, $201 265.72

EXERCISE 15.2

1. (a) 587.857   (b) 4975.571   (c) 55 452.714   (d) 702 675.429
2. (a) 34   (b) 1   (c) 1   (d) 125   (e) 128   (f) 565
   (g) 0   (h) 0   (i) 31
3. (a) 8.703   (b) 12.258   (c) 1.772   (d) 0.534   (e) 19.125   (f) 9.625
   (g) 0.080   (h) 0.253   (i) 83.289
4. (b) 178.285 38
5. (a) 3278   (b) 41 314   (c) 260 952   (d) 2 027 287

EXERCISE 15.3

3. (b) (i) 0.292   (ii) -19.903 (iii) 8.447   (iv) -29.836 (v) 0.540
4. (a) -1.400, 1.000   (b) -1.000, 1.333   (c) -1.000, 2.500
   (d) -0.833, 1.000   (e) 0.333, 0.500   (f) 0.800, -1.000
   (g) -0.287, 1.765   (h) -2.357, 0.404   (i) 0.783, 1.000
5. 20 m   6. (a) 54 km/h, 60 km/h   (b) 19 h
7. (a) $4*(.5*A6*@SQRT(A7^2+(.5*A6)^2))+A6^2$, $(A6^2*A7/3)$
   (b) 136.317 m², 92.691 m³
8. (a) $2*@PI*C4*(C5+C4)$, $@PI*C4^2*C5$
   (b) 560.774 cm², 1017.434 cm³
9. (a) $@PI*B6*(B6+@SQRT(B6^2+B7^2))$, $@PI*B6^2*B7/3$
   (b) 34 714.376 cm², 424 100.069 cm³
10. (b) 17.317 m³

EXERCISE 15.4

1. (a) Van (34)   (b) Tom (46)   (c) Sport (47)   (d) Coupe (49)
2. Road (52)   3. Answers will vary.   4. Montreal (63.5)
5. Answers will vary.   6. Answers will vary.

EXERCISE 15.5

2. (b) (i) 4.403 cm   (ii) 4.481 cm   3. (b) (i) 9.495 cm   (ii) 10.516 cm

EXERCISE 15.6

1. (a) 6.386 s, 0.429 s   (b) 5.824 s, 0.483 s   (c) 5.438 s, 0.380 s
3. (a) $3.91, $0.36   4. (a) 60 725.475 km, 15 540.494 km

EXERCISE 15.8

1. (a) $40 525.00   (b) $51 031.25   (c) $114 329.01   2. $58 326.00   3. $18 497.50

EXERCISE 15.9

1. (a) $365.77   (b) $146.31   (c) $3324.46
   (d) Total deductions: $3836.54
2. (a) $2067.00   (b) $1356.50   (c) $919.75   3. (c) 850

EXERCISE 15.10

2. (a) $188.29   (b) $180.91   (c) $199.70
3. (b) 29 months   (c) $235.89   (d) $413.00

EXERCISE 15.11

1. (i) $1333.22   (ii) $14 099.81   2. answers vary
3. $981.45   4. Grand total: $1037.23   5. answers vary

15.12 REVIEW EXERCISE

2. (b) (i) 21.1   (ii) 4.2   (iii) 9.3   (iv) 34.6
3. (a) 4.783   (b) 0.299   4. (a) 79   (b) 13
6. (a) James: 1706, Burk: 1791, Hicks: 1724, Spence: 1763
   (b) James: 142, Burk: 149, Hicks: 144, Spence: 147
   (c) James: 11, 131–153; Burk: 16, 133–165; Hicks: 24, 120–168; Spence: 18, 129–165
8. (b) (i) 40.8°, 49.2°   (ii) 40.4°, 49.6°
9. (a) −3.5, 1.0   (b) −2.2, 0.9   (c) −0.7, 1.6   (d) −1.0, 4.8
12. $126 809.05   13. Total amount: $26 962.45

GLOSSARY

absolute value   The positive number of any pair of opposite real numbers, denoted by |a|.

acute angle   An angle whose measure is between 0° and 90°.

acute triangle   A triangle with all angles acute.

adjacent angles   Two angles with a common vertex, a common side, and no interior points in common.

alternate angles   Two angles between two lines on opposite sides of a transversal.

altitude of a triangle   A line from a vertex, perpendicular to the opposite side.

amortization schedule   A schedule that shows the repayment of a loan in a series of equal payments, with the breakdown of principal and interest.

amplitude of a periodic function   The amplitude of a periodic function is $\dfrac{M - m}{2}$ where M is the maximum value and m is the minimum value of the function.

angle   A figure formed by two rays with a common endpoint called the vertex.

angle bisector   A ray that divides an angle into two angles having the same measure.

angle of elevation (depression)   The angle between a horizontal line through an observer and the line of sight from the observer through the object above (below) the observer.

annual   A period of 12 months or 1 a.

annuity   A series of payments made at regular intervals.

area   The number of unit squares contained in a region.

assessed value   The value at which a property is taxed.

average   The average of n numbers is the sum of the numbers divided by n.

axiom   A statement that is assumed to be true. Also called a postulate.

axis   A number line used for reference in locating points on a coordinate plane.

axis of symmetry   A line that is invariant under a reflection.

bank statement   A form prepared by the bank, listing all cheques cashed and deposits made over a specific period of time.

bar graph   A graph using bars to represent data.

base of a trapezoid   One of the parallel sides of the trapezoid.

BASIC   Beginners All-purpose Symbolic Instruction Code is a computer language.

binomial   A polynomial consisting of two terms.

bond   A certificate, issued by a government or a corporation, promising to pay the holder a fixed sum of money on a given date with interest.

broken line graph   A graph using line segments to represent data.

broker   An agent who buys and sells investments for others.

brokerage fee   The amount charged by a broker for buying and selling investments.

budget   A financial plan for disposing of one's income.

carrying charge   The interest that is added to the balance by a lender.

cash discount   The reduction allowed on an invoice price if paid within a specified time.

central angle of a circle   An angle subtended by an arc of a circle with the vertex at the centre.

centroid   The point of intersection of the three medians of a triangle.

chartered bank   A financial institution that provides savings, loan, and chequing services as well as payment of bills and rental of safety deposit boxes.

chord of a circle   A line segment having its endpoints on the circumference.

circle   The set of all points in the plane that are equidistant from a fixed point called the centre.

circle graph   A graph using sectors of a circle to represent data.

circumcentre   The centre of the circle that passes through the three vertices of a triangle.

circumference   The perimeter of a circle.

circumscribed circle   A circle is circumscribed about a polygon if all the vertices of the polygon lie on the circle.

collinear points   Points that lie in the same straight line.

commission   A percentage of sales that a salesperson receives as pay or incentive.

comparison shopping   The attempts of a buyer of goods and services to determine the best buy or value of goods.

complementary angles   Two angles whose sum is 90°.

compound interest   The interest paid on the principal plus any previous interest not paid.

concentric circles   Circles having the same centre.

congruent angles   Angles with the same measure.

congruent figures   Two figures that are equal in all respects — that is, there exists an isometry that maps one figure onto the other.

conic section   The intersection of a double cone and a plane — circle, ellipse, parabola, or hyperbola.

consecutive even (odd) numbers   Numbers obtained by counting by twos from any even (odd) number.

consecutive numbers   Numbers obtained by counting by ones from any given number.

consistent equations   Equations in a system that has at least one solution.

construction   The process of drawing a geometric figure using only a ruler and a compass.

coordinate   A real number paired with a point on a number line.

coordinate plane   A one-to-one pairing of all ordered pairs of real numbers with all points of a plane. Also called the Cartesian coordinate plane.

corollary   A theorem that follows directly from the proof of another theorem.

cosecant function   For any angle of rotation θ, the cosecant of θ is $\dfrac{r}{y}$.

cosecant ratio   In a right triangle, the ratio of the length of the hypotenuse to the length of the opposite side.

cosine function   For any angle of rotation θ, the cosine of θ is $\dfrac{x}{r}$.

cosine ratio   In a right triangle, the ratio of the length of the adjacent side to the length of the hypotenuse.

cotangent function   For any angle of rotation θ, the cotangent of θ is $\dfrac{x}{y}$.

cotangent ratio   In a right triangle, the ratio of the length of the adjacent side to the length of the opposite side.

coterminal angles   Angles that have the same initial and terminal rays (arms).

credit card   A card issued by banks, large stores, and companies that enables the holder to make purchases and delay payment for about 30 d, or to pay by instalments with interest.

cubic polynomial   A polynomial of the form $ax^3 + bx^2 + cx + d$, where $a \neq 0$.

deductions   Funds withheld by an employer from an employee's paycheque. Also refers to the amounts a taxpayer deducts from gross income to arrive at taxable income.

degree   A unit of angle measure equal to $\frac{1}{360}$ of a rotation.

degree of a monomial   The sum of the exponents of the variables.

degree of a polynomial   The greatest of the degrees of its terms after it has been simplified.

dependent equations   Equations in a system that has infinitely many solutions.

depreciation   The decrease in the value of a property or article due to age or wear and tear.

diagonal   A line segment with endpoints on two non-adjacent vertices of a polygon.

diameter of a circle   A chord that contains the centre of the circle. The largest chord.

direct variation   A function defined by a function of the form $y = kx$.

discount   A deduction from the original price of an article.

discriminant   The discriminant of the quadratic equation $ax^2 + bx + c = 0$ is $b^2 - 4ac$.

distance from a point to a line   The length of the perpendicular segment drawn from the point to the line.

dividend   The return or yield on an investment.

domain of a function   The set of numbers for which the function is defined. The set of all first coordinates of the ordered pairs in the function.

domain of a variable   The set of numbers that can serve as replacements for a variable.

down payment   The amount of money paid at the time that a purchase is made.

END statement   The last statement in a computer program.

estimate   To estimate is to arrive at an approximate calculation by rounding all numbers to the highest place value and calculating mentally.

equation An open sentence formed by two expressions separated by an equal sign.

equidistant At the same distance.

equilateral triangle A triangle with all sides equal.

equivalent equations Equations that have the same solution over a given domain.

exponent The number of times the base occurs in a power.

expressing in simplest form Dividing the numerator and denominator of a fraction by the highest common factor.

exterior angle of a polygon An angle formed by extending one side of a triangle and the other side at the same vertex.

factor Number that is multiplied by another number to give a product.

factorial notation Notation used to indicate the product of consecutive integers beginning with 1.

$$n! = 1 \times 2 \times 3 \times ... \times (n - 1) \times n$$

factoring Finding the factors of a number or expression over a given set.

fixed costs Regular expenses, such as rent, over which there is no control.

FOR – NEXT statement Used to loop through the same set of statements several times on a computer.

formula An equation stating the relationship among quantities that can be represented by variables.

frequency of a periodic function The number of cycles per unit of time. $f = \dfrac{1}{p}$, where p is the period of the function.

function A rule that assigns to each element in the domain a single element in the range.

geometric sequence (series) A sequence (series) in which the ratio of every pair of successive terms is constant.

greatest common factor The greatest integer that is a factor of two or more integers.

greatest monomial factor The factor of two or more monomials that has the greatest coefficient and the greatest degree.

gross profit The difference between net sales and the cost of goods sold.

histogram A bar graph used to summarize and display a large set of data.

hypotenuse The side opposite the right angle in a right triangle.

identity An equation whose sides are equivalent expressions. The equation is true for every value of the variables.

identity elements The identity element for addition is 0, since a + 0 = a. The identity element for multiplication is 1, since a × 1 = a.

imaginary unit i The number i that is a solution to the equation $i^2 = -1$.

included angle The angle whose rays contain the sides of a triangle.

inconsistent equations The equations in a system that has no solutions.

inequality Two expressions separated by an inequality symbol.

inflation During a period of inflation, available currency and credit increase beyond the available goods, resulting in price increases.

inscribed angle An angle subtended by an arc of a circle with its vertex on the circumference.

inscribed polygon A polygon with its vertices on the circle.

integer A member of the set {..., −3, −2, −1, 0, 1, 2, 3, ...}.

interest The amount of money paid as rent or earned for the use of another's money.

intersection The elements that two sets have in common.

inventory A listing of items that are on hand, and their value.

inverse variation A function defined by an equation of the form xy = k, (k ≠ 0).

invest To invest means to put money into a bank account, stocks, bonds, mutual funds, or real estate to obtain a gain or income.

irrational number A real number that cannot be expressed in the form $\frac{a}{b}$, a, b, ∈ I, and b ≠ 0.

isosceles triangle A triangle with two sides equal.

lateral area The sum of the areas of the faces of a polyhedron other than the base.

least common multiple The monomial with the smallest positive coefficient and smallest degree that is a multiple of several monomials.

LET statement Assigns a value or an expression to a variable.

linear equation   An equation in which each term is either a constant or has degree 1.

linear function   A function of the form $f(x) = mx + b$.

line segment   Two points on a line and the points between them.

line symmetry   A figure has line symmetry if there is a line such that the figure coincides with its reflection image over the line.

list price   The price that the manufacturer advises the retailer to put on the tag.

locus   A set of points that satisfy a given condition.

market price   The current price of a stock, bond, or mutual fund on the stock exchange.

mass   The amount of matter in an object. The base unit for measuring mass is the kilogram.

maturity value   The total amount due on the date of payment of a note.

mean   The sum of the values divided by the number of values.

median   The middle number when a set of numbers is arranged in order from smallest to largest or largest to smallest.

midpoint   The point that divides a line segment into two equal parts.

mixed number   A number that is part whole number and part fraction, such as $5\frac{3}{4}$.

mode   The number that occurs most often in a set of numbers.

monomial   A number, a variable, or a product of numbers and variables.

mortgage   A legal claim to certain real property of the borrower in respect of payments that have to be made for a loan.

mutual fund   A financial institution that invests the money of numerous individuals in securities of various types and gives the individual a prorated share.

natural numbers   The set of numbers {1, 2, 3, 4, 5, 6, ...}.

net   A pattern for constructing a polyhedron.

net loss   Results when the cost of goods sold and the operating expenses are greater than the gross income.

net profit   (net income)   Results when the gross income is greater than the cost of the goods sold and the operating expenses.

NEW   The first statement in a computer program.

nonagon   A polygon with nine sides.

number line   A pictorial representation of a set of numbers.

numeral   A symbol that represents a number.

obtuse angle   An angle greater than 90° but less than 180°.

obtuse triangle   A triangle with one obtuse angle.

octagon   A polygon with eight sides.

octahedron   A polyhedron with eight faces.

order of operations   The rules to be followed when simplifying expressions. These rules are sometimes referred to as BODMAS or BEDMAS.

ordered pair   A pair of numbers used to name a point on a graph.

origin   The intersection of the horizontal and vertical axes on a graph. It is described by the ordered pair (0, 0).

orthocentre   The point where the altitudes of a triangle intersect.

PACED plan   A process of decision making in which one identifies the problem, states some alternative solutions to the problem, lists criteria for making the decision, evaluates each alternative based on the criteria, and makes the decision.

palindrome   A number such as 232 that reads the same forwards as backwards.

parallel lines   Two lines in the same plane that never meet.

parallelogram   A quadrilateral with opposite sides parallel.

parameter   An arbitrary constant.

partial variation   A relation between two variables that involves a fixed amount plus a variable amount such as $C = nd + 15$.

pentagon   A polygon with five sides.

percent   A fraction (or ratio) in which the denominator is 100.

perimeter   The distance around a polygon.

periodic   Occurring at regular time intervals.

perpendicular bisector   The line that cuts a line segment into two equal parts at right angles.

perpendicular lines   Lines that intersect at right angles.

pi (π)   The quotient that results when the circumference of a circle is divided by the diameter.

pictograph   A graph using pictures to represent data.

polygon   A closed figure formed by line segments.

polyhedron   A three-dimensional object having polygons as faces.

polynomial   A monomial or the sum of monomials.

population   The entire set of items from which data are taken.

portfolio   The list of investments, such as bonds, stocks, or certificates, held by an investor.

postulate   A statement that is accepted without proof.

power   A product obtained by using a base as a factor one or more times.

present value   The principal amount that must be invested now to produce a given amount at a later date.

prime number   A number with exactly two factors — itself and 1.

principal   The amount of money that is borrowed.

principal square root   The positive square root.

prism   A polyhedron with two parallel and congruent bases in the shape of polygons.

proportion   An equation stating that two ratios are equal.

pyramid   A polyhedron with three or more triangular faces and the base in the shape of a polygon.

Pythagorean theorem   The area of the square drawn on the hypotenuse of a right-angled triangle is equal to the sum of the areas of the squares drawn on the other two sides.

quadrant   One of the four regions formed by the intersection of the x-axis and y-axis.

quadratic equation   A polynomial equation of degree 2.

quadratic formula   The formula
$$x = \frac{-b \pm \sqrt{b^2 - 4ac}}{2a}$$
for the roots of a quadratic equation.

quadrilateral   A polygon with four sides.

quotient   The result of a division.

radian   If an angle that is the central angle of a circle cuts off an arc whose length is equal to the length of the radius of the circle, then the measure of the central angle is 1 rad.

radical sign   The symbol $\sqrt{}$.

radius   The length of the line segment that joins the centre and a point on the circumference of a circle.

random sample   A sample in which each member of the population has the same chance of being selected.

range   The set of all values of a function. The set of all second coordinates of the ordered pairs of a relation.

rate   A ratio of two measurements having different units.

rate of return   An indicator, expressed as a percent, of whether an investment is profitable.

ratio   A comparison of two numbers.

rational number   A number that can be expressed as the ratio of two integers.

ray   Part of a line extending in one direction without end.

real numbers   The set of all the rational and irrational numbers.

reciprocals   Two numbers that have a product of 1.

rectangle   A parallelogram with four right angles.

reflex angle   An angle whose measure is greater than 180° and less than 360°.

regular polygon   A polygon in which all sides and angles are equal.

relation   A set of ordered pairs.

repeating decimal   A decimal in which one or more digits repeat without end.

retail price   The price at which goods are sold to consumers.

rhombus   A parallelogram in which all sides are equal.

right angle   An angle whose measure is 90°.

right cone   A cone in which the axis is perpendicular to the base.

right cylinder   A cylinder in which the sides are perpendicular to the bases.

right prism   A prism in which the lateral edges are perpendicular to the bases.

right triangle   A triangle with one right angle.

root of an equation   A solution of the equation.

rounding   The process of replacing a number by an approximate number.

scalar   A term used for real numbers when working with vectors.

scale drawing   A drawing in which distances are reductions or enlargements of actual distances.

scalene triangle   A triangle with no two sides equal.

scientific notation   Numbers written with one digit (not zero) to the left of the decimal place and a power of ten.

$$2700 = 2.7 \times 10^3$$

secant function   For any angle of rotation θ, the secant of θ is $\frac{r}{x}$.

secant ratio   In a right triangle, the ratio of the length of the hypotenuse to the length of the adjacent side.

sector angle   An angle with vertex at the centre of a circle and subtended by an arc of the circle.

sector of a circle   A region bounded by two radii and an arc.

securities   The written statements of the ownership of an investment in stocks or bonds.

segment of a circle   A region bounded by a chord and an arc.

semi-annual   Twice a year, or every 6 months.

sequence   A set of numbers written in a definite order.

set   A collection of objects.

share (of stock)   A part ownership in a corporation.

shell   A three-dimensional object whose interior is empty.

similar figures   Figures having corresponding angles equal and corresponding sides proportional.

sine function   For any angle of rotation θ, the sine of θ is $\frac{y}{r}$.

sine ratio   In a right triangle, the ratio of the length of the opposite side to the length of the hypotenuse.

skeleton   A representation of the edges of a polyhedron.

slope of a line   For a non-vertical line containing two distinct points, (x_1, y_1) and (x_2, y_2), the number

$$m = \frac{y_2 - y_1}{x_2 - x_1}.$$

solid   A three-dimensional object whose interior is completely filled.

solution set   A replacement for a variable that results in a true sentence.

sphere   The set of all points in space that are a given distance from a given point.

spreadsheet   The electronic spreadsheet is a computer application that allows the storing of information in cells and the performing of a variety of computations using formulas.

square   A quadrilateral with four congruent sides and four right angles.

square root   The square root of a number is the number that multiplies itself to give the number.

standard form of a linear equation   A linear equation written in the form $ax + by + c = 0$.

statistics   The science of collecting and analysing numerical information.

stem and leaf plot   A graph using digits of numbers to display data.

stock exchange   A place where shares and bonds are sold.

straight angle   An angle whose measure is $180°$.

supplementary angles   Two angles whose sum is $180°$.

surface area   The sum of all the areas of all faces of a polyhedron.

tangent function   For any angle of rotation θ, the tangent of θ is $\frac{y}{x}$.

tangent ratio   In a right triangle, the ratio of the length of the opposite side to the length of the adjacent side.

tangent to a circle   A line in the plane of a circle that intersects the circle in exactly one point.

tax refund   The amount of overpayment that has been made and is returned to the taxpayer.

term of a polynomial   The product of one or more numerical factors and variable factors.

terminating decimal   A decimal whose digits terminate.

tetrahedron   A polyhedron with four triangular faces.

theorem   A mathematical statement that can be proved.

trade discount   The reduction in the list price given by a manufacturer to retailers.

transversal   A line that intersects two lines in the same plane in two distinct points.

trapezoid   A quadrilateral with one pair of parallel sides.

triangle   A polygon with three sides.

trinomial   A polynomial with three terms.

union of sets   The set of all elements that belong to at least one of the sets.

unit price   The price of an item stated as the price for a single unit of the item.

variable   A letter or symbol used to represent a number.

variable costs   Costs, such as labour and materials, that are flexible and change from time to time.

vector   A directed line segment.

vertex of an angle   The common endpoint of two rays.

vertex of a polygon   The point where two adjacent sides meet in a polygon.

volume   The number of cubic units contained in a solid.

whole numbers   Numbers in the set $\{0, 1, 2, 3, 4, 5, ...\}$.

x-axis   The horizontal line used as a scale for the independent variable in the Cartesian coordinate system.

x-intercept   The x-coordinate of the point where a curve crosses the x-axis.

y-axis   The vertical line used as a scale for the dependent variable in the Cartesian coordinate system.

y-intercept   The y-coordinate of the point where a curve crosses the y-axis.

zero-product property   If $ab = 0$, then $a = 0$ or $b = 0$.

INDEX

NOTES AND PHOTOGRAPH CREDITS